FOR **2015** EXAM

NEW

CONCISE

PROJECT
MATHS 1

FOR JUNIOR CERT

GEORGE HUMPHREY, BRENDAN GUILDEA, GEOFFREY REEVES
LOUISE BOYLAN

g **GILL** EDUCATION

Gill Education
Hume Avenue
Park West
Dublin 12
www.gilleducation.ie

Gill Education is an imprint of M.H. Gill & Co.

978 07171 5356 5

Print origination by MPS Limited, a Macmillan Company

*The paper used in this book is made from the wood pulp of managed forests. For
every tree felled, at least one tree is planted, thereby renewing natural resources.*

Any links to external websites should not be construed as an endorsement
by Gill Education of the content or views of the linked materials.

For permission to reproduce photographs, the authors and publisher
gratefully acknowledge the following:

© Alamy: 223; © Getty Images: 76, 120, 130, 479, 242B,
242T, 481L, 481R.

The authors and publisher have made every effort to trace all copyright
holders, but if any has been inadvertently overlooked we would be
pleased to make the necessary arrangement at the first opportunity.

Contents

*Note: Higher Level candidates **must** cover these chapters from *New Concise Project Maths 1 (for the 2015 exam and onwards)* before moving on to *New Concise Project Maths 2 (for the 2015 exam)*. The remaining chapters from *New Concise Project Maths 1 (for the 2015 exam and onwards)* can be started directly from *New Concise Project Maths 2 (for the 2015 exam)*, for Higher Level candidates.

Preface

New Concise Project Maths 1 (for the 2015 exam and onwards) covers in one volume the complete course for Junior Certificate Mathematics, Ordinary Level. It contains strands 1–5 of the Project Maths syllabus, including the **common introductory course**. *New Concise Project Maths 2 (for the 2015 exam)* completes the Higher Level course.

New Concise Project Maths 1 incorporates the approach to the teaching of mathematics envisaged in **Project Maths**. It reflects the greater emphasis on the understanding of mathematical concepts, developing problem-solving skills and relating mathematics to everyday events.

The authors strongly sympathise with the main aims and objectives of the new Project Maths syllabus and examination. In the worked examples, a numbered, step-by-step approach is used throughout the book to help with problem solving. The constructions are demonstrated with excellent diagrams. There is a comprehensive range of carefully graded exercises to reflect the new exam. Exam-style context questions are included to enhance students' understanding of everyday practical applications of mathematics. The emphasis is on a clear and practical presentation of the material. Simple and concise language is used throughout instead of technical language, which is not required in the exam.

Additional teachers' resources, including a **Digital FlipBook**, are provided online at www.gillmacmillan.ie.

The authors would like to thank Colman Humphrey, Elaine Guildea and Sorcha Forde, who helped with proofreading, checking the answers and making many valuable suggestions that are included in the final text.

George Humphrey
Brendan Guildea
Geoffrey Reeves
Louise Boylan
March 2012

Acknowledgments

The authors wish to express their thanks to the staff of Gill & Macmillan, and special thanks to Kristin Jensen for her advice, guidance and untiring assistance in the preparation and presentation of the book.

Order of operations

When a calculation involves more than one operation we must do the calculations in the correct order. This is sensible as we have to avoid having two or more possible answers to a problem. It has been agreed that calculations are done in the following order:

1.	**BRACKETS**	Do calculations in **brackets** first.
2.	**EXPONENTS**	Then do **powers** or **roots** next.
3.	**MULTIPLICATION** or **DIVISION**	Then do any **multiplication** or **division** next.
4.	**ADDITION** or **SUBTRACTION**	Then do any **addition** or **subtraction**.

A useful memory aid is

This order of operations ensures that the answer is unique. In other words, there is only one correct answer. It is always good practice to show your work with one set of operations at a time. This order of operations is built into your calculator and is called **algebraic logic**.

Notation

Multiplication
There are three ways to denote multiplication. 3 multiplied by 4 can be written as:
(i) 3×4 **(ii)** $3(4)$ **(iii)** $(3)(4)$

Division
There are three ways to denote division. 20 divided by 5 can be written as:

(i) $20 \div 5$ **(ii)** $\frac{20}{5}$ **(iii)** $20/5$

EXAMPLE

Calculate: **(i)** $2 + 3 \times 4$ **(ii)** $6(8 - 3)$ **(iii)** $5(3 + 1) + 7$ **(iv)** $18 \div (4 + 2) - 1$

Solution:

(i) $2 + 3 \times 4$
     $= 2 + 12$ (multiplication)
     $= 14$ (addition)

(ii) $6(8 - 3)$
     $= 6(5)$ (brackets)
     $= 30$ (multiplication)

(iii) $5(3 + 1) + 7$
     $= 5(4) + 7$ (brackets)
     $= 20 + 7$ (multiplication)
     $= 27$ (addition)

(iv) $18 \div (4 + 2) - 1$
     $= 18 \div 6 - 1$ (brackets)
     $= 3 - 1$ (division)
     $= 2$ (subtraction)

Exercise 1.1

Calculate each of the following in questions 1–21.

1. 2×8
2. $3 \times 2 + 4$
3. $3 + 4 \times 5$
4. $4 + 3 \times 5$
5. $20 \div 5 + 3$
6. $12 \div 6 + 8$
7. $8 + 12 \div 4$
8. $6 + 15 \div 3$
9. $3 + 12 \div 6$
10. $24 - 24 \div 6$
11. $20 \div 4 + 2 \times 3$
12. $3(8 - 6)$
13. $15 + 6 \div 2$
14. $8 + 20 \div 4$
15. $4 - 18 \div 6$
16. $32 \div 8 + 2 + 5 \times 4$
17. $18 \div (4 + 5)$
18. $30 \div (7 - 2) - 6$
19. $(8 - 2) \div (5 - 2)$
20. $(40 \div 10) \div (12 \div 3)$
21. $(48 \div 6) \div (2 \times 4)$

22. Use $+, -, \times, \div$ or $(\ )$ in each of the following equations to make each true.

    (i) $6 \quad 2 \quad 5 = 3$ **(ii)** $4 \quad 5 \quad 3 = 23$ **(iii)** $6 \quad 2 \quad 4 = 14$

    (iv) $12 \quad 2 \quad 6 = 4$ **(v)** $4 \quad 3 \quad 2 = 10$ **(vi)** $20 \quad 8 \quad 2 = 6$

23. Aishling and Brian tried to answer the following problem: Calculate $4 + 5 \times 3$. Aishling got the answer 27 and Brian got the answer 19. Who is correct? Justify your answer.

24. Mary says that $10 - 2 \times 3$ is 24. Explain why Mary's answer is incorrect.

25. Frank has a piece of rope 20 m in length. He wants to use his calculator to work out how much rope he would have left over if he cut six pieces, each of length 3 m, off the rope. Write down the correct order in which he should enter the calculation into his calculator.

26. Below is a list of numbers, some symbols and one pair of brackets. Use all of them once to make a correct calculation.

$$3, 2, 4, 20, +, =, (\ )$$

Exponents

Powers

Powers can be thought of as repeated multiplication. The power simply tells you how many times a number is multiplied by itself.

2 to the power of 3 is written as 2^3. $2^3 = 2 \times 2 \times 2 = 8$

Square roots

The **square root** of a number is the value that when multiplied by itself gives the original number.

For example, 5 is the square root of 25 because $5 \times 5 = 25$.

The symbol $\sqrt{}$ is used to denote square root. For example, $\sqrt{25} = 5$.

Note: $\sqrt{25}$ can also be written $25^{\frac{1}{2}}$ or $(25)^{\frac{1}{2}}$.

EXAMPLE

Calculate the following. **(i)** $2(3 + 2)^2 + 3\sqrt{4}$ **(ii)** $\dfrac{6 + 5 \times 3}{11 - 4}$

Solution:

(i) $2(3 + 2)^2 + 3\sqrt{4}$
$= 2(5)^2 + 3\sqrt{4}$ (brackets first)
$= 2(25) + 3(2)$ (powers and square roots next)
$= 50 + 6$ (multiplication next)
$= 56$ (addition last)

(ii) $\dfrac{6 + 5 \times 3}{11 - 4}$ The line acts like a bracket (see note below).
First calculate the top and bottom separately.

Top $= 6 + 5 \times 3$ Bottom $= 11 - 4$
$\quad = 6 + 15$ (multiplication) $= 7$ (subtraction)
$\quad = 21$ (addition)

$\therefore \dfrac{6 + 5 \times 3}{11 - 4} = \dfrac{21}{7} = 3$

Note: $\dfrac{6 + 5 \times 3}{11 - 4} = (6 + 5 \times 3) \div (11 - 4)$

Note: If two operations are of the same order, then we work from **left to right**. For example:

$4 + 5 - 2 = 9 - 2 = 7$ $12 \times 2 \div 6 = 24 \div 6 = 4$

Exercise 1.2

Calculate each of the following in questions 1–36.

1. 3^2

2. 4^2

3. 2^4

4. $3^2 + 4^2$

5. $2^3 + 1^2$

6. 5×2^2

7. $4(3)^2$

8. $6(5)^2$

9. $3(6-4)^2$

10. $(12 \div 3)^2$

11. $(2 \times 3 - 1)^2$

12. $(8 - 2 \times 3)^3$

13. $(5-1)^2 + 9$

14. $(3-1)^2 + 3 \times 2$

15. $(5-1)^2 \div 8$

16. $12 \times 2 \div 8$

17. $24 \div 6 \times 2$

18. $30 \div 15 \times 2$

19. $3(2)^2 + 4(2)$

20. $5^2 + 3 \times 2$

21. $3^2 + 2(3) + 1$

22. $4^2 + 2 \times 5$

23. $5 \times 4 + 3^2$

24. $3 \times 5^2 + 20 \div 4$

25. $\sqrt{9}$

26. $\sqrt{16} + \sqrt{25}$

27. $\sqrt{36} - \sqrt{4}$

28. $3\sqrt{4}$

29. $2\sqrt{100}$

30. $5\sqrt{49}$

31. $\dfrac{10 + 2}{6}$

32. $\dfrac{20 + 10}{8 - 2}$

33. $\dfrac{4 \times 3 + 8}{11 - 1}$

34. $\dfrac{4 + 8 \times 3}{9 - 2}$

35. $\dfrac{3 \times 6 + 2}{17 - 3 \times 4}$

36. $\dfrac{20 + 12 \div 6}{3^2 + 2}$

37. Charlie and Cerda tried to answer the following problem: Calculate $\dfrac{8+4}{4-2}$.

   Charlie got the answer 7 and Cerda got the answer 6. Who is correct? Justify your answer.

38. Fergal says that $5(2)^2 = (10)^2 = 100$. Explain why Fergals's answer is incorrect. What is the correct answer?

39. Use the following list of numbers, some symbols and one pair of brackets to make a correct calculation: 5, 3, 1, 80, +, = and $(\ )^2$.

   Use each number or symbol once to make a correct calculation.

Natural numbers

The whole numbers 1, 2, 3, 4, 5 . . . are called the counting numbers and are denoted by $\mathbb{N}$.

$$\mathbb{N} = 1, 2, 3, 4, 5, \ldots.$$

The dots indicate that the numbers go on forever and have no end (infinite).
Natural numbers can be classified in many different ways. For example:

Even numbers: 2, 4, 6, 8, 10 . . .
Odd numbers: 1, 3, 5, 7, 9, 11 . . .
Square numbers: 1, 4, 9, 16, 25 . . .

Factors (divisors)

> The **factors (divisors)** of any whole number are the whole numbers that divide exactly into the given number, leaving no remainder.

For example, 4 is a factor of 20 because 4 divides exactly into 20, leaving no remainder.
10 is also a factor of 20 because 10 divides exactly into 20, leaving no remainder.

> 1 is a factor of every number.
> Every number is a factor of itself.

To find all the factors of a number, we write out all the pairs of factors that make up the number and then write down every number that occurs. Always start with 1 and the number itself. Then try 2, then try 3, then try 4 and so on in pairs, and stop when the pairs of factors begin to repeat. Do not repeat any factors.

Note: A calculator can help you to find all the factors by putting the number in memory, which you can keep recalling to do the divisions. Write down all the numbers that divide exactly and show your work.

EXAMPLE 1

Find the factors of: (i) 30   (ii) 36

Solution:

Write down all the pairs of factors.

(i) $\dfrac{30}{1 \times 30}$ Thus, the factors of 30 are:
        2×15 1, 2, 3, 5, 6, 10, 15, 30
        3×10
        5×6

(As the next pair of factors is 6 × 5, we have all the factors.)

(ii) $\dfrac{36}{1 \times 36}$ Thus, the factors of 36 are:
        2×18 1, 2, 3, 4, 6, 9, 12, 18, 36
        3×12 (Notice that 6 is only written once.)
        4×9
        6×6

(As the next pair of factors is 9 × 4, we have all the factors.)

Highest common factor (HCF)

> The **highest common factor** of two or more numbers is the largest
> factor that is common to each of the given numbers.

In other words, the highest common factor of two or more numbers is the **largest** number that will divide exactly into each number.

For example, the highest common factor of 6 and 8 is 2, as 2 is the largest number that divides exactly into 6 and 8.

The highest common factor of two or more numbers is found with the following steps:

> 1. Write down all the factors of each number.
> 2. Write down the common factors of each number and select the largest.

Note: If the numbers are small, the highest common factor can be written down from inspection. For example, the highest common factor of 10 and 15 is 5.

EXAMPLE 2

Find the highest common factor of: (i) 8 and 12   (ii) 18 and 30

Solution:

(i)

8	12
1 × 8	1 × 12
2 × 4	2 × 6
	3 × 4

(ii)

18	30
1 × 18	1 × 30
2 × 9	2 × 15
3 × 6	3 × 10
	5 × 6

The common factors are 1, 2 and 4.

∴ The highest common factor of 8 and 12 is 4. In other words, 4 is the largest number that will divide into both 8 and 12 evenly.

The common factors are 1, 2, 3 and 6.

∴ The highest common factor of 18 and 30 is 6.

In other words, 6 is the largest number that will divide into both 18 and 30 evenly.

Exercise 2.1

Find all the factors (divisors) of each of the following numbers in questions 1–18.

1. 6   2. 8   3. 10   4. 12   5. 15   6. 18

7. 20   8. 24   9. 28   10. 35   11. 32   12. 40

13. 48   14. 50   15. 4   16. 9   17. 16   18. 25

Find the common factors of the following in questions 19–21.

19. 8 and 12   20. 10 and 15   21. 24 and 36

Find the highest common factor of each of the following in questions 22–29.

22. 6 and 10   23. 9 and 12   24. 12 and 18   25. 10 and 40

26. 45 and 60   27. 18 and 45   28. 15, 25 and 30   29. 8, 12 and 20

30. (i) Show that the factors of 28, excluding 28 itself, add up to 28.

(ii) There is another even number less than 28 that has the same property. Find this number.

31. Find two numbers which when multiplied give 10 and when added give 7.

32. Find two numbers which when multiplied give 24 and when added give 11.

33. Pick a number from the list: 6, 8, 3, 12, 15, 10, 4, 9.

Start →

5	14	25	3	18	29	4	1	21	11
22	16	10	26	30	8	13	9	6	24
7	17	23	15	28	27	20	12	2	19

Write out all the factors for that number and then add the factors. Take this total and count the same number of places across the grid above, starting at 5, and you will find the number that you picked. Do the same for all the numbers.

34. In these productogons, the number in each square is the product of the numbers in the circles on each side of it. Find the missing numbers in each of these productogons.

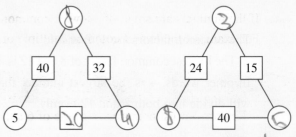

35. The highest common factor of two numbers is 8. What could the two numbers be? 8 - 16

36. The highest common factor of two numbers is 6. Write down three possible pairs of numbers.

37. 1, 4, 9, 16, . . . are square numbers. Mary says, 'All square numbers have an odd number of factors, and all other numbers have an even number of factors.' Is Mary correct? Justify your answer.

Multiples and the lowest common multiple (LCM)

> The **multiples** of a number are found by multiplying the number by 1, 2, 3 . . . and so on.

The multiples of 3 are 3, 6, 9, 12, 15, 18, 21 . . .
The multiples of 5 are 5, 10, 15, 20, 25, 30, 35 . . .

Note: This is similar to **skip counting**. However, skip counting starts at any number and skips forward or skips backwards from that number.

> The **lowest common multiple** of two or more numbers is the **smallest multiple** that is common to each of the numbers.

In other words, the lowest common multiple is the **smallest** number into which each of the numbers will divide exactly.

For example, the lowest common multiple of 2, 4 and 5 is 20, as 20 is the smallest number into which 2, 4 and 5 will divide exactly.

The lowest common multiple of two or more numbers is found with the following steps:

1. Write down the multiples of each number.
2. The lowest common multiple is the smallest (first) multiple they have in common.

Note: If the numbers are small, the lowest common multiple can be written down from inspection. For example, the lowest common multiple of 2, 3 and 4 is 12.

EXAMPLE

Find the lowest common multiple of 6 and 8.

Solution:

Multiples of 6: 6, 12, 18, (24), 30, 36, . . .
Multiples of 8: 8, 16, (24), 32, 40, 48, . . .
24 is the first number in both sets of multiples of 6 and 8.
∴ 24 is the lowest common multiple of 6 and 8.
In other words, 24 is the smallest number that 6 and 8 will divide into evenly.

Exercise 2.2

In questions 1–10, use skip counting to find the missing numbers.

1.	2	4	6		10			16					26
2.	4	7		13			22				34		
3.	5	9			21				37				
4.	20			35									
5.	21			39	45								
6.	50	48				40							
7.	80		70			55							
8.	40	37			28					13			4
9.	100		92				76						
10.	120			102					72				

11. Write the first six multiples of 3, 4, 5, 6, 10, 12.

12. M is the set of natural numbers from 1 to 20, inclusive.

    (i) List the elements of M that are multiples of 3.

    (ii) List the elements of M that are multiples of 5.

    (iii) Write down the lowest common multiple of 3 and 5.

Find the lowest common multiple of each of the following in questions 13–24.

13. 3 and 4	14. 4 and 5	15. 3 and 8	16. 10 and 15
17. 12 and 18	18. 5 and 9	19. 6 and 9	20. 5 and 7
21. 2, 3 and 4	22. 3, 4 and 5	23. 3, 5 and 10	24. 6, 12 and 15

25. A ship, S, is anchored between two lighthouses, L_1 and L_2, as shown. The beam from L_1 shines on the ship every 30 seconds. The beam from L_2 shines on the ship every 40 seconds. How often do both beams shine on the ship at the same time? What assumption have you made?

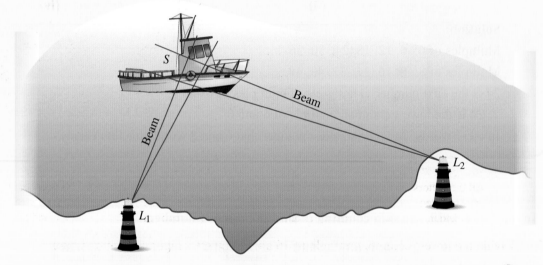

26. Andrew, Breda and Catherine regularly go swimming. Andrew swims every two days, Breda every three days and Catherine every five days. They all went swimming together on Monday, 1st June. On what date in June will they all next go swimming together again? On what day of the week did this take place?

27. Angela, Brendan and Colm are three security officers. They have to contact the control centre at regular times. Angela has to call in every 5 minutes, Brendan every 8 minutes and Colm every 10 minutes. If they all start at the same time, how long is it before they all call in at the same time?

28. In a faraway galaxy, three planets are lined up around a giant sun. They have orbits of 4, 6 and 10 years, respectively.
    (i) After how many years will the three planets be in line?
    (ii) How many orbits will each planet have completed before they are back in alignment?

29. Work out what number is written on each football shirt by solving these problems.

   (i)   **(ii)**   **(iii)**   **(iv)**

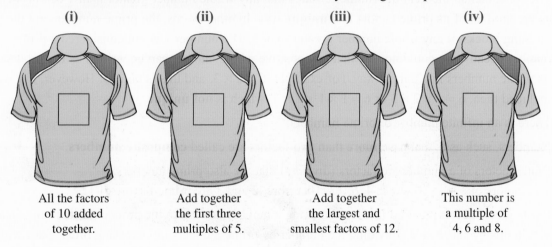

   All the factors   Add together   Add together   This number is
   of 10 added   the first three   the largest and   a multiple of
   together.   multiples of 5.   smallest factors of 12.   4, 6 and 8.

30. Divide the lowest common multiple of 16 and 24 by their highest common factor.

31. The diagram shows the starting position of a system of cogs *P*, *Q* and *R*. The cogs start to rotate.
    (i) How many revolutions does cog *R* make when cogs *R* and *Q* return to their starting positions for the first time?
    (ii) How many revolutions does cog *P* make when cogs *P* and *Q* return to their starting positions for the first time?

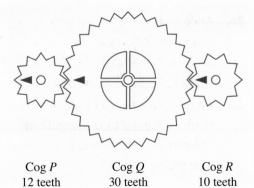

   Cog *P*   Cog *Q*   Cog *R*
   12 teeth   30 teeth   10 teeth

(iii) How many revolutions does cog Q make when cogs P and R return to their starting positions for the first time?

32. A rectangular board measures 40 cm by 24 cm. What is the largest square tile that can be used to cover the floor without having to cut any tile? A diagram may help.

Prime numbers

> A **prime number** is a whole number greater than 1 that has only two factors, 1 and itself.

For example, 7 is a prime number, as it has only two factors (divisors), 1 and 7.

The first 15 prime numbers are: 2, 3, 5, 7, 11, 13, 17, 19, 23, 29, 31, 37, 41, 43, 47.

The fundamental theorem of arithmetic states that any whole number greater than 1 can be written as the product of its prime factors in a **unique** way. In other words, the prime numbers are the building blocks of any whole number greater than 1. The number 1 is not considered a prime number because we could not say that any positive whole number can be written as the product of its prime numbers in a unique way. For example, $6 = 2 \times 3$, and this is unique. However, if 1 was included then, $6 = 1 \times 2 \times 3$ or $6 = 1 \times 1 \times 2 \times 3$, which is **not unique**.

There is an infinite number of prime numbers.

Numbers, such as 8, that have **more** than two factors are called **composite numbers**.

Prime factors of a number are factors (divisors) that are also prime numbers.
The factors of 12 are: 1, ②, ③, 4, 6, 12. Therefore, 2 and 3 are prime factors of 12.

Prime factor **decomposition** involves breaking a number down into the product of its prime factors. We do this by successively dividing the number by prime numbers in increasing order. Start with the smallest prime number that divides exactly into the number and repeat if necessary. Try the next prime number in the same way and stop when you are left with 1. You can do the divisions with a calculator, but show your work step by step.

EXAMPLE

Express **(i)** 12 **(ii)** 90 **(iii)** 105 as the product of its prime factors.

Solution:

(i)

2	12
2	6
3	3
	1

(ii)

2	90
3	45
3	15
5	5
	1

(iii)

3	105
5	35
7	7
	1

$12 = 2 \times 2 \times 3$

or $12 = 2^2 \times 3$

$90 = 2 \times 3 \times 3 \times 5$

or $90 = 2 \times 3^2 \times 5$

$105 = 3 \times 5 \times 7$

Exercise 2.3

Express each of the following numbers in questions 1–18 as the product of its prime factors.

1. 6
2. 10
3. 15
4. 14
5. 18
6. 20
7. 24
8. 28
9. 36
10. 40
11. 45
12. 56
13. 84
14. 120
15. 108
16. 150
17. 180
18. 300

In questions 19–24, write down the prime factors of the number.

19. 8
20. 21
21. 26
22. 30
23. 9
24. 25

25. Using the 1 to 100 number square, find all the prime numbers between 1 and 100.

    - Cross out 1, it is not a prime number.
    - Circle 2, it is the first prime number. Cross out all other multiples of 2.
    - Circle 3, the next prime number. Cross out all other multiples of 3.
    - Circle 5, the next prime number. Cross out all other multiples of 5.

    Continue until you have only prime numbers left. Make a list of all the prime numbers from 1 to 100.

1	2	3	4	5	6	7	8	9	10
11	12	13	14	15	16	17	18	19	20
21	22	23	24	25	26	27	28	29	30
31	32	33	34	35	36	37	38	39	40
41	42	43	44	45	46	47	48	49	50
51	52	53	54	55	56	57	58	59	60
61	62	63	64	65	66	67	68	69	70
71	72	73	74	75	76	77	78	79	80
81	82	83	84	85	86	87	88	89	90
91	92	93	94	95	96	97	98	99	100

26. Explain why the numbers 69, 205 and 77 are not prime.

27. Here is a list of numbers: 5, 10, 33, 35, 25 and 55. From this list, write down:

    (i) An even number   **(ii)** A number divisible by 3   **(iii)** A multiple of 7

    (iv) A prime number   **(v)** A perfect square   **(vi)** A factor of 110

28. Mary was born on the 1st of January in the year $2^2 \times 3^2 \times 5 \times 11$. What age, in full years, is she now?

29. For security, your credit card is encrypted using prime factors. A huge number is assigned to each individual card and it can only be verified by its prime factor decomposition. Find the natural number which is assigned to the following credit cards whose prime factor decomposition is:

    (i) $2^2 \times 3^3 \times 5^2 \times 7^2 \times 23$ **(ii)** $5 \times 7^2 \times 11^3 \times 13^2$ **(iii)** $2 \times 13^2 \times 17^2 \times 19^3$

30. To break a security code, the prime factor decomposition of the number is required. Find the code to break the following numbers.

    (i) 72   **(ii)** 210   **(iii)** 4,200

31. Write the number 10 in the following ways.

    (i) As the product of prime numbers   **(ii)** As the sum of prime numbers in **four different** ways

32. Tom has written down two pairs of prime numbers. The sum of the numbers is 24 and their difference is 10. Find the pair of prime numbers that Tom has written down.

33. Mary put a combination lock on a present that she is going to send to her friend in the post. She has e-mailed her friend with clues to open the lock.

    Multiply all the prime factors of 8, 12, 14, 15 and 39 by each other where each prime factor can only be used once in the multiplication.

    This will give the combination to open the lock.

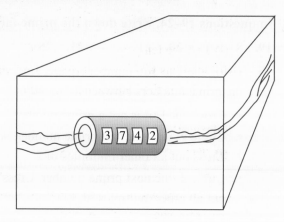

    What is the combination that will open the lock?

34. Decide whether each of the following statements is true or false. In each case, justify your answer.

    (i) There are no even prime numbers

    (ii) There are no square numbers that are prime

CHAPTER 3

INTEGERS

Integers

Negative numbers are numbers below zero. Positive and negative **whole** numbers, including zero, are called **integers**. −4 can be read as **minus four** or **negative 4**. A number without a sign before it is assumed to be positive. +3 has the same value as 3. Negative numbers have uses in the real world in areas such as banking, temperatures and depths below sea level.

The integers are denoted by the letter $\mathbb{Z}$.

$$\mathbb{Z} = \ldots -3, -2, -1, 0, 1, 2, 3, \ldots$$

Integers can also be represented on a number line:

As you move from left to right, the numbers get bigger (increasing).

As you move from right to left, the numbers get smaller (decreasing).

Integers to the right of 0 are called **positive integers**.

Integers to the left of 0 are called **negative integers**.

EXAMPLE

(i) List the temperatures 7°C, −2°C, 3°C, 10°C and −5°C from coldest to hottest.
(ii) Joan has €23 in her current bank account. She goes to the bank and withdraws €30. What is the balance now in her current bank account?

Solution:

(i) 7°C, −2°C, 3°C, 10°C, −5°C
   −5°C, −2°C, 3°C, 7°C, 10°C   (in increasing order)

(ii) Balance was €23. She withdrew €30.
   Thus, she owes the bank €7.
   This is indicated with a minus sign.
   Therefore, the balance now in her current account is −€7.

Note: The euro symbol is often omitted.

Exercise 3.1

1. For each of the following number lines, write down the value of a, b, c and d.

(i)
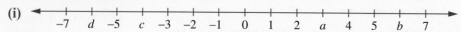

(ii)
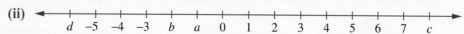

(iii)
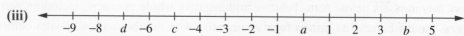

2. Frank has €40 in his current bank account. He writes a cheque for €65. What is his new balance?

3. (i) Celia's current bank account is overdrawn by €30. How is this recorded in her bank account?
   (ii) How much does she have in her current account if she lodges €100 into it?

4. Put these numbers in order. Start with the lowest.
   (i) 5, −1   (ii) 4, 0, −3, 2   (iii) −4, 3, −5, −2

5. Find the final temperature.
   (i) Start at 5°C and rise by 2°C   (ii) Start at −4°C and rise by 7°C
   (iii) Start at −3°C and rise by 3°C   (iv) Start at −5°C and rise by 2°C

6. (i) A submarine is 40 m below sea level. How would this be recorded in the ship's log?
   (ii) The submarine then dives a further 25 m. What is the new depth of the submarine below sea level?

7. In Dublin the temperature was −2°C. In Cork the temperature was 7°C warmer. What was the temperature in Cork?

8. In Amsterdam the temperature was 4°C. In Helsinki the temperature was −8°C. How many degrees warmer was it in Amsterdam than in Helsinki?

9. A plane is flying 200 m above sea level. It drops a sonar beacon to the bottom of the ocean. The beacon falls by 450 m from the plane to reach the bottom of the ocean. How deep is the ocean at the point where the beacon comes to rest?

10. The table shows the scores of some golfers in the first round of a competition. A score of −5 means five strokes fewer than expected (five below par). In a game of golf, the player with the lowest score wins.

Name	Andrew	Brendan	Ciara	Dorothy	Edward	Fiona	Greg	Hilda
Score	8	−1	5	−5	3	−2	0	−4

(i) Which of the players is (a) in the lead (b) last?

(ii) List the players in order. Start with the current leader.

11. At midnight on New Year's Day the temperatures in some cities
were as shown in the table.

New York	1°C
Dublin	−2°C
Moscow	−22°C
Cairo	4°C
Rome	−3°C

   (i) Which city recorded the:

      (a) highest temperature   (b) lowest temperature?

  (ii) List the temperatures from coldest to hottest.

 (iii) Which city was 3°C warmer than New York?

 (iv) What is the difference in temperature between

      (a) New York and Dublin (b) Moscow and Rome?

12. Find the number x that is halfway between each pair of numbers.

   (i)

     2   x 10

  (ii)

    −3 x 5

 (iii)

    −8 x −2

13. Put the symbol < (less than) or > (greater than) in the box to make each statement true.

   (i)   3 ☐ 5   (ii) 7 ☐ 2   (iii) 3 ☐ −2   (iv) 1 ☐ −2

   (v) −3 ☐ 4   (vi) 0 ☐ −2   (vii) −3 ☐ −7   (viii) −4 ☐ −3

Addition and subtraction

Two integers can be added or subtracted using two methods.

Method 1:

Find the starting position on the number line, then move right (adding) or move left (subtracting) to find the finished position.

Method 2:

Use one of the two rules:

1. When the signs are the same, add the numbers and keep their sign.
2. When the signs are different, take the smaller number from the bigger number and keep the sign of the bigger number.

EXAMPLE 1

Calculate the following.   **(i)** $-2 + 7$ **(ii)** $-6 + 4$ **(iii)** $-1 - 5$

Solution:

Method 1

(i) $-2 + 7$

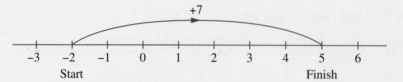

Start at -2 and move seven units to the right to finish at 5. $\therefore -2 + 7 = 5$

(ii) $-6 + 4$

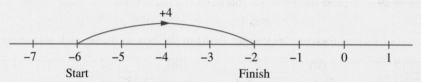

Start at -6 and move four units to the right to finish at -2. $\therefore -6 + 4 = -2$

(iii) $-1 - 5$

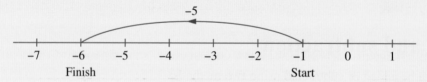

Start at -1 and move five units to the left to finish at -6. $\therefore -1 - 5 = -6$

Method 2

(i) $-2 + 7 = 5$ (different signs; subtract the smaller number, 2, from the larger number, 7, and keep the sign of the larger number, **+**)

(ii) $-6 + 4 = -2$ (different signs; subtract the smaller number, 4, from the larger number, 6, and keep the sign of the larger number, **−**)

(iii) $-1 - 5 = -6$ (same sign, both **−**; add the numbers and keep the **−**)

It is often a good idea to think of positive numbers as having money in a bank and negative numbers as owing money to the bank.

Thus, $-2 - 5 = -7$: if you owe 2 and you owe 5, then you owe 7.

$-4 + 7 = 3$: if you owe 4 and you have 7, then you have 3.

$-6 + 1 = -5$: if you owe 6 and you have 1, then you owe 5.

Dealing with more than two numbers

Often we have to do calculations with more than two numbers being added or subtracted.

When this happens, do the following:

> 1. Add up all the positive and negative numbers separately to give two numbers of different signs.
> 2. Subtract the smaller number from the larger number and keep the sign of the larger number.

EXAMPLE 2

Calculate the following.   (i) $21 + 3 - 8 + 5 - 16$ (ii) $-6 + 3 + 8 - 11 + 5 - 1 - 7$

Solution:

(i) $21 + 3 - 8 + 5 - 16$

     $= 29 - 24$ (add the positive and negative numbers separately)

     $= 5$ (subtract the smaller number, 24, from the larger number, 29, and keep the sign of the larger number, +)

(ii) $-6 + 3 + 8 - 11 + 5 - 1 - 7$

     $= 16 - 25$ (add the positive and negative numbers separately)

     $= -9$ (subtract the smaller number, 16, from the larger number, 25, and keep the sign of the larger number, −)

Exercise 3.2

1.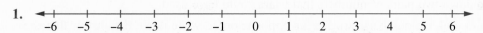

    (i) Use the number line above to calculate each of the following.

      (a) $2 + 4$ (b) $3 - 2$ (c) $-2 + 5$ (d) $6 - 7$

      (e) $-1 - 4$ (f) $-2 - 4$ (g) $-4 + 3$ (h) $-3 + 3$

    (ii) Use the number line to show that (a) $4 - 5 = -5 + 4$ (b) $-3 + 7 = 7 - 3$.

Calculate each of the following in questions 2–27.

2. $8 - 6$ 3. $5 - 3$ 4. $10 - 7$ 5. $2 - 2$

6. $11 - 4$ 7. $-5 + 7$ 8. $-1 + 6$ 9. $-2 + 5$

10. $-2 - 4$ 11. $-1 - 3$ 12. $-1 - 1$ 13. $-5 - 3$

14. $-6 + 4$ 15. $-4 + 6$ 16. $-10 + 13$ 17. $8 - 10$

18. $4 - 6$ 19. $6 - 9$ 20. $-1 - 6$ 21. $-9 + 12$

22. $8 + 4 - 10$

23. $6 + 1 - 3$

24. $4 + 5 - 1 - 6$

25. $3 + 7 - 4 - 6$

26. $9 - 8 + 7 - 5$

27. $6 + 3 - 12 + 5$

28. Find the missing number in each box.

    (i) $\boxed{} + 5 = 8$ **(ii)** $\boxed{} + 3 = 7$ **(iii)** $8 + \boxed{} = 11$

    (iv) $\boxed{} - 6 = 4$ **(v)** $-4 - \boxed{} = -6$ **(vi)** $\boxed{} - 1 = -4$

29. Write down the value of a in each of the following number lines.

    (i)

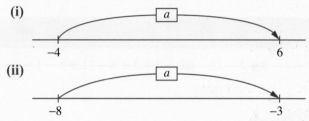

    (ii)

30. Write down the value of a and the value of b in the following number line.

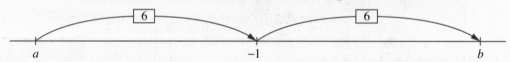

31. Fill in two negative numbers to make each of the following true.

    (i) $\boxed{} + \boxed{} = \boxed{-6}$ **(ii)** $\boxed{} - \boxed{} = \boxed{-6}$

32. A submarine is 25 m below sea level. It dives in three bursts of 20 m each and then rises by 15 m. What is the new depth of the submarine below sea level?

33. Ciara thinks of two integers. She takes one away from the other and gets an answer of -3.

    (i) Write down two pairs of numbers that Ciara could have used.

    (ii) If Ciara took the numbers away in the opposite order, write down the answer that she would get.

34. Complete these addition pyramids. The number in each brick is found by adding the two directly below it.

    (i)

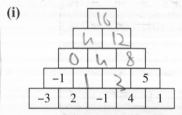

    (ii)

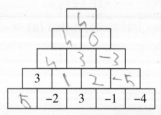

35. In a magic square, the numbers in any row, column or diagonal add up to give the same answer. Copy and complete each of these magic squares.

(i)

(ii)

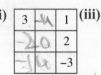

(iii)

36. The diagram shows the caves and mountains in a certain area. Base camp is indicated as 0 m.

   (i) How high above cave 1 is the summit?

   (ii) How far below the summit is camp 1?

   (iii) How far is cave 1 above cave 2?

   (iv) How far below camp 1 is cave 2?

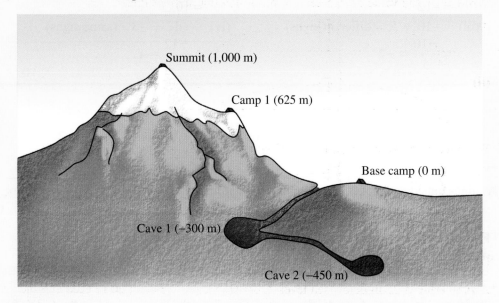

Summit (1,000 m)

Camp 1 (625 m)

Base camp (0 m)

Cave 1 (–300 m)

Cave 2 (–450 m)

Multiplication and division of two integers

The following two rules are applied to the **multiplication** or **division** of two integers:

> 1. If the signs are the same, then the answer will be positive.
> 2. If the signs are different, then the answer will be negative.

Same signs give +
$+ \times + = +$
$- \times - = +$
$+ \div + = +$
$- \div - = +$

Different signs give −
$+ \times - = -$
$- \times + = -$
$+ \div - = -$
$- \div + = -$

It is good practice to work the sign out first, then multiply or divide the numbers.

EXAMPLE

Calculate: (i) 3×-4 (ii) $-2(-5)$ (iii) $-10 \div 5$ (iv) $-12 \div -3$

Solution:

(i) 3×-4 (different signs)
 $= -12$

(ii) $-2(-5)$ (same signs)
 $= 10$

(iii) $-10 \div 5$ (different signs)
 $= \dfrac{-10}{5} = -2$

(iv) $-12 \div -3$ (same signs)
 $= \dfrac{-12}{-3} = 4$

Note: $\dfrac{-10}{5} = -2$ and $\dfrac{10}{-5} = -2$, therefore $\dfrac{-10}{5}$ or $\dfrac{10}{-5}$ can be written as $-\dfrac{10}{5} = -2$.

$-(-2) = -1(-2) = -1 \times -2 = 2$.

A minus outside a bracket means multiply what is in the bracket by -1.

Exercise 3.3

Calculate each of the following in questions 1–28.

1. $-2(2)$
2. $3(-5)$
3. $-6(-3)$
4. $-5(4)$

5. $2(-3)$
6. $-4(-4)$
7. $-8(3)$
8. $(-3)(-5)$

9. $-12 \div 6$
10. $20 \div -4$
11. $-24 \div 8$
12. $-20 \div -4$

13. $\dfrac{-8}{4}$
14. $\dfrac{-12}{-3}$
15. $\dfrac{-15}{5}$
16. $\dfrac{-14}{-7}$

17. $(-1)(-1)$
18. $(-3)(-3)$
19. $-28 \div -7$
20. $24 \div -3$

21. $11(-2)$
22. $-27 \div 9$
23. $21 \div -3$
24. $-100 \div -20$

25. $-(2)$
26. $-(-3)$
27. $-(-7)$
28. $-(4)$

29. Subtract the number in the right-hand brick from the number in the left-hand brick to find the number in the brick below.

(i)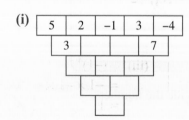

(ii)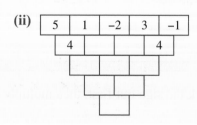

30. **(i)** Find the missing number in the box.

    (a) $\boxed{} \times 4 = -8$ **(b)** $5 \times \boxed{} = -15$ **(c)** $-12 \div \boxed{} = 3$

  (ii) Find missing pairs of numbers in the boxes such that:

    (a) $\boxed{} \times \boxed{} = 6$ **(b)** $\boxed{} \times \boxed{} = -10$ **(c)** $\boxed{} \div \boxed{} = -4$

31. Copy and complete the following two-way tables.

(i)

+	2	4		−2
5	7			
4			3	
−2				
−5				

(ii)

×	1	3		−5
4		12		
2				
−1				
			12	30

32. In these diagrams, the number in each square is the product of the numbers in the circles on each side of it. Find the missing numbers in each case.

(i)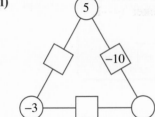

(ii)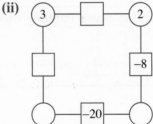

Exponents

An **even** number of minus signs give plus when multiplying.

An **odd** number of minus signs give minus when multiplying.

EXAMPLE

Calculate: **(i)** $(-3)^2$ **(ii)** $(-2)^3$ **(iii)** $(-1)^4$

Solution:

(i) $(-3)^2$
      $= -3 \times -3$
      $= 9$

(ii) $(-2)^3$
      $= -2 \times -2 \times -2$
      $= -8$

(iii) $(-1)^4$
      $= -1 \times -1 \times -1 \times -1$
      $= 1$

Exercise 3.4

Calculate each of the following.

1. 3^2
2. 5^2
3. 7^2
4. 1^2
5. 2^3
6. 3^3
7. 4^3
8. $(-2)^2$
9. $(-4)^2$
10. $(-5)^2$
11. $(-6)^2$
12. $(-1)^2$
13. $(-1)^3$
14. $(-5)^3$
15. $(-7)^2$
16. $(-3)^3$
17. $(-2)^4$
18. $(-10)^2$
19. $(-8)^2$
20. $(-12)^2$

Order of operations

The order of operations for integers is the same as that for natural numbers. The memory aid for the order of operations is BEMDAS (**b**rackets, **e**xponents, **m**ultiplication and **d**ivision, **a**ddition and subtraction):

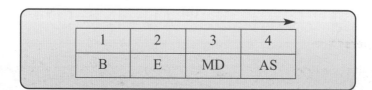

1	2	3	4
B	E	MD	AS

EXAMPLE 1

Calculate: (i) $5 \times 4 - 30 \div 6 + 3$ (ii) $4 + 54 \div -9$

Solution:

(i) $5 \times 4 - 30 \div 6 + 3$
  $= 20 - 5 + 3$ (multiplication and division)
  $= 23 - 5$ (addition)
  $= 18$ (subtraction)

(ii) $4 + 54 \div -9$
  $= 4 - 6$ (division)
  $= -2$ (subtraction)

Exercise 3.5

Calculate each of the following.

1. $3 \times 5 + 2$
2. $4 + 2 \times 3$
3. $5 + 2 \times 4 + 1$
4. $20 \div 4 + 3$
5. $3 + 8 \div 4$
6. $6 \div 3 + 10 \div 2$
7. $15 \div 5 + 2$
8. $24 \div 6 - 1$
9. $5 \times 2 + 20 \div 5$
10. $6 \div 2 + 6 \times 3$
11. $3 \times 2 - 15 \div 3$
12. $4 \times 5 - 30 \div 5$
13. $20 \div 2 - 2 \times 4$
14. $8 - 12 \div 6$
15. $7 - 15 \div 3$
16. $5(4) + 2(-6)$
17. $3(5) - 2(4)$
18. $10(2) - 4(-3)$
19. $5(-2) + 4(3) + 1$
20. $6(-2) - 5(-3) - 3$
21. $5(-4) + 4(3)$
22. $-20 \div -5$
23. $14 \div -7$
24. $-10 \div 2$
25. $-12 \div -4 + 2$
26. $15 \div -3 + 1$
27. $-30 \div 6 + 7$
28. $36 \div 9 + 5(2) - 11$
29. $6(-1) + 12 \div 2$
30. $-20 \div -2 \times 4$

Further order of operations

> ### EXAMPLE 2
>
> Calculate: **(i)** $15 \div (9 - 6)$ **(ii)** $3(-2)^3$ **(iii)** $2(1 - 4)^2 - 5(6 - 2)$
>
> **Solution:**
>
> **(i)** $\quad 15 \div (9 - 6)$
> $\quad\quad = 15 \div 3 \quad$ (brackets)
> $\quad\quad = 5 \quad\quad$ (division)
>
> **(ii)** $\quad 3(-2)^3$
> $\quad\quad = 3(-8) \quad$ (exponents)
> $\quad\quad = -24 \quad$ (multiplication)
>
> **(iii)** $\quad 2(1 - 4)^2 - 5(6 - 2)$
> $\quad\quad = 2(-3)^2 - 5(4) \quad$ (brackets)
> $\quad\quad = 2(9) - 5(4) \quad$ (exponents)
> $\quad\quad = 18 - 20 \quad$ (multiplication)
> $\quad\quad = -2 \quad$ (subtraction)

Note: A minus sign on its own outside a bracket can be replaced by multiplication with -1.

For example, $-(8 - 5) = -1(8 - 5) = -1(3) = -3$ or $-(3)^2 = -1(3)^2 = -1 \times 9 = -9$.

Exercise 3.6

Calculate each of the following in questions 1–39.

1. $3(4 + 2)$
2. $5(6 - 2)$
3. $2(8 - 5)$
4. $(3 + 5) \div 2$
5. $(18 - 4) \div 7$
6. $(21 + 3) \div 8$
7. $24 \div (6 + 2)$
8. $20 \div (12 - 2)$
9. $(20 \div 5) \div (5 - 1)$
10. $(8 + 4) \div (6 - 3)$
11. $(100 \div 2) \div (60 \div 12)$
12. $(60 \div 5) \div (45 \div 15)$
13. $5(2 \times 3 - 4)$
14. $6(5 \times 3 - 11)$
15. $2(2 + 3 \times 4)$
16. $6(2 - 4)$
17. $-3(1 - 6)$
18. $-2(-3 + 5)$
19. $3(20 \div 5 - 2)$
20. $4 + 20 \div (7 - 2)$
21. $8 - 22 \div (9 + 2)$
22. $-(3 - 5)$
23. $3(2 + 5) - (4 - 7)$
24. $2(5 - 7) - (4 - 8)$
25. 3^2
26. $2(3)^2$
27. $4(2)^2$
28. $3(-2)^2$
29. $2(4)^2$
30. $3(-4)^2$
31. $3(2)^2 + 4(2)$
32. $3(4)^2 + 2(4) + 5$
33. $3(-2)^2 - 5(-2) - 20$
34. $(4 - 1)^2$
35. $(5 - 8)^2$
36. $(100 \div 25)^2$
37. $5(6 - 2)^2$
38. $3(3 - 5)^2$
39. $4(5 - 3)^2 + 4(3 + 1)$

In questions 40–45, first calculate the top and bottom separately before doing the division. The bar, — , acts exactly like a bracket.

40. $\dfrac{10 + 2}{5 - 1}$
41. $\dfrac{2 \times 3 + 8}{5 \times 2 - 3}$
42. $\dfrac{2(5 - 1) + 2}{3 \times 6 - 4 \times 2}$
43. $\dfrac{18 + 2 \times 3}{2(5 - 1)}$
44. $\dfrac{6 \times 3 + 12 \div 4 + 9}{3(8 - 1) - 2(4 - 1)}$
45. $\dfrac{5^2 - 7}{3^2 - 7}$

46. Explain why $-4^2 \neq (-4)^2$.

Equivalent fractions

A fraction is written as **two whole numbers**, one over the other, separated by a bar.

For example, $\frac{4}{5}, \frac{7}{8}, \frac{4}{3}$ and $-\frac{5}{4}$ are fractions.

The top number is called the **numerator** and the bottom number is the **denominator**.

$$\text{Fraction} = \frac{\text{Numerator}}{\text{Denominator}}$$

Equivalent fractions are fractions that are equal. For example:

$$\frac{1}{2} = \frac{2}{4} = \frac{3}{6} = \frac{4}{8} = \frac{5}{10}.$$

This can be shown on a diagram where the same proportion is shaded in each circle.

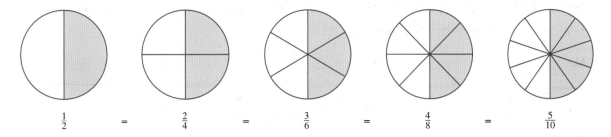

$$\frac{1}{2} \quad = \quad \frac{2}{4} \quad = \quad \frac{3}{6} \quad = \quad \frac{4}{8} \quad = \quad \frac{5}{10}$$

To find an equivalent fraction, multiply or divide the top and bottom by the same number (except zero).

$$\overset{\times 4}{\underset{\times 4}{\frac{2}{5} = \frac{8}{20}}} \qquad \text{(multiply the top and bottom by 4)}$$

$$\overset{\div 3}{\underset{\div 3}{\frac{12}{18} = \frac{4}{6}}} \qquad \text{(divide the top and bottom by 3)}$$

Lowest terms

When we can no longer divide the top and bottom evenly by the same whole number, we say that the fraction is in its **lowest terms**. This process is also called **simplifying the fraction**.

$$\frac{5}{20} = \frac{1}{4}$$ (divide the top and bottom by 5)

Exercise 4.1

1. Express each of the following fractions in its lowest terms.

   (i) $\frac{5}{10}$ (ii) $\frac{3}{12}$ (iii) $\frac{4}{16}$ (iv) $\frac{6}{8}$ (v) $\frac{6}{18}$

   (vi) $\frac{8}{16}$ (vii) $\frac{14}{21}$ (viii) $\frac{21}{30}$ (ix) $\frac{30}{45}$ (x) $\frac{11}{33}$

2. Express the fraction of each shape that is shaded, giving your answer in its lowest terms.

   (i) 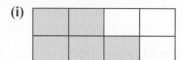   (ii) 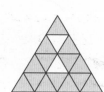   (iii)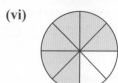

   (iv) 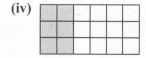   (v)   (vi)

   (vii) 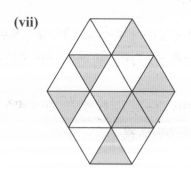   (viii) 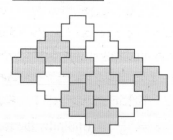   (ix)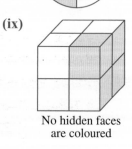

   No hidden faces are coloured

3. (i) Shade in $\frac{2}{3}$ of this shape.   (ii) What fraction of this shape is **not** shaded?

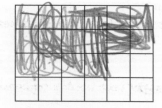   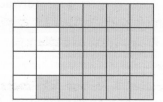

4. Find the missing number in each of these equivalent fractions.

(i) $\frac{1}{4} = \frac{\Box}{8}$ (ii) $\frac{2}{3} = \frac{\Box}{9}$ (iii) $\frac{2}{5} = \frac{8}{\Box}$ (iv) $\frac{4}{6} = \frac{\Box}{3}$

(v) $\frac{10}{15} = \frac{2}{\Box}$ (vi) $\frac{12}{24} = \frac{\Box}{4}$ (vii) $\frac{12}{9} = \frac{\Box}{3}$ (viii) $\frac{3}{4} = \frac{\Box}{20}$

(ix) $\frac{8}{24} = \frac{2}{\Box}$ (x) $\frac{\Box}{30} = \frac{1}{5}$ (xi) $\frac{\Box}{24} = \frac{3}{4} = \frac{6}{\Box}$ (xii) $\frac{5}{\Box} = \frac{1}{2} = \frac{\Box}{\Box}$

5. Is the shaded fraction of each shape an equivalent fraction? Justify your answer.

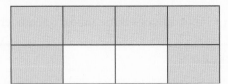 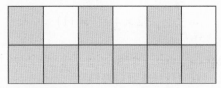

6. Which of the three fractions $\frac{4}{18}$, $\frac{5}{20}$ and $\frac{6}{27}$ are equivalent? Justify your answer.

7. John says that $\frac{2}{3} = \frac{9}{12}$. Is John correct? Justify your answer.

8. (i) Express the fraction $\frac{16}{64}$ in its lowest terms.

    (ii) Mary answers the question like this:

       Cancel the 6s, $\frac{16}{64} = \frac{1}{4}$. Therefore $\frac{16}{64} = \frac{1}{4}$.

       (a) Explain why Mary is **not** right.

       (b) Make up a similar question that shows that Mary's method is wrong.

9. Which of the fractions $\frac{3}{5}$ or $\frac{2}{3}$ is larger? Copy the grids to justify your answer.

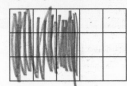 

10. Pam got 10 out of 15 for her test and Tom got 15 out of 20 in his test. Kate said that they both did equally well because they both got five questions wrong. Is Kate correct? Explain your answer.

11. Estimate how much of the rectangle below is shaded.

    (i) Between 0 and $\frac{1}{4}$ (ii) Between $\frac{1}{4}$ and $\frac{1}{2}$ (iii) Between $\frac{1}{2}$ and $\frac{3}{4}$ (iv) Between $\frac{3}{4}$ and 1

Types of fractions

Proper fraction

If the top is smaller than the bottom, the fraction is called a **proper fraction** or a **bottom-heavy fraction** and is less than 1, for example $\frac{2}{5}, \frac{3}{4}$.

Improper fraction

If the top is bigger than the bottom, the fraction is called an **improper fraction** or a **top-heavy fraction** and is greater than 1, for example $\frac{4}{3}, \frac{7}{5}$.

Mixed number

A number such as $2\frac{3}{4}$ is called a **mixed number** or a **mixed fraction**.

EXAMPLE

(i) Express $2\frac{3}{4}$ as an improper fraction.

(ii) Express $\frac{19}{5}$ as a mixed number.

Solution:

(i) $2\frac{3}{4}$

    $= \frac{11}{4}$ $(2 \times 4 + 3 = 11)$

(ii) $\frac{19}{5}$

    $= 3\frac{4}{5}$ (5 into 19 goes three times, remainder 4)

Order of operations

The order of operations for fractions is the same as that for natural numbers and integers.

Remember: **BEMDAS**.

However, if you are adding, subtracting, multiplying, dividing, raising to a power or taking a square root of a fraction, it is good practice to write all mixed numbers first as top-heavy (improper) fractions.

Addition and subtraction of fractions

> You can add and subtract fractions that have the same denominator.

EXAMPLE 1

Mary eats $\frac{1}{5}$ of a pizza and John eats $\frac{2}{5}$ of the same pizza.

What fraction of the pizza has been eaten?

Solution:

Mary and John eat $\frac{1}{5} + \frac{2}{5} = \frac{1+2}{5} = \frac{3}{5}$.

They eat $\frac{3}{5}$ of the pizza.

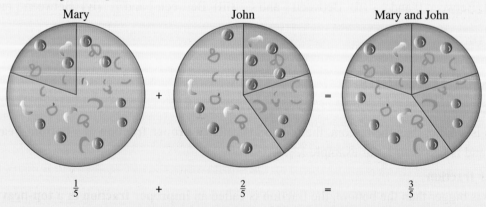

Mary		John		Mary and John
$\frac{1}{5}$	+	$\frac{2}{5}$	=	$\frac{3}{5}$

When the **denominators** are the same, you can just add the **numerators**.

Fractions with different denominators

> You can add or subtract fractions with different denominators by writing each fraction as an **equivalent fraction** with the same denominator.

EXAMPLE 2

Express the following as one fraction. (i) $\frac{1}{4} + \frac{2}{3}$　　(ii) $\frac{4}{3} - \frac{1}{5}$

Solution:

(i) $\frac{1}{4} + \frac{2}{3}$

Method 1

The common denominator of 4 and 3 is 12.

$$\overset{\times 3}{\underset{\times 3}{\frac{1}{4} = \frac{3}{12}}} \qquad \overset{\times 4}{\underset{\times 4}{\frac{2}{3} = \frac{8}{12}}}$$

$$\therefore \frac{1}{4} + \frac{2}{3} = \frac{3}{12} + \frac{8}{12} = \frac{3+8}{12} = \frac{11}{12}$$

Method 2

$$\frac{1}{4} + \frac{2}{3}$$
$$= \frac{3(1) + 4(2)}{12} = \frac{3+8}{12} = \frac{11}{12}$$

(ii) $\frac{4}{3} - \frac{1}{5}$

Method 1

The common denominator of 3 and 5 is 15.

$$\overset{\times 5}{\underset{\times 5}{\frac{4}{3} = \frac{20}{15}}} \qquad \overset{\times 3}{\underset{\times 3}{\frac{1}{5} = \frac{3}{15}}}$$

$$\therefore \frac{4}{3} - \frac{1}{5} = \frac{20}{15} - \frac{3}{15} = \frac{20-3}{15} = \frac{17}{15} = 1\frac{2}{15}$$

Method 2

$$\frac{4}{3} - \frac{1}{5}$$
$$= \frac{5(4) - 3(1)}{15} = \frac{20-3}{15} = \frac{17}{15} \text{ or } 1\frac{2}{15}$$

EXAMPLE 3

Express the following as one fraction. (i) $3\frac{2}{5} - 1\frac{3}{4}$　　(ii) $3\frac{1}{3} - 1\frac{5}{6} - 2\frac{1}{4}$

Solution:

(i) $\quad 3\frac{2}{5} - 1\frac{3}{4}$

$$= \frac{17}{5} - \frac{7}{4}$$

$$= \frac{4(17) - 5(7)}{20}$$

$$= \frac{68 - 35}{20} = \frac{33}{20} \text{ or } 1\frac{13}{20}$$

(ii) $\quad 3\frac{1}{3} - 1\frac{5}{6} - 2\frac{1}{4}$

$$= \frac{10}{3} - \frac{11}{6} - \frac{9}{4}$$

$$= \frac{4(10) - 2(11) - 3(9)}{12}$$

$$= \frac{40 - 22 - 27}{12}$$

$$= \frac{40 - 49}{12} = -\frac{9}{12} = -\frac{3}{4}$$

Exercise 4.2

Express each of the following mixed fractions as an improper (top-heavy) fraction in questions 1–12.

1. $2\frac{1}{4}$ 2. $2\frac{3}{5}$ 3. $4\frac{3}{4}$ 4. $3\frac{3}{4}$ 5. $1\frac{2}{5}$ 6. $3\frac{3}{10}$

7. $1\frac{7}{8}$ 8. $3\frac{3}{8}$ 9. $4\frac{2}{5}$ 10. $5\frac{2}{3}$ 11. $4\frac{2}{7}$ 12. $8\frac{3}{5}$

Express each of the following improper fractions as a mixed number in questions 13–24.

13. $\frac{7}{4}$ 14. $\frac{13}{6}$ 15. $\frac{25}{4}$ 16. $\frac{11}{3}$ 17. $\frac{17}{7}$ 18. $\frac{19}{8}$

19. $\frac{22}{5}$ 20. $\frac{7}{2}$ 21. $\frac{3}{2}$ 22. $\frac{20}{9}$ 23. $\frac{33}{5}$ 24. $\frac{41}{6}$

Express each of the following as one fraction in its lowest terms in questions 25–45.

25. $\frac{3}{5}+\frac{1}{5}$ 26. $\frac{4}{7}+\frac{2}{7}$ 27. $\frac{1}{9}+\frac{7}{9}-\frac{5}{9}$

28. $\frac{7}{8}-\frac{6}{8}$ 29. $\frac{5}{6}-\frac{1}{6}$ 30. $\frac{3}{10}+\frac{7}{10}-\frac{1}{10}$

31. $\frac{1}{2}+\frac{1}{4}$ 32. $\frac{2}{3}+\frac{1}{2}$ 33. $\frac{3}{4}+\frac{2}{3}$

34. $\frac{5}{6}+\frac{2}{3}$ 35. $\frac{3}{4}-\frac{2}{5}$ 36. $\frac{2}{5}-\frac{3}{10}$

37. $2\frac{3}{4}+2\frac{1}{8}$ 38. $4\frac{1}{5}+1\frac{1}{4}$ 39. $2\frac{3}{8}+3\frac{1}{4}$

40. $4\frac{3}{5}-2\frac{1}{10}$ 41. $3\frac{1}{3}-2\frac{5}{12}$ 42. $2\frac{1}{3}-3\frac{1}{4}$

43. $4\frac{1}{2}+1\frac{1}{4}-2\frac{3}{8}$ 44. $3\frac{1}{4}-2\frac{1}{3}+2\frac{1}{6}$ 45. $4\frac{3}{4}-2\frac{1}{5}-3\frac{7}{10}$

46. The bristles on a hairbrush are $8\frac{3}{4}$ cm in length. The handle is $11\frac{1}{3}$ cm in length. Find the total length of the hairbrush.

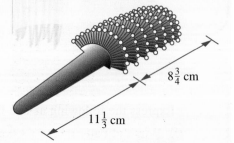

$8\frac{3}{4}$ cm

$11\frac{1}{3}$ cm

47. Two lengths of piping are joined together. The total length is $25\frac{1}{4}$ cm. The length of piping marked b is $8\frac{2}{3}$ cm. Calculate the length of piping marked a.

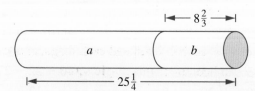

$8\frac{2}{3}$

a

b

$25\frac{1}{4}$

48. Fiona is training for the women's mini-marathon. During a certain week she trained on three evenings. On one evening she ran $2\frac{3}{4}$ km, on another evening $3\frac{7}{12}$ km and on the third evening she ran $4\frac{1}{6}$ km. How many kilometres did Fiona run during that week?

49. Ann, Bren and Liam are the only candidates in a school election. Ann got $\frac{7}{20}$ of the votes. Bren got $\frac{2}{5}$ of the votes.

    (i) What fraction of the votes did Liam get?

    (ii) Which candidate won the election? Justify your answer.

50. Indicate the following on the number line. (i) $1\frac{1}{2}$ (ii) $2\frac{1}{4}$ (iii) $3\frac{2}{3}$ (iv) $4\frac{7}{8}$

$$\overset{\displaystyle 0 \qquad\quad 1 \qquad\quad 2 \qquad\quad 3 \qquad\quad 4 \qquad\quad 5}{\rule{0pt}{0pt}}$$

51. $\frac{1}{3} + \frac{1}{2} = x$. Indicate x on the number line.

$$\overset{\displaystyle 0 \hspace{11cm} 1}{\rule{0pt}{0pt}}$$

52. Write the following fractions in order of size, starting with the **smallest**.

    (i) $\frac{7}{10}, \frac{3}{5}$ (ii) $\frac{1}{2}, \frac{1}{4}, \frac{3}{8}$ (iii) $\frac{5}{16}, \frac{3}{4}, \frac{1}{8}, \frac{1}{2}$

53. Which of the fractions $\frac{4}{5}, \frac{19}{20}, \frac{7}{10}$ or $\frac{1}{4}$ lie between $\frac{1}{2}$ and $\frac{3}{4}$? Justify your answer.

54. Paul and Lisa have identical glasses containing some water. Paul's glass is $\frac{1}{2}$ full and Lisa's glass is $\frac{1}{3}$ full. The water from both their glasses will be poured into an identical empty glass. They want to find what fraction of the empty glass will contain water. Paul puts six equally spaced markings on the empty glass, where the sixth mark is at the top of the glass.

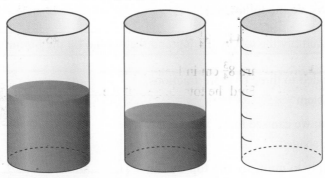

    (i) Why did Paul use six markings?

    (ii) What fraction of the third glass does **not** contain water?

55. Rory is trying to subtract $\frac{1}{5}$ from $\frac{7}{8}$. His attempt is shown here: $\frac{7}{8} - \frac{1}{5} = \frac{6}{3} = 2$.

    (i) Explain what Rory has done wrong.

    (ii) Write out the correct solution.

56. In a magic square, each row, each column and each diagonal add up to the same number. Copy and complete this magic square.

$\frac{1}{3}$		
$\frac{1}{4}$	$\frac{1}{3}$	$\frac{5}{12}$

57. (i) What fraction of this figure is shaded?

(ii) How many more squares would have to be shaded for $\frac{3}{4}$ of the figure to be shaded?

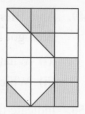

58. What is the missing fraction in each of these balance diagrams?

(i) 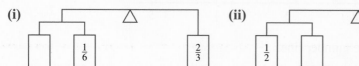 (ii)

$\frac{1}{6}$ $\frac{2}{3}$ $\frac{1}{2}$ $\frac{4}{5}$

59. Clocks have 12 divisions round the face. What fraction of a full turn does:

(i) The minute hand turn through from 08:15 to 08:35

(ii) The minute hand turn through from 09:20 to 10:05

(iii) The hour hand turn through from 02:00 to 07:00

(iv) The hour hand turn through from 03:00 to 04:30

Multiplication of fractions

To multiply two fractions, do the following:

> Multiply the top by the top and the bottom by the bottom.

Note: This can be extended to three or more fractions.

Consider the problem $\frac{2}{3} \times \frac{4}{5}$.

From the diagram, we can see that $\frac{2}{3} \times \frac{4}{5} = \frac{8}{15}$.
Eight squares are shaded.

A shortcut is simply to **multiply the top by the top and the bottom by the bottom**.

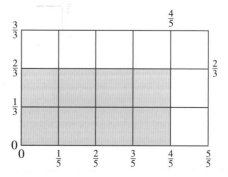

EXAMPLE

Express the following as one fraction. (i) $\frac{3}{7} \times \frac{2}{5}$ (ii) $2\frac{1}{2} \times 1\frac{4}{5}$

Solution:

(i) $\frac{3}{7} \times \frac{2}{5} = \frac{6}{35}$ (multiply the top by the top and the bottom by the bottom)

(ii)　$2\frac{1}{2} \times 1\frac{4}{5}$

$= \frac{5}{2} \times \frac{9}{5}$　　(write both fractions as top-heavy fractions)

$= \frac{45}{10}$　　(multiply the top by the top and the bottom by the bottom)

$= \frac{9}{2}$ or $4\frac{1}{2}$　　(divide the top and bottom by 5)

Alternatively, we can divide the top and bottom by common factors before multiplying:

$2\frac{1}{2} \times 1\frac{4}{5} = \frac{5}{2} \times \frac{9}{5_1} = \frac{9}{2}$ or $4\frac{1}{2}$

Exercise 4.3

Express each of the following as a single fraction in its lowest terms in questions 1–16.

1. $\frac{2}{3} \times \frac{5}{7}$　　　　2. $\frac{3}{4} \times \frac{1}{5}$　　　　3. $\frac{5}{7} \times \frac{3}{4}$　　　　4. $\frac{3}{5} \times \frac{5}{9}$

5. $\frac{2}{3} \times \frac{4}{7}$　　　　6. $\frac{5}{6} \times \frac{9}{10}$　　　　7. $1\frac{1}{2} \times \frac{5}{8}$　　　　8. $2\frac{1}{2} \times 1\frac{1}{5}$

9. $1\frac{1}{4} \times \frac{2}{3}$　　　　10. $3\frac{1}{2} \times \frac{7}{6}$　　　　11. $2\frac{1}{2} \times \frac{3}{5}$　　　　12. $2\frac{3}{4} \times 1\frac{3}{11}$

13. $2\frac{2}{3} \times 3\frac{3}{4}$　　　　14. $\frac{2}{3} \times \frac{3}{4} \times \frac{5}{8}$　　　　15. $2\frac{1}{4} \times 1\frac{5}{11} \times 1\frac{1}{2}$　　　　16. $2\frac{1}{3} \times \frac{2}{3} \times \frac{5}{8}$

17. **(i)** The diagram shows a 5×4 grid. Using shading or otherwise, show that $\frac{3}{4}$ of $\frac{4}{5} = \frac{12}{20} = \frac{3}{5}$.

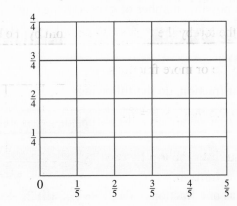

(ii) Construct a 4×3 grid. Using shading or otherwise, show that $\frac{2}{3}$ of $\frac{3}{4} = \frac{1}{2}$.

18. Which is larger, $\frac{4}{5}$ of $4\frac{1}{8}$ or $\frac{2}{5}$ of $8\frac{1}{2}$? Justify your answer.

19. Each lap of a race is $1\frac{3}{5}$ km long. What is the total length of a $6\frac{1}{4}$ lap race?

20. A litre bottle is $\frac{2}{3}$ full of apple juice. Breda drinks $\frac{4}{5}$ of the apple juice.

    What fraction of a litre of apple juice **(i)** does Breda drink **(ii)** is left in the bottle?

21. The diagram shows a rectangular flowerbed of length $13\frac{1}{2}$ m and width $5\frac{1}{3}$ m.

    (i) What is the area of the flowerbed?

    (ii) What is the perimeter (distance around the edges) of the flowerbed?

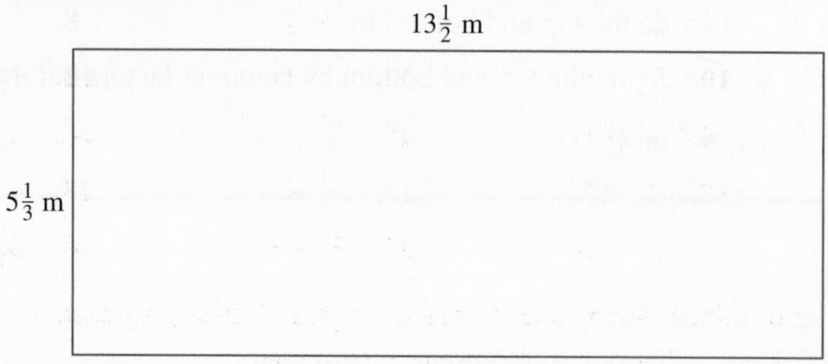

$$13\frac{1}{2}\ \text{m}$$

$5\frac{1}{3}$ m

22. Aideen has two cats. One cat eats $\frac{1}{3}$ of a tin of cat food in the morning and exactly the same in the evening. Her second cat eats $\frac{1}{2}$ of a tin of cat food once per day. How many tins of cat food does she need to buy to feed her cats for one week?

23. Jack eats $\frac{1}{5}$ of a bag of sweets. He shares the remaining sweets equally among Tom, Paul and Lisa.

    (i) What fraction of the bag of sweets does Tom get?

    (ii) What is the smallest possible number of sweets in the bag?

Division of fractions

To divide one fraction by another fraction, do the following:

> Turn the fraction we are dividing by upside down and multiply.

EXAMPLE

Express the following as one fraction. **(i)** $2\frac{1}{3} \div 1\frac{5}{6}$ **(ii)** $2\frac{3}{5} \div 4$

Solution:

(i)
$$2\frac{1}{3} \div 1\frac{5}{6}$$
$$= \frac{7}{3} \div \frac{11}{6}$$
$$= \frac{7}{3} \times \frac{6}{11}$$
$$= \frac{42}{33}$$
$$= \frac{14}{11} \text{ or } 1\frac{3}{11}$$

(ii)
$$2\frac{3}{5} \div 4$$
$$= \frac{13}{5} \div \frac{4}{1}$$
$$= \frac{13}{5} \times \frac{1}{4}$$
$$= \frac{13}{20}$$

Note: $4 = \frac{4}{1}$ as a top-heavy fraction

Note: $\frac{5}{3}$ is the reciprocal of $\frac{3}{5}$. Similarly, the reciprocal of $3\left(\frac{3}{1}\right)$ is $\frac{1}{3}$.

Exercise 4.4

Express each of the following as a single fraction in its lowest terms in questions 1–24.

1. $\frac{3}{5} \div \frac{4}{7}$

2. $\frac{2}{5} \div \frac{1}{3}$

3. $\frac{2}{3} \div \frac{5}{3}$

4. $\frac{4}{5} \div \frac{3}{5}$

5. $\frac{3}{8} \div \frac{1}{4}$

6. $\frac{7}{9} \div \frac{14}{3}$

7. $\frac{1}{2} \div \frac{1}{4}$

8. $\frac{8}{3} \div \frac{2}{3}$

9. $1\frac{1}{5} \div 3\frac{3}{5}$

10. $2\frac{1}{4} \div 3\frac{3}{5}$

11. $\frac{2}{3} \div 1\frac{2}{3}$

12. $1\frac{1}{2} \div 1\frac{3}{4}$

13. $1\frac{4}{5} \div 2\frac{7}{10}$

14. $4\frac{1}{4} \div 1\frac{5}{12}$

15. $5\frac{1}{4} \div 10\frac{1}{2}$

16. $2\frac{5}{8} \div \frac{3}{4}$

17. $4\frac{4}{5} \div 1\frac{1}{7}$

18. $4\frac{1}{3} \div 1\frac{6}{7}$

19. $3\frac{1}{8} \div \frac{5}{12}$

20. $8 \div 2\frac{1}{2}$

21. $4 \div \frac{1}{5}$

22. $3\frac{1}{2} \div 10$

23. $3\frac{1}{8} \div \frac{5}{16}$

24. $6\frac{1}{4} \div 1\frac{7}{8}$

25. Paula has 3 kg of mince. She wishes to make burgers of mass $\frac{1}{6}$ kg each. How many burgers can she make? Draw a diagram to represent the problem.

26. Sean has invited 17 friends to a party in his house. He has ordered 12 pizzas and has decided that each friend and himself is to get $\frac{2}{3}$ of a pizza. Has he ordered enough pizzas? Justify your answer.

27. How many $2\frac{1}{4}$ cm lengths of wire can be cut from a roll $49\frac{1}{2}$ cm in length?

28. A ball bearing has a mass of $1\frac{1}{6}$ grams. How many ball bearings have a total mass of 49 grams?

29. A race is $5\frac{2}{5}$ km is length. Each lap is $\frac{9}{20}$ km long. How many laps would an athlete complete if he finished the race?

Exponents: Powers of fractions

Just as $2^3 = 2 \times 2 \times 2 = 8$, so $\left(\frac{4}{5}\right)^3 = \frac{4}{5} \times \frac{4}{5} \times \frac{4}{5} = \frac{64}{125}$.

Simply multiply the top by the top by the top and the bottom by the bottom by the bottom. Fractions to other powers can be calculated in the same way.

Always write mixed numbers as top-heavy fractions first.

EXAMPLE

Write the following fractions without exponents (powers). (i) $\left(\frac{1}{2}\right)^3$ (ii) $\left(1\frac{1}{2}\right)^2$

Solution:

(i) $\left(\frac{1}{2}\right)^3$

$= \frac{1}{2} \times \frac{1}{2} \times \frac{1}{2}$

$= \frac{1}{8}$

(ii) $\left(1\frac{1}{2}\right)^2$

$= \left(\frac{3}{2}\right)^2$ (top-heavy fraction)

$= \frac{3}{2} \times \frac{3}{2} = \frac{9}{4}$ or $2\frac{1}{4}$

Exercise 4.5

Write the following as fractions without exponents (powers).

1. $\left(\frac{1}{2}\right)^2$
2. $\left(\frac{2}{3}\right)^2$
3. $\left(\frac{3}{4}\right)^2$
4. $\left(\frac{4}{5}\right)^2$
5. $\left(\frac{1}{4}\right)^2$

6. $\left(\frac{1}{3}\right)^2$
7. $\left(\frac{1}{3}\right)^3$
8. $\left(\frac{1}{5}\right)^3$
9. $\left(\frac{3}{5}\right)^3$
10. $\left(\frac{5}{4}\right)^2$

11. $\left(1\frac{1}{3}\right)^2$
12. $\left(1\frac{3}{4}\right)^2$
13. $\left(3\frac{1}{3}\right)^2$
14. $\left(2\frac{2}{5}\right)^2$
15. $\left(1\frac{1}{2}\right)^3$

16. $\left(1\frac{4}{5}\right)^2$
17. $\left(\frac{2}{3}\right)^3$
18. $\left(2\frac{1}{2}\right)^3$
19. $\left(-\frac{1}{2}\right)^2$
20. $\left(-\frac{2}{3}\right)^2$

Order of operations for fractions

The order of operations for fractions is the same as that for integers. Keep **BEMDAS** in mind.

EXAMPLE

Write the following as one fraction. (i) $\frac{1}{2} \times \frac{3}{4} + \frac{5}{16}$ (ii) $\frac{6}{5}\left(\frac{5}{12} + \frac{1}{4}\right)$

(i) $\frac{1}{2} \times \frac{3}{4} + \frac{5}{16}$

   $= \frac{3}{8} + \frac{5}{16}$ (multiplication first)

   $= \frac{11}{16}$ (addition)

(ii) $\frac{6}{5}\left(\frac{5}{12} + \frac{1}{4}\right)$

   $= \frac{6}{5}\left(\frac{2}{3}\right)$ (brackets first)

   $= \frac{12}{15}$ (multiplication)

   $= \frac{4}{5}$ (simplify)

Exercise 4.6

Express each of the following as one fraction in its lowest terms in questions 1–18 (keep **BEMDAS** in mind).

1. $\frac{1}{4} \times \frac{3}{5} + \frac{7}{10}$
2. $\frac{3}{2} \times \frac{1}{5} + \frac{3}{10}$
3. $\frac{3}{4} \times \frac{5}{3} + \frac{1}{2}$

4. $\frac{5}{2}\left(\frac{7}{10} - \frac{3}{5}\right)$
5. $\frac{3}{4}\left(\frac{1}{2} + \frac{1}{3}\right)$
6. $\frac{1}{2} + \frac{2}{3} \times \frac{5}{4}$

7. $\frac{2}{3} \div \frac{4}{9} + \frac{1}{2}$
8. $\frac{1}{2} + \frac{1}{4} \div \frac{2}{3}$
9. $1\frac{5}{16} + 2\frac{1}{4} \div 3\frac{3}{5}$

10. $\left(4\frac{2}{3} - 2\frac{3}{4}\right) \div 1\frac{8}{15}$
11. $\frac{3}{4}\left(1\frac{1}{5} \div 3\frac{3}{5}\right)$
12. $\left(2\frac{1}{5} - 1\frac{3}{10}\right) \div \left(\frac{1}{2} + \frac{2}{5}\right)$

13. $\left(2\frac{1}{2} - 1\frac{3}{4}\right) \div \left(1\frac{1}{4} - 1\frac{1}{8}\right)$
14. $\frac{4}{9}\left(\frac{3}{4} \times \frac{2}{3} + \frac{5}{8}\right)$
15. $\frac{3}{17}\left(\frac{3}{5} + \frac{2}{5} \div \frac{3}{4}\right)$

16. $\frac{3}{4} + \left(\frac{1}{2}\right)^2$
17. $\left(\frac{1}{2} + \frac{1}{3}\right)^2$
18. $\frac{10}{3}\left(\frac{3}{5} - \frac{1}{2}\right)^2$

19. Verify that $\frac{3}{4}\left(\frac{4}{5} + \frac{1}{3}\right) = \frac{3}{4} \times \frac{4}{5} + \frac{3}{4} \times \frac{1}{3}$.

20. Express $\dfrac{\frac{2}{5} + \frac{3}{4}}{1\frac{1}{5} + 2\frac{1}{4}}$ as one fraction in its lowest terms.

21. Hazel spent $\frac{1}{4}$ of her income on food and $\frac{2}{5}$ of the remainder of her income on rent. What fraction of her income did Hazel:

(i) Not spend on food

(ii) Spend on rent

(iii) Spend on food and rent

(iv) Not spend on food or rent

22. A bag of sugar weighs 1 kg. Pat uses $\frac{1}{4}$ of the bag to make some biscuits. Lisa uses $\frac{2}{3}$ of the remaining sugar to make a cake.

(i) How many grams of sugar are left?

(ii) What fraction of the bag of sugar is left?

(**Note:** 1 kg = 1,000 g)

23. Choose a starting fraction, such as $\frac{2}{5}$.

(i) Calculate a new fraction $= \dfrac{1 - \text{starting fraction}}{1 + \text{starting fraction}}$ then calculate $\dfrac{1 - \text{new fraction}}{1 + \text{new fraction}}$.

(ii) Repeat for several different starting fractions.

(iii) Write down what you notice.

Problems involving fractions

Note: $\frac{3}{5}$ of 20 means $\frac{3}{5} \times 20$.

EXAMPLE

(i) Express 45 minutes as a fraction of 3 hours.

(ii) $\frac{4}{5}$ of a number is 32. What is the number?

Solution:

(i) First change 3 hours to minutes.

3 hours $= 3 \times 60 = 180$ minutes

45 minutes as a fraction of 3 hours $= \frac{45}{180} = \frac{1}{4}$

(ii) $\frac{4}{5}(\text{number}) = 32$ (given)

$4\,(\text{number}) = 160$ (multiply both sides by 5)

$\text{number} = 40$ (divide both sides by 4)

Note: An alternative method is to find $\frac{1}{5}$ of the number by dividing both sides by 4 and then multiplying both sides by 5 or simply divide both sides by $\frac{4}{5}$. Whatever method you use, make sure you are doing the same thing to both sides.

Exercise 4.7

Express the first number as a fraction of the second number in questions 1–8.

1. 15; 20
2. 18; 30
3. 28; 42
4. 20; 100
5. 20; 32
6. 9; 27
7. 15; 90
8. 14; 56

Express the first quantity as a fraction of the second quantity in questions 9–20.

9. 35c; €1·05
10. 4 days; 2 weeks
11. 50 cm; 1 m
12. 750 m; 1 km
13. 90c; €3
14. 20 minutes; 1 hour
15. 800 g; 1 kg
16. 15 hours; 2 days
17. 18 seconds; $1\frac{1}{2}$ minutes
18. 8 mm; 2 cm
19. 12 days; 4 weeks
20. 8 months; 2 years

21. A man spent $2\frac{1}{2}$ hours gardening on Saturday morning. He spent 60 minutes trimming the hedge, 50 minutes cutting grass and the rest of the time weeding. What fraction of this time did he spend:

    (i) Trimming the hedge   (ii) Cutting the grass   (iii) Weeding

22. In a bag containing 240 marbles, 80 are red, 72 are green, 48 are blue and the remainder are white. What fraction of these marbles are:

    (i) Red   (ii) Green   (iii) Blue   (iv) White

23. Simplify: (i) $3 \times \frac{2}{3}$ (ii) $5 \times \frac{4}{5}$ (iii) $7\left(\frac{5}{7}\right)$ (iv) $8\left(\frac{9}{8}\right)$

Calculate the number in questions 24–29.

24. $\frac{1}{4}$ of the number is 10
25. $\frac{2}{3}$ of the number is 16
26. $\frac{3}{5}$ of the number is 12
27. $\frac{5}{6}$ of the number is 20
28. $\frac{7}{8}$ of the number is 28
29. $\frac{8}{9}$ of the number is 48

30. Sean spent $\frac{3}{4}$ of his pocket money and had €10 left. How much had he at first?

31. In a club, $\frac{3}{5}$ of the members are girls. The remaining 180 members are boys.
    How many members are there altogether?

32. The table below shows some information about the number of people attending a school play.

	Men	Women	Children
Fraction of people	$\frac{1}{8}$	$\frac{1}{4}$	P
Number of people	30	Q	R

    (i) Find the value of the fraction marked P.   (ii) Calculate the numbers Q and R.

33. A ball is dropped onto a hard surface. Each time it bounces, it rebounds to exactly $\frac{4}{5}$ of the height from which it fell. After the first bounce, the ball rises to a height of 60 cm. From what height was it originally dropped?

CHAPTER 5 DECIMALS

Decimals and place value

A decimal is another way of writing a fraction. Decimals are used for parts of a number that are smaller than 1. The decimal point separates a number into its whole number part and its fractional part.

For example, consider the numbers 256·7, 45·83 and 1·478.

	Hundreds	Tens	Units	•	Tenths	Hundredths	Thousandths	separate parts
256·7:	2	5	6	•	7			$= 200 + 50 + 6 + \frac{7}{10}$
45·83:		4	5	•	8	3		$= 40 + 5 + \frac{8}{10} + \frac{3}{100}$
1·478:			1	•	4	7	8	$= 1 + \frac{4}{10} + \frac{7}{100} + \frac{8}{1{,}000}$

Fractions with 10, 100, 1,000, etc. on the bottom can easily be written as decimals.

For example, $\frac{7}{10} = 0{\cdot}7$, $\frac{3}{100} = 0{\cdot}03$, $\frac{23}{1{,}000} = 0{\cdot}023$.

(These decimals can be verified on your calculator.)

Other fractions can be written as decimals by simply dividing the bottom into the top, using your calculator.

For example, $\frac{3}{5} = 0{\cdot}4$, $\frac{3}{8} = 0{\cdot}375$, $\frac{5}{4} = 1{\cdot}25$.

Exercise 5.1

Write each of the following as a decimal in questions 1–40.

1. $\frac{2}{10}$	**2.** $\frac{3}{10}$	**3.** $\frac{1}{100}$	**4.** $\frac{7}{100}$	**5.** $\frac{4}{100}$
6. $\frac{3}{100}$	**7.** $\frac{9}{1{,}000}$	**8.** $\frac{6}{10}$	**9.** $\frac{6}{100}$	**10.** $\frac{2}{100}$
11. $\frac{1}{1{,}000}$	**12.** $\frac{7}{1{,}000}$	**13.** $\frac{9}{100}$	**14.** $\frac{8}{10}$	**15.** $\frac{3}{1{,}000}$
16. $\frac{56}{10}$	**17.** $\frac{23}{100}$	**18.** $\frac{4}{100}$	**19.** $\frac{2}{1{,}000}$	**20.** $\frac{27}{1{,}000}$
21. $\frac{3}{5}$	**22.** $\frac{1}{2}$	**23.** $\frac{1}{5}$	**24.** $\frac{1}{8}$	**25.** $\frac{5}{8}$
26. $\frac{7}{8}$	**27.** $\frac{5}{2}$	**28.** $\frac{3}{2}$	**29.** $\frac{7}{4}$	**30.** $\frac{7}{5}$
31. $\frac{3}{20}$	**32.** $\frac{12}{5}$	**33.** $\frac{13}{4}$	**34.** $\frac{13}{16}$	**35.** $\frac{24}{50}$
36. $2\frac{1}{5}$	**37.** $4\frac{1}{2}$	**38.** $2\frac{3}{4}$	**39.** $1\frac{7}{40}$	**40.** $1\frac{3}{16}$

41. (i) Write down the number shown by the arrow.

(ii) Write down the number shown by the arrow.

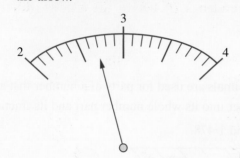

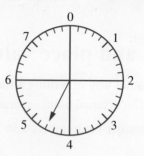

42. Insert a decimal point in the number:

(i) 2,347 so that the digit 3 represents (a) 3 (b) three-tenths

(ii) 1,638 so that the digit 6 represents (a) 60 (b) six-tenths

(iii) 51,296 so that the digit 2 represents (a) 200 (b) two-hundredths

(iv) 23,584 so that the digit 5 represents (a) 5 (b) 50 (c) five-tenths

43. Use all the cards shown once: | 5 | 0 | 6 | · |

(i) Write down the largest number you can make if the last digit cannot be zero and there must be at least one digit after the decimal point.

(ii) Write down the smallest number you can make if the first digit cannot be zero and there must be at least one digit before the decimal point.

Writing decimals as fractions

To write a decimal as a fraction, do the following:

1. Write the decimal number over 1.
2. Multiply the top and bottom by 10, 100, 1,000, etc. until the top is a whole number.
3. Simplify this fraction (if possible).

EXAMPLE

Write the following as a fraction in its lowest terms. (i) 0·8   (ii) 0·55   (iii) 1·125

Solution:

(i)   0·8

$$= \frac{0·8}{1}$$

$$= \frac{8}{10}$$

$$= \frac{4}{5}$$

(ii)   0·55

$$= \frac{0·55}{1}$$

$$= \frac{55}{100}$$

$$= \frac{11}{20}$$

(iii)   1·125

$$= \frac{1·125}{1}$$

$$= \frac{1,125}{1,000}$$

$$= \frac{9}{8}$$

Exercise 5.2

Express each of the following decimals as a fraction in its lowest terms in questions 1–25.

1. 0·4
2. 0·7
3. 0·6
4. 0·2
5. 0·9
6. 0·25
7. 0·75
8. 0·15
9. 0·35
10. 0·55
11. 0·125
12. 0·375
13. 1·1
14. 2·3
15. 3·8
16. 0·05
17. 2·45
18. 3·24
19. 2·8
20. 0·0625
21. 1·16
22. 3·625
23. 2·44
24. 1·08
25. 2·05

26. In each of the following numbers, express the underlined digit as a fraction in its lowest terms.

    (i) 0·8̲6   (ii) 2·24̲5   (iii) 45·38̲7   (iv) 120·00̲5

Order of operations

The order of operations for decimals is the same as that for integers. Keep **BEMDAS** in mind.

EXAMPLE

Calculate: (i) 5(2·3) + 2·1   (ii) 3·2 − 23·52 ÷ 4·2

             (iii) 8(5·6 − 2·5)   (iv) 5(0·4 + 0·2)^2

Solution:

(i)   5(2·3) + 2·1

    = 11·5 + 2·1   (multiplication)

    = 13·6   (addition)

(ii) $3 \cdot 2 - 23 \cdot 52 \div 4 \cdot 2$

$= 3 \cdot 2 - 5 \cdot 6$ (division)

$= -2 \cdot 4$ (subtraction)

(iii) $8(5 \cdot 6 - 2 \cdot 5)$

$= 8(3 \cdot 1)$ (brackets)

$= 24 \cdot 8$ (multiplication)

(iv) $5(0 \cdot 4 + 0 \cdot 2)^2$

$= 5(0 \cdot 6)^2$ (brackets)

$= 5(0 \cdot 36)$ (exponents)

$= 1 \cdot 8$ (multiplication)

Exercise 5.3

Calculate each of the following in questions 1–28.

1. $4 \cdot 6 + 3 \cdot 2 + 1 \cdot 7$

2. $10 \cdot 3 + 4 \cdot 8 - 8 \cdot 9$

3. $3(4 \cdot 5) + 8 \cdot 4$

4. $8(2 \cdot 7) - 10 \cdot 5$

5. $9 \cdot 62 \div 3 \cdot 7$

6. $12 \cdot 88 \div 4 \cdot 6 + 1 \cdot 2$

7. $6 \cdot 3 + 0 \cdot 42 \div 0 \cdot 07$

8. $2 \cdot 1 + 3 \cdot 4(6 \cdot 5)$

9. $3(8 \cdot 2) + 2(5 \cdot 4)$

10. $5(8 \cdot 7) - 7(3 \cdot 4)$

11. $8(5 \cdot 6 - 2 \cdot 4)$

12. $2 \cdot 7(7 \cdot 3 - 5 \cdot 1)$

13. $(38 \cdot 48 - 7 \cdot 43) \div 6 \cdot 9$

14. $4 \cdot 5 - 28 \cdot 35 \div 6 \cdot 3$

15. $5 \cdot 5 \div 0 \cdot 25 + 4 \cdot 5 \div 0 \cdot 9$

16. $2 \cdot 45(16 \cdot 32 - 11 \cdot 28)$

17. $6 \cdot 2(3 \cdot 4 - 5 \cdot 2)$

18. $50 \cdot 46 \div (10 \cdot 1 - 1 \cdot 4)$

19. $3 \cdot 1(1 \cdot 84 \div 0 \cdot 8 + 2 \cdot 7)$

20. $(2 \cdot 4 + 1 \cdot 3)(2 \cdot 4 - 1 \cdot 3)$

21. $(2 \cdot 4)^2 + (0 \cdot 3)^2$

22. $(1 \cdot 6)^2 - (0 \cdot 8)^2$

23. $3(0 \cdot 2)^2 + 4(0 \cdot 5)^2$

24. $6 \cdot 4(1 \cdot 2 + 1 \cdot 3)^2$

25. $\dfrac{2 \cdot 2 + 4 \cdot 4}{0 \cdot 11}$

26. $\dfrac{3 \cdot 04 + 4 \cdot 76}{0 \cdot 29 - 0 \cdot 05}$

27. $\dfrac{10(7 \cdot 168 + 2 \cdot 832)}{8(8 \cdot 762 - 5 \cdot 637)}$

28. (i) $(0 \cdot 6)^2$ (ii) $1 - (0 \cdot 6)^2$ (iii) $\dfrac{4}{1 - (0 \cdot 6)^2}$ (iv) $\sqrt{\dfrac{4}{1 - (0 \cdot 6)^2}}$

29. Consider the diagrams below. On each straight line, the numbers in the circles multiply together to make the number in the rectangle. Copy and complete the diagrams by filling in the missing numbers.

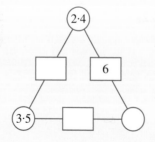 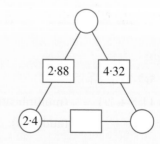

30. Carl the plumber has a 7·5 m length of copper pipe. He
    needs to cut it into 40 cm lengths.

    (i) How many complete pieces will he get?

    (ii) What is the length of the piece left over?

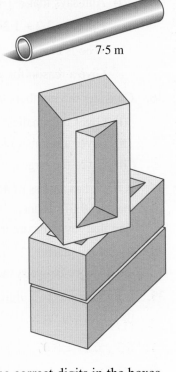

7·5 m

31. Consider the brick shown.

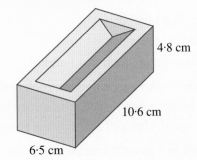

4·8 cm

10·6 cm

6·5 cm

If you have to stack the bricks one on top of the other, find the
difference between the maximum possible height and the
minimum possible height.

32. Use all the digits 1, 3, 5 and 7 once to make two
    decimal numbers so that the difference between these
    two numbers is less than 2 but greater than 0. There is
    more than one solution.

Put the correct digits in the boxes.

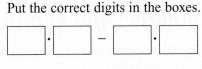

33. Joan has stamps costing 54c each and stamps costing 38c each. How many of each stamp
    should she use to post a parcel costing exactly €3·14?

34. On his birthday, Thomas is given a big jar of very small sweets.

    He wants to find out how many sweets are in the jar, but it would take
    too long to count them.

    A label on the jar tells him that the total mass of the sweets is 600 g.
    He weighs five sweets. The mass of the five sweets is 3·75 g.

    (i) Calculate the mass of one sweet.

    (ii) How many sweets are in the jar?

35. **(i)** Ann says that $3\cdot2 + 1\cdot34 = 4\cdot36$.

   Bill says $3\cdot2 + 1\cdot34 = 4\cdot54$.

   Who is correct?

   Give a reason for your answer.

(ii) Tom says that $4\cdot6 - 1\cdot32 = 3\cdot28$.

   Ian says $4\cdot6 - 1\cdot32 = 3\cdot32$.

   Who made the mistake?

   Give a reason for your answer.

36. Consider the numbers $0\cdot3$, $2\cdot6$, $0\cdot8$, $15\cdot6$ and $1\cdot5$. Which two of these numbers:

   (i) Gives the smallest number when multiplied? Find that number.

   (ii) Gives a number closest to 4 when multiplied? Find that number.

   (iii) Gives the largest number when one is divided by the other? Find that number.

37. A truck has a mass of $4\cdot8$ tonnes when empty. It is loaded with 72 metal ingots, each having a mass of $0\cdot075$ tonnes. The truck wants to drive over a bridge when loaded. The bridge has a sign that says 'maximum 10 tonnes'. Should the truck use the bridge? Justify your answer.

38. Rivets are placed $32\cdot4$ mm apart. If 21 rivets are placed in a straight line assembly, calculate the distance between the first and last rivet.

39. A number has two digits after the decimal point. It is greater than $30\cdot1$ and less than $30\cdot2$. Its digits add up to 10. What is the number?

Rounding and approximation

In real life it is not always necessary to give exact answers, for example the number of people that attended a rock concert. It may even be impossible to give an exact answer, for example the number of hairs on your head. A number can be rounded to an approximate number. We round numbers according to how accurately we wish to give the details.

Rounding to the nearest 10, 100, 1,000 and so on

If there were 8,427 people at a football match, a newspaper may report that '8,000 attended the football match'. The number 8,427 can be rounded to the nearest 10, 100 or 1,000.

8,427 rounded to the nearest 10 is 8,430

8,427 rounded to the nearest 100 is 8,400

8,427 rounded to the nearest 1,000 is 8,000

Note: It is a convention to round a number which is in the middle to the to the higher number.
   For example:

85 to the nearest 10 is 90

550 to the nearest 100 is 600

3,500 to the nearest 1,000 is 4,000

Exercise 5.4

1. Complete the following table.

Number	Nearest 10	Nearest 100	Nearest 1,000
2,436	2440	2400	2000
1,289	1290	1300	1000
13,238	13240	13200	13000
45,621	45620	45600	46000
75,273	75270	75300	75000

2. It was reported that 54,573 people watched Dublin play Cork in Croke Park.
   Round the number of people to the nearest **(i)** 10 **(ii)** 100 **(iii)** 1,000 **(iv)** 10,000.

3. Write down each of the following figures to an appropriate degree of accuracy.

   (i) A class raised €69·73 for a certain charity

   (ii) The distance between two towns is 189 km

   (iii) The population of a town is 11,355

   (iv) The area of a field is 12,103 m^2

4. A lifeguard says, 'There are about 80 people in the pool today.' This figure is correct to the nearest 10. What is the **(i)** smallest **(ii)** largest number of people in the pool?

5. The number of people at a rock concert is 2,400 to the nearest 100.
   What is the **(i)** smallest **(ii)** largest number of people at the concert?

6. 18,537 people signed a petition. A report stated, '19,000 people sign petition.' To what degree of accuracy is the number given in the report?

7. **(i)** Rearrange the digits 6, 5, 7 and 4 to make the smallest possible number.

   (ii) Round your number to the nearest **(a)** 10 **(b)** 100 **(c)** 1,000.

8. Round off these readings to **(a)** the nearest 10 **(b)** the nearest 100.

9. Cian bought a new car for €19,495. His friend says, 'That's €20,000 to the nearest €1,000.'
   Is he correct? Explain your answer.

10. An equilateral triangle has lengths of sides of 10 cm, correct to the nearest cm.
    Calculate the smallest possible perimeter of the triangle.

Rounding to a certain number of decimal places

The number of digits after the decimal point, including zeros, is the number of decimal places.

Decimal numbers can be rounded off to a given number of decimal places with the following steps:

1. Count the digits after the decimal point to the required number of decimal places.
2. Look at the **next** digit to the right.
   (i) If it is 5 or more, increase the previous digit by 1.
   (ii) If it is less than 5, leave the previous digit as it is.
3. Remove all the digits to the right.

EXAMPLE

(i) Write 2·817 correct to two decimal places.

(ii) Write 54·73 correct to one decimal place.

Solution:

(i) 2·8 1 7
    ①②③

The third digit after the decimal point is 7. This is greater than 5, so round up. 1 is increased to 2.

∴ 2·817 = 2·82, correct to two decimal places

(ii) 54·7 3
      ①②

The second digit after the decimal point is 3. This is less than 5, so round down. Leave 7 as 7.

∴ 54·73 = 54·7, correct to one decimal place.

Exercise 5.5

1. Write each of the following numbers correct to one decimal place.
   (i) 8·77   (ii) 3·54   (iii) 23·35   (iv) 1·75   (v) 3·86

2. Write each of the following numbers correct to two decimal places.
   (i) 6·137   (ii) 9·144   (iii) 31·271   (iv) 0·638   (v) 0·00586

3. Write each of the following numbers correct to three decimal places.
   (i) 4·5766   (ii) 0·1234   (iii) 15·2891   (iv) 0·0376   (v) 2·4796

4. Write the answer to each of the follow calculations correct to two decimal places.
   (i) $2 \cdot 8 \times 4 \cdot 12$ (ii) $73 \div 4 \cdot 2$ (iii) $(6 \cdot 28)^2$ (iv) $\sqrt{6 \cdot 5}$

5. Write each of the following fractions as decimals correct to two decimal places.

   (i) $\frac{1}{7}$ (ii) $\frac{5}{3}$ (iii) $\frac{6}{11}$ (iv) $\frac{5}{18}$ (v) $\frac{1}{17}$

6. The display on a calculator shows the result of $31 \div 7$.

   What is the result correct to:

   (i) One decimal place   (ii) Two decimal places

4·428571429

7. The scales show Anthony's mass. Write Anthony's mass correct to:

   (i) One decimal place   (ii) Two decimal places

   (iii) Nearest kg   (iv) Nearest 10 kg

68·248
kg

8. $\frac{2}{9} = 0·222$ correct to three decimal places. Is $\frac{5}{9} = 0·555$ correct to three decimal places? Justify your answer.

Rounding to a certain number of significant figures

The most significant figure in a number is the figure which has the greatest value. In other words, the first figure on the left (except 0) is called the first significant figure, the next figure is called the second significant figure and so on. Significant means important.

To round a number to a given number of significant figures, do the following:

1. Start at the most significant figure and count the required number of figures.
2. Look at the next figure to the right.
   (i) If it is 5 or more, increase the previous figure by 1.
   (ii) If it is less than 5, leave the previous figure as it is.
3. Add zeros, as necessary, to preserve place value.

EXAMPLE

(i) Write 268·71 correct to two significant figures.

(ii) Write 0·0438 correct to one significant figure.

Solution:

(i) 2 6 8 · 7 1
    ①②③ ④ ⑤

The third significant figure is 8.
This is greater than 5, so round up.
6 is increased to 7.

Add one zero to locate place value.
∴ $268·71 = 270$, correct to two significant figures.

(ii) 0·04 3 8
     ①②③

The second significant figure is 3.
This is less than 5, so round down.
Leave 4 as 4.

∴ $0·0438 = 0·04$, correct to one significant figure.

Exercise 5.6

1. Write each of the following numbers correct to one significant figure.
   (i) 18   (ii) 623   (iii) 351   (iv) 24·6   (v) 0·087

2. Write each of the following numbers correct to two significant figures.
   (i) 467   (ii) 352   (iii) 4754   (iv) 28·6   (v) 0·0681

3. Write each of the following numbers correct to three significant figures.
   (i) 4,584   (ii) 7,587   (iii) 3,278   (iv) 24·86   (v) 0·07955

4. Write the answer to each of the follow calculations correct to two significant figures.
   (i) 243×34 (ii) $2·58 \times 3·6$ (iii) $124 \div 355$ (iv) $0·31 \times 0·94$

5. Write each of the following fractions as decimals correct to two significant figures.
   (i) $\frac{2}{3}$ (ii) $\frac{11}{7}$ (iii) $\frac{7}{11}$ (iv) $1\frac{7}{9}$ (v) $\frac{1}{18}$

6. The display shows the result of $199 \div 7$. What is the result correct to:
   (i) Two decimal places
   (ii) One decimal place

   28·42857143

   (iii) Two significant figures
   (iv) One significant figure

7. Mary thinks 578 correct to two significant figures is 58. Is she correct? Justify your answer.

Estimation and approximation

Being able to estimate the answer to a problem before using your calculator to make an exact calculation is an important skill. The estimate of the answer will show whether an error has been made, which could easily happen if you press a wrong key on your calculator.

EXAMPLE

(i) By rounding each of the numbers to its nearest whole number, calculate an approximate answer for:
$$\frac{48·27 + 12·146}{14·82 - 3·02}$$

(ii) Find the exact answer using your calculator.

Solution:

(i) If we write each number correct to the nearest whole number, the problem now reduces to:

$$\frac{48 + 12}{15 - 3} = \frac{60}{12} = 5$$

Therefore, 5 is an approximate answer.

(ii)

$$\frac{48 \cdot 27 + 12 \cdot 146}{14 \cdot 82 - 3 \cdot 02} = \frac{60 \cdot 416}{11 \cdot 8} = 5 \cdot 12$$

Therefore, the exact answer is 5·12 (very close to our estimate).

Exercise 5.7

In questions 1–12, round off each number to its nearest whole number and calculate an approximate answer. Then, using your calculator or otherwise, find the exact answer. In each case, calculate the positive difference between the exact value and the approximate value.

1. $4 \cdot 3 \times 5 \cdot 7$

2. $30 \cdot 08 \div 4 \cdot 7$

3. $2 \cdot 8 \times 5 \cdot 7 + 2 \cdot 04$

4. $\dfrac{9 \cdot 15 \times 2 \cdot 196}{5 \cdot 5815}$

5. $\dfrac{14 \cdot 18 - 4 \cdot 086}{1 \cdot 96}$

6. $\dfrac{18 \cdot 207}{3 \cdot 7 + 2 \cdot 08}$

7. $\dfrac{24 \cdot 092}{6 \cdot 1 - 2 \cdot 93}$

8. $\dfrac{66 \cdot 88 - 27 \cdot 36}{7 \cdot 6}$

9. $\dfrac{56 \cdot 214}{2 \cdot 31 + 5 \cdot 79}$

10. $\dfrac{15 \cdot 332 + 8 \cdot 94}{9 \cdot 1 - 3 \cdot 18}$

11. $\dfrac{3 \cdot 95 \times 8 \cdot 42 + 2 \cdot 948}{1 \cdot 8 \times 4 \cdot 3 + 1 \cdot 2}$

12. $\dfrac{30 \cdot 317}{\sqrt{24 \cdot 7009}}$

13. Terry uses his calculator to evaluate $38 \cdot 5 \times 4 \cdot 2$. The answer he got was $16 \cdot 17$. Use approximations to show that his answer is wrong.

14. (i) Write the numbers 608 and 19 correct to one significant figure.
    (ii) Hence, calculate an estimate of $608 \div 19$.
    (iii) Calculate the exact value of $608 \div 19$.
    (iv) Calculate the difference between your estimate and the exact value.

15. Part of a football stadium has 59 rows of seats and each row seats 99 people.
    (i) Estimate the number of people the stand can seat.
    (ii) Is your estimate bigger or smaller than the actual number?
        Justify you answer without calculating the exact value.

16. Kevin thinks that $4 \cdot 2 \times 10 = 4 \cdot 20$. How would you explain to Kevin why his answer is wrong? It is not enough just to give the correct answer.

17. Sean had to do the following calculation: $\dfrac{20 \cdot 8 - 4 \cdot 8}{1 \cdot 6}$.

First, he made an estimate of what his answer should be. Then he used his calculator to do the calculation. He got the answer 17·8.

Because of his estimate, he realised this answer could not be correct.

  (i) Show how Sean might have made a suitable estimate.

 (ii) Find the correct answer to the calculation.

(iii) Sean got his answer by keying the following into his calculator:

$$20 \cdot 8 \;\boxed{-}\; 4 \cdot 8 \;\boxed{\div}\; 1 \cdot 6 \;\boxed{=}$$

Explain why this did not give the correct answer to the calculation.

Notation used in algebra

Algebra is sometimes called the language of mathematics. Algebra can be used to communicate mathematically with other people.

Written	Means
a	$1 \times a$ or $1a$
$3a$	$3 \times a$ or $a + a + a$
ab	$a \times b$
$2ab$	$2 \times a \times b$ or $ab + ab$
a^2	$a \times a$
$4a^2$	$4 \times a \times a$ or $a^2 + a^2 + a^2 + a^2$
a^3	$a \times a \times a$
$\dfrac{a}{5}$	$a \div 5$ or $\frac{1}{5}a$
$-a$	$-1 \times a$ or $-1a$
$\dfrac{ab}{c}$	$(a \times b) \div (c)$

Substituting numbers for letters

A **substitute** is used to replace something. In football, a substitute replaces another player. In algebra, when we replace letters with numbers when evaluating expressions we call it **substitution**. When you are substituting numbers in an expression, it is good practice to put a bracket around the number that replaces the letter. (Remember: **BEMDAS**.)

EXAMPLE 1

If $a = 2$ and $b = 7$, find the value of the following.

(i) $2a + 5b$ (ii) $3ab + 4$ (iii) $(b - a)^2$

Solution:

(i) $2a + 5b$
$= 2(2) + 5(7)$
$= 4 + 35$
$= 39$

(ii) $3ab + 4$
$= 3(2)(7) + 4$
$= 42 + 4$
$= 46$

(iii) $(b - a)^2$
$= (7 - 2)^2$
$= (5)^2$
$= 25$

EXAMPLE 2

(i) If $x = 4$, find the value of $x^2 - x + 5\sqrt{x}$.

(ii) If $a = 3 \cdot 25$ and $b = 9$, find the value of $\sqrt{a^2 - b}$.

Solution:

(i) $\quad x^2 - x + 5\sqrt{x}$

$\quad = (4)^2 - (4) + 5\sqrt{4}$

$\quad = 16 - 4 + 5(2)$

$\quad = 16 - 4 + 10$

$\quad = 26 - 4$

$\quad = 22$

(ii) $\quad \sqrt{a^2 - b}$

$\quad = \sqrt{(3 \cdot 25)^2 - 9}$

$\quad = \sqrt{10 \cdot 5625 - 9}$

$\quad = \sqrt{1 \cdot 5625}$

$\quad = 1 \cdot 25$

Exercise 6.1

1. If $a = 3$, find the value of:

   (i) $a + 2$ (ii) $2a$ (iii) $4a + 1$ (iv) a^2

2. If $x = 5$, find the value of:

   (i) $x + 3$ (ii) $4x$ (iii) $3x + 2$ (iv) $2x - 5$

   (v) x^2 (vi) $12 + 2x$ (vii) $8 - x$ (viii) $\sqrt{x + 4}$

3. If $a = 2$ and $b = 5$, find the value of:

   (i) $a + b$ (ii) $b - a$ (iii) $a + 2b$ (iv) ab

   (v) $ab + 10$ (vi) $2ab - 20$ (vii) a^2 (viii) $a^2 + 3a + 6$

4. Find the value of $\dfrac{x + 2}{4}$ when (i) $x = 6$ (ii) $x = 18$ (iii) $x = 26$.

5. If $p = 2$, $q = 3$ and $r = 4$, find the value of $\dfrac{3pq + 6}{r}$.

6. When $x = 2$, find the value of $3x^2 + 5$.

7. If $x = 4$, find the value of $x^2 + 9\sqrt{x} - 20$.

8. When $a = 5$ and $b = 4$, find the value of $a^2 - 3\sqrt{b}$.

9. If $v = \sqrt{u^2 + 2as}$, find the value of v when $u = 8$, $a = 2$ and $s = 20$.

10. If $x = -2$, find the value of:

    (i) $x + 5$ (ii) $2x$ (iii) $3x + 7$ (iv) $x + 2$

    (v) $5 - 2x$ (vi) $1 - 3x$ (vii) $2x + 5$ (viii) $2x - 3$

11. If $p = 2$ and $q = -1$, find the value of:

   (i) $p + q$ (ii) $p - q$ (iii) $3p + 2q$ (iv) pq
   (v) $-4pq$ (vi) $p^2 - 5q$ (vii) $\sqrt{p^2 - 5q}$ (viii) $(p + q)^p$

12. If $x = 2$ and $y = -1$, find the value of $(x - y)^2$.

13. A gardener uses the formula $c = 10h + 1$ to calculate what he charges for work, where c = the cost in euro and h = the number of hours worked. Calculate what the gardener charges to work for (i) 2 hours (ii) 5 hours (iii) 8 hours (iv) $\frac{1}{2}$ hour.

14. The formula for the cost of a newspaper advert is given by the formula $C = 2w + 9$, where C = the cost in euro and w = the number of words. Calculate the cost of an advert that contains (i) 10 words (ii) 13 words (iii) 27 words.

15. The rule for converting degrees Fahrenheit into degrees Celsius is $C = \frac{5}{9}(F - 32)$. Using this rule, convert (i) 50°F (ii) 77°F into degrees Celsius.

16. The number of bacteria, N, in a colony is given by $N = 500(1 + gt)$, where g is the growth factor and t is the time in hours.

   (i) Calculate the value of N when $g = 0.2$ and $t = 4$.

   (ii) Write down the value of N when $t = 0$.

17. Two mobile companies calculate their bills in the following way:

   Easy Talk: Bill = €$(10 + 0.15\, m + 0.1\, t)$

   Talk On: Bill = €$(0.4\, m + 0.05\, t)$

   where m is the number of minutes and t is the number of texts.

   Calculate which company each of the people in the table should choose to have the cheapest bill.

Name	Minutes spent on calls	Number of text messages
Alice	62	15
Brian	8	120
Ciara	40	50
Dean	150	0

Language

Variable:	When letters are used to stand for different numbers, they are called **variables** or **unknowns**.
Constant:	Anything that has a fixed value (can't be changed) is called a **constant**. For example, 5, −3 and $\frac{1}{2}$ are constants because their values do not change.
Term:	A **term** is a single unit containing one or more variables, often with a constant in front or a constant on its own. For example, x, $3x^2$, $5ab$, $-4pq$ and 9 are terms.

Coefficient:	The number in front of a term is called the **coefficient** of the term.
	In the term $5x$, 5 is the coefficient of x.
	In the term $-4pq$, -4 is the coefficient of pq.
	In the term $-y$, -1 is the coefficient of y (as $-y = -1y$).
Expression:	An **expression** is a collection of terms separated by + and − symbols.
	$3a + 2b$ is an expression with two terms.
	$x^2 - 2x - 8$ is an expression with three terms.

Adding and subtracting terms

> Only terms that are the same can be added.

This rule ensures that algebra and arithmetic give the same result.

$2x$ and $3x$ are like terms. $3pq$ and $5pq$ are like terms. $4x^2$ and x^2 are like terms.

$2a$ and $5b$ are **not** like terms. $3x^2$ and $4x^3$ are **not** like terms.

Adding and subtracting like terms is often called **collecting like terms** or **simplifying the expression**.

Note: $p \times q = q \times p$, so $pq = qp$. However, we usually write the letters in alphabetical order.

EXAMPLE 1

Simplify each of the following expressions.

(i) $5x + 2x + x$ (ii) $2a + 5a - 4a$ (iii) $2x^2 + 4x^2 - 7x^2$

Solution:

(i) $5x + 2x + x$
     $= 5x + 2x + 1x$
     $= 8x$

(ii) $2a + 5a - 4a$
     $= 7a - 4a$
     $= 3a$

(iii) $2x^2 + 4x^2 - 7x^2$
     $= 6x^2 - 7x^2$
     $= -x^2$

EXAMPLE 2

Simplify each of the following expressions.

(i) $4a + 3b + 6 - 3a - 5b + 1$ (ii) $6x^2 - 3x - 7 - 2x^2 + 8x - 2$

Solution:

(i) $4a + 3b + 6 - 3a - 5b + 1$
     $= 4a - 3a + 3b - 5b + 6 + 1$
     $= a - 2b + 7$

(ii) $6x^2 - 3x - 7 - 2x^2 + 8x - 2$
     $= 6x^2 - 2x^2 - 3x + 8x - 7 - 2$
     $= 4x^2 + 5x - 9$

Exercise 6.2

Simplify each of the following expressions in questions 1–38.

1. $2a + 3a$
2. $4b + 5b$
3. $2x + 5x$
4. $5y + 3y$
5. $a + a + a$
6. $x + x + x + x$
7. $2x + x$
8. $5x + x$
9. $x + 6x$
10. $x + 2x + 3x$
11. $2a + a + a$
12. $3q + q + 4q$
13. $3a + 2 + 2a + 1$
14. $3x + 5 + 4x + 1$
15. $2a + 5b + 4a + 3b$
16. $4p^2 + 3p^2$
17. $5x^2 - 2x^2$
18. $6a^2 - 5a^2$
19. $5p - 2p + 4p$
20. $12x - 5x - 3x$
21. $10q + 3q - 8q + q$
22. $6ab + 3ab$
23. $5ab + ab$
24. $4ab - ab$
25. $3x - 5x$
26. $4x - 7x$
27. $12a - 14a$
28. $8x - 9x$
29. $4x - 5x$
30. $7a - 9a$
31. $5x - 3x + 4x - x$
32. $8x - 3x - 5x$
33. $-10x + 11x - 3x + 5x$
34. $x^2 + 2x + 4x + 8$
35. $x^2 + 3x - x - 15$
36. $x^2 - 4x - x + 4$
37. $3xy + 4xy - 5xy - 2xy$
38. $2x^2 - 5x + 4 - x^2 + 2x - x^2 + 3x - 2$

39. $6p + 2p = 8p$. Verify the result by letting (i) $p = 1$ (ii) $p = 3$ (iii) $p = 6$.

40. $5ab - 3ab = 2ab$. Verify the result by letting (i) $a = 2$ and $b = 1$ (ii) $a = 5$ and $b = 3$.

41. Express the masses shown on each scale as simply as possible, where all masses are in grams.

   (i)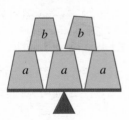

   (ii)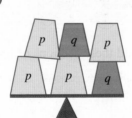

   (iii)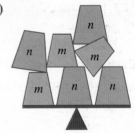

42. Write down the card that always has the same value as:

   (i) $a + a$
   (ii) $3a + a$
   (iii) $3a - 2a$
   (iv) $a + a + b$
   (v) $5ab + ab$
   (vi) $3a^2 - a^2$

43. (i) Express, in terms of x, the length of the beads that make up this bracelet, where all lengths are in cm.

   (ii) Express half the length of the beads in terms of x.

   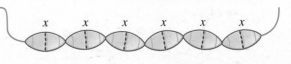

44. A necklace is made from two kinds of beads of length x cm and y cm, as shown.
Express the total length of the necklace in terms of x and y.

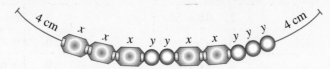

45. The diagram shows three piles of parcels, where all masses are in kg.

Express the mass of each pile as simply as possible.

(i)   **(ii)**   **(iii)**

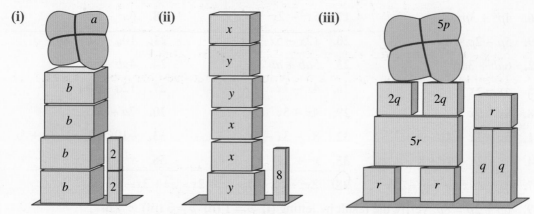

46. The diagram shows 10 sections of flexible construction fencing, each of length a metres.

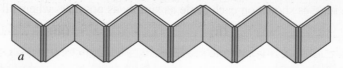

Which of the shapes below could these sections of fencing fit exactly around?
In each case, explain your answer.

(i)   **(ii)**   **(iii)**

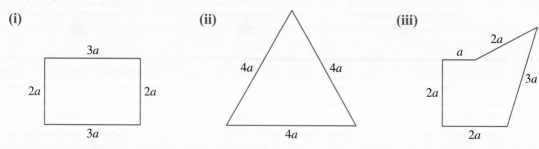

47. In a magic square, each row, each column and each diagonal add up to the same amount. Show that both squares below are magic squares.

$p-2$	$p-1$	$p+3$
$p+5$	p	$p-5$
$p-3$	$p+1$	$p+2$

$a+c$	$a+b-c$	$a-b$
$a-b-c$	a	$a+b+c$
$a+b$	$a-b+c$	$a-c$

48. Sketch a rectangle and a triangle where $12a + 24$ is the perimeter.

49. The answer to a maths problem is $5a$. Write down three questions that have this answer.

Multiplying terms

$a \times a = a^2$ pronounced 'a squared'.

$a \times a \times a = a^3$ pronounced 'a cubed'.

$a \times a \times a \times a = a^4$ pronounced 'a to the power of 4'.

> The order to follow when multiplying terms in algebra is:
> **1.** Sign   **2.** Numbers   **3.** Letters (separately)

When you are multiplying, it is good practice to group the numbers and the **same** letters together, putting the letters in alphabetical order.

EXAMPLE

Simplify each of the following.

  (i) $2 \times 4a$ (ii) $3x \times 5x$ (iii) $-2x \times 6x$

(iv) $2a \times 5b$ (v) $-1 \times -7x^2$ (vi) $-2x \times x^2$

Solution:

(i) $\quad 2 \times 4a$
$= 2 \times 4 \times a$
$= 8a$

(ii) $\quad 3x \times 5x$
$= 3 \times 5 \times x \times x$
$= 15x^2$

(iii) $\quad -2x \times 6x$
$= -2 \times 6 \times x \times x$
$= -12x^2$

(iv) $\quad 2a \times 5b$
$= 2 \times 5 \times a \times b$
$= 10ab$

(v) $\quad -1 \times -7x^2$
$= -1 \times -7 \times x^2$
$= 7x^2$

(vi) $\quad -2x \times x^2$
$= -2 \times x \times x^2$
$= -2x^3$

Exercise 6.3

Simplify the expressions in questions 1–36.

1. 3×4	2. 5×-3	3. -2×4	4. -6×-3
5. $2 \times 5a$	6. $4 \times 3b$	7. $5 \times 2x$	8. $8 \times 2y$
9. $4 \times 2m$	10. $6 \times 5x$	11. $x \times 4$	12. $x \times 7$
13. $a \times a$	14. $2a \times 3a$	15. $5a \times 2a^2$	16. $3a^2 \times 4a$
17. $3a \times 2b$	18. $4p \times 3q$	19. $2p \times q$	20. $k \times 3k$
21. $-2p \times 4q$	22. $-3a \times -5b$	23. $-2k \times -6k$	24. $-4a \times 3b$
25. $-5x \times 2x$	26. $-3x \times -2x$	27. $4x \times -2x$	28. $-x \times 2x$
29. $-1 \times 2x$	30. $-1 \times -5x$	31. $4x \times -1$	32. $-3x^2 \times -1$
33. $x \times -x^3$	34. $x \times -2x^2$	35. $-2 \times -2x^2$	36. $-x \times -5x^2$

37. Sort these cards into pairs of equivalent algebraic expressions.

$3 \times a \times a$	$6a^2b$	$3a \times 2$	$6ab$
$3a \times 2b$	$3a^2$	$3a \times 2ab$	$6a$

38. In these algebraic pyramids, each brick is the product of the two bricks below it. Complete both pyramids.

(i)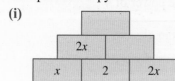

(ii)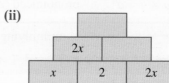

39. $3x \times 2x = 6x^2$. Verify the result by letting (i) $x = 2$ (ii) $x = 5$ (iii) $x = 8$.

40. $4p \times 3q = 12pq$. Verify the result by letting (i) $p = 2$ and $q = 3$ (ii) $p = 4$ and $q = -1$.

Expanding brackets and simplifying 1

Note: Removing brackets is called **expanding the brackets**.

To remove brackets with a term outside the bracket, do the following:

> 1. Multiply each term inside the bracket by the term outside the bracket.
>
> 2. Any term not in a bracket is brought down to the next line unchanged.
>
> 3. Simplify (add and subtract terms that are the same).

No sign or number in front of a bracket means that every term is multiplied by 1 or left unchanged. If the term outside the bracket is negative, then the sign of every term inside the brackets will change. In particular, a minus sign on its own outside the bracket means that every term inside the bracket is multiplied by −1, or in practice simply change the sign of every term inside the bracket.

For example:

$$-(-2x^2 + 3x - 4) = -1(-2x^2 + 3x - 4) = 2x^2 - 3x + 4$$

(every sign is changed)

EXAMPLE

Remove the brackets and simplify each of the following.

(i) $3(x + 4) - 5$

(ii) $6 - 2(3x - 5)$

(iii) $3(4x + 5) - 2(6x + 4)$

(iv) $2(2x^2 - 5) - (3x^2 - 10)$

Solution:

(i) $3(x + 4) - 5$

$= 3x + 12 - 5$

$= 3x + 7$

(ii) $6 - 2(3x - 5)$

$= 6 - 6x + 10$

$= 16 - 6x$

(iii) $3(4x + 5) - 2(6x + 4)$

$= 12x + 15 - 12x - 8$

$= 12x - 12x + 15 - 8$

$= 7$

(iv) $2(2x^2 - 5) - 1(3x^2 - 10)$

$= 4x^2 - 10 - 3x^2 + 10$

$= 4x^2 - 3x^2 - 10 + 10$

$= x^2$

Exercise 6.4

In questions 1–33, remove the brackets and simplify.

1. $2(x + 5)$

2. $3(x + 2)$

3. $4(2x + 1)$

4. $4(3x + 2)$

5. $3(3 + 5a)$

6. $5(3 + 2p)$

7. $3(3a - 2)$

8. $2(3 - 4b)$

9. $2(3x + 2y)$

10. $2(x + 5) + 3$

11. $4 + 3(a + 2)$

12. $1 + 5(2a + 1)$

13. $3(2x + 1) + 2x$

14. $5(3x - 2) - 11x$

15. $6(2x + 1) + 4x$

16. $4x + 2(x + 4)$

17. $10a + 3(4a - 3)$

18. $9x + 4(3 - 2x) - 12$

19. $-2(5 - 4x)$

20. $-(3 - 7x)$

21. $-(-1 - 3x)$

22. $3(2x + 4) + 2(5x + 3)$

23. $3(2x + 1) + 5(x + 2)$

24. $4(2x + 3) - 2(4x - 6)$

25. $5(2x - 3) - 3(3x - 5)$

26. $8(x + 1) - 4(2x - 1)$

27. $6(x + 2) - 3(2x + 5)$

28. $5(2x + 3) - 2(4 + 3x) - 7$

29. $3(4 + 2x) - 5(x + 2) - 2$

30. $2(3a - 5b) - 2(2a - 5b + 1) + 2$

31. $3(2x + 4) - 3(x + 5) + 3 + 2x$

32. $2(1 - 3x - x^2) - (2 - 6x - 3x^2)$

33. $4(2x^2 + 3x) - 6(x^2 + 2x) - 2x^2$

34. Show that $3(4x + 5) - 2(6x + 4)$ reduces to a constant and find that constant.

35. $3(p + q) = 3p + 3q$. Verify the result by letting (i) $p = 1$ and $q = 2$ (ii) $p = 5$ and $q = 3$.

36. $5(4x - 1) = 20x - 5$. Verify the result by letting (i) $x = 1$ (ii) $x = 3$ (iii) $x = -2$.

37. Sort these cards into pairs of equivalent algebraic expressions.

| $4(x + 2)$ | $4(2 - x) + 4x$ | $2(6x + 1)$ | $2(2x + 4) + 8x$ |

| $12x + 2$ | $12x + 8$ | 8 | $8 + 4x$ |

38. Find, in terms of x, the difference in area between rectangle A and rectangle B.

Rectangle A: width 4, length $2x + 3$.
Rectangle B: width 3, length $x + 4$.

39. Richard wrote the following: $5(2x - 1) + 3(x + 1) = 7x - 5 + 3x + 3 = 10x + 2$.

Richard has made two mistakes in his working. Explain the mistakes Richard has made.

Expanding brackets and simplifying 2

EXAMPLE

Simplify each of the following.

(i) $2x(x - 1) - 3(x + 2)$ (ii) $2(x^2 + 3x) - x(2x + 5) + x$

Solution:

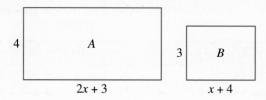

(i) $2x(x - 1) - 3(x + 2)$

$= 2x^2 - 2x - 3x - 6$

$= 2x^2 - 5x - 6$

(ii) $2(x^2 + 3x) - x(2x + 5) + x$

$= 2x^2 + 6x - 2x^2 - 5x + x$

$= 2x^2 - 2x^2 + 6x + x - 5x$

$= 2x$

Exercise 6.5

In questions 1–22, remove the brackets and simplify.

1. $2x(x + 3)$
2. $3x(2x + 5)$
3. $4x(x + 2)$
4. $5a(a + 4)$
5. $2p(p + 3)$
6. $3q(q - 1)$
7. $7x(x - 2)$
8. $6x(4 - x)$
9. $10x(x - 3)$
10. $-2x(x - 3)$
11. $-3x(2x + 1)$
12. $-x(x - 4)$
13. $x(x + 2) + 3(x + 2)$
14. $x(x + 3) + 3(x + 3)$
15. $3x(3x - 2) + 2(3x - 2) + 4$
16. $2x(x + 2) - 4(x - 1) - 4$
17. $3x(2x + 1) - 2x(x - 3)$
18. $x(3x - 4) - 3x(x - 2)$
19. $3a(2a + 3) - 2a(3a + 5) + a$
20. $a(a + 1) + 2a(a - 3) + 3(2a - a^2)$
21. $4x(2x^2 - 3x + 6) + 6(2x^2 - 4x)$
22. $x(x - y) + y(x - y) + y^2$
23. $x(x + 3) = x^2 + 3x$. Verify the result by letting (i) $x = 2$ (ii) $x = 5$ (iii) $x = -1$.
24. $2a(a - 5) = 2a^2 - 10a$. Verify the result by letting (i) $a = 3$ (ii) $a = 1$ (iii) $a = -4$.

Multiplying expressions

To multiply two expressions, do the following:

1. Multiply each term separately in the second expression by each term in the first expression.
2. Simplify (add and subtract terms that are the same).

Note: Multiplication is often indicated by brackets.

EXAMPLE

In each of the following, remove the brackets and simplify.

(i) $(x + 2)(x + 5)$ (ii) $(2x - 3)(x + 4)$ (iii) $(x + 3)^2$

Solution:

(i) $(x + 2)(x + 5)$
$= x(x + 5) + 2(x + 5)$
$= x^2 + 5x + 2x + 10$
$= x^2 + 7x + 10$

(ii) $(2x - 3)(x + 4)$
$= 2x(x + 4) - 3(x + 4)$
$= 2x^2 + 8x - 3x - 12$
$= 2x^2 + 5x - 12$

(iii) $(x + 3)^2 = (x + 3)(x + 3)$
$= x(x + 3) + 3(x + 3)$
$= x^2 + 3x + 3x + 9$
$= x^2 + 6x + 9$

Exercise 6.6

In questions 1–32, remove the brackets and simplify.

1. $(x + 1)(x + 2)$
2. $(x + 2)(x + 3)$
3. $(x + 4)(x + 5)$
4. $(x + 6)(x + 1)$
5. $(x + 5)(x + 2)$
6. $(x + 7)(x + 3)$
7. $(2x + 3)(x + 1)$
8. $(2x + 1)(x + 5)$
9. $(3x + 2)(x + 5)$
10. $(x + 5)(x - 2)$
11. $(x + 3)(x - 2)$
12. $(x + 5)(x - 3)$
13. $(x - 4)(x - 2)$
14. $(x - 6)(x - 3)$
15. $(x - 1)(x - 2)$
16. $(2a + 3)(a - 1)$
17. $(2a - 1)(a + 5)$
18. $(2x - 5)(x + 2)$
19. $(3a - 1)(a - 3)$
20. $(2p - 1)(p - 3)$
21. $(3x - 4)(x + 5)$
22. $(3x + 1)(2x + 3)$
23. $(4a + 1)(2a - 3)$
24. $(2x - 3)(2x + 3)$
25. $(x - 5)(x + 5)$
26. $(x - 3)(x + 3)$
27. $(x - 1)(x + 1)$
28. $(x + 1)^2$
29. $(x - 3)^2$
30. $(2x + 1)^2$
31. $(x + 3)(x + 1) - x(x + 3) - 3$
32. $(x - 3)(x + 5) - x(x + 2) + 15$

33. $(x + 2)(x + 4) = x^2 + 6x + 8$. Verify the result by letting **(i)** $x = 1$ **(ii)** $x = 3$ **(iii)** $x = 6$.

34. $(2a + 1)(a - 3) = 2a^2 - 5a - 3$. Verify the result by letting **(i)** $a = 2$ **(ii)** $a = 4$ **(iii)** $a = -2$.

35. The diagram shows a rectangle of length $l = (2x - 1)$ and breadth $b = (x + 5)$. Express, in terms of x, the:

    (i) perimeter **(ii)** area of the rectangle.

    Note: Perimeter $= 2l + 2b$ and area $= l \times b$.

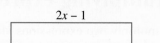

36. Express, in terms of x, the area of the shaded regions.

    (i)   **(ii)**   **(iii)**

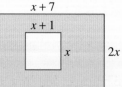
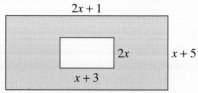

37. The diagram shows a rectangle of length $l = (x + 3)$ and breadth $b = (x + 2)$.

    (i) Express the area of the rectangle in terms of x.
    (ii) Calculate the area of each of the four smaller rectangles separately and add your results.
    (iii) Hence, show that $(x + 3)(x + 2) = x^2 + 5x + 6$.

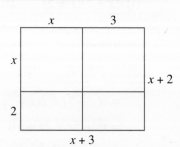

LINEAR EQUATIONS

CHAPTER 7

Equation

> An equation is a statement in which
> two **different** algebraic expressions are equal.

For example, $3x + 1 = x + 13$ is an equation.

Notes: 1. The left-hand part of an equation is referred to as the **LHS** – the left-hand side.
Similarly, the RHS refers to the right-hand side.

2. $x + x = 2x$ is an **identity**, not an equation, because the two expressions are the same.

Balance

In order to solve equations, we must first understand the idea of **balance**.

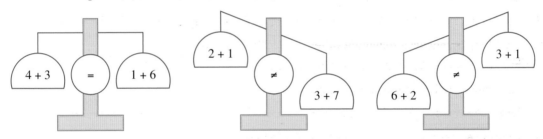

Exercise 7.1

1. What is the value of ★ which will balance the scales?

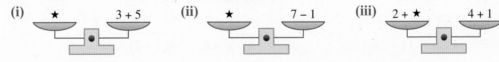

   (i)   ★   3 + 5   (ii)   ★   7 − 1   (iii) 2 + ★   4 + 1

2. What is the value of ⊛ which will balance the scales?

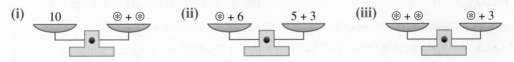

   (i)   10   ⊛ + ⊛   (ii) ⊛ + 6   5 + 3   (iii) ⊛ + ⊛   ⊛ + 3

Solution of an equation

To solve an equation means to find the value of the letter that makes both sides equal in value. The aim is to end up with **letter = number**. The number that makes both sides equal in value is called the **solution** or **root** of the equation.

Consider the equation $x + 2 = 7$.

When $x = 5$, both sides are equal to 7. We say that 5 is the **solution** or **root** of the equation $x + 2 = 7$.

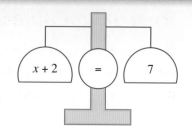

EXAMPLE

(i) Verify that $t = 4$ is the root of $3t + 2 = 14$.

(ii) Show that $x = 3$ is the solution to the equation $2x + 5 = 5x - 4$.

Solution:

(i) Check: $t = 4$

LHS	RHS
$3t + 2$	14
$3(4) + 2$	
$12 + 2$	
14	

LHS = RHS ✓

(ii) Check: $x = 3$

LHS	RHS
$2x + 5$	$5x - 4$
$2(3) + 5$	$5(3) - 4$
$6 + 5$	$15 - 4$
11	11

LHS = RHS ✓

Exercise 7.2

In questions 1–20, verify that the given root satisfies the equation.

1. $x = 2$, $\quad x + 4 = 6$
2. $x = 5$, $\quad 2x - 3 = 7$
3. $t = 1$, $\quad 2t + 4 = 3t + 3$
4. $t = 3$, $\quad 3t - 2 = 2t + 1$
5. $x = 7$, $\quad 2(x + 1) = 16$
6. $p = 6$, $\quad 4(p + 2) = 32$
7. $x = 2$, $\quad 3(x + 2) = 2x + 8$
8. $h = 1$, $\quad 6(h + 4) + 5 = 35$
9. $f = 10$, $\quad 7(f - 1) - 50 = f + 3$
10. $m = 12$, $\quad 4(m - 3) - 9 = 2m + 3$
11. $x = -3$, $\quad x + 8 = 5$
12. $x = -2$, $\quad 4x + 10 = 2$
13. $t = -4$, $\quad 2(t + 5) = 2$
14. $t = -3$, $\quad 3(t + 5) + 4 = t + 13$
15. $x = -5$, $\quad 2x + 3 = 3(x + 2) + 2$
16. $x = -1$, $\quad 3(x - 3) + 7 = -5$
17. $x = 2$, $\quad 2(x - 3) + 3x + 1 = 5$
18. $d = 8$, $\quad 2(4 - d) + 5 = -3$
19. $w = 13$, $\quad 3(w - 5) + 2(4 - w) = 6$
20. $y = 15$, $\quad 8 - y = 7(y - 16)$

Rule of equations

The two sides of an equation can be thought of as scales in **balance**. The scale will stay **balanced** provided we do the same thing to both sides.

We do the same thing to both sides of an equation until we end up with:

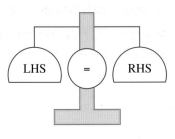

> letter = number

Then we say the equation is **solved**.

> What we do to one side of an equation, we must do (the same) to the other side.

This means we can:

1. **Add** or **subtract** the same quantity to both sides.
2. **Multiply** or **divide** both sides by the same quantity.

Remember: You must carry out the same operation on each side of the equation to keep it **in balance**. It is good practice to check your answer by substitution.

EXAMPLE 1

Solve for x: $2x + 3 = 11$ and verify your solution.

Solution:

$$2x + 3 = 11$$
$$2x + 3 - 3 = 11 - 3 \quad \text{(subtract 3 from both sides)}$$
$$2x = 8 \quad \text{(simplify each side)}$$
$$\frac{2x}{2} = \frac{8}{2} \quad \text{(divide both sides by 2)}$$
$$x = 4$$

Check: $x = 4$

LHS	RHS
$2x + 3$	11
$2(4) + 3$	
$8 + 3$	
11	

LHS = RHS when $x = 4$.

Therefore, $x = 4$ is the correct solution.

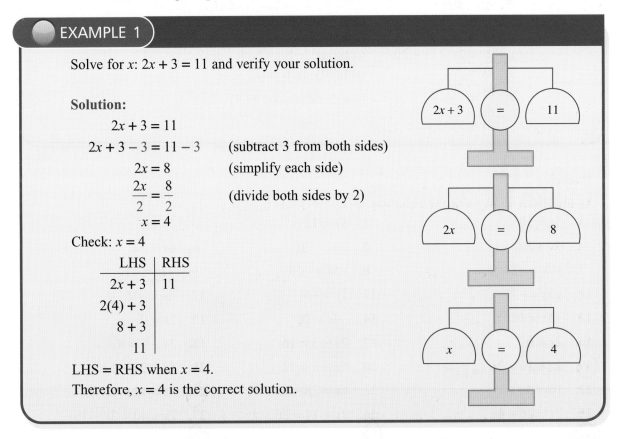

Note: It is not necessary to draw the scales to solve an equation, but always keep **balance** in mind.

EXAMPLE 2

Solve for x: $-3x = 12$.

Solution:

$$-3x = 12$$
$$-3x \times -1 = 12 \times -1 \quad \text{(multiply both sides by } -1\text{)}$$
$$3x = -12 \quad \text{(simplify each side)}$$
$$\frac{3x}{3} = \frac{-12}{3} \quad \text{(divide both sides by 3)}$$
$$x = -4$$

EXAMPLE 3

Solve for x: $6x - 7 = 2x + 13$.

Solution:

$$6x - 7 = 2x + 13$$
$$6x - 7 + 7 = 2x + 13 + 7 \quad \text{(add 7 to both sides)}$$
$$6x = 2x + 20 \quad \text{(simplify each side)}$$
$$6x - 2x = 2x - 2x + 20 \quad \text{(subtract } 2x \text{ from both sides)}$$
$$4x = 20 \quad \text{(simplify each side)}$$
$$\frac{4x}{4} = \frac{20}{4} \quad \text{(divide both sides by 4)}$$
$$x = 5$$

Exercise 7.3

In questions 1–30, solve the equation.

1. $5x = 10$
2. $3x = 12$
3. $2x = 6$
4. $4x = 20$
5. $10x = 30$
6. $6x = 30$
7. $-7x = -21$
8. $-5x = -10$
9. $-2x = -12$
10. $-3x = -33$
11. $2x = -4$
12. $5x = -15$
13. $-3x = 18$
14. $-4x = 20$
15. $5x = 0$
16. $2x = 0$
17. $7x - 5 = 16$
18. $3x - 7 = 8$
19. $2x + 16 = 24$
20. $5x - 8 = 22$
21. $5x - 2 = -12$
22. $10 = 3x + 1$
23. $4x = 28 - 3x$
24. $5x = 12 + 8x$
25. $7x = 26 - 6x$
26. $2x + 14 = 26 - 4x$
27. $7x + 40 = 2x - 10$
28. $8x + 2 = 5x - 16$
29. $7x + 11 = 3x + 27$
30. $2x - 5 = 1 - x$

In questions 31–36, find the value of *x*.

31.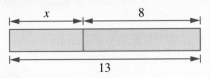

32.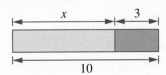

33.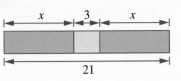

34.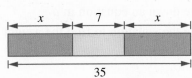

35.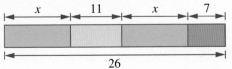

36.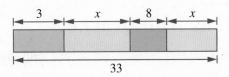

In questions 37–44, the number in a lower box is calculated by adding the two numbers above it. In questions 37–38, find the value of *t*.

37.

3	5	6
8	*t*	

38.

In questions 39–44, form an equation in *x* and hence solve for *x*.

39.

2	*x*	7
x + 2	*x* + 7	
15		

40.

41.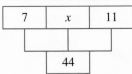

42.

x	2	*x*
	14	

43.

44.

3	2*x*	1
	48	

45. Mike is weighing tins of soup. Let *t* represent the weight of a tin of soup.

  (i) Explain why $4t + 5$ represents the weight on the left side.

  (ii) Write down an expression for the weight on the right side.

  (iii) Write down an equation in *t*.

  (iv) Solve the equation to find the weight of a tin of soup.

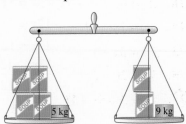

46. Caroline is weighing apples. Let a represent the weight of an apple.

    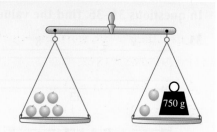

    (i) Write down an expression for:
       (a) The weight on the left side
       (b) The weight on the right side
    (ii) Write down an equation in a.
    (iii) Solve the equation to find the weight of an apple.

Equations with brackets

Equations that contain brackets are solved with the following steps:

1. Remove the brackets (any term not in a bracket is moved down to the next line unchanged).
2. Simplify the sides.
3. Arrange so that the left-hand side only contains a letter term and the right-hand side contains a number.
4. Divide both sides by the number in front of the letter.
   (If the number in front of x is negative, it is good practice to first multiply both sides by -1.)

● EXAMPLE

Solve for x: $11 - 7(x + 2) = 5(x - 3)$.

Solution:

$$11 - 7(x + 2) = 5(x - 3)$$
$$11 - 7x - 14 = 5x - 15 \qquad \text{(remove the brackets)}$$
$$-7x - 3 = 5x - 15 \qquad \text{(simplify both sides)}$$
$$-7x - 3 + 3 = 5x - 15 + 3 \qquad \text{(add 3 to both sides)}$$
$$-7x = 5x - 12 \qquad \text{(simplify both sides)}$$
$$-7x - 5x = 5x - 5x - 12 \qquad \text{(subtract } 5x \text{ from both sides)}$$
$$-12x = -12 \qquad \text{(simplify both sides)}$$
$$12x = 12 \qquad \text{(multiply both sides by } -1\text{)}$$
$$\frac{12x}{12} = \frac{12}{12} \qquad \text{(divide both sides by 12)}$$
$$x = 1$$

Exercise 7.4

In questions 1–30, solve the equation.

1. $3(x + 4) = 18$
2. $5(x - 2) = 10$
3. $3(x + 4) = 2(x + 8)$
4. $6(x + 3) = 4(x + 5)$
5. $7(x - 2) = 4(x + 1)$
6. $4(x + 4) = 2(x + 3)$
7. $5(x - 3) + 7(x + 2) = 11$
8. $5(x + 4) - 3(x - 4) = 40$
9. $3(x - 1) + 5(x + 1) = 18$
10. $4(x - 1) - 3(x - 2) = 6$
11. $5(x - 1) - 2(x + 2) = 3$
12. $4(x + 5) - 2(x + 3) = 12$
13. $3x + 4(x - 6) + 3 = 0$
14. $x + 2(x + 1) = 11$
15. $10(x + 4) - 3(2x + 5) - 1 = 0$
16. $5(2x + 3) - 4 = 4(2x + 1) + 11$
17. $4(x - 3) + 3(x + 7) = 16$
18. $3(2x + 1) - 3(x + 4) = 0$
19. $5(x + 4) - 3(x - 4) = 3x + 29$
20. $2(7 + x) - 4(x + 3) = 15(x - 1)$
21. $7(x - 6) + 2(x - 7) = 5(x - 4)$
22. $4(x - 3) - 2(x - 1) = 3(x - 2)$
23. $2 - 6(2 - x) = 5(x + 3) - 23$
24. $5 - 4(x - 3) = x - 2(x - 1)$
25. $1 + 4(2x - 6) - 3(x + 4) = 0$
26. $5 = 3(3 - 2x) + 4(6 - 2x)$
27. $11 + 4(3x - 1) = 5(2x + 1) + 2(2x - 5)$
28. $8 + 2(2x - 11) - 2x = 4(x - 4)$
29. $5(3x - 2) + 1 - 3(2x + 1) = 2(x + 1)$
30. $2 + 5(3x - 1) = 4(2x - 3) + 2(x - 3)$

Equations with fractions

Equations with fractions are solved with the following steps:

1. Put brackets on top.
2. Multiply each part of the equation by the LCD of the numbers on the bottom.
3. Divide the bottom into the top (this removes all fractions).
4. Proceed as when solving previous equations.

EXAMPLE 1

Solve for x: $\dfrac{2x}{3} + \dfrac{x}{4} = \dfrac{11}{6}$.

Solution:

The LCD of 3, 4 and 6 is 12. Therefore, we multiply each part of the equation by 12.

$$\frac{2x}{3} + \frac{x}{4} = \frac{11}{6}$$

$$\frac{(2x)}{3} + \frac{(x)}{4} = \frac{(11)}{6} \qquad \text{(put brackets on top)}$$

$$\frac{12(2x)}{3} + \frac{12(x)}{4} = \frac{12(11)}{6} \qquad \text{(multiply each part by 12)}$$

$$4(2x) + 3(x) = 2(11) \qquad \text{(divide the bottom into the top)}$$

$$8x + 3x = 22 \qquad \text{(remove the brackets)}$$

$$11x = 22 \qquad \text{(simplify the left-hand side)}$$

$$\frac{11x}{11} = \frac{22}{11} \qquad \text{(divide both sides by 11)}$$

$$x = 2$$

EXAMPLE 2

Solve for x: $\dfrac{x + 1}{2} = \dfrac{2x + 1}{10} + \dfrac{x + 2}{3}$.

Solution:

The LCD of 2, 10 and 3 is 30. Therefore, we multiply each part of the equation by 30.

$$\frac{x + 1}{2} = \frac{2x + 1}{10} + \frac{x + 2}{3}$$

$$\frac{(x + 1)}{2} = \frac{(2x + 1)}{10} + \frac{(x + 2)}{3} \qquad \text{(put brackets on top)}$$

$$\frac{30(x + 1)}{2} = \frac{30(2x + 1)}{10} + \frac{30(x + 2)}{3} \qquad \text{(multiply each part by 30)}$$

$$15(x + 1) = 3(2x + 1) + 10(x + 2) \qquad \text{(divide the bottom into the top)}$$

$$15x + 15 = 6x + 3 + 10x + 20 \qquad \text{(remove the brackets)}$$

$$15x + 15 = 16x + 23 \qquad \text{(simplify the right-hand side)}$$

$$15x + 15 - 15 = 16x + 23 - 15 \qquad \text{(subtract 15 from both sides)}$$

$$15x = 16x + 8 \qquad \text{(simplify both sides)}$$

$$15x - 16x = 16x - 16x + 8 \qquad \text{(subtract 16x from both sides)}$$

$$-x = 8 \qquad \text{(simplify both sides)}$$

$$x = -8 \qquad \text{(multiply both sides by -1)}$$

Note: If a part of the equation is not a fraction, it can be changed into a fraction form by putting it over 1.

For example, $5 = \dfrac{5}{1}$, $2x = \dfrac{2x}{1}$.

Exercise 7.5

Solve each of the following equations.

1. $\dfrac{x}{2} + \dfrac{x}{3} = \dfrac{5}{2}$

2. $\dfrac{x}{4} + \dfrac{x}{2} = \dfrac{15}{4}$

3. $\dfrac{x}{3} + \dfrac{x}{4} = \dfrac{7}{12}$

4. $\dfrac{x}{4} + \dfrac{x}{5} = \dfrac{27}{20}$

5. $\dfrac{x}{2} - \dfrac{x}{5} = \dfrac{3}{10}$

6. $\dfrac{x}{3} - \dfrac{x}{5} = \dfrac{2}{3}$

7. $\dfrac{2x}{5} + \dfrac{x}{3} = \dfrac{22}{15}$

8. $\dfrac{3x}{4} - \dfrac{2x}{3} = \dfrac{5}{12}$

9. $\dfrac{2x}{5} = \dfrac{3}{2} + \dfrac{x}{4}$

10. $\dfrac{4x}{9} - \dfrac{x}{2} = \dfrac{2}{3}$

11. $\dfrac{x+2}{4} + \dfrac{x-3}{2} = \dfrac{1}{2}$

12. $\dfrac{x+4}{3} = \dfrac{x+1}{4} + \dfrac{1}{6}$

13. $\dfrac{3x+4}{2} - \dfrac{4x-11}{5} = 0$

14. $\dfrac{x-3}{4} + \dfrac{4}{3} = \dfrac{3x-1}{6}$

15. $\dfrac{x+4}{3} - \dfrac{x+2}{4} = \dfrac{7}{6}$

16. $\dfrac{x-8}{7} + \dfrac{x-3}{3} - \dfrac{5}{21} = 0$

17. $\dfrac{2x-3}{3} - \dfrac{1}{6} = \dfrac{x+2}{4}$

18. $\dfrac{x-5}{3} + \dfrac{1}{15} = \dfrac{x-2}{5}$

19. $\dfrac{3x-1}{2} - \dfrac{x}{4} = \dfrac{9}{2}$

20. $\dfrac{x}{5} - \dfrac{x-3}{6} = \dfrac{11}{15}$

CHAPTER 8

RATIO AND PROPORTION

Ratio

A ratio is a comparison between two similar quantities measured in the same units.

It is written in a given order.

The ratio 7 to 4 is written 7 : 4 or as a fraction, $\frac{7}{4}$.

The ratio of cats to dogs is 2 : 3. What is the ratio of dogs to cats?

Simplifying ratios

A ratio is unchanged if we multiply or divide each part by the same number. It is usual to make each part of the ratio as small as possible. However, each part must be a whole number.

EXAMPLE 1

Express each of the following ratios in its simplest form.

(i) 12 : 15   (ii) 14 : 28 : 35   (iii) $2 : 1\frac{1}{2}$ (iv) 0·25 : 0·75

Solution:

(i) $12 : 15 = 4 : 5$ (divide each part by 3)

(ii) $14 : 28 : 35 = 2 : 4 : 5$ (divide each part by 7)

(iii) $2 : 1\frac{1}{2} = 4 : 3$ (multiply each part by 2)

(iv) $0·25 : 0·75 = 25 : 75$ (multiply each part by 100)

          $= 1 : 3$ (divide each part by 25)

To express one quantity as a ratio of another, do the following:

1. Make sure both quantities are in the same units.
2. Remove the units and write the numbers as a ratio.
3. Simplify this ratio.

EXAMPLE 2

Express the ratio 800 m to 2 km in its simplest form.

1. First express both in metres.

    2 km = 2,000 m

2. Therefore, 800 m : 2 km

    =   800 m : 2,000 m

    =   800 : 2,000   (remove the units)

3. =   8 : 20   (divide each part by 100)

    =   2 : 5   (divide each part by 4)

Exercise 8.1

In questions 1–34, express the ratio in its simplest form.

1. 4 : 8
2. 15 : 20
3. 3 : 9
4. 12 : 30
5. 6 : 10
6. 14 : 21
7. 15 : 12
8. 50 : 30
9. 30 : 25
10. 36 : 24
11. 40 : 50
12. 20 : 100
13. 24 : 16
14. 36 : 27
15. 88 : 77
16. 125 : 200
17. 8 : 12 : 20
18. 15 : 20 : 25
19. 2 : 8 : 10
20. 18 : 24 : 42
21. 20 cm : 50 cm
22. €18 : €24
23. 12 m : 18 m
24. 8 km : 24 km
25. 400 m : 2 km
26. 75 cm : 2 m
27. 600 cm^3 : 2 litres
28. 900 g : 1 kg
29. 4 days : 2 weeks
30. 2 hours : 40 minutes
31. 9 months : 2 years
32. 25% : 125%
33. 15 minutes : 2 hours 30 minutes
34. 800 kg : $1\frac{1}{2}$ tonnes

35. If $a = 4$, $b = 6$ and $c = 12$, simplify each of the following ratios.

    (i) $a : c$ (ii) $2b : c$ (iii) $a^2 : 2c$ (iv) $(a + b) : (2c - a)$

36. In a class of 30 pupils, there are 20 girls. Find the ratio of:

    (i) The number of boys to the number of girls

    (ii) The number of boys to the number of pupils in the whole class.

37. A girl is 15 years old and her father is 45 years old. Calculate the ratio of:

    (i) The girl's age to her father's age now

    (ii) The girl's age to her father's age in five years' time

    (iii) The father's age to the girl's age three years ago

38. A man was earning €400 a week. He received an extra €80 a week in salary. Calculate the ratio of the new salary per week to the old salary per week.

39. The world's tallest buildings include:

Name	Location	Height (m)
Burj Khalifa	Dubai	828
Taipei 101	Taipei	508
World Financial Centre	Shanghai	492

   (i) What is the ratio of their heights in descending order?

   (ii) Express your answer in its simplest form.

40. A football pitch has a length of 120 m and its width is 80 m. Calculate:

   (i) The ratio of its length to its width

   (ii) The ratio of its length to its perimeter

   (iii) The ratio of its perimeter to its width

41. A car travelling at 75 km/h overtakes a motorbike travelling at 1 km/min. Calculate, at the moment of overtaking, the ratio of the car's speed to the motorbike's speed.

Proportion

A proportion of an object is usually given as a fraction comparing a part of the object with the complete object. For example, if a basket of 20 flowers contains 8 roses, then the proportion of the roses in the basket is $\frac{8}{20}$ or $\frac{2}{5}$. Comparing the top with the bottom, we can say that 2 out of every 5 flowers are roses.

A proportion can also be given as a percentage. We could say that $\frac{2}{5} = 40\%$ of the flowers are roses.

Note: It is sometimes easier to compare proportions if they are converted to percentages.

 EXAMPLE 1

(i) A class of 30 students contains 25 who own a mobile phone. What proportion do not own a mobile phone?

(ii) In an election, the proportion of voters who supported the Happy Party was 55%. There were 12,000 voters in total.

(a) Express the proportion as a fraction.

(b) Find the number of Happy Party supporters.

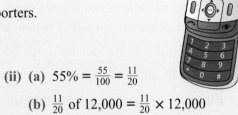

Solution:

(i) There are $30 - 25 = 5$ students who do not own a mobile phone. The proportion is $\frac{5}{30}$ or $\frac{1}{6}$.

(ii) (a) $55\% = \frac{55}{100} = \frac{11}{20}$

(b) $\frac{11}{20}$ of $12,000 = \frac{11}{20} \times 12,000$

$= 6,600$ supporters

 EXAMPLE 2

A packet of 12 sweets contains three flavours: strawberry, lemon and orange. There are four strawberry and six lemon sweets. The rest are orange flavoured.

(i) How many are orange?

(ii) Find the proportions of each flavour.

(iii) Show that the total of the proportions add up to 1.

(iv) If the flavours are supposed to be equal, what proportion should there be of each flavour?

Solution:

(i) There are 12 sweets in the packet, so:

Orange = $12 - (\text{Strawberry} + \text{Lemon}) = 12 - (4 + 6) = 2$

(ii) Strawberry: $\frac{4}{12} = \frac{1}{3}$; Lemon: $\frac{6}{12} = \frac{1}{2}$; Orange: $\frac{2}{12} = \frac{1}{6}$.

(iii) Using the unsimplified fractions $\frac{4}{12} + \frac{6}{12} + \frac{2}{12} = \frac{12}{12} = 1$.

(iv) 12 sweets, 3 flavours, so ideally $12 \div 3 = 4$ sweets per flavour. Proportion: $\frac{4}{12} = \frac{1}{3}$.

OR

3 flavours, so $\frac{1}{3}$ per flavour would be expected.

Exercise 8.2

1. There are three rotten apples at the bottom of a barrel containing 12 apples. Express the proportion of rotten apples as a (simplified) fraction and as an exact percentage.

2. A prize fund of €1,200 is distributed as follows: $\frac{1}{2}$ for first prize, $\frac{2}{5}$ for second prize and the remainder for third prize.

   (i) Calculate the proportion of the third prize.

   (ii) How much is the third prize worth?

3. In a survey, the proportion of people who watched a football match on television was $\frac{3}{8}$.

   (i) What proportion did not watch the match?

   (ii) If 240,000 people did not watch the match, how many did?

4. €400 is $\frac{8}{11}$ of a prize fund. Find the total prize fund.

5. When a cyclist had travelled a distance of 17 km she had completed $\frac{5}{8}$ of her journey. What was the length of the journey?

Proportional parts (dividing quantities in a given ratio)

Ratios can be used to divide, or share, quantities.

To divide, or share, a quantity in a given ratio, do the following:

> 1. Add the ratios to get the total number of parts.
> 2. Divide the quantity by the total of the parts (this gives one part).
> 3. Multiply this separately by each ratio.

EXAMPLE

(i) Divide €28 in the ratio 2 : 5.   (ii) Divide 300 kg in the ratio 2 : 5 : 8.

Solution:

(i) 1. $2 + 5 = 7$ parts

2. 1 part $= \dfrac{€28}{7} = €4$

3. 2 parts $= 2 \times €4 = €8$

   5 parts $= 5 \times €4 = €20$

Therefore, €28 divided in the ratio 2 : 5 is €8, €20.

Check: €8 + €20 = €28 ✓

(ii) 1. $2 + 5 + 8 = 15$ parts

2. 1 part $= \dfrac{300 \text{ kg}}{15} = 20$ kg

3. 2 parts $= 2 \times 20$ kg $= 40$ kg

   5 parts $= 5 \times 20$ kg $= 100$ kg

   8 parts $= 8 \times 20$ kg $= 160$ kg

Therefore, 300 kg divided in the ratio 2 : 5 : 8 is 40 kg, 100 kg, 160 kg.

Check: (40 + 100 + 160) kg = 300 kg ✓

Exercise 8.3

In questions 1–20, divide the quantity in the given ratio.

	Quantity	Ratio
1.	€18	1 : 2
2.	€30	2 : 3
3.	€24	1 : 3
4.	40 kg	3 : 5
5.	28 mins	3 : 4
6.	50 cm	3 : 2
7.	9 months	2 : 1
8.	36	5 : 4
9.	88	7 : 4
10.	€120	5 : 3

	Quantity	Ratio
11.	450 pupils	4 : 5
12.	260 g	6 : 7
13.	150	3 : 2
14.	€24·36	2 : 1
15.	€15·30	2 : 3
16.	€180	2 : 8 : 5
17.	480 g	5 : 4 : 3
18.	€4,000	5 : 7 : 8
19.	170 kg	3 : 6 : 8
20.	162 cm	4 : 3 : 2

21. Divide €24 into three equal parts. Hence or otherwise, divide €24 in the ratio 1 : 2.

22. Divide €50 in the ratio 7 : 3.

23. A prize of €30 is shared between two people in the ratio 1 : 2. How much does each person receive?

24. €1,040 was divided in the ratio 6 : 7. The larger amount was given to charity. How much was this?

25. The total attendance at a concert over two nights was 450. The nightly attendances were in the ratio of 2 : 3. Find the attendance on the first night.

26. €105 was shared among three people in the ratio 1 : 2 : 4. Calculate the smallest share.

27. A man has two children, a boy aged 8 years and a girl aged 12 years. If he divides €400 in the ratio of their ages, how much does each child get?

28. The sides of a triangle are in the ratio 3 : 4 : 5. If the perimeter of the triangle is 60 cm, find the length of each side.

29. An alloy consists of copper, zinc and tin in the ratio 7 : 4 : 3 (by weight). Find the weight of each metal in 84 kg of alloy.

30. Two schools are to receive a grant from the Department of Education in proportion to their number of pupils. If one school has 450 pupils and the other has 720, how would a grant of €56,160 be divided between them?

31. The profits of a business are divided in the ratio of money invested. A, B and C invest €24,000, €16,000 and €12,000, respectively. How much will each receive from a profit €6,500?

Given the ratios in disguise

In some questions the ratios are given in disguise.

> ## EXAMPLE
>
> €560 is shared between A, B and C so that A gets twice as much as B and B gets twice as much as C. How much does each receive?
>
> **Solution:**
> Let the smallest share be 1 part.
> Therefore, C receives 1 part (smallest share), B receives 2 parts (twice as much as C) and A receives 4 parts (twice as much as B).
>
> Now the requirement is to divide €560 in the ratio 1 : 2 : 4.
> 1. $1 + 2 + 4 = 7$ parts
> 2. 1 part $= \dfrac{€560}{7} = €80$
> 3. C's share is 1 part = €80
>   B's share is 2 parts = $2 \times €80 = €160$
>   A's share is 4 parts = $4 \times €80 = €320$
>   Check: €80 + €160 + €320 = €560 ✓

Exercise 8.4

1. €120 is shared between A and B. How much does each receive if:

   (i) A and B receive equal shares

   (ii) A gets twice as much as B

   (iii) A gets three times as much as B

2. €280 is divided between A, B and C so that A gets twice as much as B and B gets twice as much as C. How much does each receive?

3. €120 is shared between P, Q and R so that P gets twice as much as Q and Q and R get equal shares. How much does P receive?

4. €42 is divided between A, B and C so that A gets twice as much as B and B gets twice as much as C. How much does B receive?

5. €70 is divided between A, B and C so that A gets twice as much as B and C gets twice as much as A.

   (i) Who received the smallest share?

   (ii) How much does each receive?

6. €300 is divided between X, Y and Z so that Y gets three times as much as X and Z gets twice as much as Y.

   (i) Who received the smallest share?

   (ii) How much does each receive?

Given the value of some of the parts (proportions)

Sometimes we are given the value of some of the parts. Look for the equation given in disguise.

EXAMPLE

A and B share a sum of money in the ratio 4 : 3. If B's share is €15, calculate:

   (i) The total amount shared between A and B

   (ii) The amount that A received

Solution:

   (i) $4 + 3 = 7$, so there are 7 parts altogether.

   Equation given in disguise: 3 parts = €15   (B's share)

   Therefore, 1 part = €5   (divide both sides by 3)

   Therefore, 7 parts = €35   (multiply both sides by 7)

   Therefore, the total sum of money shared is €35.

   (ii) A's share is 4 parts = $4 \times €5 = €20$

Note: This problem could also be solved using fractions.

   Given: $\frac{3}{7}$ of total = €15, therefore $\frac{1}{7}$ of total = €5, etc.

Exercise 8.5

1. A and B share a sum of money in the ratio 2 : 3. If A's share is €40, calculate B's share.

2. A sum of money was divided in the ratio 3 : 4. If the larger share was €24, calculate:

   (i) The sum of money

   (ii) The smaller share

3. A prize fund was divided between two people in the ratio 2 : 3. If the larger prize was €120, calculate the total prize fund.

4. In a school, the ratio of girls to boys is 4 : 5. If there are 364 girls, calculate:

   (i) The total number of pupils in the school

   (ii) The number of boys in the school

5. The ratio of the speeds of two cars is 3 : 2. If the faster car is travelling at 96 km/h, calculate the speed of the slower car.

6. The ages of a father and daughter are in the ratio 8 : 3. If the father is 48 years old, how old is the daughter?

7. At a football match, the ratio of the home supporters to away supporters was 5 : 3. 15,000 away supporters attended the match. How many home supporters were at the match?

8. A piece of string was cut into two pieces in the ratio 5 : 9. The larger piece was 36 cm long.

   (i) How long was the piece of string before it was cut?

   (ii) How long was the shorter piece?

9. Two lengths are in the ratio 8 : 5. If the larger length is 120 cm, find the other length.

10. Two lengths are in the ratio 7 : 5. If the shorter length is 45 cm, calculate the other length.

11. The lengths of the sides of a triangle are in the ratio 4 : 3 : 2. If the shortest side is of length 36 cm, calculate the perimeter of the triangle.

12. A, B and C share a sum of money in the ratio 2 : 3 : 4. If C's share is €48, find:

    (i) The total sum of money shared

    (ii) The amount A and B received

13. The first three money prizes in a draw are in the ratio 5 : 3 : 2. If the second-largest prize is €240, calculate the first and third prizes.

14. A sum of money was divided in the ratio 5 : 2. If the larger share was €39 more than the smaller share, calculate the sum.

15. A woman gave some money to her four children in the ratio 2 : 3 : 5 : 9. If the difference between the largest and the smallest share is €11·76, how much money did she give altogether?

Direct proportion

If two quantities increase or decrease in the same ratio, they are said to be in **direct proportion**.
Direct proportion problems, using the unitary method, are solved with following steps:

> **1.** Write down the equation given in disguise.
> (Put the quantity that we want to find on the right-hand side.)
> **2.** Divide both sides by the first quantity that is given.
> (This gives the amount for one unit of the first quantity.)
> **3.** Multiply both sides by the first quantity required.

Note: Strictly speaking, these are not equations, but using equations makes the working easier.

EXAMPLE

(i) A woman earns €280 for working 40 hours. How much would she earn if she worked 33 hours for the same rate of pay?

(ii) A car can travel 75 km on 5 litres of petrol. How far will it travel on 8 litres of petrol at the same rate of consumption?

Solution:

(i) 1. Given: 40 hours = €280   (answer required in euro, therefore euro on the right)

    2.   1 hour   = €7   (divide both sides by 40)

    3.   33 hours = €231   (multiply both sides by 33)

(ii) 1. Given: 5 litres   = 75 km   (answer required in kilometres, therefore kilometres on the right)

    2.   1 litre   = 15 km   (divide both sides by 5)

    3.   8 litres   = 120 km   (multiply both sides by 8)

Exercise 8.6

1. If 5 chairs cost €400, find the cost of **(i)** 1 chair **(ii)** 7 chairs.

2. 7 pens cost €1·75. Calculate the cost of **(i)** 1 pen **(ii)** 3 pens **(iii)** 12 pens.

3. 8 apples cost €1·92. How much will 10 apples cost?

4. A machine produces 200 bolts every 5 minutes. How many bolts will the machine produce in **(i)** 1 minute **(ii)** 8 minutes **(iii)** 30 seconds?

5. A woman earns €376 for working 40 hours. How much would she earn if she worked 32 hours at the same rate of pay?

6. 8 m of cloth cost €11·60. What is the cost of 14 m of the same cloth?

7. A laser printer can print 800 pages in 40 minutes. How many pages can it print in
   (i) 1 minute (ii) 70 minutes (iii) 1 hour (iv) 55 minutes at the same rate of printing?

8. If 12 books weigh 2·4 kg, find the weight of (i) 1 book (ii) 3 books (iii) 40 books.

9. The train fare for a return journey for an adult from Galway to Dublin is €32. The child's fare is three-quarters of the adult fare. Calculate the cost of a return journey from Galway to Dublin for (i) 3 adults (ii) 1 child (iii) 2 adults and 3 children (iv) 5 children and 1 adult.

10. Seven tubes of toothpaste have a weight of 840 g. Calculate the weight of 8 tubes of the same toothpaste.

11. A hotel charges €343 per person for seven days. Calculate the charge for 12 days at the same rate.

12. A candle that is 24 cm tall will burn for 8 hours. What height remains when the candle has been burning for 3 hours 30 minutes?

13. If 450 people attend a concert, the takings amount to €5,625. How many people attended on the following evening, when the takings amounted to €6,000? (Assume that all seats were sold at the same price on both evenings.)

14. On a map, 10 km is represented by 1 cm.

    (i) What distances are represented on the map by:
        (a) 2 cm   (b) 8 cm   (c) 0·5 cm   (d) 1·5 cm   (e) 0·35 cm?

    (ii) What distances on the map represent:
        (a) 40 km   (b) 60 km   (c) 75 km   (d) 150 km   (e) 12·5 km?

15. A model car is built 72 times smaller than the real car.

    (i) What are the real measurements represented by (a) 4 cm (b) $\frac{1}{2}$ cm (c) $3\frac{1}{4}$ cm on the model?

    (ii) A part on the real car is 2·16 m long. What size will this be on the model?

16. It costs €120 to carpet a rectangular room measuring 5 m by 4 m.
    How much would it cost to cover a room measuring $7\frac{1}{2}$ m by 6 m with the same carpet?
    (Hint: Calculate the cost of carpeting in 1 m^2.)

17. 7 books cost €12 more than 5 books cost. How much would (i) 1 book (ii) 30 books cost?

18. 9 cups cost €4·50 more than 6 cups. How much would 20 cups cost?

CHAPTER 9

PERCENTAGES

Percentages, fractions and decimals

The words **'per cent'** mean 'per 100' or 'in every 100'. The symbol for per cent is %.

Thus, 15 per cent means '15 in every 100,' written as 15%.

A percentage is a fraction with 100 on the bottom. It tells you an amount out of 100.

Percentages, fractions and decimals are linked:

$$7\% \quad = \quad \frac{7}{100} \quad = \quad 0{\cdot}07$$

$$\uparrow \qquad\qquad \uparrow \qquad\qquad \uparrow$$

percentage   fraction   decimal

Changing percentages to fractions and decimals

To change a percentage into a fraction, do the following:

> Write the number as a fraction with 100 on the bottom
> and simplify this fraction.

EXAMPLE 1

Write the following as a fraction in its simplest form. **(i)** 15%   **(ii)** 48%

Solution:

(i)   15%

$$= \frac{15}{100} \quad \text{(put over 100)}$$

$$= \frac{3}{20} \quad \text{(divide top and bottom by 5)}$$

(ii)   48%

$$= \frac{48}{100} \quad \text{(put over 100)}$$

$$= \frac{12}{25} \quad \text{(divide top and bottom by 4)}$$

To change a percentage into a decimal, do the following:

> Divide the number by 100.

EXAMPLE 2

Write the following as decimals. **(i)** 32%   **(ii)** 85%

Solution:

(i)   32%

$= \dfrac{32}{100}$ (put over 100)

$= 0{\cdot}32$

(ii)   85%

$= \dfrac{85}{100}$ (put over 100)

$= 0{\cdot}85$

Changing fractions and decimals to percentages

To change a fraction or a decimal to a percentage, do the following:

> Multiply the fraction or decimal by 100 and put the percentage symbol, %, at the end.

EXAMPLE 3

Write the following as percentages. **(i)** 0.42   **(ii)** $\frac{3}{5}$ **(iii)** $\frac{7}{20}$

Solution:

(i) $0{\cdot}42$

$= 0{\cdot}42 \times 100\%$

$= 42\%$

(ii) $\frac{3}{5}$

$= \frac{3}{5} \times 100\%$

$= 60\%$

(iii) $\frac{7}{20}$

$= \frac{7}{20} \times 100\%$

$= 35\%$

Exercise 9.1

In questions 1–25, express each of the following percentages as **(i)** a fraction in its simplest form and **(ii)** a decimal.

1. 20%	2. 30%	3. 50%	4. 25%	5. 10%
6. 5%	7. 40%	8. 75%	9. 80%	10. 60%
11. 35%	12. 45%	13. 65%	14. 95%	15. 55%
16. 12%	17. 4%	18. 15%	19. 2%	20. 88%
21. 120%	22. 150%	23. 110%	24. 180%	25. 225%

Express each of the following decimals as a percentage in questions 26–35.

26. 0·12   27. 0·3   28. 0·23   29. 0·18   30. 0·03

31. 0·68   32. 0·02   33. 0·04   34. 1·6   35. 2·4

Express each of the following fractions as a percentage in questions 36–50.

36. $\frac{1}{2}$ 37. $\frac{1}{4}$ 38. $\frac{3}{4}$ 39. $\frac{1}{5}$ 40. $\frac{2}{5}$

41. $\frac{3}{10}$ 42. $\frac{9}{10}$ 43. $\frac{11}{25}$ 44. $\frac{17}{20}$ 45. $\frac{33}{50}$

46. $\frac{9}{100}$ 47. $\frac{1}{50}$ 48. $\frac{6}{5}$ 49. $\frac{3}{2}$ 50. $\frac{1}{8}$

51. Express the shaded portion of the rectangle as a:

     (i) fraction   (ii) decimal   (iii) percentage.

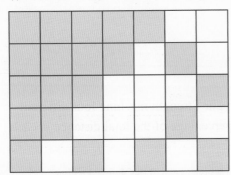

52. Express $\dfrac{2,000 - 800}{1,500}$ as a (i) fraction   (ii) decimal   (iii) percentage.

53. Write these numbers in order of size. Start with the smallest number.

         22% $\frac{1}{5}$ 0·3 $\frac{2}{7}$

54. Four cakes have been cut into eight different-sized pieces. Which pieces go together to make the four full cakes?

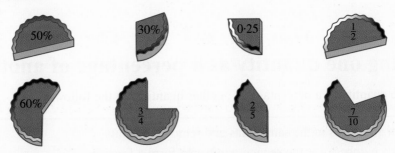

55. Match these 12 cards into four sets that show the same number.

$\frac{3}{4}$ 50%   0·25   0·75   75% $\frac{1}{10}$ $\frac{1}{4}$ 10% $\frac{1}{2}$ 0·1   25%   0·5

56. These are the marks scored by Keith in his recent exams.

   (i) In which subject did he do the best? Explain your answer.

   (ii) In which subject did he do the worst? Explain your answer.

   (iii) Put the subjects in order from Keith's worst result to his best result.

REPORT CARD

English	15/20
Maths	81%
Science	7/10
French	68%
History	11/25
Geography	66%
Irish	13/20

57. The picture shows how far up the scale of a Test your Strength machine four different people have hit the weight. Approximately what percentage of the total distance is each weight from the bottom?

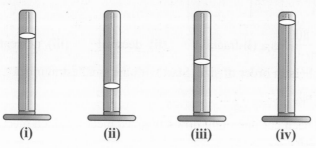

    (i)   **(ii)**   **(iii)**   **(iv)**

Expressing one quantity as a percentage of another

To express one quantity as a percentage of another quantity, do the following:

1. Write both quantities in the same units and remove the units.
2. Put the first number over the second number to form a fraction.
3. Multiply this fraction by 100 and put in the percentage symbol, %, at the end.

   In short:

$$\frac{\text{First number}}{\text{Second number}} \times 100\%$$

EXAMPLE

Express: (i) 80c as a percentage of €2·40   (ii) 400 m as a percentage of 2 km

Solution:

(i)   1. €2·40 = 240c

2. $\dfrac{80}{240}$

3. $\dfrac{80}{240} \times 100\%$

= $33\frac{1}{3}\%$

(ii)   1. 2 km = 2,000 m

2. $\dfrac{400}{2,000}$

3. $\dfrac{400}{2,000} \times 100\%$

= 20%

Exercise 9.2

In questions 1–24, express the first quantity as a percentage of the second.

1. 15, 20
2. 20, 50
3. 3, 5
4. 60, 300

5. 12, 15
6. 36, 300
7. 20, 8
8. 18, 12

9. 15 cm, 60 cm
10. 300 m, 1 km
11. 4 mm, 2 cm
12. 900 g, 2 kg

13. 80 cm, 2 m
14. 750 m, 5 km
15. €1·50, €7·50
16. 18 hours, 3 days

17. 60°, 180°
18. €1·26, €8·40
19. €1·20, €1
20. 60 km/h, 80 km/h

21. 63c, €1·80
22. 800 g, $2\frac{1}{2}$ kg
23. 700 cm³, 2 litres
24. 640 kg, 4 tonnes

25. There are 15 girls in a class of 25.

   (i) What percentage of the class are girls?

   (ii) What percentage are boys?

26. A boy gains 142 marks out of 200 marks in an exam. What percentage is this?

27. There are 40 red, 60 green, 100 blue and 50 white marbles in a bag. What percentage of the total number of marbles is each colour?

28. Which is the better record, 20 wins in 25 or 30 wins in 40?

29. An auctioneer received €4,100 as commission when she sold a house for €164,000. What percentage commission did the auctioneer receive for selling the house?

30. An article that costs €240 is increased in price by €60.

   (i) What is the increase as a percentage of the old price?

   (ii) What is the increase as a percentage of the new price?

31. A large bar of chocolate has 40 squares. Louise eats 28 of the squares. What percentage of the bar does she eat?

32. The diagram shows four different bottles of olive oil.

    (i) Express B as a percentage of A.

    (ii) Express C as a percentage of B.

    (iii) Express D as a percentage of A.

    (iv) Express (B + C) as a percentage of A.

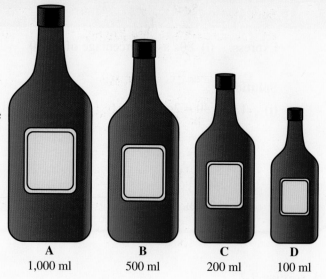

A	B	C	D
1,000 ml	500 ml	200 ml	100 ml

Finding the percentage change in a quantity

Often we have to express a change in a quantity as a percentage change.

Always express the change in the quantity as a percentage of the **original** quantity, using the following formula:

$$\text{Percentage change in a quantity} = \frac{\text{Change in quantity}}{\text{Original quantity}} \times 100\%$$

EXAMPLE

(i) A woman's salary was increased from €40,000 to €44,800.

Calculate her percentage increase in salary.

(ii) A man went on a diet and reduced his weight from 120 kg to 111 kg.

Calculate his percentage decrease in weight.

Solution:

(i) Increase = €44,800 − €40,000

   = €4,800

Percentage increase in salary

$$= \frac{\text{Increase in salary}}{\text{Original salary}} \times 100\%$$

$$= \frac{4{,}800}{40{,}000} \times 100\%$$

$$= 12\%$$

(ii) Decrease = 120 kg − 111 kg

   = 9 kg

Percentage decrease in weight

$$= \frac{\text{Decrease in weight}}{\text{Original weight}} \times 100\%$$

$$= \frac{9}{120} \times 100\%$$

$$= 7\tfrac{1}{2}\%$$

Exercise 9.3

Calculate the percentage increase or decrease in each of the following quantities in questions 1–18.

	Original quantity	New quantity
1.	25 kg	30 kg
2.	40 m	60 m
3.	60 marks	45 marks
4.	50c	45c
5.	€4·20	€4·41
6.	25 litres	22 litres

	Original quantity	New quantity
7.	800 kg	856 kg
8.	€120	€109·20
9.	250 m	215 m
10.	475 pupils	513 pupils
11.	€1·60	€1·40
12.	80 km/h	84 km/h

	Original quantity	New quantity
13.	50 cm	46·5 cm
14.	€250	€212·50
15.	72 marks	81 marks
16.	€2,700	€3,064·50
17.	360 kg	240 kg
18.	120 litres	40 litres

19. In 2010 a school had 450 pupils on the roll. In 2011 the number of pupils had increased to 477. Calculate the percentage increase in the number of pupils attending the school.

20. A maths book had 350 pages. A new edition was published with 343 pages. Calculate the percentage decrease in the number of pages in the book.

21. A man's salary was increased from €30,900 to €33,063. Calculate his percentage increase in salary.

22. A car, including four passengers, had a weight of 1,680 kg. Two of the passengers got out of the car and the weight was reduced to 1,478·4 kg.

   (i) Calculate the weight of the two passengers who got out.

   (ii) Calculate the percentage decrease in weight.

23. During a fever, the temperature of a child rose from 37°C to 38·85°C. Calculate the percentage increase in temperature.

Finding a given percentage of a quantity

There are several ways to find percentages of quantities. Here are two methods:

> **Method 1:**
> 1. Find 1%.
> 2. Multiply this by the percentage asked for in the question.
>
> **Method 2:**
> 1. Write the percentage as a decimal (or a fraction).
> 2. Multiply the quantity by the decimal (or the fraction).

EXAMPLE 1

Find 12% of €284.

Solution:

Method 1:
1. 100% = 284
   1% = 2·84
   (divide both sides by 100)
2. 12% = €2·84 × 12
   = €34·08

Method 2:
1. 12% = 0·12%   (as a decimal)
2. Therefore, 12% of €284
   = €284 × 0·12
   = €34·08

Exercise 9.4

In questions 1–20, find:

1. 10% of €380
2. 20% of €150
3. 25% of €3·36
4. 75% of €72·40
5. 5% of €120
6. 50% of 184 m
7. $12\frac{1}{2}$% of 400 m
8. 30% of €270·50
9. 35% of €520·20
10. 45% of 168·80
11. 11% of €350
12. 13% of $2\frac{1}{2}$ km
13. 31% of €120
14. 48% of €250
15. 8% of €50
16. 17% of €140
17. $7\frac{1}{2}$% of 6,160
18. $2\frac{1}{2}$% of €80·40
19. $33\frac{1}{3}$% of 900 m
20. $66\frac{2}{3}$% of €180
21. A school concert raised €2,480 for charity. After a vote it was decided to give 20% to charity A, 25% to charity B, 40% to charity C and the remainder to charity D. How much was given to each charity?

22. Add 18% of €35 and 14% of €23.

23. A car costing €12,000 in cash can be bought on credit by paying a 25% deposit and followed by 24 monthly payments of €400.

   (i) How much will the car cost on credit?

   (ii) What is the extra cost above the cash price?

24. A racing bike that normally costs €960 can be bought using three different plans:

Plan	Deposit	Number of payments	Each payment
A	20%	24	€45
B	50%	12	€40
C	10%	36	€35

   (i) Work out how much the bike costs using each plan.

   (ii) Work out the extra cost of each plan compared to the cash price.

   (iii) Calculate the percentage increase in price as a percentage of the original price for each plan.

25. This pie chart shows the contents of a large chocolate bar. The bar weighs 200 g.

   (i) What percentage is carbohydrate?

   (ii) Calculate the amount of protein, carbohydrate and fat in the bar.

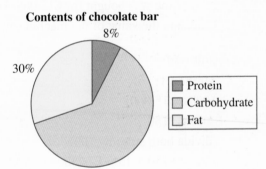

Contents of chocolate bar

Increasing or decreasing a quantity by a given percentage

A change in a quantity, whether an increase or a decrease, is often described by a percentage.

We will use two methods to increase or decrease a quantity by a percentage.

EXAMPLE 1

In 2010 the population of a town was 5,400. In 2012 it increased by 12%.
What was the population of the town in 2012?

Solution:

Method 1:

100% = 5,400

1% = 54

(divide both sides by 100)

Therefore, 12% = 54 × 12 = 648.

Therefore, the population in 2012

= 5,400 + 648 = 6,048.

Method 2:

As a percentage, the population in 2012 is

100% + 12% = 112% of the population in

2010.

Therefore, the population in 2012

= 112% of 5,400

= 1·12 × 5,400 = 6,048

EXAMPLE 2

A machine was bought for €15,000. During the year its value depreciated by 15%.
Calculate the value of the machine at the end of the year.

Solution:

Method 1:

100% = 15,000

1% = 150

(divide both sides by 100)

15% = €150 × 15 = €2,250

Therefore, the value of the machine after

a year

= €15,000 − €2,250

= €12,750

Method 2:

As a percentage the new value is

100% − 15% = 85% of the old value.

Therefore, the value of the machine after

a year

= 85% of €15,000

= €15,000 × 0.85

= €12,750

Exercise 9.5

1. Calculate these percentage changes.

   (i) Increase 300 by 10%

   (iii) Decrease 120 km by 20%

   (v) Decrease €320 by 55%

   (ii) Decrease 200 by 5%

   (iv) Increase 520 m by 15%

   (vi) Increase €80 by 8%

2. A packet of biscuits normally weighs 180 g. During a promotion it is marked '10% extra free'. What is the weight of biscuits in this packet?

3. A bag of crisps usually weighs 60 g. It is marked '15% extra free'.

   (i) Calculate 15% of 60 g.   (ii) What is the weight of crisps in this bag?

4. Sarah earns €520 per week. She receives a pay rise of 4%. How much does she earn each week after the pay rise?

5. A bus ticket now costing €28 is due to rise by 12% in the new year. What will the price of the bus ticket be in the new year?

6. A lorry is carrying 750 kg of sand. For safety reasons, it has to reduce its load by 18%. Calculate the new weight the lorry is carrying after the reduction.

7. Before it was serviced a car's top speed was 120 km/h. After a service its top speed increases by 9%. What is the new top speed?

8. During a sale the following items were reduced in price. Calculate the sale price.

(i)

€ 80
Take 20% off

(ii)

€ 180
Take 25% off

(iii)

€ 90
Take 33⅓% off

(iv)

€ 16
Take 40% off

9. In a sale, a supermarket reduced all its prices by 30%. On Fun Friday, the supermarket reduced its sale prices by 20%. Gail says, 'That means all prices are reduced by half.' Is Gail wrong? Justify your answer.

10. During a sale, a shop had two identical pairs of jeans on sale. The label on one pair said '33⅓% discount'. The label on the other pair said '⅖ off'. Which pair of jeans would you buy? Explain your answer.

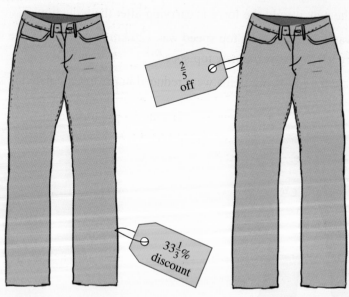

$\frac{2}{5}$
off

33⅓%
discount

11. **(i)** Eoin measures the height of a flower as 50 cm. The next day it is 12% taller. What is its new height?

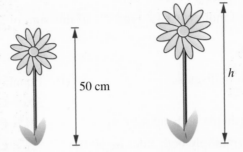

50 cm

h

(ii) Another plant grows from 60 cm to 69 cm. Calculate the percentage change in height.

12. A shop is having a three-day sale. Each day the prices of goods are reduced by 20% of the price from the previous day. The day before the sale a washing machine cost €650.

Pre-sale	€650
Day 1	
Day 2	
Day 3	

 (i) Complete the table on the right.
 (ii) Has the price of the washing machine been reduced by 60% during the third day of the sale? Justify your answer.

13. **(i)** In 2008 the population of a town was 2,400. In 2009 the population had decreased by 10% of the 2008 figure. In 2010 the population of the town increased by 10% of the 2009 figure. Find the population of the town in **(a)** 2009 **(b)** 2010.

 (ii) By what percentage has the population changed from 2008 to 2010?

14. Ciara spends €1,600 each year on heating her house. By adding extra insulation in the attic, she can reduce this by 15%.

 (i) How much will Ciara save on her heating bills each year if she gets the insulation?

 (ii) It will cost €920 to have the extra insulation put in. Ciara will get a grant of €200 towards this cost. How many years will it take for the savings on her heating bills to recover the rest of the cost?

Given a percentage of a quantity

In some questions on percentages we will be given an equation in disguise.

When this happens, do the following:

> **1.** Write down the equation given in disguise.
> **2.** From this equation, find 1%.
> **3.** Calculate the required percentage.

EXAMPLE 1

(i) 8% of a number is 20. Find the number.

(ii) 3% of a sum of money is €45. Find 7% of this sum of money.

Solution:

(i) Equation given in disguise:

$8\% = 20$

$1\% = 2{\cdot}5$ (divide both sides by 8)

$100\% = 250$ (multiply both sides by 100)

Check: 8% of 250 = 0·08 × 250 = 20 ✓

(ii) Equation given in disguise:

$3\% = €45$

$1\% = €15$ (divide both sides by 3)

$7\% = €105$ (multiply both sides by 7)

Check: 3% = €15 × 3 = €45 ✓

Reverse percentage problems

EXAMPLE 2

(i) The price of a holiday is increased by 6% to €1,537. What was the original cost of the holiday?

(ii) A bicycle was sold for €544 at a loss of 15%. Find the original cost of the bicycle.

Solution:

(i) | cost of holiday | $\xrightarrow{\ +6\%\ }$ | €1,537 | $= 106\%$

Think of the original cost as 100%.   100% + 6% = 106%

∴ $106\% = €1,537$ (equation given in disguise)

$1\% = €14{\cdot}5$ (divide both sides by 106)

$100\% = €1,450$ (multiply both sides by 100)

Therefore, the original cost of the holiday was €1,450.

(ii) | cost of bicycle | $\xrightarrow{\ -15\%\ }$ | €544 | $= 85\%$

Think of the original cost as 100%.   100% − 15% = 85%

∴ $85\% = €544$ (equation given in disguise)

$1\% = €6{\cdot}4$ (divide both sides by 85)

$100\% = €640$ (multiply both sides by 100)

Therefore, the original cost of the bicycle was €640.

Exercise 9.6

1. 5% of a number is 15. Find the number.

2. 20% of a sum of money is €80. Find this sum of money.

3. 8% of the population of a town is 96. Calculate the population of the town.

4. 6% of a number is 30. Find 11% of the number.

5. 110% of a sum of money is €660. Calculate the sum of money.

6. 80% of a number is 600. Calculate the number.

7. Trevor saves 12% of his monthly salary. Each month he saves €180. What is his monthly salary?

8. 15% of an orange's weight is peel. If the peel weighs 12 g, find the weight of the orange.

9. Rory received a 4% increase in his salary. His new salary is €572 per week. What was Rory's salary per week before the increase?

10. During a promotion a bottle of shampoo contained an extra 10% more than a normal bottle. The promotion bottle contains 550 ml. Calculate the volume of a normal bottle.

11. In an election the winning candidate received 189 votes, which was 54% of all the votes cast. How many votes were cast?

12. In a maths test Ross answered 80% of the questions correctly. He answered 20 questions correctly. How many questions were on the maths test?

13. The price of a holiday is increased by 8% to €583·20. What was the original cost of the holiday?

14. A piece of elastic was stretched by 15% to a length of 9·2 cm. Calculate its unstretched original length.

9·2 cm

15. A one-year-old car is worth €24,000. This is a decrease in value of 25% of its value from new. What was the price of the car when it was new?

16. A bat colony has 156 bats. This was an increase of 30% on the numbers the previous year. What was the size of the bat colony last year?

17. 205 g of a breakfast cereal provides 72 mg of vitamin C. This is 18% of the recommended daily intake of vitamin C. What daily intake of vitamin C is recommended?

18. A salesperson's wages for a week was €620. This was made up of a basic pay of €540 plus a commission of 4% of sales. Calculate the amount of the sales for the week.

Introduction to sets

> A **set** is a well-defined collection of objects.

The set of whole numbers between 4·7 and 8·2 is a well-defined set, but the set of good films is not (different people will give different answers).

The objects that make up a set are called **elements** or **members** of that set.

Sets are written as a list within braces { } with the elements separated by commas. For example, a set of wild animals might look like {**lion, elephant, bear**}.

When graphed, we use a Venn diagram, which represents each set as a closed curve (or loop) and shows each element as a labelled point within the curve.

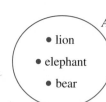

Notes:

1. When listing the elements of a set or showing a set with a Venn diagram, **an element is never repeated**.
2. The **order** in which the elements are listed or shown is **not** important.
3. The condition, or rule, describing the elements of a set is often put inside braces. For example, $M = \{$months of the year$\}$.

EXAMPLE 1

(i) If $A = \{$letters of the word MISSISSIPPI$\}$, list the elements of A.

(ii) If $F = \{$factors of 6$\}$, list the elements of F and represent F with a Venn diagram.

Solution:

(i) **MISSISSIPPI**

There are 11 letters in the word MISSISSIPPI, but only four different letters are used. These four different letters are M, I, S and P.

Therefore, $A = \{$M, I, S, P$\}$.

(ii) The factors of 6 are 1, 2, 3 and 6.

Therefore, $F = \{1, 2, 3, 6\}$.

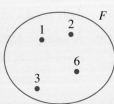

Membership of a set

$\in$ means **is an element of**
$\notin$ means **is not an element of**

EXAMPLE 2

$A = \{\text{the first five letters in the alphabet}\}$.
Insert $\in$ or $\notin$ in each of the following statements: (i) $d \ \square \ A$ (ii) $g \ \square \ A$

Solution:

$$A = \{\text{the first five letters in the alphabet}\}$$
Therefore, $A = \{a, b, c, d, e\}$

(i) d is an element of A,   therefore $d \in A$.
(ii) g is not an element of A,   therefore $g \notin A$.

Exercise 10.1

In questions 1–10, list the elements of the set and represent the set with a Venn diagram.

1. $A = \{\text{even numbers between 1 and 9}\}$
2. $B = \{\text{odd numbers between 0 and 10}\}$
3. $C = \{\text{factors of 12}\}$
4. $D = \{\text{letters of the word SUCCESSES}\}$
5. $E = \{\text{prime numbers less than 14}\}$
6. $F = \{\text{letters of the word ARRANGEMENT}\}$
7. $G = \{\text{vowels in the alphabet}\}$
8. $H = \{\text{vowels in the word MATHEMATICS}\}$
9. $I = \{\text{numbers between 2 and 22 that can be divided evenly by 3}\}$
10. $J = \{\text{numbers between 4 and 31 that can be divided evenly by 5}\}$

In questions 11–15, list the elements of the set.

11. $X = \{\text{days of the week}\}$
12. $Y = \{\text{days of the week beginning with the letter S}\}$
13. $Z = \{\text{months of the year beginning with the letter J}\}$
14. $M = \{\text{whole numbers between 1 and 9, including 1 and 9}\}$
15. $S = \{\text{the squares of the first six natural numbers}\}$

In questions 16–19, say whether each statement is true or false.

16. $7 \in \{$odd numbers$\}$

17. $8 \notin \{$even numbers$\}$

18. Monday $\in \{$days of the week$\}$

19. Friday $\notin \{$months of the year$\}$

If $X = \{a, b, c, d, e\}$, $Y = \{0, 2, 4, 6, 8\}$ and $Z = \{1, 4, 9, 16, 25, 36\}$, insert $\in$ or $\notin$ in each of the following statements.

20. $d \boxed{\in} X$

21. $5 \boxed{\notin} Y$

22. $a \boxed{\notin} Y$

23. $5 \boxed{\notin} Z$

24. $b \boxed{\notin} Y$

25. $c \boxed{\notin} Y$

26. $49 \boxed{\notin} Z$

27. $b \boxed{\in} X$

28. $25 \boxed{\notin} Y$

29. $\sqrt{16} \boxed{\in} Y$

30. $\sqrt{16} \boxed{\in} Z$

31. $\sqrt{64} \boxed{\notin} X$

Number of elements in a set

The number of elements in the set A is denoted by $\#A$.

$$\#A = \text{the number of elements in set } A.$$

EXAMPLE

$A = \{a, b, c, d, e\}$ and $X = \{2, 4, 6, 8\}$.

(i) Find $\#A$.   (ii) Calculate $\#A - \#X$.

Solution:

(i) Since A contains five elements, then $\#A = 5$.

(ii) Since X contains four elements, then $\#X = 4$.
Therefore, $\#A - \#X = 5 - 4 = 1$.

Equality of sets

Sets are said to be **equal** if they contain exactly the same elements.

The **order** in which the elements are listed is **not** important. For example, if $A = \{a, b, c, d)$ and $B = \{b, c, d, a\}$, then $A = B$, as they contain exactly the same elements.

The null set

The set that contains **no** elements is called the **null** or **empty** set.
The null set is denoted by Ø or { }.

> The **null set**, Ø or { }, is the set that contains no elements.

Examples of the null set:

{months of the year that have more than 31 days}

{odd numbers that can be divided evenly by 2}

Note: {0} is **not** the null set.

{0} is a set that contains one element, 0, so it is **not** empty.

Exercise 10.2

1. **(i)** Which of the following sets are equal?

$$P = \{2, 4, 6, 8\}, \quad Q = \{3, 5, 7\}, \quad R = \{5, 7, 3\}, \quad S = \{8, 2, 4, 6\}$$

(ii) Evaluate: **(a)** $\#P + \#Q$ **(b)** $(\#S)^2$

2. If $A = \{p, q, r\}$ and $B = \{p, q, s\}$, explain why $A \neq B$.

3. $A = \{2, 4, 6, 8\}$ and $B = \{$even numbers between 1 and 9$\}$.

(i) Is $A = B$? **(ii)** Evaluate $\#(A) + \#(B)$.

4. $C = \{$days of the week containing nine letters$\}$.

$D = \{$days of the week beginning with the letter W$\}$.

Does $C = D$?

5. $P = \{$vowels in the word 'median'$\}$, $Q = \{$vowels in the word 'mean'$\}$.

(i) List the elements in **(a)** P **(b)** Q.

(ii) Is $P = Q$? **(iii)** Evaluate $\#(P) - \#(Q)$.

6. $A = \{p, q\}$, $B = \{1, 2, 3\}$ and $C = \{m, i, s, t\}$. Evaluate each of the following.

(i) $\#A + \#B + \#C$ **(ii)** $5(\#A) + 4(\#B) + 3(\#C)$

(iii) $[\#A]^2 + [\#B]^2 + [\#C]^2$ **(iv)** $[\#(A) + \#(B)]^2$

7. $A = \{$even numbers between 6·7 and 7·9$\}$.

(i) List the set A. **(ii)** Evaluate $\#(A)$.

8. $A = \{$letters in the word 'rearrange'$\}$, $B = \{$letters in the word 'ranger'$\}$.

(i) List the elements **(a)** of A **(b)** of B.

(ii) Does $A = B$?

(iii) Evaluate $\#A - \#B$.

Membership of a set defined by a rule

A set can also be described by using a rule.

Consider the set $P = \{$prime numbers less than 8$\}$. This set can also be written as:

$$P = \{x \mid x \text{ is a prime number less than } 8\}$$

This is read as:

P   is   the set   of all values of x such that x is a prime number less than 8
↓   ↓   ↓   ↓   ↓   ↓

P   =   { x | x is a prime number less than 8}

This is the **rule method** of describing a set.

EXAMPLE

$A = \{x \mid x \text{ is an even number between 3 and 11}\}$. List the elements of A.

Solution:

Using the rule, $x = 4, 6, 8, 10$.

Therefore, $A = \{4, 6, 8, 10\}$.

Exercise 10.3

In questions 1–14, list the elements of the set.

1. $A = \{x \mid x \text{ is an even number between 5 and 15}\}$

2. $B = \{x \mid x \text{ is an odd number between 2 and 12}\}$

3. $C = \{x \mid x \text{ is a letter of the word 'TENNESSEE'}\}$

4. $D = \{x \mid x \text{ is a letter of the word 'TOMORROW'}\}$

5. $E = \{x \mid x \text{ is a factor of 28}\}$

6. $F = \{x \mid x \text{ is a factor of 36}\}$

7. $G = \{x \mid x \text{ is a whole number between 3 and 25 and divisible by 4}\}$

8. $P = \{x \mid x \text{ is a prime number less than 20}\}$

9. $V = \{x \mid x \text{ is a vowel}\}$

10. $M = \{x \mid x \text{ is a vowel in the word 'NOTORIOUS'}\}$

11. $W = \{x \mid x \text{ is a day of the week beginning with } T\}$

12. $R = \{x \mid x \text{ is a whole number between } 2\frac{1}{4} \text{ and } 2\frac{1}{2}\}$

13. $T = \{x \mid x \text{ is a vowel in the word 'DRY'}\}$

14. $S = \{x \mid x \text{ is an even number between } 4\frac{1}{2} \text{ and } 5\frac{1}{2}\}$

Subsets (sets within sets)

If every element of a set B is also an element of a set A, then B is said to be a subset of A. This is written as $B \subset A$.

> $\subset$ means **is a subset of**
> $\not\subset$ means **is not a subset of**

EXAMPLE 1

$A = \{1, 3, 5, 7, 9\}$, $B = \{3, 5\}$ and $C = \{3, 6\}$.
(i) Say why B is a subset of A.   (ii) Is $B \subset C$?
(iii) Represent A and B with a Venn diagram.

Solution:

(i) Every element in B is also in A,
therefore B is a subset of A, i.e. $B \subset A$.

(ii) The element 5 is in B and not in C,
therefore B is not a subset of C,
i.e. $B \not\subset C$.

(iii)

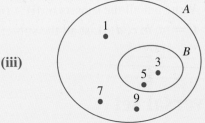

Set B is contained within set A.

Notes: 1. Every set is a subset of itself.   **2.** The null set is a subset of every set.

EXAMPLE 2

$A = \{p, q\}$. Write out all the subsets of A.

Solution:
The subsets of A are $\{\ \}$, $\{p\}$, $\{q\}$ and $\{p, q\}$.

Exercise 10.4

1. $A = \{1, 2, 3, 4, 5, 6, 7, 8\}$, $B = \{4, 5, 6, 7\}$, $C = \{\ \}$, $D = \{3, 4, 8, 9\}$, $E = \{2\}$, $F = \{4, 6\}$.
State whether each of the following is true or false.

(i) $B \subset A$ (ii) $E \subset B$ (iii) $C \subset E$ (iv) $D \subset D$
(v) $F \not\subset B$ (vi) $E \subset A$ (vii) $A \subset D$ (viii) $F \not\subset C$
(ix) $D \subset C$ (x) $F \subset B \subset A$

2. $H = \{1, 2, 3, 4, 5, 6, 7, 8, 9, 10\}$. List the following subsets of H.

   (i) {even numbers}   (ii) {odd numbers}   (iii) {numbers divisible by 3}

   (iv) {prime numbers}   (v) {multiples of 5}   (vi) {factors of 24}

   (vii) {perfect squares}   (viii) {perfect cubes}   (ix) {numbers divisible by 17}

3. Represent each of the following with Venn diagrams.

   (i) $A = \{1, 3, 5, 7, 9\}$ and $B = \{1, 3\}$

   (ii) $P = \{6, 9\}$ and $Q = \{2, 5, 6, 7, 9, 12\}$

   (iii) $C = \{x \mid x$ is an even number between 1 and 19$\}$ and

        $D = \{x \mid x$ is a number between 3 and 17 that is divisible by 4$\}$

4. If $A = \{231, 43, 141, 600, 501, 430, 610, 35\}$, write down a subset of A in which the sum of the digits in each number is 6.

5. $A = \{p, q, r\}$, $B = \{1, 2, 3, 4\}$.

   Write out all the subsets of (i) A (ii) B.

6. $C = \{a, b, c, d\}$. List all the subsets of C that contain exactly three elements.

Universal set

The **universal set** is the set containing all the elements used in a given question. It is denoted by U. In a Venn diagram the universal set is represented by a rectangle.

Intersection

> The **intersection** of two sets, A and B, is the set of elements that are in both A and B.

It is written as $A \cap B$, pronounced 'A intersection B'.

Union

> The **union** of two sets, A and B, is the set of elements formed by joining together all the elements of A and B.

It is written as $A \cup B$, pronounced 'A union B'.

EXAMPLE

$U = \{1, 2, 3, 4, 5, 6, 7, 8, 9, 10\}$, $A = \{1, 3, 4, 7\}$ and $B = \{3, 6, 7, 8, 9\}$.

   (i) Represent U, A and B with a Venn diagram.

   (ii) List the elements of $A \cap B$ and $A \cup B$.

   (iii) Evaluate $\#(A \cup B) - \#(A \cap B)$.

Solution:

   (i)

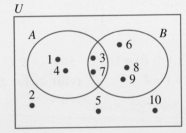

   (ii) $A \cap B = \{3, 7\}$

          $A \cup B = \{1, 3, 4, 6, 7, 8, 9\}$

   (iii) $\#(A \cup B) - \#(A \cap B)$

          $= 7 - 2 = 5$

Note: U need not be included if it is not relevant to the question.

Exercise 10.5

  1. $A = \{1, 2, 3, 4, 5\}$ and $B = \{4, 5, 6, 7\}$.
     (i) Represent A and B with a Venn diagram.
     (ii) List the elements of $A \cap B$ and $A \cup B$.
     (iii) Evaluate $\#(A \cup B) - \#(A \cap B)$.
     (iv) Is $(A \cap B) \subset A$? Explain your answer.

  2. $C = \{a, b, c, d\}$ and $D = \{b, d, e, f, g, h\}$.
     (i) Represent C and D with a Venn diagram.
     (ii) List the elements of $C \cap D$ and $C \cup D$.
     (iii) Evaluate $\#D - \#(C \cap D)$.

  3. $U = \{a, b, c, d, e, f, g, h, i, j\}$, $A = \{c, d, e, f\}$ and $B = \{e, f, g, h\}$.
     (i) Represent U, A and B with a Venn diagram.
     (ii) List the elements of $A \cap B$ and $A \cup B$.
     (iii) Evaluate $\#(A \cup B) - \#(A \cap B)$.

  4. $U = \{2, 3, 4, 5, 6, 7, 8, 9\}$, $A = \{2, 4, 5\}$ and $B = \{2, 5, 6, 8\}$.
     (i) Represent U, A and B with a Venn diagram.
     (ii) List the elements of $A \cup B$ and $A \cap B$.
     (iii) Explain why $(A \cup B) \subset U$.
     (iv) Evaluate $\#U - \#(A \cup B)$.

5. From the Venn diagram shown here, say whether each of the following statements is true or false.

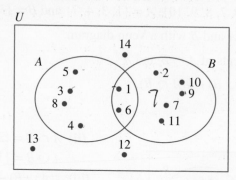

(i) $6 \in A$ (ii) $6 \in B$ (iii) $(A \cap B) = \emptyset$ (iv) $13 \in U$

(v) $1 \in (A \cap B)$ (vi) $12 \in (A \cup B)$ (vii) $\#A = 4$ (viii) $\#(A \cap B) = 2$

(ix) $\#A > \#B$ (x) $\#U - \#B = 6$

(xi) List the elements of U that are not in $A \cup B$.

6. $A = \{1, 2, 6\}$, $B = \{1, 2, 3, 4, 5\}$ and $U = \{1, 2, 3, 4, 5, 6, 7\}$.

(i) Explain why $B \subset U$.

(ii) Represent U, A and B with a Venn diagram.

(iii) Evaluate $\#U - \#(A \cup B)$.

(iv) List the elements of U that are not in A or B.

7. Link each of the following with $\in, \notin, =, \neq, \subset, \cup$ or $\cap$.

(i) $5 \square \{2, 3, 4, 5, 6\}$ (ii) $\{t, r\} \square \{r, t\}$ (iii) $\{a, b\} \square \{a, b, c\}$ (iv) $\{4\} \square \{3, 4, 5\}$

(v) $\{p, q, r\} \square \{r, p, q\}$ (vi) $q \square \{m, n, o\}$ (vii) $\{a, b, c\} \square \{c, d, e\} \square \{a, b, c, d, e\}$

(viii) $\{1, 2, 3, 4, 5\} \square \{4, 5, 6, 7, 8\} \square \{4, 5\}$ (ix) $\{1, 3\} \square \{1, 3, 5, 9\} \square \{1, 3, 5, 7, 9\}$

8. $U = \{1, 4, 9, 12, 15, 18, 19, 20\}$.

$A = \{$numbers in U divisible by 2$\}$.

$B = \{$numbers in U divisible by 3$\}$.

Copy and complete the Venn diagram.

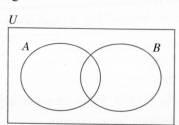

Set difference

> $A \setminus B$ is the set of elements that are in A but not in B.

$A \setminus B$ is pronounced 'A less B' or 'A not B' or 'A but not in B'.
In some ways it is like the subtraction of one set from another.

EXAMPLE 1

$A = \{a, b, c, d, e, f\}$ and $B = \{e, f, g, h\}$.
Represent A and B with a Venn diagram.
List the elements of **(i)** $A \setminus B$ **(ii)** $B \setminus A$.

Solution:

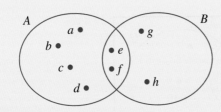

(i) $A \setminus B$
$= \{a, b, c, d, e, f\} \setminus \{e, f, g, h\}$
$= \{a, b, c, d\}$
(all the elements in A that are not in B)

(ii) $B \setminus A$
$= \{e, f, g, h\} \setminus \{a, b, c, d, e, f\}$
$= \{g, h\}$
(all the elements of B that are not in A)

Note: If brackets are involved, the operation inside the brackets must be done first.

EXAMPLE 2

$P = \{a, b, c\}$, $\quad Q = \{c, d, e\}$, $\quad R = \{a, c, e, f\}$.
List the elements of **(i)** $(P \cup Q) \setminus R$ **(ii)** $Q \setminus (P \cap R)$.

Solution:
(i) $(P \cup Q) \setminus R$
$P \cup Q$ (brackets first)
$= \{a, b, c\} \cup \{c, d, e\}$
$= \{a, b, c, d, e\}$

Therefore, $(P \cup Q) \setminus R$
$= \{a, b, c, d, e\} \setminus \{a, c, e, f\}$
$= \{b, d\}$

(ii) $P \cap R$ (brackets first)
$= \{a, b, c\} \cap \{a, c, e, f\}$
$= \{a, c\}$

Therefore, $Q \setminus (P \cap R)$
$= \{c, d, e\} \setminus \{a, c\}$
$= \{d, e\}$

Exercise 10.6

1. $A = \{1, 2, 3, 4, 5, 6\}$ and $B = \{4, 5, 6, 7, 8\}$.
   (i) Represent A and B with a Venn diagram.
   (ii) List the elements of (a) $A \setminus B$ (b) $B \setminus A$.

2. $P = \{a, b, c, d\}$ and $Q = \{a, c, e, f, g\}$.
   (i) Represent P and Q with a Venn diagram.
   (ii) List the elements of (a) $P \setminus Q$ (b) $Q \setminus P$.
   (iii) Evaluate $\#(Q \setminus P) - \#(P \setminus Q)$.

3. $X = \{p, q, r, s\}$ and $Y = \{p, q, u, v, w\}$. List the elements of:
   (i) $X \setminus Y$ (ii) $Y \setminus X$ (iii) $(X \setminus Y) \cup (Y \setminus X)$ (iv) $(X \setminus Y) \cap (Y \setminus X)$

4. From the Venn diagram shown, answer true or false to each of the following statements.
   (i) $\#U = 10$ (ii) $P \cap Q = \{3, 4\}$ (iii) $Q \setminus P = \{9, 10\}$ (iv) $\#(P \setminus Q) = 2$
   (v) $(P \cup Q) \setminus (P \cap Q) = \{1, 6, 7, 9, 10\}$

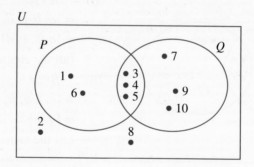

5. $A = \{1, 2, 3, 4, 5\}$, $B = \{1, 2, 6, 7, 8\}$ and $C = \{2, 5, 7, 9\}$. List the elements of:
   (i) $A \setminus B$ (ii) $A \setminus C$ (iii) $B \setminus A$ (iv) $B \setminus C$
   (v) $A \cup B$ (vi) $(A \cup B) \setminus C$ (vii) $B \cap C$ (viii) $A \setminus (B \cap C)$
   (ix) $B \cup C$ (x) $(B \cup C) \setminus (B \cap C)$ (xi) $(B \cap C) \setminus A$

A\B = Everything in B that is not in B.

A =

Complement of a set

The **complement** of a set A is the set of elements in the universal set, U, that are **not** elements of A.

> $$A' = U \setminus A$$
> Every element in the universal set U except those in A.

The complement of a set A is written A' (pronounced 'A complement' or 'A dashed').
It is an extension of set difference.

$$(A \cup B)' = U \setminus (A \cup B) \quad \text{and} \quad (A \cap B)' = U \setminus (A \cap B)$$

The four regions for the three sets U, A **and** B

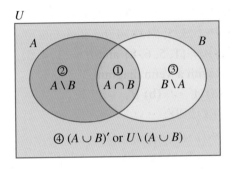

Note: If the universal set, U, is not involved, there are only three regions.

When drawing a Venn diagram, always work from the centre outwards.

EXAMPLE

$U = \{1, 2, 3, 4, 5, 6, 7, 8, 9\}$, $A = \{1, 3, 4, 7\}$ and $B = \{2, 3, 5, 7, 9\}$.

Represent U, A and B with a Venn diagram.

List the elements of **(i)** A' **(ii)** B' **(iii)** $A' \cup B'$ **(iv)** $(A \cup B)'$

Solution:

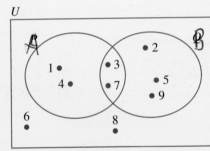

(i) $A' = U \setminus A$

     $= \{1, 2, 3, 4, 5, 6, 7, 8, 9\} \setminus \{1, 3, 4, 7\}$

     $= \{2, 5, 6, 8, 9\}$

(ii) $B' = U \setminus B$

     $= \{1, 2, 3, 4, 5, 6, 7, 8, 9\} \setminus \{2, 3, 5, 7, 9\}$

     $= \{1, 4, 6, 8\}$

(iii) $A' \cup B'$

     $= \{2, 5, 6, 8, 9\} \cup \{1, 4, 6, 8\}$

     $= \{1, 2, 4, 5, 6, 8, 9\}$

(iv) $(A \cup B)'$

     $(A \cup B)$ (brackets first)

     $= \{1, 3, 4, 7\} \cup \{2, 3, 5, 7, 9\}$

     $= \{1, 2, 3, 4, 5, 7, 9\}$

     $(A \cup B)'$

     $= U \setminus (A \cup B)$

     $= \{1, 2, 3, 4, 5, 6, 7, 8, 9\}$

     $\setminus \{1, 2, 3, 4, 5, 7, 9\}$

     $= \{6, 8\}$

Exercise 10.7

1. $U = \{a, b, c, d, e\}$ and $A = \{c, d, e\}$. List the elements of A'.
2. $U = \{3, 4, 5, 6, 7, 8\}$ and $P = \{3, 5, 7\}$. List the elements of P'.
3. $U = \{1, 2, 3, 4, 5, 6, 7, 8\}$, $A = \{1, 5, 6, 8\}$ and $B = \{1, 4, 5\}$.
   (i) Represent U, A and B with a Venn diagram.
   (ii) List the elements of (a) A' (b) B'.
   (iii) Verify that $A' \cap B' = (A \cup B)'$.
4. $U = \{a, b, c, d, e, f, g\}$, $P = \{a, d, f, g\}$ and $Q = \{a, b, g\}$.
   (i) Represent U, P and Q with a Venn diagram.
   (ii) List the elements of (a) P' (b) Q' (c) $P' \cap Q'$ (d) $(P \cup Q)'$.
   (iii) Evaluate $\#(P') + \#(Q') - \#(P' \cap Q')$.
5. The Venn diagram shows the sets U, A and B.

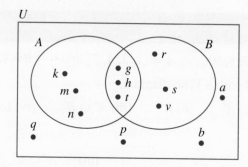

List the elements of the following sets.

(i) U (ii) A (iii) B (iv) $A \cap B$

(v) $A \cup B$ (vi) $A \setminus B$ (vii) $B \setminus A$ (viii) A'

(ix) B' (x) $A' \cap B'$ (xi) $(A \cup B)'$ (xii) $A' \cap B$

(xiii) $A \cap B'$ (xiv) $(B \setminus A)'$

Numerical problems on two sets

When using Venn diagrams to solve numerical problems, we put the actual number of elements in a region on the diagram. It is important at this stage that the meanings of the symbols used are considered.

Set notation	Meaning
$\cup$	or
$\cap$	and, both
$A \cup B$	in A or in B
$A \cap B$	in A and in B
$A \setminus B$	in A but not in B, in A only
$B \setminus A$	in B but not in A, in B only
U	universal set
A' or $U \setminus A$	in U but not in A
$(A \cup B)'$ or $U \setminus (A \cup B)$	in U but not in A or B
$(A \cup B)'$ or $U \setminus (A \cap B)$	in U but not in A and B

When putting the values into a Venn diagram, always work from the centre outwards.

EXAMPLE 1

In a class of 34 pupils, 22 study music, 18 study science and 8 study both.

Draw a Venn diagram to illustrate the information and use it to find the number of pupils in the class who study **(i)** music only **(ii)** science only **(iii)** neither music nor science.

Solution:

Draw a Venn diagram showing U for the class, M for music and S for science.

Given: $\#U = 34$, $\#M = 22$, $\#S = 18$ and $\#(M \cap S) = 8$.

Put 8 in the middle intersecting part of the diagram.

(i)　Number who study music only

　　$= \#(M \setminus S)$

　　$= 22 - 8$

　　$= 14$

(ii)　Number who study science only

　　$= \#(S \setminus M)$

　　$= 18 - 8$

　　$= 10$

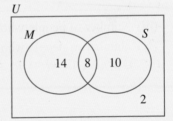

(iii)　Number who study neither music nor science

　　$= \#[U \setminus (M \cup S)]$

　　$= 34 - (14 + 8 + 10)$

　　$= 34 - 32 = 2$

Check: $14 + 8 + 10 + 2 = 34$ ✓

In some questions the number of elements in the intersection of the two sets is not given. This leads to the problem of **double counting**.

EXAMPLE 2

In a survey of 32 people, 20 said they liked rock music, 13 said they liked classical music and 4 said they like neither.

   (i) How many liked both rock and classical music?

   (ii) Represent the survey with a Venn diagram.

(iii) How many only liked rock music?

(iv) How many liked only one of these types of music?

Solution:

On the Venn diagram, let U represent the number of people in the survey, R the number who liked rock music and C the number who liked classical music.

   (i) The number of people in the survey who liked rock music, classical music or neither
   $$= 20 + 13 + 4 = 37.$$
   The number of people in the survey $= 32$.

   Therefore, the number of people counted twice $= 37 - 32 = 5$.

   Thus, 5 people liked both rock and classical music.

   (ii) U

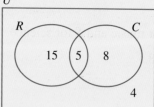

$\#(R \cap C) = 5$
$\#(R \setminus C) = 20 - 5 = 15$
$\#(C \setminus R) = 13 - 5 = 8$
Check: $15 + 5 + 8 + 4 = 32$ ✓

(iii) Number of people who only liked rock music $= \#(R \setminus C) = 15$.

(iv) Number of people who liked only one of these types of music
   $$= \#(R \setminus C) + \#(C \setminus R) = 15 + 8 = 23.$$

Exercise 10.8

1. 66 pupils were asked in a survey if they liked rock music, R, or classical music, C, or neither. The results are shown in the Venn diagram.

   How many said they liked:

   (i) Both

   (iii) Classical music

   (v) Only one of these types of music

   (ii) Rock music

   (iv) Neither

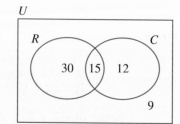

2. Each of the 50 members of a club were asked if they played chess (*C*), hockey (*H*) or neither. The results are shown in the Venn diagram. How many said they played **(i)** both **(ii)** chess **(iii)** hockey **(iv)** neither **(v)** only one of these games?

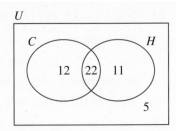

3. In a class of 30 pupils, 18 play basketball (*B*), 14 play football (*F*) and 2 play neither. Copy the Venn diagram and complete it. How many pupils in the class play **(i)** both games **(ii)** only one of these games **(iii)** at least one of these games?

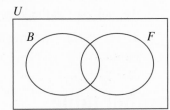

4. In a class of 30 pupils, 16 study French, 17 study German and 5 study both French and German. How many pupils in the class study **(i)** French only **(ii)** German only **(iii)** neither?

5. In a survey of 80 people, 58 said they had a television set, 45 had a radio and 30 said that they had both. How many people in the survey had **(i)** television only **(ii)** radio only **(iii)** neither?

6. In a class of 32 girls, 19 play hockey and 22 play tennis. If all the girls play at least one of these games, how many girls in the class play both games?

7. In a survey, 100 people were asked if they liked oranges or grapefruit. 75 people said they liked oranges, 50 said they liked grapefruit and 10 said they liked neither. How many people in the survey said they liked both?

8. In a survey of 300 houses, 250 had television sets, 180 had a phone and 20 had neither a television nor a phone. How many households in the survey had both?

9. The Venn diagram shows the number of elements in the sets *U*, *A* and *B*. Evaluate each of the following.

   (i) $\#(U)$ **(ii)** $\#(A \cap B)$ **(iii)** $\#(A \setminus B)$
   (iv) $\#(B \setminus A)$ **(v)** $\#(A \cup B)$ **(vi)** $\#(A \cup B)'$
   (vii) $\#(A')$ **(viii)** $\#(B')$ **(ix)** $\#[U \setminus (A \cap B)]$

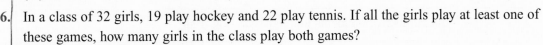

Use a Venn diagram to solve each of the following in questions 10–14.

10. If $\#A = 20$, $\#B = 15$ and $\#(A \cap B) = 8$, find $\#(A \cup B)$.

11. If $\#(X) = 16$, $\#(Y) = 18$ and $\#(X \cup Y) = 24$, find $\#(X \cap Y)$.

12. If $\#(A) = 22$, $\#(A \cup B) = 35$ and $\#(A \cap B) = 12$, find $\#(B)$.

13. If $\#(X) = 1$, $\#(Y) = 13$ and $\#(X \cup Y) = 23$, find **(i)** $\#(X \setminus F)$ **(ii)** $\#(Y \setminus X)$.

14. If $\#(U) = 35$, $\#(X) = 19$, $\#(Y) = 17$ and $\#(X \cap Y) = 7$, find $\#[U \setminus (X \cup Y)]$.

15. The Venn diagram shows the number of girls in a class of 30 who study maths (M), economics (E) or both. If each girl must study one of these subjects, how many girls in the class study **(i)** both subjects **(ii)** maths only **(iii)** economics only?

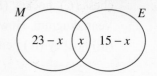

16. All 22 pupils in a class took part in the long (L) or the high (H) jump in a sports day. 16 took part in the long jump and 12 took part in the high jump.

If $\#(L \cap H) = x$, write an equation in x and find the value of x.

Symbol table

Symbol	Meaning	Example
$\in$	is an element of	$5 \in \{1, 2, 4, 5, 9\}$
$\notin$	is not an element of	$8 \notin \{1, 2, 4, 5, 9\}$
$\#$	the number of elements in	$\#\{cat, dog, fish\} = 3$
$=$	is equal to	$\{t, e, a\} = \{e, a, t\}$
$\varnothing$	the empty (or null) set	$\varnothing = \{\ \}$
$\subset$	is a subset of	$\{1, 3\} \subset \{1, 2, 3, 4, 5\}$
$\not\subset$	is not a subset of	$\{p, e, n\} \not\subset \{c, a, s, e\}$
U	the universal set	all the elements
$\cap$	intersection	$\{1, 2, 3\} \cap \{2, 4, 6\} = \{2\}$
$\cup$	union	$\{1, 2, 3\} \cup \{2, 4, 6\} = \{1, 2, 3, 4, 6\}$
$\setminus$	set difference	$\{2, 3, 5, 7, 11\} \setminus \{1, 2, 3, 6\} = \{5, 7, 11\}$
$'$	complement	$U = \{1, 2, 3, 4\}$, $S = \{2, 3\} \Rightarrow S' = \{1, 4\}$

The 24-hour clock

To avoid confusion, timetables generally use the 24-hour clock instead of a.m. and p.m. In the 24-hour clock system, all times are written using four digits. The first two digits show the number of hours past midnight and the last two digits show the number of minutes past the hour. Nowadays a colon is used to separate the hours from the minutes.

13:00 is pronounced 'thirteen hours' or 'thirteen hundred hours'.
15:21 is pronounced 'fifteen twenty-one' or 'fifteen twenty-one hours'.
07:30 is pronounced 'seven thirty' or 'seven thirty hours'.

Note: The 24-hour clock runs from 00:00 hours (midnight) to 24:00 hours (midnight again). Therefore, 00:00 = 24:00.

Adding and subtracting times in the 24-hour clock system

> **Remember:** 1 hour = 60 minutes.

EXAMPLE

(i) A train left Dublin at 18:31 hours. It arrived in Drogheda 39 minutes later. At what time did the train arrive in Drogheda?

(ii) A train left Kildare at 10:45 hours and arrived in Mallow at 13:19 hours. How many hours and minutes did the journey take?

Solution:

(i) Add 39 minutes to 18:31.

$$
\begin{array}{r}
18{:}31 \\
+\ 00{:}39 \\
\hline
18{:}70 \\
=\ 19{:}10
\end{array}
$$

$18{:}70 = 18{:}00 + 00{:}70$
$\qquad = 18{:}00 + 01{:}10$
$\qquad = 19{:}10$

> 70 minutes
> = 1 hour and 10 minutes

The train arrived in Drogheda at 19:10.

(ii) The problem here is that the number of minutes in the earlier time is greater than the number of minutes in the later time. This problem is solved by one of three methods.

Method 1:

Transfer one hour into the minutes column

$$\begin{array}{r} 13{:}19 \\ -10{:}45 \\ \hline \end{array} = \begin{array}{r} 12{:}79 \\ -10{:}45 \\ \hline 2{:}34 \end{array}$$

Therefore, the time taken is 2 hours 34 minutes.

Method 2:

Add the same number of minutes to both times to make the earlier time an even number of hours

$$\begin{array}{r} 13{:}19 \\ -10{:}45 \\ \hline \end{array} = \begin{array}{r} 13{:}34 \\ -11{:}00 \\ \hline 2{:}34 \end{array} \quad \begin{array}{l} \text{(add 15 minutes to} \\ \text{both times)} \end{array}$$

Therefore, the time taken is 2 hours 34 minutes.

Method 3:

Divide the time up.

	Hours	Minutes
10:45 to 11:00		15
11:00 to 13:00	2	
13:00 to 13:19		19
	2	34

Therefore, the time taken is 2 hours 34 minutes.

Exercise 11.1

1. Convert the following into minutes.

   (i) $\frac{1}{2}$ hour   (ii) $\frac{3}{4}$ hour   (iii) $\frac{1}{10}$ hour

   (iv) $\frac{2}{5}$ hour   (v) $\frac{1}{12}$ hour   (vi) 0·25 hour

   (vii) $\frac{2}{3}$ hour   (viii) 0·7 hour   (ix) $\frac{8}{15}$ hour

2. Convert the following minutes into hours.

   (i) 30 minutes   (ii) 15 minutes   (iii) 20 minutes

   (iv) 90 minutes   (v) 24 minutes   (vi) 42 minutes

3. Copy the table and calculate the duration for each of the following journeys.

	(i)	(ii)	(iii)	(iv)	(v)
Start time	18:00	15:07	15:50	11:48	09:32
Duration of journey					
Arrival time	21:00	17:07	18:30	14:17	13:18

4. Copy the table and calculate the arrival time for each of the following journeys.

	(i)	(ii)	(iii)	(iv)	(v)
Start time	14:05	11:08	09:33	17:50	22:15
Duration of journey	1 hr 35 mins	1 hr 55 mins	2·75 hrs	200 mins	7 hrs 50 mins
Arrival time					

5. Copy the table and calculate the departure (start) time for each of the following journeys.

	(i)	(ii)	(iii)	(iv)	(v)
Departure (start) time					
Duration of journey	48 mins	8 hrs 40 mins	98 mins	$2\frac{1}{5}$ hrs	$\frac{1}{8}$ day
Arrival time	11:33	05:30	13:05	12:15	18:25

6. A train leaves Dublin at 07:42 and arrives in Killarney at 11:22. How many hours and minutes does the journey take?

7. A coach left Dublin at 17:15. It arrived in Maynooth 47 minutes later. At what time did the coach arrive in Maynooth?

8. A train arrived in Waterford from Dublin at 17:35. The journey took 2 hours 20 minutes. At what time did the train leave Dublin?

9. Ian sets his video recorder to record a film. The film begins at 20:40 and ends at 22:15.

   (i) Calculate the running time of the film.

   (ii) If Ian uses a new 240-minute tape, how much recording time will be left on the tape?

10. A lorry must reach its destination by 17:15 and the journey takes 3 hours 20 minutes. What is the latest time at which the driver should set out?

11. A ferry journey takes $3\frac{3}{4}$ hours and the ferry was due to leave at 21:50. However, it was delayed by $1\frac{1}{2}$ hours. What time did the ferry arrive at its destination?

12. A school's lessons begin at 09:00 and end at 15:40, with a 65-minute break at lunchtime and a 20-minute break in mid-morning. If there are nine lessons of equal length, how long is a lesson?

13. A pupil arrived home from school at 17:10. She immediately began her maths homework, which took 35 minutes. She then took a 20-minute break. After this she spent 30 minutes studying history, then she took a 12-minute break and spent 25 minutes each on science, English and Irish. Complete the following table.

Arrived home	Finished maths	Finished first break	Finished history	Finished second break	Finished science	Finished English	Finished Irish
17:10			18:35				

14. A turkey needs to be cooked for lunch at 13:45. The cooking time is 20 minutes per kilogram, plus 30 minutes. If the turkey weighs 6 kg, what is the latest time at which the turkey should be put in the oven?

15. Gavin is alone underground. He looks at his watch to see what time it is. Using the 24-hour clock, what are the two different times it could be?

16. Copy and complete this table.

12-hour clock	7:00 a.m.	7:00 p.m.			10:20 p.m.	
24-hour clock			17:15	07:45		22:49

17. The following is a partial log on the sinking of *Titanic*.

Event	Lookout sounds warning	Ship hits iceberg	Captain arrives on bridge	First lifeboat launched	First distress rocket fired	Stern rose out of sea	*Titanic* sinks
Time	23:38		23:48				02:20

Two minutes after the lookout sounded the warning, *Titanic* struck the iceberg. The first lifeboat was launched at 25 minutes past midnight. The first distress rocket was fired one hour after the captain arrived on the bridge. The stern rose out of the sea 10 minutes before the ship sank.

 (i) Copy and complete the log given above.

 (ii) How long did it take from the collision with the iceberg until *Titanic* sank?

 (iii) Give a reason why the captain was not on the bridge.

18. A director of a variety show for TV has a strict time schedule he must keep with.

 Here are the times for each section of the show.

 The times are given in minutes and seconds, e.g. Act 3 takes 3 minutes 45 seconds.

Show introduction	2.30	Commercial break	3.15
Act 1	4.15	Act 7	2.55
Act 2	5.40	Act 8	4.23
Act 3	3.45	Act 9	5.07
Commercial break	3.15	Commercial break	3.15
Act 4	3.20	Closing comments	3.30
Act 5	4.18		
Act 6	4.28		

 (i) How long are the three commercial breaks in total?

 (ii) How long are the nine acts in total?

 (iii) How long is the entire show?

19. A factory manufacturing widgets operates 24/7 (i.e. all day, all week). A widget is manufactured every 2 minutes.

 (i) Find the number of widgets manufactured in a working week.

 (ii) After a refit of the factory, a widget can be manufactured every 108 seconds. Find the number of widgets that can now be produced in a working week.

20. (i) Eoin and Siobhan are flying from Dublin to New York. They depart Dublin at 10:45 on Wednesday. The estimated flight time is 6 hours 20 minutes. Local time in New York is five hours behind local time in Dublin. Calculate their estimated (local) time of arrival in New York.

 (ii) They depart New York the following Monday at 17:45 local time. The estimated flight time to Dublin is 6 hours 40 minutes. Calculate their estimated (local) time of arrival in Dublin.

Timetables

Transport timetables are usually printed in the 24-hour clock system using a two-way table. Frequently the separator is left out. For example, 17:23 is given as 1723.

EXAMPLE

Below is an extract from the Galway to Dublin bus timetable.

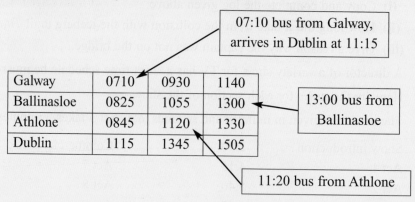

07:10 bus from Galway, arrives in Dublin at 11:15

Galway	0710	0930	1140
Ballinasloe	0825	1055	1300
Athlone	0845	1120	1330
Dublin	1115	1345	1505

13:00 bus from Ballinasloe

11:20 bus from Athlone

(i) Calculate the difference in travelling time to Dublin between the 07:10 bus and the 09:30 bus.

(ii) Calculate how long it takes the 11:20 bus from Athlone to get to Dublin.

(iii) John lives in Ballinasloe and needs to catch the 13:00 bus to Athlone. It takes him 17 minutes to walk from his house to the bus stop in Ballinasloe. What is the latest time at which he can leave his house to catch the 13:00 bus if he has to walk?

Solution:

(i) $\begin{array}{r} 11:15 \\ -07:10 \\ \hline 4:05 \end{array}$ Therefore, the 07:10 bus takes 4 hours 5 minutes.

$\begin{array}{r} 13:45 \\ -09:30 \\ \hline 4:15 \end{array}$ Therefore, the 09:30 bus takes 4 hours 15 minutes.

In conclusion, the 09:30 bus from Galway takes 10 minutes longer to travel to Dublin.

(ii) $\begin{array}{r} 13:45 \\ -11:20 \\ \hline 2:25 \end{array}$ Therefore, the 11:20 bus from Athlone takes 2 hours 25 minutes to get to Dublin.

(iii) John needs to leave his house at 17 minutes before 13:00 at the latest. In other words, he has to leave his house at 12:43 at the latest.

$\begin{array}{r} 12:60 \\ -00:17 \\ \hline 12:43 \end{array}$

Exercise 11.2

1. Calculate the time it takes for the bus to travel between each station.

Letterkenny	06:50
Monaghan	07:43
Castleblayney	08:29
Carrickmacross	09:04
Slane	10:09
Ashbourne	10:51
Dublin	11:27

2. Find the time taken by the train to travel from Pearse Station to each station.

Pearse Station	1732
Connolly Station	1736
Howth Junction	1745
Malahide	1753
Skerries	1805
Drogheda	1817
Dundalk	1835

3. This is an extract from a railway timetable:

Dublin	Departing	0810	1245	1730
Portlaoise	Departing	0905	1350	1815
Thurles	Departing	0940	1430	1900
Mallow	Departing	1045	1540	1955
Killarney	Departing	1200	1620	2040
Tralee	Arriving	1235	1650	2115

   (i) How long, in hours and minutes, does it take to go from Dublin to Tralee on each train?

  (ii) Find the difference in time between the fastest and the slowest train from Dublin to Tralee.

 (iii) It takes Colman 12 minutes to travel from his home to the railway station in Portlaoise. What is the latest time at which he can leave his house to catch the 08:10 train from Dublin to Tralee at Portlaoise railway station?

4. A DART train passes Howth Junction every 15 minutes. The first train passes at 06:45 and the last train is at 23:30.

   (i) Calculate the length of time between the first and last train.

  (ii) Calculate the number of DART trains that pass the station in a day.

 (iii) Calculate the number of trains that pass Howth Junction before 12:00.

5. An airline's timetable for flights between Cork Airport and Dublin Airport are shown.

Dublin to Cork										
Flight	Depart	Arrive	M	T	W	T	F	S	S
AB511	07:15	08:05	•	•	•	•	•	–	–
AB513	08:45	09:30	–	–	–	–	–	•	•
AB515	11:20	12:00	–	–	–	–	–	•	–
AB521	16:35	17:25	–	–	–	–	–	•	•
AB523	19:40	20:35	•	•	•	•	•	–	•

Cork to Dublin										
Flight	Depart	Arrive	M	T	W	T	F	S	S
AB512	08:35	09:25	•	•	•	•	•	–	–
AB514	09:55	10:50	–	–	–	–	–	•	•
AB516	12:35	13:15	–	–	–	–	–	•	–
AB522	17:45	18:30	–	–	–	–	–	•	•
AB524	21:00	21:45	•	•	•	•	•	–	•

Key: • indicates flight available that day.   – indicates no flight available that day.

(i) If Emily travels on Saturday, what is the earliest flight she can get from Cork to Dublin?

(ii) Jack takes the latest flight on Sunday from Dublin to Cork. How long does this flight take?

(iii) Dessie must check in at Dublin Airport 45 minutes before his flight. It takes him 90 minutes to reach the airport from home. What is the latest time he can leave home to get flight AB523 on Sunday?

6.

| Bell of the Ball Outfits | | | | | | | Time Card |

Name: Ned Ward   Department: Men's Clothes   Work Number 1234

Week Number 23

	Saturday	Sunday	Monday	Tuesday	Wednesday	Thursday	Friday
Start	08:30	10:30	14:00	08:50	08:45	09:00	09:35
Finish	17:30	13:00	20:40	18:10	18:30	18:55	18:55
Lunch Break	1 hr	–	–	1 hr	1 hr	1 hr	1 hr
Daily Hours							

| SUMMARY | Total Sat/Sun hours | | Total weekday hours Mon–Fri | |

(i) Calculate the daily hours worked by Ned Ward each day.

(ii) Copy and complete the summary section of the time card to show the total number of weekend hours and total number of weekday hours Ned worked.

7.

	Mon	Tues	Wed	Thurs	Fri
09:00–09:45	Maths	Geography	English	Geography	Maths
09:45–10:30	Geography	Maths	Geography	English	Maths
10:30–11:10	Accounting	Geography	Maths	Irish	Irish
11:10–11:25	Break	Break	Break	Break	Break
11:25–12:00	Irish	Accounting	Geography	English	English
12:00–12:40	English	Accounting	Maths	Accounting	Accounting
12:40–13:15	English	Irish	Irish	Irish	Accounting

The timetable above shows the programme for a one-week revision course.

From the information provided:

  (i) Find the total amount of time, excluding breaks, on this course.

 (ii) State **(a)** which subject has the most class time

           (b) which subject has the least class time.

(iii) Justify your answers to **(a)** and **(b)**.

8. A timetable for the train service from Dublin to Ballina and Westport is shown. Use the timetable to answer the questions below.

		Monday to Saturday							Sunday			
		FX										
Dublin	dep.	08:30		13:00		18:05			09:20		18:00	
Athlone	arr.	10:12		14:38		19:34			11:17		19:48	
Athlone	dep.	10:13		14:39		19:36			11:20		19:50	
Roscommon	dep.	10:41		15:08		20:06			11:48		20:20	
Castlerea	dep.	11:02		15:29		20:29					20:42	
Ballyhaunis	dep.	11:20		15:46		20:46			12:26		21:00	
Claremorris	dep.	11:35		16:01		21:01					21:15	
Manulla Junc.	arr.	11:49		16:15		21:15			12:55		21:28	
Manulla Junc.	dep.	11:50	11:51	16:16	16:17	21:17	21:22		12:57	12:58	21:29	21:30
Foxford	dep.		12:08		16:34		21:39			13:14		21:47
Ballina	dep.		12:25		16:50		21:55			13:30		22:05
Castlebar	dep.	11:57		16:24		21:23			13:04		22:37	
Westport	arr.	12:15		16:45		21:45			13:25		22:55	

FX = Not on Friday

(i) How many hours and minutes does it take the 13:00 train from Dublin to get to Roscommon?

(ii) For how long does the 08:30 train from Dublin stop at Manulla Junction?

(iii) On Fridays, if you want to get from Athlone to Ballina, what is the earliest time you can get a train from Athlone?

(iv) On Sundays, how many trains stop at Castlerea on the way to Westport?

(v) On Friday, you want to go from Claremorris to Ballina, but you need to visit a friend in Foxford along the way. At what time will you catch the train in Claremorris and at what time will you continue your journey to Ballina?

Distance, speed and time

There are three formulas to remember when dealing with problems involving distance (D), speed (S) and time (T). It can be difficult to remember these formulas; however, the work can be made easier using a triangle and the memory aid Dad's Silly Triangle.

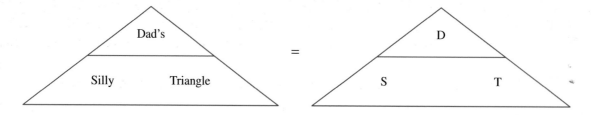

Consider the triangle on the right. By covering the quantity required, D, S or T, any of the three formulas above can be found by inspection.

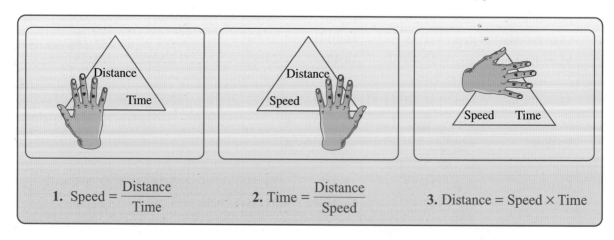

1. Speed = $\dfrac{\text{Distance}}{\text{Time}}$ **2.** Time = $\dfrac{\text{Distance}}{\text{Speed}}$ **3.** Distance = Speed × Time

Note: Speed here means average speed.

Common units of speed

> 1. Kilometres per hour, written as km/h.
> 2. Metres per second, written as m/s.

Note: 'per' means 'divided by'.

Converting minutes to hours

To convert minutes to hours, **divide** by 60.

For example, 48 minutes $= \frac{48}{60}$ h $= \frac{4}{5}$ h or 0.8 h.

However, the following occur quite often and are easy to memorise:

30 minutes $= \frac{1}{2}$ hour	20 minutes $= \frac{1}{3}$ hour	50 minutes $= \frac{5}{6}$ hour
15 minutes $= \frac{1}{4}$ hour	40 minutes $= \frac{2}{3}$ hour	12 minutes $= \frac{1}{5}$ hour
45 minutes $= \frac{3}{4}$ hour	10 minutes $= \frac{1}{6}$ hour	24 minutes $= \frac{2}{5}$ hour

EXAMPLE

(i) A train takes 2 hours 30 minutes to travel a distance of 250 km. Calculate the average speed of the train in km/h.

(ii) A cyclist travels $2\frac{1}{4}$ km at an average speed of 15 m/s. How long does the journey take?

(iii) A car travels for 3 hours 20 minutes at an average speed of 75 km/h. How far does it travel?

Solution:

(i) Time has to be expressed in hours.

2 hours 30 minutes $= 2\frac{1}{2}$ hours.

$$\text{Speed} = \frac{\text{Distance}}{\text{Time}}$$

$$= \frac{250}{2\frac{1}{2}}$$

$$= \frac{500}{5} \quad \text{(multiply top and bottom by 2)}$$

$$= 100$$

Therefore, the average speed is 100 km/h.

(ii) km has to be expressed in m.

$2\frac{1}{4}$ km $= 2{,}250$ m.

$$\text{Time} = \frac{\text{Distance}}{\text{Speed}}$$

$$= \frac{2{,}250}{15}$$

$$= 150$$

Therefore, the time taken $= 150$ seconds (or $2\frac{1}{2}$ minutes).

(iii) Time has to be expressed in hours. 3 hours 20 minutes $= 3\frac{1}{3}$ hours.

$$\text{Distance} = \text{Speed} \times \text{Time}$$
$$= 75 \times 3\frac{1}{3}$$
$$= 250$$

Therefore, the distance travelled $= 250$ km.

Exercise 11.3

1. Calculate the average speed in km/hour of each of the following.

	(i)	(ii)	(iii)	(iv)	(v)	(vi)
Distance	120 km	250 km	520 km	25 km	6,000 m	100 m
Time	6 hours	4 hours	8 hours	30 mins	$\frac{1}{4}$ hour	10 secs

2. Calculate the distance travelled in km for each of the following.

	(i)	(ii)	(iii)	(iv)	(v)	(vi)
Time	78 mins	2 hours	3·5 hours	45 secs	$4\frac{1}{3}$ hours	$1\frac{1}{2}$ mins
Speed	78 km/h	37·5 km/h	1·4 km/min	1,200 km/h	96 km/h	20 m/sec

3. Calculate the time taken in hours for each of the following.

	(i)	(ii)	(iii)	(iv)	(v)	(vi)
Distance	312 km	75 km	3,000 km	8,000 m	1,500 m	1,400 km
Speed	312 km/h	150 km/h	1.25 km/min	12 km/h	33 km/h	1·75 km/min

4. The tables below show some information on problems concerning distance, speed and time. Complete the tables.

Distance	Speed	Time
240 km		3 hours
360 km	90 km/h	
140	70 km/h	2 hours
232 km	58 km/h	
1,080 m	12 m/s	
400 m		80 seconds
	15 m/s	200 seconds

Distance	Speed	Time
240 km		2 hours 30 mins
72 km	16 km/h	
280 km		3 hours 30 mins
	64 km/h	3 hours 15 mins
	90 km/h	1 hour 20 mins
50 km		1 hour 15 mins
	75 km/h	1 hour 40 mins

5. How long does it take a bus to travel 260 km at an average speed of 52 km/h?

6. A tractor travels 45 km in 3 hours. Calculate its average speed in km/h.

7. A car travelled for 5 hours at an average speed of 60 km/h. Calculate the distance it travelled.

8. (i) Express 2 hours 30 minutes in hours.
   (ii) A train starts a journey of 180 km at 14:15 and completes the journey at 16:45. Calculate the average speed of the train in km/h.

9. A bus travelled at an average speed of 100 km/h between 12:55 and 14:25. What distance did it travel?

10. Find the average speed of a car that completes a journey of 208 km in 3 hours 15 minutes.

11. A girl ran a distance of 3,600 m in 15 minutes. Calculate her average speed in m/s.

12. A motorcyclist begins a journey of 280 km at 15:00. If the average speed is 80 km/h, find the time at which the journey is completed.

13. (i) Express 4 hours 15 minutes in hours.
    (ii) A train starts a journey of 255 km at 09:40 and completes the journey at 13:55. What was the average speed of the train?

14. A car travels 54 km in 45 minutes. Calculate its average speed in km/h.

15. A train travels 52 km in 40 minutes. How far will it travel in 1 hour 10 minutes at the same average speed?

16. A train began a non-stop journey of 147 km at 10:50 and completed the journey at 12:35.
    (i) How long did the journey take in hours and minutes?
    (ii) Calculate the average speed of the train in km/h.

17. A non-stop bus left Cork at 12:24 and arrived in Dublin at 15:09.
    (i) For how long was the bus travelling?
    (ii) By leaving Cork at 12:24, the bus was 34 minutes late. At what time was it due to leave Cork?
    (iii) The distance travelled was 258.5 km. Calculate the average speed of the bus in km/h.

18. This table shows the flight times (in hours) between some major European cities. For example, the highlighted reading shows that the flight time from Dublin to London is 1 hour.

Dublin					
2·9	Madrid				
2·7	3·8	Berlin			
①	2·9	2·1	London		
3·75	2·9	2·6	$2\frac{2}{3}$	Rome	
2·9	4·5	2	2·6	3·9	Oslo

(i) Which two cities are the same flight time from Dublin?

(ii) Which city is further from London – Oslo or Berlin? Justify your answer.

(iii) If the average speed of a flight from Madrid to Oslo is 550 km/hour, find the total distance (in km) between them.

(iv) The distance from Berlin to Rome is 1,222 km. Find the average speed of the flight.

(v) A plane departs Oslo on Monday at 23:15, destination Rome. What is the expected day and arrival time in Rome, given that both cities are in the same time zone (i.e. no time difference between the two cities)?

19. (i) The distance from the earth to the moon is 390,000 km. A spacecraft from Earth can cover this distance in 8 hours 40 minutes. Find the speed of the spacecraft in km per hour.

(ii) Light can travel at a speed of 300,000 km per second. Find how long it would take light to travel from Earth to the moon.

20. The robotic spacecraft *Voyager*, launched in 1997, is moving at $\frac{1}{18,000}$ the speed of light.

Calculate, in kilometres, the distance *Voyager* travels in one year.

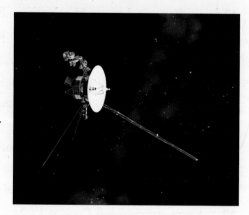

Note: The speed of light is approximately 300,000 km/s.

COLLECTING AND PROCESSING DATA

Types of data

Data is a collection of facts. It can be numbers, measurements, descriptions or observations. On our course we consider **two** types of data.

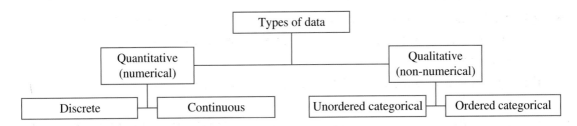

Quantitative data (numerical)

Discrete numerical data	Continuous numerical data
Discrete numerical data are data which can only have certain values.	Continuous data are data which can take any numerical value within a certain range.
Examples are number of students in a school, number of goals scored in a match and shoe sizes (including half-sizes).	Examples are time, weight, height, temperature, pressure and area. (Accuracy depends on the measuring device used.)

Qualitative data (non-numerical)

Unordered categorical data	Ordered categorical data
Unordered categorical data is data that can be sorted according to a category but have **no** order or ranking (rating scale). It can be counted but not measured.	Ordered categorical data is data that can be sorted according to a category and have an order or ranking. It can be counted and ordered but not measured.
Examples are colours, blood groups and gender (male or female).	Examples are examination grades, football divisions and opinion scales.

Note: Ordered categorical data are sometimes called **ordinal data**.

If a code is used to put data into a category, the data is called **nominal data**. The data are assigned a code in the form of a number or letter. The numbers or letters are simply labels. For example, males could be coded as 1 and females as 2. Marital status can be coded as M if married or S if single. Nominal data can be counted but not measured or ordered.

Exercise 12.1

In questions 1–18, classify the data as either discrete numerical, continuous numerical, unordered categorical or ordered categorical.

1. Number of cars in a car park
2. Temperatures of patients in a hospital
3. Colour of balloons
4. Subject grades A, B, C, D, E, F and NG
5. Gender (male or female)
6. Year groups in a school
7. Height of a plant
8. Number of rooms in a house
9. Tyre pressure
10. School subjects
11. Number of socks in a drawer
12. Position in a race
13. Age in complete years
14. Area of a field
15. Crops grown on a farm
16. Volume of a cube
17. Cost of posting a parcel
18. Distance from Cork to Dublin

19. The illustration shows a red car. State a variable about the car that is:

    (i) Categorical

    (ii) Discrete numerical

    (iii) Continuous numerical

20. Write a short question where the answer given will contain data that is:

    (i) Discrete numerical data
    (ii) Continuous numerical data
    (iii) Unordered categorical data
    (iv) Ordered categorical data

Tallying and frequency tables

You collect raw data by counting or measuring. However, lists of numbers can be difficult to understand and reach conclusions quickly. One way data can be sorted easily is by using a **frequency table**.

A frequency table is a table showing each piece of data with its corresponding frequency (the number of times it occurs). A frequency table makes it easier to understand a collection of data, see any patterns and draw conclusions. Frequency tables can be used to record discrete and continuous data. Frequency tables are also called data collection sheets, observation sheets, data capture sheets or tally charts.

To help us construct a frequency table, we can use tallies. Tallying is another name for counting.

When using tallies:

|||| = 4   ⊮ = 5   ⊮ | = 6   ⊮ ⊮ ||| = 13, etc.

Note: ⊮ is called a gate.

We use tallies to help us enter the data in a frequency table.

EXAMPLE 1

A sample survey of 48 households found the following number of children in each household.

$$
\begin{array}{cccccccccccc}
2 & 3 & 4 & 3 & 2 & 1 & 3 & 5 & 0 & 3 & 3 & 2 \\
1 & 0 & 3 & 2 & 3 & 4 & 2 & 4 & 3 & 4 & 3 & 3 \\
2 & 5 & 2 & 4 & 1 & 4 & 3 & 5 & 4 & 1 & 0 & 3 \\
3 & 1 & 3 & 2 & 3 & 0 & 4 & 2 & 1 & 3 & 3 & 2 \\
\end{array}
$$

Using tallies, represent the data with a frequency table.

Solution:

Number of children	0	1	2	3	4	5
Tally	IIII	IIII I	IIII IIII	IIII IIII IIII II	IIII III	III
Number of households	4	6	10	17	8	3

Note: Unless asked, it is not essential to include tallies in a frequency table.

Grouped data

When data are collected in groups they are called **grouped frequency distribution**. The groups that the data are put into are called **class intervals**.

For example, the following table gives information on the percentage marks students obtained in an examination.

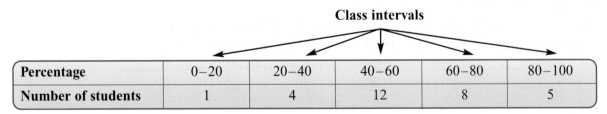

Class intervals

Percentage	0−20	20−40	40−60	60−80	80−100
Number of students	1	4	12	8	5

Note: 0−20 means 0 is included but 20 is not, and so on.

133

EXAMPLE 2

The pulse rates of 26 students, while resting, were recorded. The raw data was recorded as follows:

$$86 \quad 72 \quad 92 \quad 84 \quad 81 \quad 79 \quad 88 \quad 87 \quad 94 \quad 77 \quad 85 \quad 90 \quad 76$$
$$75 \quad 80 \quad 81 \quad 89 \quad 83 \quad 78 \quad 84 \quad 88 \quad 85 \quad 82 \quad 71 \quad 86 \quad 77$$

Represent the data in a grouped frequency table.

Solution:

The lowest value is 71 and the highest is 94.

Weight in kg	70–75	75–80	80–85	85–90	90–95
Tally	||	⅏ |	⅏ ||	⅏ |||	|||
Frequency	2	6	7	8	3

Note: 70–75 means 70 is included but 75 is not, and so on.

Note: Different class intervals could be used, such as 70–80, 80–90, 90–100.

Because this data is discrete the class intervals could be 70–74, 75–78, and so on.

Exercise 12.2

1. The tally chart below shows the number of glass bottles put into a bottle bank during a 15-minute period:

Colour of glass	Tally				
Brown	⅏	⅏	⅏	⅏	⅏
Clear	⅏	⅏	⅏	||	
Green	⅏	⅏	⅏	|||	

(i) How many bottles were put in the bottle bank during this 15-minute period?

(ii) How many more brown bottles than clear bottles were put in the bottle bank?

(iii) Complete the following frequency table.

Colour of glass	Brown	Clear	Green
Frequency			

2. In a designed experiment, 30 pupils were asked to throw a die once. The raw data was recorded as follows:

$$1 \quad 4 \quad 6 \quad 3 \quad 3 \quad 2 \quad 1 \quad 6 \quad 5 \quad 4$$
$$1 \quad 5 \quad 3 \quad 5 \quad 4 \quad 6 \quad 5 \quad 2 \quad 6 \quad 3$$
$$3 \quad 4 \quad 6 \quad 6 \quad 1 \quad 5 \quad 6 \quad 3 \quad 6 \quad 5$$

Complete the following data capture sheet.

Score	1	2	3	4	5	
Tally						ⅢⅠ ‖‖
Frequency	4					

3. Geraldine asked some students in her school, 'How many keys do you have on your key ring?' She recorded the results as follows:

$$4 \quad 1 \quad 2 \quad 3 \quad 3 \quad 5 \quad 2 \quad 1 \quad 3 \quad 4 \quad 5 \quad 1$$
$$2 \quad 4 \quad 5 \quad 5 \quad 3 \quad 1 \quad 2 \quad 1 \quad 5 \quad 4 \quad 4 \quad 5$$
$$3 \quad 3 \quad 5 \quad 1 \quad 1 \quad 5 \quad 4 \quad 3 \quad 3 \quad 2 \quad 1 \quad 1$$

(i) How many students did Geraldine ask?

(ii) Using tallies, complete the following frequency table.

Number of keys	Tally	Frequency

(iii) Explain why the data recorded is primary data.

4. On one Friday evening of term, a school held a disco. The following Monday a random sample of 40 students who attended were asked to rate the disco on a 5-point scale A, B, C, D, E, where A represents the highest score and E the lowest score. The raw ratings are shown below:

B   C   A   A   B   C   E   C   A   B   B   A   C   A   A   B   B   C   E   D

D   C   A   A   A   B   B   C   A   B   D   C   A   B   B   A   A   B   C   A

(i) Design and complete a frequency table for the ratings.

(ii) The organisers claim the disco was a success. Do you agree? Give a reason for your answer.

5. A maths teacher gave her students a maths test. The test was marked out of 100 marks. The results of the test were recorded as follows:

$$25 \quad 85 \quad 55 \quad 74 \quad 60 \quad 19 \quad 54 \quad 48 \quad 41 \quad 79 \quad 81 \quad 73 \quad 88 \quad 74 \quad 38$$
$$57 \quad 65 \quad 90 \quad 76 \quad 98 \quad 42 \quad 50 \quad 59 \quad 17 \quad 68 \quad 79 \quad 20 \quad 64 \quad 35 \quad 71$$

(i) Complete the following frequency table.

Marks	0–20	20–40	40–60	60–80	80–100
Tally					
Number of students					

Note: 0–20 means 0 or more but less than 20.

(ii) How many students took the test?

(iii) The pass mark is 40%. What percentage of the students passed the test?

(iv) Is this primary or secondary data? Give a reason for your answer.

(v) Is the data discrete or continuous? Justify your answer.

6. A shop recorded the number of newspapers sold on each day in March. The raw data is as follows:

$$51 \quad 57 \quad 54 \quad 42 \quad 48 \quad 49 \quad 58 \quad 43 \quad 53 \quad 59$$
$$47 \quad 47 \quad 52 \quad 53 \quad 42 \quad 53 \quad 55 \quad 53 \quad 59 \quad 47$$
$$44 \quad 49 \quad 53 \quad 47 \quad 58 \quad 54 \quad 52 \quad 49 \quad 43 \quad 53 \quad 59$$

(i) Design and complete a grouped frequency table, using class intervals 40–45, 46–50, etc.

(ii) The shop owner decided that she will only stock 54 newspapers each day.
In March, on how many days would she have sold out of newspapers?

7. Mary goes to an all-girls' school. She decided to do a sample survey to find out the time spent studying by students per week in her area. Mary chose 40 students randomly from her own school register and asked each of these students the time, to the nearest hour, they spent studying per week. The raw data were recorded as follows:

$$7 \quad 9 \quad 14 \quad 6 \quad 1 \quad 10 \quad 2 \quad 6 \quad 7 \quad 11 \quad 10 \quad 1 \quad 10 \quad 2 \quad 6 \quad 3 \quad 5 \quad 3 \quad 0 \quad 5$$
$$11 \quad 7 \quad 13 \quad 10 \quad 1 \quad 9 \quad 5 \quad 2 \quad 15 \quad 6 \quad 6 \quad 11 \quad 6 \quad 4 \quad 0 \quad 12 \quad 9 \quad 13 \quad 4 \quad 8$$

Complete the following grouped frequency table.

Time spent studying, in hours	0–4	4–8	8–12	12–16
Tally				
Number of students				

Note: 4–8 means 4 or more but less than 8.

(i) Is this primary or secondary data? Give a reason for your answer.

(ii) Is the data discrete or continuous? Explain your answer.

(iii) Give two reasons why this may be a biased sample.

(iv) Suggest two ways Mary could improve her sample to make it more representative.

Questionnaires

Designing a questionnaire

Always have a clear aim for your survey and ask questions in a logical order.

> A questionnaire is a set of questions used to obtain data from a population.
> Anyone who answers a questionnaire is called a **respondent**.
> The part where you give your answer is called the **response section**.

The questionnaire should:

Be clear about who is to complete it.	Be as brief as possible.
Start with simple questions.	Be able to be answered quickly.
Be clear how the answers are to be recorded.	Be clear where the answers are to be recorded.

The questions should:

Be short and use simple language.	Not be leading in any way. This can influence the answer.
Provide tick boxes.	Not cause embarrassment or offend (avoid personal questions).
Be clear about what is asked.	Be relevant to the survey.
Allow a 'yes' or 'no' answer, a number or a response from a choice of answers.	Not be open ended, which might produce long or rambling answers which are difficult to analyse.

Single-response questions

Question	Comment
Gender: **Male** ☐ **Female** ☐	Good, clear question.

Multiple-response questions

Question	Comment
How old are you?	Personal question, as people may be embarrassed to give their age. No indication of accuracy.
A better question would be: Which is your age group, in years? Under 18 18–40 41–60 Over 60 ☐ ☐ ☐ ☐	Only one response required. No gaps and no overlapping of boxes.
You prefer to go out on Saturdays, don't you?	A leading question. It forces an opinion on the person being surveyed.
A better question is: On which day do you prefer to go out? Please tick one box. Mon Tue Wed Thu Fri Sat Sun ☐ ☐ ☐ ☐ ☐ ☐ ☐	A much better question. Respondents have a choice. Better accuracy for the survey.
How much TV do you watch on a school weeknight? A lot ☐ A bit ☐ Very little ☐	This question is too vague.
A better question is: How many hours of TV, to the nearest hour, do you watch on a school weeknight? Please tick one box. 0 1 2 3 4 or more ☐ ☐ ☐ ☐ ☐	This is more precise. Better accuracy for the survey.

Opinion scale

In some questions the response uses an opinion scale to measure attitudes and reactions. For example:

The local shops sell high-quality goods. Please tick one box.
☐   ☐   ☐   ☐   ☐ Strongly   Disagree   No opinion   Agree   Strongly disagree   agree

Exercise 12.3

1. What is the difference between primary data and secondary data?

2. Write down which of the following is primary data and which is secondary data.

    (i) Tom counted the number of red cars that passed through a road junction in his area.

    (ii) Jane looked on the internet to find the number of babies born in Ireland in 2010.

    (iii) For his homework, Ian used a table of statistics on the ages of footballers from a newspaper.

    (iv) Gillian threw a die 100 times and recorded the results to investigate if the die is biased.

3. Give one difference between a census and a sample.

4. A company that makes batteries wants to carry out a study to see how long their batteries last. Should they use a census or a sample? Justify your answer.

5. Make **one** critisism of each question why it is unsuitable for a questionnaire.

    (i) Saturday is the best day to have a disco, wouldn't you agree?

    (ii) How many emails did you send today?   0–5 ☐   0–10 ☐   10 or more ☐

    (iii) The waiter service in this restaurant is: Excellent ☐   Very good ☐`

    (iv) What do you think of our new and improved apple juice?

    (v) Sweets are bad for your teeth. Do you eat many sweets?

    (vi) Have you stolen goods from a shop?

6. The owner of a local cinema wants to find out how often teenagers attend the cinema. As teenagers left the cinema, the owner gave them a questionnaire containing the following question.

    > How often do you attend the cinema?
    > Tick one box.
    >
    > ☐ Sometimes   ☐ Occasionally   ☐ Regularly

    (i) Write down **two** criticisms of the response section.

    (ii) Write a better question for this questionnaire. Include tick boxes.

7. A teacher is investigating the number of hours her pupils spend on the internet in a month. One of her questions is shown below.

    > How many hours do you spend on the internet in a month?
    > Tick one box.
    >
    > ☐ 0–10   ☐ 10–20   ☐ 20–30   ☐ 30–40   ☐ 40+

    (i) (a) Write one criticism of the question.

        (b) Write one criticism of the response.

    (ii) Write a better question. Include tick boxes.

8. Alex is taking a survey about how far, to the nearest km, people have to travel to their workplace. Here is his response section.

   Tick one box.

   ☐ 1–2   ☐ 2–3   ☐ 5–6   ☐ Over 6

   State three **criticisms** of his response section.

9. As each customer left a shop, the owner gave them a questionnaire containing the following question.

How much money did you spend in the shop today?
Tick one box.
Less than €20   Less than €40   Less than €60   €60 or more
☐   ☐   ☐   ☐

   Write down one reason why the response section of this question is unsuitable.

10. A builder used the following question in a survey: 'How much do you pay each month on your mortage?' (Tick one box.)

    Under €400 ☐   €400–€600 ☐   €600–€1,000 ☐

    (i) Give two criticisms of the response section.

    (ii) Give one criticism of the question asked.

11. Helen is collecting data about the speed of cars in her town. She decides to collect data during the rush hour. Comment on Helen's choice of sample.

12. A market research company wishes to interview a sample of 50 adults in a large town in order to obtain their views on the proposed construction of a bypass around the town. The company interviewed the first 50 adults leaving the local train station on a Friday in June.

    (i) List two reasons why this method of sample selection is not suitable.

    (ii) Suggest how a random sample of 50 adults could be selected from the town.

    (iii) One question the company used was: 'Do you think we should have a bypass to make our village safer?' What is wrong with this question?

13. Maura is carrying out an investigation into the cost of food in the school canteen. She asks students in the queue for the school canteen, 'Do you agree that the food in the school canteen is overpriced?'

    (i) (a) Why is her sample likely to be biased?   (b) Why is her question biased?

    (ii) Suggest two reasons for her to carry out a sample survey.

    (iii) For a different investigation, Maura selects a sample of 60 students from the 800 students in her school. Describe how she could select a simple random sample.

14. A company that makes toothpaste says the new brand is better than the old brand. A dentist wants to investigate this claim. He chooses 40 boys and 40 girls at random from his patients. The boys are given the new brand and the girls are given the old brand. After four months the dentist compares the boys' and girls' teeth.

    (i) Write down two reasons why this is not a reliable experiment.

    (ii) Give two ways in which this experiment could be improved.

15. A company produces compost for germinating seeds. It develops Better Grow, a new compost, which the company claims helps seeds germinate much more quickly than its competitors' compost. Design a simple statistical experiment that could be carried out to test the company's claim.

16. Brian wants to use a questionnaire to find out what kind of music the students at his school like. He also wants to find out if the boys and girls in his school like the same type of music and if there is a difference between year groups. Write down three questions that Brian might include in his questionnaire. Include tick boxes.

CHAPTER 13

AVERAGES AND THE SPREAD OF DATA

Averages

Much of our work in analysing data is concerned with finding a value that in some way is typical or representative of all the values in a distribution. The three most widely used are:

1. **The mode** 2. **The median** 3. **The mean**

They are often called **measures of central tendency**.

> The **mode** is the value that occurs most often.

In other words, the mode is the value with the highest frequency or the most popular value.

> The **median** is the middle value when the values are arranged in order of size.

Half the values lie below and half above the median. For an even number of values, the median is halfway between the two middle values (the mean of the two middle values).

> The **mean** of a set of values is
> the sum of all the values divided by the number of values.

That is:

$$\text{Mean} = \frac{\text{Sum of all the values}}{\text{Number of values}}$$

Note: The mean is the proper name for what most people call the average.

This table will help you to decide which average to use.

Averages	Advantages	Disadvantages
Mode	Easy to find. Will be one of the data values. Not affected by extreme values.	Sometimes there is no mode. No further mathematical applications.
Median	Easy to calculate. Not affected by extreme values.	Not always one of the given data. No further mathematical applications.
Mean	Uses all the data values. Has further mathematical applications.	Not always one of the given data. Always affected by extreme values.

The **range** is the difference between the highest and lowest value.

That is: Range = (Highest value) − (Lowest value)

This gives a measure of how spread out the data are (it is not an average). Sometimes it is called a measure of variability.

Mathematical shorthand for the mean

μ, pronounced 'mu', is the symbol for the mean.

Σ, pronounced 'sigma', means the sum of (add up).

Σx, pronounced 'sigma x', means add up all the x values.

The formula is often written as: $\text{Mean} = \mu = \dfrac{\Sigma x}{n}$ where n is the number of values.

EXAMPLE 1

The price, in cent, of a bar of chocolate in nine different shops was recorded as follows:

$$79, 75, 79, 72, 90, 75, 75, 80, 77$$

Find the **(i)** mean   **(ii)** median   **(iii)** mode   **(iv)** range of these prices.

Solution:

(i) Mean = $\dfrac{\text{Sum of the prices}}{\text{Number of prices}}$

$$= \frac{79 + 75 + 79 + 72 + 90 + 75 + 75 + 80 + 77}{9} = \frac{702}{9} = 78 \text{ cent}$$

(ii) Median: First write the prices in ascending order.

$$72, 75, 75, 75, \widehat{77}, 79, 79, 80, 90$$

The median is the middle price. Thus, the median is 77 cent.

(iii) Mode: Price which occurs most often.

75 occurs most often. Therefore, the mode is 75 cent.

Note: Sometimes we say the modal price is 75 cent.

(iv) Range = (Highest price) − (Lowest price)

$$= 90 - 72 = 18 \text{ cent}$$

EXAMPLE 2

Cormac counted the number of books on different shelves in a library. He recorded the following numbers: 41, 43, 29, 52, 40, 46.

Find the median of the number of books on each shelf.

Solution:

Median: First write the numbers in ascending order.

$$29, 40, (41, 43), 46, 52$$

There is an even number of numbers.

$\therefore$ The median is the mean of the two middle values $= \dfrac{41 + 43}{2} = \dfrac{84}{2} = 42$ books.

Exercise 13.1

In questions 1–9, find the:

(i) Mean	(ii) Mode	(iii) Median	(iv) Range

1. 1, 1, 2, 4, 7
2. 2, 2, 5, 9, 12
3. 3, 4, 3, 8, 7
4. 9, 5, 6, 5, 10, 5, 9
5. 7, 4, 4, 8, 7, 8, 4
6. 9, 4, 9, 2, 1
7. 10, 2, 4, 2, 7, 6, 4, 8, 2
8. 1, 8, 0, 3, 8
9. 0, 8, 5, 10, 3, 0, 2

In questions 10–12, find (i) the median and (ii) the mean of each of the following arrays of numbers.

10. 1, 2, 4, 9
11. 5, 4, 8, 7, 4, 2
12. 8, 12, 11, 3, 7, 10, 16, 5

13. Write the following numbers in increasing size: 1·6, 2·5, 0·8, 1·3, 0·8. Hence, find the:

(i) mean (ii) median (iii) mode (iv) range of these numbers.

14. Four movies last for 123 minutes, 136 minutes, 142 minutes and 167 minutes. Find (i) the mean length and (ii) the range of the four movies.

15. The boot sizes of 15 players in a football team were recorded as follows:

    10   9   11   10   9   10   10   10   12   8   9   11   10   11   7

(i) Write the data in increasing order.

(ii) Write down the (a) modal and (b) median boot size.

(iii) Calculate the (a) mean boot size and (b) the range of boot sizes.

16. The times taken by five girls to complete a training run were recorded as follows: 11 min 15 sec, 10 min 43 sec, 13 min 12 sec, 14 min 18 sec and 12 min 42 sec. Find the **(i)** mean time **(ii)** median time **(iii)** range for the five girls to complete the training run.
    (iv) Explain why there is no modal time for the training run.

17. A golfer plays five rounds of golf. His scores were 98, 93, 98, 91 and 90. What type of average, the mean, median or mode, will he prefer to call his average? Explain your answer.

18. A manufacturer of confectionery bars claims that the average weight of each bar is at least 66 grams. One bar was chosen from 10 different shops and weighed. Their weights, to the nearest gram, were recorded as follows:

    $$64 \quad 67 \quad 69 \quad 66 \quad 67 \quad 68 \quad 68 \quad 71 \quad 67 \quad 70$$

    Do you think that the manufacturer is justified in making this claim? Explain your answer.

Given the mean

Sometimes we are given the mean and we need to find one of the values. Essentially, we are given an equation in disguise and by solving this equation we calculate the missing value.

EXAMPLE 1

The mean of the five numbers 10, 5, 4, 8 and x is 6. Calculate the value of x.

Solution:

Method 1

$$\text{Mean} = 6$$

$$\therefore \quad \frac{10 + 5 + 4 + 8 + x}{5} = 6$$

$$\frac{27 + x}{5} = 6$$

$$27 + x = 30$$

(multiply both sides by 5)

$$x = 3$$

Method 2

The mean of the five numbers is 6

$\therefore$ the numbers must add up to 30

$\left(\text{because } 5 \times 6 = 30 \quad \text{or} \quad \dfrac{30}{5} = 6 \right)$

$$\therefore \quad 10 + 5 + 4 + 8 + x = 30$$

$$27 + x = 30$$

$$x = 3$$

EXAMPLE 2

The mean of eight numbers is 9. When one of the numbers is taken away, the mean is increased by 1. Find the number that was taken away.

Solution:

Old situation (8 numbers)	**New situation** (7 numbers)
The mean of the 8 numbers is 9.	The mean of the remaining 7 numbers is 10.
Therefore, the numbers must add up to 72	Therefore, the numbers must add up to 70
$\left(\text{because } 8 \times 9 = 72, \text{ or } \dfrac{72}{8} = 9\right)$	$\left(\text{because } 7 \times 10 = 70, \text{ or } \dfrac{70}{7} = 10\right)$

$$72 - 70 = 2$$

Therefore, the number taken away was 2.

Exercise 13.2

1. The mean of four numbers is 5. Find the sum of the numbers.

2. The mean of five numbers is 8. Find the sum of the numbers.

3. The mean of six numbers is 10. Find the sum of the numbers.

4. The mean of the three numbers 3, 4 and x is 4. Calculate the value of x.

5. The mean of the four numbers x, 4, 6 and 7 is 5. Calculate the value of x.

6. The mean of the five numbers 8, 5, x, 4 and 6 is 6. Calculate the value of x.

7. The mean of the six numbers 4, 2, 1, x, 2 and 4 is 3. Calculate the value of x.

8. The mean of the seven numbers 5, 7, 3, 4, x, 8 and 6 is 7. Calculate the value of x.

9. **(i)** The mean of three numbers is 5. Find the sum of the numbers. **(ii)** When another number is added on, the mean of the four numbers is 6. Find the number that was added on.

10. The mean of four numbers is 2. When another number is added on, the mean is increased by 1. Find the number that was added on.

11. The mean of five numbers is 6. When one of the numbers is taken away, the mean is increased by 1. Find the number that was taken away.

12. The mean of six numbers is 3. When one of the numbers is taken away, the mean is decreased by 1. Find the number that was taken away.

13. The rainfall, measured in centimetres, at a weather station for the first six months of a certain year was recorded in the following table:

Month	Jan	Feb	Mar	Apr	May	June
Rainfall in cm	12	10	7	6	x	2

If the mean rainfall for the six months was 7 cm, calculate the value of x.

14. The table shows a student's test results over a four-month period.

Month	Sept	Oct	Nov	Dec
Mark	62	n	78	75

If the student's mean mark for the four tests was 73, calculate the value of n.

15. The table shows the number of compact discs sold per day in a shop from Monday to Friday of a particular week.

Day	Monday	Tuesday	Wednesday	Thursday	Friday
No. of compact discs sold	32	17	48	42	61

(i) Calculate the mean number of compact discs sold per day from Monday to Friday.

(ii) The shop was also open on the Saturday of that particular week. The mean number of compact discs sold per day from Monday to Saturday was 50.

Calculate the number of compact discs sold on that Saturday.

Comparison of two sets of data

We usually compare sets of data in two parts:

> 1. How the ranges compare.
> 2. How one, or more, of the averages, mean, median or mode, compare.

Note: The higher the range, the greater the spread of the values (less consistent).

The lower the range, the smaller the spread of the values (more consistent).

EXAMPLE

A maths teacher gave a maths test to a third-year class. The marks for the boys and the girls were recorded in the following table.

Boys	59	71	58	94	18	92	14	78	72	64
Girls	53	73	59	62	40	52	76	62	50	63

Calculate the mean and range for each group. Comment briefly on how the two groups compare.

Solution:

Boys

$$\text{Mean} = \frac{59 + 71 + 58 + 94 + 18 + 92 + 14 + 78 + 72 + 64}{10}$$

$$= \frac{620}{10} = 62 \text{ marks}$$

Range = (Highest mark) − (Lowest mark)

$$= 94 - 14 = 80 \text{ marks}$$

Girls

$$\text{Mean} = \frac{53 + 73 + 59 + 62 + 40 + 52 + 76 + 62 + 50 + 63}{10}$$

$$= \frac{590}{10} = 59 \text{ marks}$$

Range = (Highest mark) − (Lowest mark)

$$= 76 - 40 = 36 \text{ marks}$$

Comment: The boys have a slightly higher mean mark than the girls. However, the girls have a much lower range of marks. Their marks are **less spread out**, which shows the girls are more consistent.

Exercise 13.3

1. Two students, A and B, take four maths tests. Their results were as follows:

   A: 69 10 88 84   B: 64 73 54 61

   (i) Calculate the mean mark and the range of marks for each student.

   (ii) Comment briefly on how the two students compare.

2. The pulse rates of 7 boys and 7 girls were recorded as follows:

   Boys: 87 88 84 91 81 85 86   Girls: 86 87 95 72 82 99 88

   (i) Calculate the median, mean and range of the pulse rates for each group.

   (ii) Comment briefly on how the two groups compare.

3. At a quiz, the individual scores of six members of two teams were recorded as follows:

   Team A: 16   58   30   2   44   30
   Team B: 30   37   23   34   30   26

   Which team is the most consistent? Explain your answer.

4. The battery life, to the nearest hour, of seven mobile phones from each of two companies, A and B, were recorded as follows:

A: 53 48 36 58 52 54 49
B: 54 42 53 40 41 54 52

(i) Complete the following two-way table.

	Mean	Median	Range
Company A			
Company B			

(ii) Which brand would you buy? Explain your answer.

5. There is one place left on the boys' senior netball team. Two boys, Brendan and Colm, are trying out for this last place. Their scores for each of their last 10 games were recorded as follows:

Brendan: 4 8 3 5 5 2 2 1 3 2
Colm: 4 5 3 4 4 2 3 3 5 3

(i) Calculate the mean number of goals per match for each boy.

(ii) Calculate the range for each boy.

(iii) Which boy should be picked for the team? Explain your answer.

Frequency distribution

Data are often summarised using a frequency distribution. This section shows you how to calculate the range, mode, median and mean when the data is given in a frequency table.

The range, mode and median can be found from the table.

However, to calculate the mean we do the following:

1. Multiply each value by its corresponding frequency.
2. sum all these products.
3. divide this sum by the total number of frequencies.

Mathematical shorthand for the mean

$$\text{Mean} = \mu = \frac{\Sigma fx}{\Sigma f}$$

(i) x is the value of each measurement.

(ii) f is the frequency of each measurement.

(iii) Σfx is the sum of all the fx values.

(iv) Σf is the sum of all the frequencies.

EXAMPLE

A survey of the number of people per car in 21 cars passing an intersection was recorded in the following table:

Number of people per car	1	2	3	4	5
Number of cars	2	7	4	5	3

Calculate the (i) range (ii) mode (iii) median (iv) mean of the number of people per car.

Solution:

(i)   Range = (Highest value) − (Lowest value) = 5 − 1 = 4 people.

(ii) The mode is the value which occurs most often. In a frequency table the mode is the value with the highest frequency.

(mode = 2 people, occurs most often)

Number of people per car	1	2	3	4	5
Number of cars	2	7	4	5	3

(highest frequency)

From the table, we can see that 2 occurs more often than any other value. Therefore, the mode is 2 people per car.

Note: Remember that the mode is the value, **not** the frequency.

(iii) In a frequency table the values are already arranged in order of size. The median is the middle value. There are 21 values (2 + 7 + 4 + 5 + 3 = 21). Thus, the median is the 11th value.

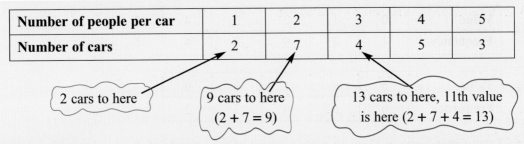

Number of people per car	1	2	3	4	5
Number of cars	2	7	4	5	3

2 cars to here

9 cars to here (2 + 7 = 9)

13 cars to here, 11th value is here (2 + 7 + 4 = 13)

The first 2 cars contain 1 person. The next 7 cars contain 2 people. The next 4 cars contain 3 people. This contains the 11th value.

Thus, the median = 3 people per car.

(iv) Mean = $\dfrac{\text{Sum of the values}}{\text{Number of values}}$

$= \dfrac{2(1) + 7(2) + 4(3) + 5(4) + 3(5)}{2 + 7 + 4 + 5 + 3}$ $\boxed{\mu = \dfrac{\Sigma fx}{\Sigma f}}$

$= \dfrac{2 + 14 + 12 + 20 + 15}{21} = \dfrac{63}{21} = 3$ people per car

Grouped frequency distribution

If the data are recorded in a grouped frequency distribution, called class intervals, then the class interval with the highest frequency is called the **modal class**. The median will also lie in a class interval.

Note: In a grouped frequency distribution, it is not possible to give exact values for the range, the mode, the median or the mean as we are not given the exact values.

Exercise 13.4

In questions 1–5, calculate the:

(i) range   (ii) mode   (iii) median   (iv) mean.

1.

Value	1	2	3	4
Frequency	4	3	2	1

2.

Value	1	3	5	7
Frequency	2	2	5	6

3.

Value	0	2	4	6	8
Frequency	4	3	5	7	2

4.

Value	0	1	2	3	4	5
Frequency	1	2	9	8	4	1

5.

Value	5	6	7	8	9
Frequency	6	5	4	3	2

6. Tins of peas come in boxes. A record is kept of the number of damaged tins in each box.

No. of damaged tins	0–2	3–5	6–8	9–11	12–14
No. of boxes	10	7	5	3	2

    (i) State the modal class.   **(ii)** Which class interval contains the median?

7. A football league has 20 teams. The frequency table shows the number of goals scored by each team on one weekend (each team played one match).

Number of goals	0	1	2	3	4
Number of teams	1	3	8	5	3

    (i) How many teams scored **(a)** 2 goals **(b)** 2 goals or more?

    (ii) Write down the modal score.

    (iii) Calculate the mean score per team.

8. 35 students hire skates at the ice rink. Their sizes are recorded in the following table.

Skate size	3	4	5	6	7	8	9	10
Frequency	1	3	5	5	7	9	3	2

    (i) Write down the modal shoe size.

    (ii) Calculate **(a)** the range and **(b)** the mean shoe size.

    (iii) Is the mean or the mode the best average to use for this group of skaters? Justify your answer.

9. In a street with 24 houses, a postman recorded the number of letters delivered to each house. The results were:

$$1 \quad 2 \quad 5 \quad 3 \quad 2 \quad 3 \quad 0 \quad 1 \quad 1 \quad 4 \quad 3 \quad 0$$
$$2 \quad 1 \quad 1 \quad 4 \quad 0 \quad 2 \quad 2 \quad 1 \quad 4 \quad 1 \quad 2 \quad 3$$

Complete the following table.

Number of letters	0	1	2	3	4	5
Tally						
Frequency					3	

(i) State the modal number of letters per house.

(ii) Calculate the mean number of letters per house.

10. A machine is designed to pack pins into boxes containing 20 pins in each box. To check the machine's accuracy, a random sample of boxes is taken at regular intervals and the number of pins per box is counted (this is called **quality control**). The results are shown below.

Number of pins	18	19	20	21	22
Number of boxes	10	9	3	2	1

(i) How many boxes were sampled?　(ii) Write down the modal number of pins per box.

(iii) Calculate (a) the range (b) the mean number of pins per box.

(iv) Describe briefly the machine's performance.

11. The mass, to the nearest kilogram, of 21 parcels was recorded in the following table.

Mass, in kg	1	2	3	4	5
Number of parcels	2	7	4	5	3

(i) Write down (a) the mode and (b) the median.

(ii) Calculate (a) the range and (b) the mean.

(iii) Explain briefly why none of these answers can be exact.

12. The temperatures at midnight in January 2010 in a certain town were measured and recorded in the following table.

Temperature in °C	−2	−1	0	1	2	3	4
Number of nights	5	2	3	7	8	4	2

(i) State the modal and median temperature.

(ii) Calculate the range and mean of the temperatures.

Diagrams

Many people find numerical data easier to understand if it is presented in a diagram. On our course there are five ways of representing data in a diagram.

1. **Bar charts**
2. **Line plots**
3. **Pie charts**
4. **Histograms**
5. **Stem and leaf plots**

When drawing a statistical diagram, the following is important:

1. Label both axes (where necessary) and include a title.
2. Use scales that are easy to read and give a clear overall impression.

Bar charts

Bar charts are a simple and effective way of displaying categorical, ordinal and discrete data. The bars can be drawn vertically or horizontally. The height, or length, of each bar represents the frequency. Each bar must be the same width and leave the same space between the bars. The bar with the greatest height, or longest length, represents the mode.

Note: A bar chart **cannot** be used to represent continuous data. This is the reason a gap is left between the bars.

EXAMPLE

A survey was taken of a number of students to find out the number of text messages that they sent on a particular day. The frequency table shows the results of the survey.

Number of text messages	0	1	2	3	4	5
Number of students	1	3	6	8	5	2

  (i) Draw a bar chart of the data.
 (ii) How many students took part in the survey?
(iii) What percentage of the students sent three or more text messages on that particular day?

Solution:

(i) Bar chart

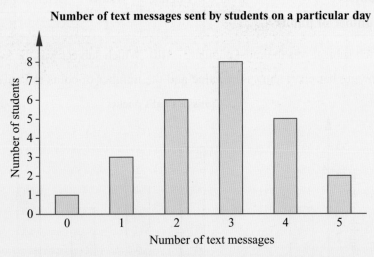

Number of text messages sent by students on a particular day

(ii) Total number of students in the survey = 1 + 3 + 6 + 8 + 5 + 2 = 25

(iii) Number of students who sent three or more text messages = 8 + 5 + 2 = 15

Percentage of students who sent three or more text messages

$$= \frac{\text{Number of students who sent 3 or more text messages}}{\text{Total number of students in the survey}} \times 100\%$$

$$= \frac{15}{25} \times 100\% = 60\%$$

Exercise 14.1

1. A first-year class was asked to state their favourite subject in school. The results are shown in the bar chart below.

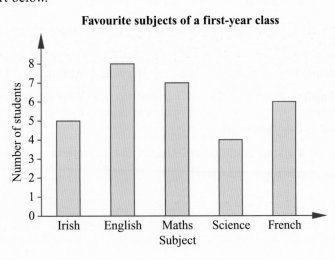

Favourite subjects of a first-year class

(i) Complete the following table.

Subject	Irish	English	Maths	Science	French
Number of pupils					

(ii) Which subject was the most popular? **(iii)** Which subject was the least popular?

2. The following bar chart shows the value and the number of coins in Paul's pocket.

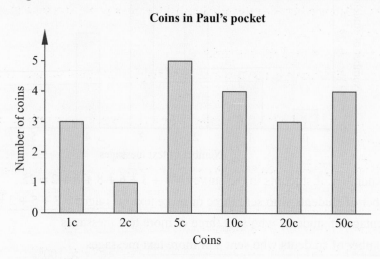

Coins in Paul's pocket

(i) Complete the following frequency table.

Coin	1c	2c	5c	10c	20c	50c
Number of coins						

(ii) Write down the mode.

(iii) How many coins are in Paul's pocket?

(iv) What is the total value of the coins in Paul's pocket?

3. The pupils in a certain class were asked how they travelled to school. The results are shown in the table below.

Mode of transport	Train	Bus	Bicycle	Walking	Car
Number of pupils	4	7	5	8	6

(i) Show the data on a bar chart.

(ii) What was **(a)** the least common and **(b)** the most common mode of travel?

(iii) How many pupils are in the class?

4. A survey was carried out on the colours of cars in a car park. The results are shown in the table below.

Colour	Blue	Red	Black	White	Green	Silver
Number of cars	4	8	6	2	3	1

(i) Illustrate the data with a bar chart.

(ii) Find the difference between the numbers of the most popular colour and the least popular colour of these cars.

(iii) How many cars were in the car park?

(iv) Express the number of black cars as a percentage of the total number of cars in the car park.

5. The following table gives the rainfall, to the nearest cm, over a six-month period in a certain district.

Month	March	April	May	June	July	August
Rainfall	7 cm	8 cm	6 cm	5 cm	1 cm	3 cm

(i) Draw a bar chart to illustrate the data.

(ii) Find the difference, in cm between the wettest and the dryest month.

(iii) What percentage of the total rainfall in the six-month period fell in May?

6. The spreadsheet below shows the number of different drinks purchased from a vending machine on a particular day.

	A	B
1	**Drink**	**Number of Drinks**
2	Tea	11
3	Coffee	12
4	Chocolate	10
5	Soup	8
6	Other	9

(i) Represent the data with a bar chart.

(ii) What was the total number of drinks sold on the day?

(iii) Express the most popular drink as a percentage of the total number of drinks sold on the day.

7. A maths test consisted of 10 questions. 1 mark was given for a correct solution and 0 marks were given for an incorrect solution. The following bar chart represents the marks obtained by a class in the test.

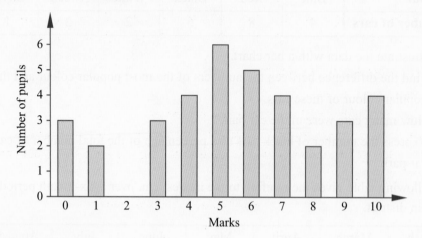

(i) Complete the following table.

Marks	0	1	2	3	4	5	6	7	8	9	10
Number of pupils	3								2		

(ii) How many pupils scored 2 marks?

(iii) How many pupils scored 8 marks or more?

(iv) Write down the modal mark.

(v) How many pupils took the test?

(vi) Calculate the mean mark.

(vii) If the pass mark is 5 or more, calculate the percentage of pupils that passed the test.

Line plots

For categorical, ordinal and discrete data, a line plot is similar to a bar chart, with the bars replaced with dots. A line plot is often called a **dot plot**. It is used for small sets of data, usually fewer than 50 values. It consists of a horizontal axis on which the values (or categories) are evenly marked, from the smallest value to the largest value, including any value in between that does not occur. Each value is indicated with a dot over the corresponding value on the horizontal axis. Each dot represents **one** value. The number of dots above each value indicates how many times each value occurs. Dots must be equally spaced over each value. Each dot is similar to a tally mark used in a frequency distribution. The main advantage of a line plot is that it can be created very quickly, even while collecting the data.

EXAMPLE

The data shows the ages of students in a youth club.

14 13 15 14 13 15 14 15 17 12 17 16 13 16
16 14 14 15 12 16 15 13 17 14 13 17 15 14

Represent this data with a line plot.

Solution:

The smallest number is 12 and the largest number is 17.
The numbers that will go on the horizontal axis are 12, 13, 14, 15, 16, 17.
Put a single dot for each value in the data over the correct value on the horizontal axis.
Space all dots equally above the line.

Ages of students in a youth club

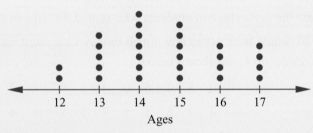

Ages

Note: Sometimes Xs are used instead of dots.

Exercise 14.2

1. The data shows the number of hours spent on homework in a particular week by a first-year class.

3 1 5 2 6 3 3 4
2 4 0 3 4 1 4 5
4 5 3 6 2 5 2 3

Represent this data on a line plot.

2. Ciana collects data from a group of students on the number of siblings (brothers or sisters) each student has. Her results are shown below.

2 0 1 4 3 1 0 2
1 3 0 3 2 5 4 1
3 4 3 1 5 0 2 3

(i) Construct a line plot to represent this data.

(ii) How many of these students have no siblings?

3. The marks, out of five, scored in a test by 20 students are shown below.

$$5 \quad 1 \quad 3 \quad 1 \quad 3 \quad 4 \quad 5 \quad 1 \quad 3 \quad 5$$
$$4 \quad 3 \quad 1 \quad 2 \quad 3 \quad 5 \quad 3 \quad 2 \quad 5 \quad 2$$

(i) Complete the following frequency table.

Marks scored	1	2	3	4	5
Tally					
Number of students					

(ii) Represent the data with a line plot.

(iii) How many students scored (a) 5 marks (b) 0 marks?

(iv) Calculate the percentage of students who scored 4 marks or more.

4. In a survey, 30 people were asked how much money they spent each week on the National Lottery. The results, in €, are shown below.

$$4 \quad 0 \quad 8 \quad 4 \quad 6 \quad 0 \quad 4 \quad 2 \quad 4 \quad \quad 0 \quad 2 \quad 4 \quad 0 \quad 6 \quad 2$$
$$10 \quad 4 \quad 8 \quad 6 \quad 4 \quad 6 \quad 8 \quad 4 \quad 8 \quad \quad 10 \quad 4 \quad 2 \quad 6 \quad 0 \quad 6$$

(i) Complete the following data capture sheet.

Amount, in €	0	2	4	6	8	10
Tally						
Number of people						

(ii) Represent the data with a line plot.

(iii) Write down the modal amount of money spent per week on the lottery for these 30 people.

(iv) Calculate the mean amount of money spent on the lottery for these 30 people.

5. Colin surveyed some students on the number of movies they watched on their holidays. His results are shown on the line plot below.

Number of movies watched by students on holidays

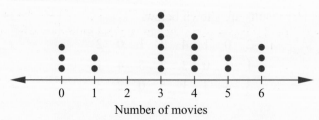

Number of movies

(i) Complete the following frequency distribution table.

Number of movies watched	0	1	2	3	4	5	6
Number of students							

(ii) What does each dot represent?

(iii) Write down the modal number of movies watched.

(iv) How many students did Colin survey?

(v) Calculate the mean number of movies watched.

6. The number of goals scored by football teams in a certain league on a particular Saturday afternoon is shown in the line plot below.

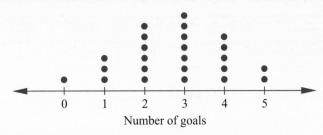

Number of goals scored by football teams in a certain league

Number of goals

(i) Complete the following frequency distribution table.

Number of goals	0	1	2	3	4	5
Number of teams						

(ii) What does each dot represent?

(iii) Write down the modal score.

(iv) How many teams are in the league?

(v) Calculate the mean score.

Pie chart

A pie chart is a circle divided into sectors in proportion to the frequency of the data. It displays the proportions as angles measured from the centre of the circle (but not the actual frequencies). The largest sector represents the mode. It is a good way of representing data when you want to show how things are shared or divided.

Steps in drawing a pie chart:

1. Add up all the frequencies.
2. Divide this into 360°.
3. Multiply the answer in step 2 by each individual frequency.
   (This gives the size of the angle for each sector.)
4. Draw the pie chart, label each sector and give it a title.
   (It is a good idea to write the size of each angle on the pie chart.)

Note: It is good practice to check that all your angles add up to 360° before drawing the pie chart.

 EXAMPLE

The favourite colours of a number of students are shown in the frequency table.

Favourite colour	Purple	Red	Blue	Yellow	Black
Number of students	15	18	9	6	24

Represent this information with a pie chart.

Solution:

$15 + 18 + 9 + 6 + 24 = 72$, therefore there are 72 pupils altogether.

In a circle there are 360°. The whole circle has to include all 72 pupils, so it is first necessary to find out how many degrees one pupil will represent on the pie chart. This is then multiplied by the number of pupils in each category.

   So we have: 72 pupils = 360°.

      Therefore, 1 pupil = 5° (divide both sides by 72).

In other words, one pupil will take up 5° on the pie chart. We make up a table to work out the angle for each sector.

Sector	Number of pupils	Angle
Purple	15	$15 \times 5° = 75°$
Red	18	$18 \times 5° = 90°$
Blue	9	$9 \times 5° = 45°$
Yellow	6	$6 \times 5° = 30°$
Black	24	$24 \times 5° = 120°$
Total	72 pupils	360°

Make sure your total is 360°

Students' favourite colour

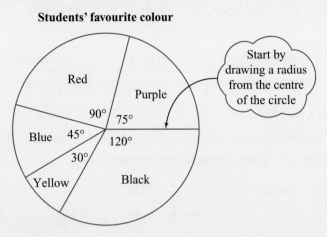

Start by drawing a radius from the centre of the circle

Note: An alternative method to calculate the angles is to use fractions.

Sector	Number of pupils	Fraction	Angle
Purple	15	$\frac{15}{72}$	$\frac{15}{72} \times 360° = 75°$
Red	18	$\frac{18}{72}$	$\frac{18}{72} \times 360° = 90°$
Blue	9	$\frac{9}{72}$	$\frac{9}{72} \times 360° = 45°$
Yellow	6	$\frac{6}{72}$	$\frac{6}{72} \times 360° = 30°$
Black	24	$\frac{24}{72}$	$\frac{24}{72} \times 360° = 120°$
Total	72 pupils	$\frac{72}{72}$	360°

Exercise 14.3

1. The languages taken by first-year students and the angle in each sector in the pie chart are shown in the table below. Represent the data with a pie chart.

Language	German	French	Italian	Spanish
Angle in sector	60°	150°	30°	120°

2. The ages of 18 boys in a local youth club were as follows.

Age	13	14	15
Number	9	6	3

Represent this data with a pie chart.

3. 24 fifth-year pupils were asked to choose from an option of four subjects. The results are in the table below.

Applied Maths	Chemistry	French	Accounting
12	6	4	2

Illustrate the data with a pie chart.

4. A survey was carried out in a class of 36 primary school pupils to see how they travelled to school. The results of the survey are shown in the following table.

Mode of travel	Walked	Bus	Bike	Car	Train
Number of pupils	12	2	4	10	8

Represent this information on a pie chart.

5. A box of coloured balloons contains the following numbers of balloons of each colour.

Colour	Blue	White	Red	Green	Orange
Number of balloons	20	15	30	20	x

(i) If there were 90 balloons in the box, calculate the value of x.

(ii) Illustrate the data with a pie chart.

6. 12 students were asked how many times they had gone to the cinema in the last month. The results were as follows:

$$3 \quad 4 \quad 1 \quad 2 \quad 0 \quad 4 \quad 3 \quad 2 \quad 1 \quad 2 \quad 3 \quad 2$$

(i) Copy and complete the following spreadsheet.

	A	B
	Number of trips to the cinema	**Number of students**
1		
2	0	
3	1	
4	2	
5	3	
6	4	

(ii) Represent the data with a pie chart.

(iii) Write down the mode.

(iv) Calculate the mean.

7. In a survey, 120 girls were asked for their shoe size. The results of the survey were as follows.

Shoe size	2	3	4	5	6	7
Number of girls	10	15	25	35	30	5

    (i) Represent the data on a pie chart.

    (ii) How many girls wear (a) a size 5 (b) a size 5 or smaller?

    (iii) Write down (a) the modal shoe size and (b) calculate the mean shoe size.

    (iv) Comment on the actual shoe sizes recorded. Does this seem realistic? Justify your answer.

8.   (i) Calculate $360° \div 100$.

    (ii) In a certain district, the percentages of land used for specific purposes were recorded in the following table.

Purpose	Industry	Farming	Housing	Parks	Hospital
Percentage	35	5	30	10	20
Angle					

    (a) Copy and complete the table.

    (b) Draw a pie chart to show this data.

Given the pie chart

In some questions we are given the pie chart, or the angles in a pie chart, and we have to work backwards to calculate the numbers in each category.

In each question we are given an equation in disguise, and from this we can work out the number represented by $1°$.

EXAMPLE

An election for a leader is held between four candidates A, B, C and D.

The pie chart represents the number of people who voted in the election for each candidate.

If 180 people voted for candidate A, how many people voted for candidates B, C and D?

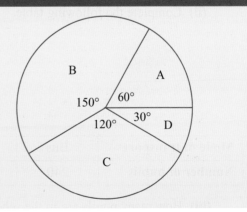

Solution:

In this example we work in reverse. So we have:

$60° = 180$ people   (equation given in disguise)

$1° = 3$ people   (divide both sides by 60)

In other words, $1°$ represents three people on the pie chart.

B: Angle = $150°$ Number of people = $3 \times 150 = 450$

C: Angle = $120°$ Number of people = $3 \times 120 = 360$

D: Angle = $30°$ Number of people = $3 \times 30 = 90$

450 voted for B, 360 voted for C and 90 voted for D.

Exercise 14.4

1. A survey was taken of the people entering a
   supermarket during a certain day. The results are
   shown in the pie chart.

   (i) What angle represents the number of men?

   (ii) 180 children were counted in the survey.
   What was the total number of people counted
   entering the supermarket?

   (iii) How many men were counted entering the
   supermarket?

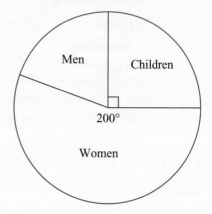

2. The pie chart on the right shows the means of transport
   used by all the pupils in a school.

   (i) What angle represents the bicycle as a means of
   transport?

   (ii) Complete the following table.

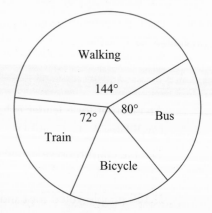

Mode of transport	Bus	Walking	Train	Bicycle
Number of pupils	240			

   (iii) How many pupils are in the school?

3. A group of students was surveyed to find their favourite channel from four given TV channels.
   The pie chart represents the results of the survey.
   (i) What is the measure of the angle for TG4?
   (ii) 15 students replied that RTÉ2 was their favourite channel. How many students were surveyed?
   (iii) How many gave TV3 as their reply?

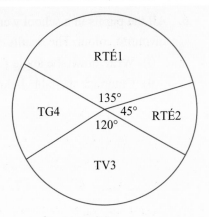

4. Each student in a class studies one of the four languages French, German, Spanish or Italian.
   The pie chart represents the number of students that study each language.
   (i) What is the measure of the angle for Italian?
   (ii) 10 students study French. How many students study German?
   (iii) How many students are in the class?
   (iv) How many students do not study Spanish?

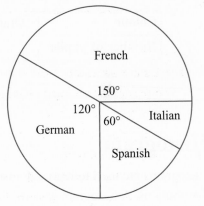

5. An examination was taken by a number of pupils and each obtained a grade of A, B, C, D or E.
   The pie chart illustrates the grades obtained.
   (i) What is the angle representing grade E?
   (ii) Complete the following table.

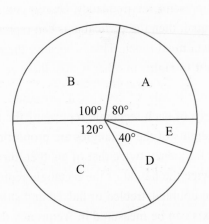

Grade	A	B	C	D	E
Number of pupils	40				

6. All the pupils in a school were asked to name their
   favourite colour. The results are in the pie chart shown.
   (i) Write down the angle representing red.
   (ii) Complete the table below.

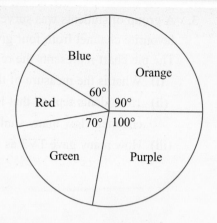

Colour	Orange	Blue	Red	Green	Purple
Number of pupils					150

Histogram

Histograms are used to represent discrete or continuous data, usually contained in grouped frequency distributions. A histogram uses rectangles to represent frequency. The area of each rectangle represents the frequency. On our course the class intervals will have equal widths. If the widths are equal, then the vertical axis can represent frequency. In a histogram, the rectangles representing the data **must** touch. This is because the numbers on the horizontal axis form a **continuous range from left to right**. In other words, there are no gaps in the numbers along the horizontal axis.

For the sake of drawing a histogram or using a histogram to work out frequencies, we say that the area of each rectangle represents the frequency. However, in a histogram with equal widths, the heights of the rectangles are proportional to the frequencies. In other words, if one class interval has a frequency twice that of another, then the height of the rectangle representing this class will be twice the height of the rectangle representing the other class. Also, all the heights in a histogram can be doubled, trebled or halved and still represent the same distribution. In other words, the vertical axis can be measured in **frequency density**.

Note: Bar charts and histograms are often confused with each other. The differences are that bar charts **cannot** represent continuous data and in a histogram the rectangles **must** touch.

EXAMPLE

The duration of each log-on to the internet in a public library was recorded over a certain period. The results are summarised in the following table.

Duration (minutes)	0–5	5–10	10–15	15–20	20–25	25–30
Number of log-ons	2	4	7	10	8	5

Note: 5–10 means 5 minutes or more but less than 10 minutes, etc.

Draw a histogram to illustrate the data in the table.

Solution:

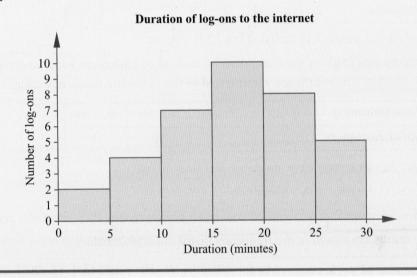

Duration of log-ons to the internet

Exercise 14.5

Construct a histogram to represent each of the following grouped frequency distributions in questions 1–4.

1.

Interval	0–2	2–4	4–6	6–8
Frequency	3	5	4	2

Note: 0–2 means 0 is included but 2 is not, etc.

2.

Interval	0–10	10–20	20–30	30–40	40–50
Frequency	2	6	5	4	3

Note: 0–10 means 0 is included but 10 is not, etc.

3.

Interval	0–5	5–10	10–15	15–20	20–25	25–30
Frequency	1	4	7	6	5	2

Note: 5–10 means 5 is included but 10 is not, etc.

4.

Interval	0–4	4–8	8–12	12–16	16–20	20–24
Frequency	2	4	8	7	5	1

Note: 8–12 means 8 is included but 12 is not, etc.

5. A survey was made of the time spent by each of 26 customers while shopping in a supermarket. The results are summarised in the following frequency table.

Time (minutes)	0–20	20–40	40–60	60–80
No. of customers	5	7	10	4

Note: 20–40 means 20 or more but less than 40, etc.

Represent the data with a histogram.

6. 42 first-year students were asked how much pocket money they spent in a certain week.

The results are shown in the frequency distribution table below.

Amount of pocket money in €	0–5	5–10	10–15	15–20	20–25
Number of students	8	10	12	x	5

Note: 5–10 means €5 or more but less than €10, etc.

   (i) Find the value of x.

   (ii) Represent the data with a histogram.

   (iii) Write down the modal class.

7. The heights of 36 students, correct to the nearest cm, were recorded in the following frequency table.

Height (cm)	130–140	140–150	150–160	160–170	170–180	180–190	190–200
No. of students	2	7	10	8	5	3	1

Note: 130–140 means 130 is included but 140 is not, etc.

   (i) Represent the data with a histogram.

   (ii) Write down the modal class

   (iii) Could this data be represented with a bar chart? Justify your answer.

8. The marks obtained by 31 candidates in a maths examination were as follows.

   25 85 55 74 60 19 54 48 41 79 81 73 88 74 38 77

   57 65 90 76 98 42 50 59 17 68 79 20 64 45 71

   (i) Complete the following frequency table.

Marks	0–20	20–40	40–60	60–80	80–100
Tally					
Number of students					

   Note: 40–60 means 40 or more but less than 60, etc.

   (ii) Illustrate the data with a histogram.

   (iii) Write down the modal class.

   (iv) In which class interval does the median lie?

   (v) Could this data be represented with a bar chart? Justify your answer.

9. The number of hours spent studying, per week, by 40 students in a certain school were recorded as follows.

   7   9   14   6   1   10   2   6   7   11

   10   1   10   2   6   3   5   3   0   5

   11   7   13   10   1   9   5   2   15   6

   6   11   6   4   0   12   9   13   4   8

   (i) Complete the following table.

Time in hours	0–4	4–8	8–12	12–16
Tally				
Number of students				

   Note: 4–8 means 4 or more but less than 8, etc.

   (ii) Write down the modal class.

   (iii) In which interval does the median lie?

   (iv) Represent the data with a (a) histogram and (b) pie chart.

   (v) Discuss the differences, advantages and disadvantages of using either diagram to represent this data.

10. A supermarket opens at 08:00. The histogram shows the distribution of the times employees arrive for work.

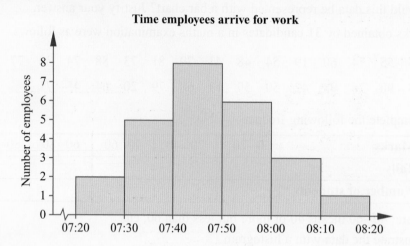

Time employees arrive for work

(i) Complete the following frequency distribution.

Time	07:20– 07:30	07:30– 07:40	07:40– 07:50	07:50– 08:00	08:00– 08:10	08:10– 08:20
No. of employees						

(ii) How many employees arrived for work that day?

(iii) How many employees arrived before 07:50?

(iv) How many employees were definitely late for work? Explain your answer.

(v) What is the modal class?

(vi) What percentage of the employees arrived before 07:40?

(vii) What is the maximum number of employees that could have arrived before 07:45?

(viii) Could this data be represented with a bar chart? Give a reason for your answer.

Stem and leaf plots (stemplots)

A stem and leaf plot groups the **actual** values and lists them in order horizontally. It is similar to a bar chart, histogram or line plot that has been drawn on its side, except that the rows are made up of digits (numbers).

The **stems** represent the first part of each number and are written on the left-hand side.

The **leaves** represent the remaining part of each number and are written on the right-hand side.

Consider the numbers 50, 52, 57, 61, 65, 68, 69, 73, 77.

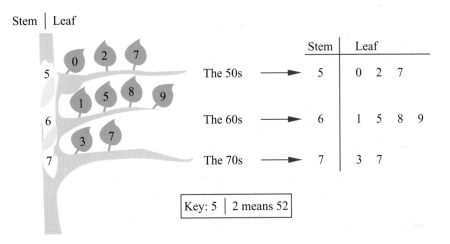

Stem | Leaf

Stem	Leaf
5	0 2 7
6	1 5 8 9
7	3 7

The 50s ⟶

The 60s ⟶

The 70s ⟶

Key: 5 | 2 means 52

In the above stem and leaf plot, the tens digits are the **stems** and the ones digits are the **leaves**.

Note: A 'stem and leaf plot' is often called a 'stemplot'.

When constructing a stem and leaf plot, do the following:

1. Write down the smallest and largest values.
2. Write the stems in a vertical line from the smallest to the largest. (Keep equal intervals and include any missing stems in between.)
3. Draw a vertical line to the right of the stems.
4. Write the leaves next to their corresponding stems.
5. Always include a **key** to show the place value that is meant.
6. Give your stem and leaf plot a heading.

The leaf always consists of **one digit**.

52 has stem 5 and leaf 2   674 has stem 67 and leaf 4

1·3 has stem 1 and leaf 3   2,839 has stem 283 and leaf 9

Usually, a stem and leaf plot is **ordered**. This simply means that the leaves are arranged in increasing order from left to right. There is no need to separate the leaves with commas since each leaf is always a single digit (number).

EXAMPLE

The number of minutes taken to complete an exercise was recorded for 24 students in a class. The results were as follows.

20 9 36 24 17 32 25 21 14 8 26 38

18 15 21 8 11 23 6 37 25 32 17 36

(i) Represent the data with a stem and leaf plot.

(ii) Calculate the range.

Solution:

(i) The smallest value is 6 and the largest value is 38.

Let the intervals be 0–9, 10–19, 20–29, 30–39.

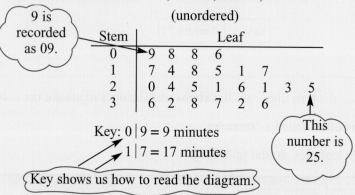

9 is recorded as 09.

(unordered)

Stem	Leaf
0	9 8 8 6
1	7 4 8 5 1 7
2	0 4 5 1 6 1 3 5
3	6 2 8 7 2 6

Key: 0|9 = 9 minutes

1|7 = 17 minutes

This number is 25.

Key shows us how to read the diagram.

Number of minutes taken to complete an experiment

(ordered)

Stem	Leaf
0	6 8 8 9
1	1 4 5 7 7 8
2	0 1 1 3 4 5 5 6
3	2 2 6 6 7 8

Key: 0|9 = 9 minutes

1|7 = 17 minutes

(ii) Range = Largest value − Smallest value = 38 − 6 = 32 minutes

Enter the leaves, crossing out the values as you record them. This is called an **unordered** stem and leaf plot. Then create a new stem and leaf plot so that the leaves are in increasing order. This is called an **ordered** stem and leaf plot.

Exercise 14.6

For questions 1–4, construct a stem and leaf plot for the given data.

1. 24 42 35 31 27 37 47 21 30 25

2. 9 11 32 29 37 12 19 2 15 22 17 21 6 27

3. 32 24 8 47 23 19 6 12 4 24 41 48 28
    15 19 34 2 30 18 23 37 45 27 32 41 25

4. 44 51 78 21 37 69 77 63 56 31 32 44
    66 45 38 71 45 66 57 62 45 54 43 53

5. The number of guests in a hotel over a two-week period was recorded as follows.

    36 43 39 53 29 43 33 47 51 27 42 31 34 22

    (i) Represent this data on a stem and leaf plot.
    (ii) Calculate the range.

6. The number of litres of diesel bought by 20 motorists was recorded as follows.

    17 22 28 11 35 43 23 26 18 15
    25 45 37 35 27 16 41 34 13 29

    (i) Construct a stem and leaf plot to represent the data.
    (ii) Calculate the (a) range and (b) the mean number of litres of diesel bought per motorist.
    (iii) Does this data contain a mode? Justify your answer.

7. The stem and leaf plot records the heights, in centimetres, of the first 30 students that entered a school on a certain morning.

Stem	Leaf
14	8 9
15	0 1 3 4 5 5 6 9
16	1 1 4 4 4 6 7 7 9
17	0 1 2 4 5 6 8
18	1 2 6 7

    (i) Write down a key.
    (ii) What does the entry 15 | 3 represent?
    (iii) What is the height of the (a) shortest person and (b) tallest person?
    (iv) Write down the range.
    (v) Write down the modal height.

   (vi) Is any student in this sample 173 cm tall?
   (vii) Calculate the mean height.
   (viii) Find the median height.
   (ix) Does this sample represent the population of this school? Explain your answer.
   (x) How could the sample be improved? Justify your answer.
   (xi) Suggest another diagram that could represent this sample. Justify your answer.

8. The time, in seconds, taken to answer 18 mobile phone calls was recorded as follows.

2·5	3·5	5·6	3·6	2·4	4·5	3·3	4·2	3·2
5·9	1·9	3·3	2·9	3·3	5·8	3·7	3·2	2·9

   (i) Copy and complete the stem and leaf plot to represent this data.

   Time, in seconds, taken to answer a mobile call

Stem	Leaf
1	
2	4
3	
4	2
5	

   Key: 2│4 means 2·4 seconds

   (ii) What was the **(a)** shortest time and **(b)** the longest time taken to answer the calls?
   (iii) Calculate the range.
   (iv) Write down the modal time taken to answer a call.
   (v) Calculate the mean time taken to answer a call.
   (vi) The time 5·3 seconds was incorrectly recorded as 3·5 seconds. Would this error increase or decrease the mean? Justify your answer.
   (vii) Calculate the change in the mean due to this error.
   (viii) Somebody suggested that the data should have been represented with a pie chart. Do you agree? Explain your answer.

Misuses of statistics

Many advertisements frequently use graphs and diagrams to present information. In most cases the graphs and diagrams are well presented and give an honest and fair representation of the facts. However, some are deliberately drawn to mislead. It is often what is left out that is important. The most common ways to present correct data in a misleading way are to use a false origin, insert no scale, or a non-uniform scale, on the vertical axis or draw graphs with unequal widths. Consider the next example.

EXAMPLE

Briefly comment on these bar charts, which represent the number of cars sold over two years on a garage forecourt.

Solution:

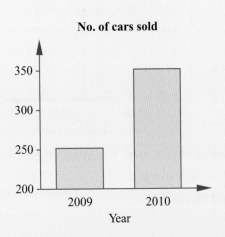

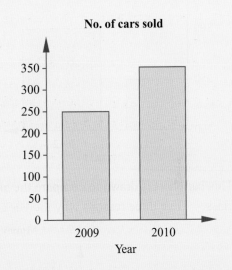

This bar chart gives the impression that car sales in 2009 were three times greater in 2010 compared to 2009 (indicating a 200% increase). However, the vertical (number) axis does not start at zero.

When we can see the whole bar chart, with the vertical (number) axis starting at zero, it shows that car sales have increased. However, they have not even doubled (actual increase was 40%).

Exercise 14.7

1. In each case, give two reasons why the graphs are misleading.

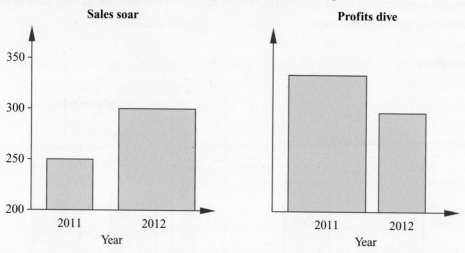

2. This bar chart is drawn to compare the amount of money, in €, raised for charity by two classes. Give three reasons why the bar chart is misleading.

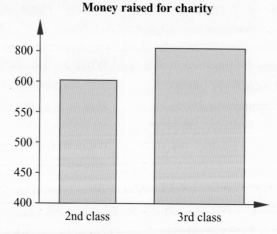

3. A car manufacturer produces two makes of car, A and B. They sell twice as much of B as A. The following diagram has been drawn to represent this information. Explain why the diagram is misleading.

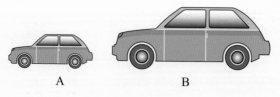

4. The diagram has been drawn to represent the number of trucks sold over a 10-year period.

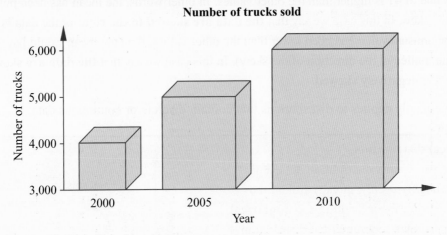

Number of trucks sold

Give two reasons why this diagram is misleading.

5. Seven people work for a company. Their annual salaries, in €, are as follows.

180,000   40,000   40,000   40,000   40,000   40,000   40,000

The company decides to advertise for another employee. The company claims in the advertisement that the average salary is €60,000 per year. Is the company trying to mislead with this advertisement? Give reasons for your answer.

6. A professor of economics once said, 'In the future we hope that economic growth rates in all countries will be above the average.' What is wrong with his statement?

Shape of a distribution

In some distributions, certain values look unusual or are not typical. Consider the values 2, 3, 4, 4, 5, 6, 7, 9 and 41. The value 41 is not typical of the rest of the values. It is often called an **outlier**. In this case, it has a small effect on the median (this is one of the reasons why they use the median value in horse sales). However, it does have a big effect on the mean.

Consider the 8 values without the value 41:

2, 3, 4, 4, 5, 6, 7, 9

$\text{Median} = \dfrac{4 + 5}{2} = 4\cdot 5$

(average of the two middle values)

$\text{Mean} = \mu = \dfrac{2 + 3 + 4 + 4 + 5 + 6 + 7 + 9}{8}$

$= \dfrac{40}{8} = 5$

Consider the 9 values including the value 41:

2, 3, 4, 4, 5, 6, 7, 9, 41

$\text{Median} = 5$

(middle value)

$\text{Mean} = \mu = \dfrac{2 + 3 + 4 + 4 + 5 + 6 + 7 + 9 + 41}{9}$

$= \dfrac{81}{9} = 9$

The value 41, outlier, increases the median by 0·5 and increases the mean by 4.

We say that the data has been **skewed** by the unusual value of 41. The mean has been increased because the unusual value of 41 is higher than the other values. In other words, the mean has been pulled in the direction of the skew. In this case we say that **the data are skewed to the right** or the data is **positively skewed**. If the unusual value had been lower than the other values, then the mean would have been lowered (again, pulled in the direction of the skew). In this case we say that **the data are skewed to the left** or the data is **negatively skewed**.

Note: Skewness only applies to distributions that contain discrete or continuous data.

Symmetrical distribution

If all of the values in a distribution are evenly spread (or roughly evenly spread) around the mean, the distribution is said to be **symmetrical**. The diagram shows a symmetrical distribution. The mean and the median coincide.

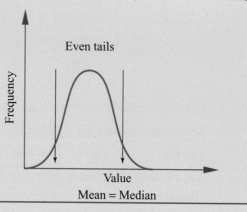

Skewed right distribution

If most of the values in a distribution are low, then the tail is on the right-hand side. The distribution is said to be **skewed to the right** (right-hand tail). It is also said to be **positively skewed**. The diagram shows a distribution that is **skewed to the right**. In this case, the mean of the data is **greater** than the median. The mean is pulled right (increased) by the right-hand skew.

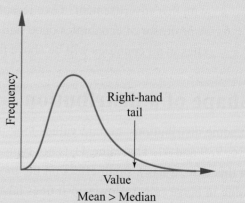

Skewed left distribution

If most of the values in a distribution are high, then the tail is on the left-hand side. The distribution is said to be **skewed to the left** (left-hand tail). It is also said to be **negatively skewed**. The diagram shows a distribution that is **skewed to the left**. In this case, the mean of the data is **less** than the median. The mean is pulled left (lowered) by the left-hand skew.

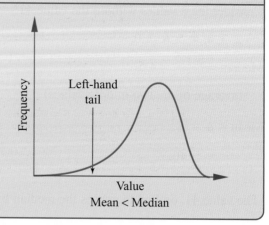

Describe the shape of each distribution. Are there any outliers?

(i)

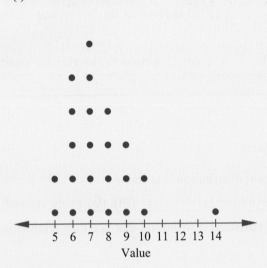

(ii)

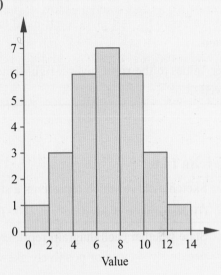

Solution:

(i)

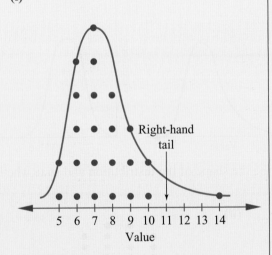

(ii)

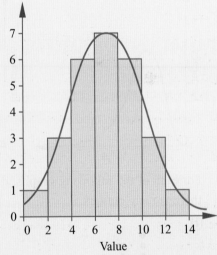

Most values are low.

∴ The distribution is skewed to the right.

There is one outlier, 14.

The values are evenly spread about the mean.

∴ The distribution is symmetrical.

There are no outliers.

When we talk about the direction of skewness, we are talking about the direction of the tail of the distribution. The tail indicates the area where there are fewer values.

> Values **evenly** spread around the mean gives two even tails, which is called **symmetrical**.
>
> Fewer values to the **left** gives a left-hand tail, which is called **skewed to the left** or **negatively skewed**.
>
> Fewer values to the **right** gives a right-hand tail, which is called **skewed to the right** or **positively skewed**.

Exercise 14.8

1. Sketch a curve which represents a statistical distribution that is:

    (i) Negatively skewed   **(ii)** Symmetrical   **(iii)** Positively skewed

2. State whether each diagram represents a statistical distribution that is either symmetrical, negatively skewed or positively skewed.

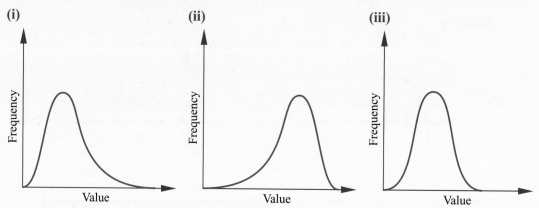

3. For each of the following graphs, describe the shape of the distribution and state whether there are any outliers.

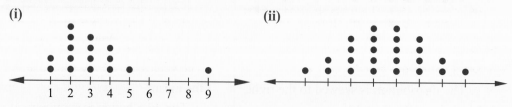

(iii)

(iv)

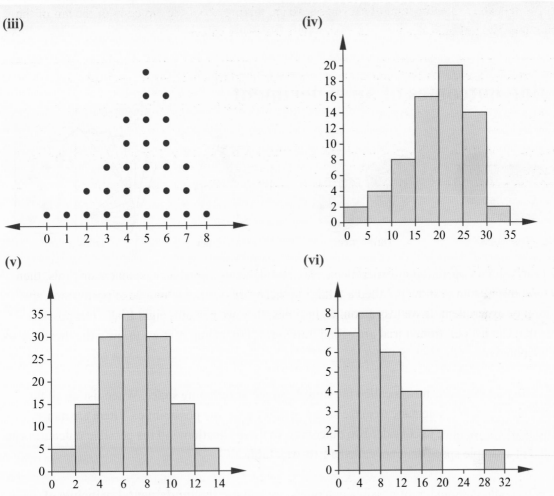

(v)

(vi)

Hint: When dealing with stem and leaf plots, it may help to rotate the page by 90°.

(vii)

Stem	Leaf					
1	1	3				
2	0	2	5			
3	1	3	4	7		
4	0	4	5	6	7	8
5	1	3	6	6	7	8	9
6	2	4	7	8	9	
7	0	1	3			

(viii)

Stem	Leaf				
10	5				
11	1	4			
12	0	1	2	5	
13	0	3	4	7	8
14	1	3	6	8	
15	2	5			
16	3				

4. A bar chart was used to record the number of students who play the sports soccer, hurling, hockey, tennis, basketball, swimming and camogie. A person looking at the bar chart stated that this distribution is skewed. Is the person correct? Justify your answer.

Listing outcomes of an experiment

Toss coins

Throw dice

Spin a spinner

Draw a card

If you carry out an operation or experiment, for example using coins, dice, spinners or cards, then each toss, throw, spin or draw is called a **trial**. In other words, a trial is **one** go at performing an operation or experiment. If we toss a coin eight times, then we perform eight trials. The possible results that can happen from a trial are called **outcomes**. For example, if we throw a die there are six possible outcomes: 1, 2, 3, 4, 5 and 6.

A list of all possible outcomes is called the **sample space** or **outcome space**. When listing all the possible outcomes, be systematic to make sure you don't miss any possibilities. There are many situations where we have to consider two outcomes. In these situations, all the possible outcomes can be listed in a sample space diagram called a **two-way table**.

To help us count the number of possible outcomes, we can use the **fundamental principle of counting**.

Fundamental principle of counting

> Suppose one operation has m possible outcomes and a second operation has n outcomes. The number of possible outcomes when performing the first operation **followed by** the second operation is $m \times n$.

Performing one operation **and** another operation means we **multiply** the number of possible outcomes.

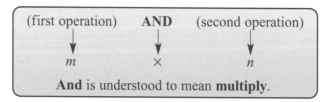

(first operation)   **AND**   (second operation)

m $\times$ n

And is understood to mean **multiply**.

Basically, we multiply the number of outcomes for each choice. The fundamental principle of counting can be extended to three or more operations.

Note: We assume that the outcome of one operation does not affect the number of outcomes of the other operation.

EXAMPLE 1

(i) A die is thrown and a coin is tossed. How many outcomes are possible?

(ii) List all the possible outcomes.

Solution:

(i) Using the fundamental principle of counting:

1. Die   There are 6 possible outcomes for a die: 1, 2, 3, 4, 5 or 6.

2. Coin   There are 2 possible outcomes for a coin: H or T.

Die   Coin

Hence, the number of different outcomes = $\boxed{6} \times \boxed{2} = 12$

(ii) Using a two-way table:

Coin	T	•	•	•	•	•	•
	H	•	•	•	•	•	•
		1	2	3	4	5	6

Die

A dot indicates an outcome.

There are 12 dots (6 × 2).

List of outcomes

$(1, H), (2, H), (3, H), (4, H), (5, H), (6, H)$

$(1, T), (2, T), (3, T), (4, T), (5, T), (6, T)$

EXAMPLE 2

A school requires a new sports kit, consisting of a jersey, shorts and socks. A local factory has four different types of jersey, two different types of shorts and three different types of socks. How many different types of kit selections are possible?

Solution:

Jersey   Shorts   Socks

The number of different kit selections = $\boxed{4} \times \boxed{2} \times \boxed{3} = 24$

Exercise 15.1

1. A restaurant makes six varieties of pizza. Each of these is available in three different sizes. How many different pizzas can be ordered?

2. Lunch in a certain hotel consists of a main course and a dessert. There are five different main courses and three different desserts. How many different lunch selections are possible?

3. A factory makes electric kettles. Kettle sizes are 1 litre, 2 litres and 3 litres. Kettles are silver, cream, brown or black. How many different types of kettle does the factory make?

4. A young person starting a new job needs an outfit consisting of a jacket, trousers and shirt. A local shop has three different types of jacket, two different types of trousers and five different types of shirt. How many different selections of outfit are possible?

5. A student must choose one subject from each of the following subject groups:
   Group A: 3 modern languages   Group B: 3 science subjects
   Group C: 2 business subjects
   How many different subject selections are possible?

6. A certain car is available as a saloon or a hatchback. Each of these is available with three different engine sizes and five different colours.

   How many different versions of the car are available?

7. Photographs can be printed in large, medium or small sizes. They can be in black and white or in colour and they can have a glossy finish or a mate finish. In how many different ways can photographs be printed?

8. A game consists of spinning a five-sided spinner labelled *P, Q, R, S* and *T* and tossing a coin. An outcome is a letter and a head or a tail.

   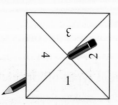

   (i) How many outcomes of the game are possible?

   (ii) List all the possible outcomes of the game.

9. A game is played with two fair spinners, as shown. An outcome of the game is a number and a colour.

   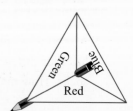

   (i) How many outcomes of the game are possible?

   (ii) List all the possible outcomes of the game.

10. A game consists of spinning a fair die
and a fair spinner which can land on *A*,
B or *C*. An outcome is a number and
a letter.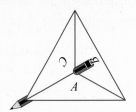

    (i) How many outcomes of the game are
possible?

    (ii) List all the possible outcomes of the game.

11. Three numbers are printed on
discs, as shown.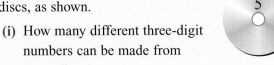

    (i) How many different three-digit
numbers can be made from
these discs?

    (ii) Rearrange the discs so that they show the **(a)** smallest three-digit number **(b)** largest
three-digit number.

12. Tickets in a raffle have a code printed on them.
The code is a letter followed by a digit.

    How many different codes are possible?
                   | X7 | (example)

Theoretical probability

Probability involves the study of the laws of chance. It is a measure of the chance, or likelihood, of
something happening. Probability is used throughout the world to predict what is likely to happen
in the future. These events can be as simple as throwing a die or as complicated as assessing an
insurance risk. **At random** means not knowing in advance what the outcome will be.

If *E* is an event, then *P*(*E*) stands for the probability that that event occurs.

P(*E*) is read as 'the probability of *E*'.

Definition

> The measure of the probability of an event, *E*, is given by:
>
> $$P(E) = \frac{\text{Number of successful outcomes}}{\text{Number of possible outcomes}}$$

The probability of an event is a number between 0 and 1, including 0 and 1. The chance of an event happening can be shown on a **probability scale**:

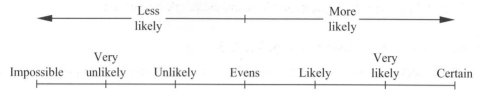

A **probability of 0** means that an event is **impossible**. If E is impossible, then $P(E) = 0$.

A **probability of 1** means an event is **certain**. If E is certain, then $P(E) = 1$.

The probabilities of some events are shown on the probability scale below.

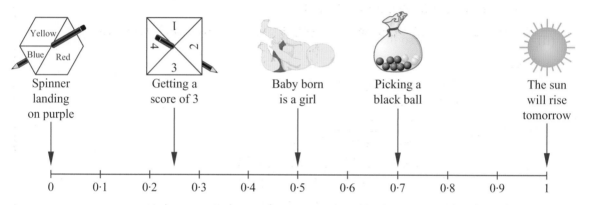

| Spinner landing on purple | Getting a score of 3 | Baby born is a girl | Picking a black ball | The sun will rise tomorrow |

Probabilities should always be written as fractions, decimals or percentages.

EXAMPLE 1

An unbiased die is thrown once. Find the probability that the number obtained is:

(i) 2   **(ii)** Odd   **(iii)** Greater than 4

Solution:

When an unbiased die is thrown, there are six possible outcomes: 1, 2, 3, 4, 5 or 6.

(i) There is only one 2.

∴ $P(2) = \frac{1}{6}$

(ii) There are three odd numbers: 1, 3 and 5.

∴ $P(\text{odd number}) = \frac{3}{6} = \frac{1}{2}$

(iii) There are two numbers greater than four: 5 and 6.

∴ $P(\text{number greater than four}) = \frac{2}{6} = \frac{1}{3}$

A pack of cards consists of 52 cards divided into four suits: clubs (black), diamonds (red), hearts (red) and spades (black). Each suit consists of 13 cards bearing the following values: 2, 3, 4, 5, 6, 7, 8, 9, 10, jack, queen, king and ace. The jack, queen and king are called **picture cards**.

The total number of outcomes if one card is picked is 52.

Notes: The phrase 'drawn at random' means each object is **equally likely** to be picked. 'Unbiased' means 'fair'.

EXAMPLE 2

A card is drawn at random from a normal pack of 52 playing cards.

What is the probability that the card will be:

(i) An ace   **(ii)** A spade   **(iii)** Black   **(iv)** Odd numbered

Solution:

(i) $P(\text{ace}) = \dfrac{\text{number of aces}}{\text{number of cards}} = \dfrac{4}{52} = \dfrac{1}{13}$

(ii) $P(\text{spade}) = \dfrac{\text{number of spades}}{\text{number of cards}} = \dfrac{13}{52} = \dfrac{1}{4}$

(iii) $P(\text{black card}) = \dfrac{\text{number of black cards}}{\text{number of cards}} = \dfrac{26}{52} = \dfrac{1}{2}$

(iv) Each suit has four odd numbers: 3, 5, 7 and 9. There are four suits. Therefore, there are 16 cards with an odd number.

$P(\text{odd-numbered card}) = \dfrac{\text{number of cards with an odd number}}{\text{number of cards}} = \dfrac{16}{52} = \dfrac{4}{13}$

Probability of an event not happening

If E is any event, then 'not E' is the event that E does not occur. Clearly, E and 'not E' cannot occur at the same time. Either E or 'not E' must occur. Thus, we have the following relationship between the probabilities of E and not E:

$$P(E) + P(\text{not } E) = 1$$
$$\text{or}$$
$$P(\text{not } E) = 1 - P(E)$$

Note: $P(\text{not } E)$ is sometimes written as $P(E')$ or $P(\overline{E})$.

EXAMPLE 3

When Richard plays golf the probability that he will lose a golf ball during a round is $\frac{3}{5}$. During his next round of golf, what is the probability that he will complete a round of golf without losing a golf ball?

Solution:

$P(\text{lose a ball}) = \frac{3}{5}$

$P(\text{will not lose a ball}) = 1 - P(\text{lose a ball})$

$$= 1 - \frac{3}{5} = \frac{2}{5}$$

Exercise 15.2

1. There are four red and two yellow marbles in a bag.
   One marble is selected at random from the bag.
   What is the probability that the marble selected is:

   (i) Red **(ii)** Yellow **(iii)** Green

2. The letters of the word MISSISSIPPI are written on separate cards, placed in a box and mixed up. A card is selected at random from the bag. What is the probability that the card shows the letter:

   (i) M **(ii)** I **(iii)** S **(iv)** P **(v)** T

3. **(i)** A box contains eight black pens and two blue pens. One pen is chosen at random from the box. Write down the probability that the pen chosen is **(a)** black **(b)** not black.

   (ii) Represent each answer on the probability scale.

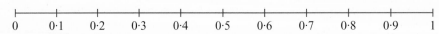

4. A card is selected at random from a full pack of 52 cards (no jokers). What is the probability the card is:

   (i) Black **(ii)** A club **(iii)** The ace of spades **(iv)** A king

5. **(i)** A bag contains five red, two blue and three green counters. One counter is chosen at random from the bag. What is the probability that the counter is **(a)** red **(b)** blue **(c)** green **(d)** red or blue?

   (ii) Represent each answer on the probability scale.

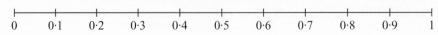

6. **(i)** A bag contains eight red discs, seven yellow discs and five white discs. A disc is selected at random from the bag. What is the probability that the disc is **(a)** yellow **(b)** not red?

   (ii) Represent each answer on the probability scale.

   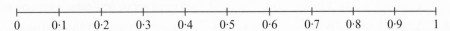

7. Of the 35 people working in a firm, 20 walk to work, 10 go by car and the remainder go by bus. One of the people working in the firm is chosen at random. What is the probability that this person goes to work by bus?

8. **(i)** Noreen bought a packet of flavoured sweets. There were 24 sweets in the packet: eight apple, five cherry, five orange and the remainder were raspberry. How many raspberry sweets were in the packet?

   (ii) Noreen takes one sweet at random from the packet. What is the probability the sweet selected is **(a)** apple flavoured **(b)** orange or raspberry flavoured **(c)** not cherry flavoured?

   (iii) Which two flavours have the same probability of being selected?

9. The probability of a train being late is 0·15. What is the probability that it will not be late?

10. **(i)** Frank has accidently put two old batteries back into his bag that also contains eight new batteries. He randomly picks out one battery from the bag. What is the probability that the battery selected is **(a)** a new battery **(b)** an old battery?

    (ii) Represent each answer on the probability scale.

    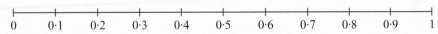

    (iii) How many batteries should he take out to be sure that at least one is new?

11. For each of the following events, say whether it is impossible, very unlikely, unlikely, evens, likely, very likely or certain.

    (i) If you buy a lotto ticket you will win the lotto jackpot.

    (ii) You will get a head when you toss a coin.

    (iii) You will pick a vowel at random from the letters of the word 'MOUSE'.

    (iv) If you pick a card from a deck of cards, it will be a spade.

    (v) One day mathematicians will find a whole number between 2 and 3.

    (vi) When a fair die is thrown it will land on one of its faces.

    (vii) A washing machine that is regularly used will break down during the next 20 years.

12. The probability of four events have been marked on a probability scale.

0   1

Event *P*: A person is over 4 metres tall. Event *Q*: Getting a score less than 7 on one roll of a die. Event *R*: A coin lands tails up. Event *S*: Pick a number greater than 1 from 1, 2, 3 and 4.

Label the arrows with the letters *P*, *Q*, *R* and *S* to show the event they represent.

13. The probability scale shows the probabilities of the events *A*, *B*, *C*, *D*, *E*. Which of the five events:

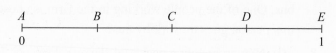

 (i) Has an even chance of happening

 (ii) Is impossible

(iii) Is certain to happen

(iv) Is unlikely to happen

 (v) Is very likely to happen

14. To play a game, you spin the pointer. You win the prize on which the pointer lands. Martin has one spin.

 (i) Which prize is Martin most likely to win?

 (ii) Explain your answer to part **(i)**.

Copy the scale below.

Sheila has one spin. On the scale, mark with a:

(iii) *P* the probability that Sheila will win €10.

(iv) *H* the probability that Sheila will win €20.

15. In a bag there are 10 numbered discs. Claire selects one disc from the bag. What is the probability that Claire selects a disc that has:

 (i) 2 on it   **(ii)** No 2 on it

(iii) A 2 and a 3 on it

(iv) A 2 or a 3 on it

16. The pie chart shows the sports played by people in a club. One person is selected at random from the club. Find the probability that the person selected plays:

(i) Soccer   (ii) Hurling   (iii) Golf

17. 200 eggs were classified according to size (large or medium) and colour (brown or white). The results are given in the following table.

	Brown	**White**
Large	40	80
Medium	32	48

(i) An egg is chosen at random. What is the probability that it is **(a)** a white egg **(b)** a brown egg **(c)** a large brown egg **(d)** a medium white egg?

(ii) Label the probability of each event with the letters A, B, C and D, respectively. Indicate the position of A, B, C and D on the probability scale.

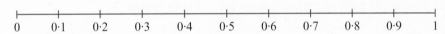

18. 150 students sitting an examination were grouped according to age (16, 17 or 18) and gender (female or male). The results are given in the following table.

	Age 16	**Age 17**	**Age 18**
Female	30	18	12
Male	60	27	3

(i) One student is chosen at random. What is the probability that the student is **(a)** male **(b)** a 16-year-old female **(c)** younger than 18 **(d)** older than 19?

(ii) Label the probability of each event with the letters P, Q, R and S, respectively. Indicate the position of P, Q, R and S on the probability scale.

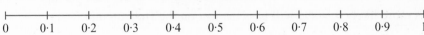

19. (i) The table shows how 40 counters are coloured and numbered. Complete the table.

	Red	Blue	Total
1	15		30
2			
Total	24		

(ii) The counters are placed in a bag and one counter is selected at random. Calculate the probability that the counter is (a) red (b) blue and numbered 1.

20. (i) This table shows the entries of some distance running events. Complete the table.

	100 m	5,000 m	Marathon	Total
Male	12			
Female		12	6	
Total	21		21	72

(ii) An athlete is chosen at random. What is the probability that the athlete chosen is a
(a) female (b) male marathon runner (c) 5,000 m runner?

21. The table shows information about the number of books in a classroom library.

	Maths	English	Total
Paperback	15	27	
Hardback	30		
Total		75	120

(i) Complete the table.
(ii) A book is chosen at random. What is the probability that the book is a (a) hardback
(b) paperback (c) maths hardback (d) English paperback?
(iii) A hardback is chosen at random. What is the probability that it is an English book?
(iv) A maths book is chosen randomly. What is the probability that it is a paperback book?

22. The probability that a woman will pass her driving test at the first attempt is 0·75. Explain why it is more likely that she will pass the test on the first attempt.

23. On each spinner, write five numbers such that each statement is true.

(i) It is certain that you will get a number that is greater than 3.	(ii) It is more likely that you will get an odd number than an even number.	(iii) It is impossible to get a number divisible by 3.
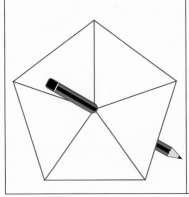	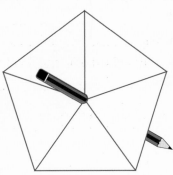	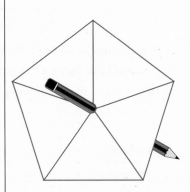

24. Copy and complete the spinner so that the probability of getting an even number is $\frac{1}{2}$ and the probability of getting a 2 is $\frac{1}{3}$.

Combining two events

There are many situations where we have to consider two outcomes. In these situations, all the possible outcomes, called the **sample space** (or **outcome space**), can be listed in a **sample space diagram** (often called a **two-way table** or a **probability space diagram**).

 EXAMPLE 1

A fair coin is tossed and a fair die is rolled. List all the outcomes in a sample space diagram. Calculate the probability of obtaining a head and an odd number.

Solution:

Sample space diagram

	T					
Coin H	•		•		•	
	1	2	3	4	5	6

Die

We indicate each successful outcome with a dot.

P(head and an odd number)

$= \frac{3}{12} = \frac{1}{4}$

EXAMPLE 2

Two unbiased spinners are spun together. Each spinner is divided into equal sectors and numbered as shown. An outcome is achieved by adding the numbers that each arrow lands on.

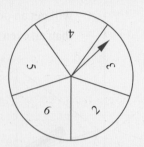 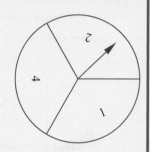

(i) Represent all the outcomes in a sample space diagram.

(ii) What is the probability that the outcome is 7?

Solution:

(i) Sample space diagram:

4	6	7	8	9	10
2	4	5	6	7	8
1	3	4	5	6	7
+	2	3	4	5	6

Second spinner (rows), First spinner (columns)

(ii) There are 15 outcomes.
7 occurs three times.
$$\therefore P(7) = \tfrac{3}{15} = \tfrac{1}{5}$$

Exercise 15.3

1. (i) A fair coin is tossed and a fair die is rolled. List all the outcomes in a sample space diagram.

   (ii) Calculate the probability of obtaining a tail and an even number.

2. For a two-course meal you can choose one main course and dessert from the menu.

   (i) List all the possible two-course meals that can be chosen.

   (ii) What is the probability that if you choose a two-course meal at random from the menu it will contain steak and ice cream?

Main course	Dessert
Fish	
Steak	Ice cream
Pizza	Fruit salad

3. **(i)** A fair coin is tossed and a fair five-sided spinner, with sides A, A, B, B, B, is spun. How many outcomes are possible?

T					
H					
	A	A	B	B	B

(ii) Find the probability of **(a)** a head and an A **(b)** a tail and a B.

4. A game is played with two fair spinners, as shown. Both are spun at the same time and the outcomes are multiplied to get a score.

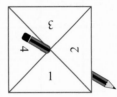

(i) Copy and complete the table.

3				12
2		4		
1				
×	1	2	3	4

(ii) Calculate the probability of an outcome of:

(a) 3   **(b)** 6   **(c)** 12

(d) 0   **(e)** An odd number   **(f)** A number divisible by 3

5. Two unbiased four-sided spinners are labelled with the numbers 1, 2, 3 and 4. An experiment consists of spinning them together and the score is calculated by subtracting the smaller number from the larger number. When the numbers are equal the score is 0.

(i) Copy and complete the following sample space diagram to show all possible outcomes.

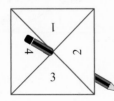

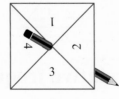

Number on second spinner	4		2		0
	3				
	2			1	
	1				
	–	1	2	3	4

Number on first spinner

(ii) Calculate the probability of a score of:

(a) 0   **(b)** 1   **(c)** 2 or 3

6. A fair die is thrown and a fair spinner is spun. The die is numbered 1 to 6 and the spinner is labelled 1 to 4.

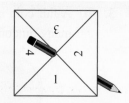

An outcome is achieved by adding the numbers which are face up when the die and spinner come to rest.

(i) List all the outcomes in the sample space diagram and complete the data capture sheet.

4						
3						
2						
1						
+	1	2	3	4	5	6

Outcome	2	3	4	5	6	7	8	9	10
Frequency									

(ii) What is the probability that the outcome is:

    (a) 6   **(b)** 8 or more   **(c)** Prime   **(d)** Divisible by 5

7. **(i)** A game consists of spinning two unbiased spinners, as shown. Using a sample space diagram, or otherwise, list all possible outcomes.

(ii) Find the probability that in any one game the outcome will be:

    (a) An *A* and an odd number

    (b) A *B* or a *C* and an even number

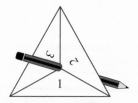

Experimental probability (relative frequency)

Often a probability can only be found by carrying out a series of experiments and recording the results. For example, if you drop a drawing pin and you want to find out the probability that it lands point up, there is no obvious method except by dropping a lot of drawing pins and recording the results. The probability of the event can then be **estimated** from these results. A probability found in this way is known as **experimental probability** or **relative frequency** of an event. Each separate experiment carried out is called a **trial**. To find the relative frequency, the experiment has to be repeated a number of times. It is important to remember that if an experiment is repeated, there will be different outcomes and that increasing the number of times an experiment is repeated generally leads to better estimates of probability.

Estimating probabilities using relative frequency

> The relative frequency of an event in an experiment is given by:
>
> $P(E)$ = relative frequency of an event = $\dfrac{\text{number of successful trials}}{\text{number of trials}}$

Relative frequency can be used to estimate how many times you would **expect** a particular outcome to happen in an experiment.

The expected number of outcomes is calculated as follows:

> Expected number of outcomes = (Relative frequency) × (Number of trials)
>
> or
>
> Expected number of outcomes = P(event) × (number of trials)

Note: To estimate the probability of some events, it is necessary to carry out a survey or look at historical data (past data).

EXAMPLE 1

To estimate the probability that a drawing pin lands point up when dropped, Andrew dropped a drawing pin 50 times and recorded the results in a frequency table, as shown.

	Point up	Point down
Frequency	18	32

(i) Estimate the probability that the drawing pin lands point up.

(ii) If Andrew drops 250 drawing pins, estimate the number of pins that will land point up.

Point up   Point down

Solution:

(i) P(drawing pin lands point up) = $\frac{18}{50} = \frac{9}{25} = 0\cdot36$

(ii) Andrew drops 200 drawing pins.

Expected number of drawing pins landing point up
= P(drawing pin lands point up) × (number of pins)
= $0\cdot36 \times 250 = 90$ drawing pins landing point up

EXAMPLE 2

A six-sided die is thrown 120 times. The results of the trials are shown in the table below.

Score	1	2	3	4	5	6
Frequency	23	8	16	22	13	38

Is the die fair? Give a reason for your answer.

Solution:

The probability of any particular number on a fair die is $\frac{1}{6}$.

The expected frequency of each number = P(event) × (number of trials) = $\frac{1}{6}$ × 120 = 20.

Therefore, we would expect that each number should occur about 20 times. With this die, the frequency of some of the numbers is very different from the expected value of 20. In fact, the number 6 occurs 38 times, almost twice the number of times expected and the number 2 occurs 8 times, less than half the number of times expected.

Thus, we could conclude that this die appears to be unfair or biased in some way. In fact, the die is biased in favour of 6 and biased against 2.

Exercise 15.4

1. Colm found by experiment that he kicked a rugby ball over the post 52 times out of 80 kicks. Estimate the probability that in his next kick he will kick the ball over the post.

2. A light bulb manufacturer tests samples of bulbs to estimate the number that are faulty. From a batch of 10,000 bulbs, 400 were selected at random and it was found that eight were faulty. Based on the sample result, estimate the number of faulty bulbs in the batch.

3. Aideen made a spinner with three colours: yellow, purple and blue. She tested it by spinning it 600 times and recording the results. Her results were as follows.

Colour	Yellow	Purple	Blue
Frequency	247	132	221

   (i) Estimate the probability of the spinner landing on purple.
   (ii) In a game, the spinner is spun 50 times. How many times would you expect the spinner to land on purple?

4. Hilda throws a die and records the number of sixes that she gets after various numbers of throws. She records her results in the following table.

Number of throws	20	50	100	200	500	1,000	2,000
Number of sixes	2	6	13	35	91	160	332

   (i) Calculate the relative frequency of a six at each stage that Hilda recorded.
   (ii) If Hilda threw the die 12,000 times, how many sixes would you expect her to get?

5. A fair spinner is labelled as shown.
   The results of the first 10 spins are:

   P   Q   R   R   Q   S   Q   P   R   S

   (i) Write down the experimental probability of the letter *Q*.

   (ii) As the number of spins increases, what do you expect
   to happen to the experimental probability of *Q*?

6. The results from 40 spins of a number spinner were recorded as follows.

   1 4 3 2 1 1 2 5 4 4 5 4 3 3 2 1 2 3 3 1
   5 4 3 4 2 1 2 3 5 3 4 3 5 1 4 2 3 4 5 2

   (i) Complete the following table.

Number	1	2	3	4	5
Tally					
Frequency					

   (ii) Use these results to estimate the probability of getting a 3 with the next spin.

   (iii) Is the spinner biased? Give a reason for your answer.

7. Catherine made a five-sided spinner. She lettered the sections as shown
   in the diagram. She thought that the spinner wasn't fair, as it seemed to
   land on some letters more than others. She spun the spinner 100 times
   and recorded the results in the table below.

Number	*A*	*B*	*C*	*D*	*E*
Frequency	14	43	8	22	13

   (i) Calculate the experimental probability of each letter.

   (ii) If the spinner was fair, how many times would you expect each letter to occur?

   (iii) Do you think the spinner is fair? Give a reason for your answer.

8. A traffic survey was carried out at a busy intersection for one hour. The results are recorded
   in the following data capture sheet.

Direction	Turn right	Turn left	Straight ahead
Number of vehicles	128	108	164

   (i) How many vehicles were recorded in the survey?

   (ii) Calculate the relative frequency of the vehicles in this survey which (a) turned right
   (b) turned left (c) went straight ahead.

   (iii) If 5,400 vehicles used the intersection during the day, estimate the number of vehicles
   that turned left.

   (iv) Give one reason why these figures may not be accurate.

VAT: Value Added Tax

Value Added Tax (VAT) is a tax on goods and services. The rate of VAT is given in the form of a percentage, for example 15% VAT.

Note: Be careful with VAT, as some prices are given inclusive of VAT (the VAT has already been added on), while other prices are given exclusive of VAT (the VAT has not been added on yet).

EXAMPLE 1

VAT at 21% is added to a bill of €160. Calculate the total bill, including the VAT.

Solution:

Method 1:

$$1\% = \frac{€160}{100} = €1·60$$
$$21\% = €1·60 \times 21 = €33·60$$

Therefore, the total bill is

€160 + €33·60 = €193·60.

Method 2:

As a percentage, the new bill is

100% + 21% = 121% of the bill without VAT

= 121% of €160

= €160 × 1·21 = €193·60

EXAMPLE 2

A garage bill came to €120. When VAT was added to the bill it amounted to €138. Calculate the rate of VAT.

Solution:

VAT added = bill including VAT − bill excluding VAT

= €138 − €120 = €18

$$\text{Rate of VAT} = \frac{\text{VAT added on}}{\text{bill excluding VAT}} \times 100\% = \frac{18}{120} \times 100\% = 15\%$$

Often a price includes VAT and we have to **work in reverse** to calculate the VAT or the price before VAT was added on.

EXAMPLE 3

A garage bill for repairs to a car came to €295·20, including VAT at 23%. Calculate the bill before VAT was added.

Solution:

Think of the bill before VAT was added on as 100%.

$$100\% + 23\% = 123\%$$

Therefore, 123% = €295·20   (equation given in disguise)

       1% = €2·40   (divide both sides by 123)

    100% = €240   (multiply both sides by 100)

Check: 123% of €240 = €240 × 1·23 = €295·20 ✓

Exercise 16.1

Copy and complete the following table, where the bill does not include VAT.

	Bill	VAT rate	VAT	Bill including VAT
1.	€140	10%		
2.	€540	23%		
3.	€600	$12\frac{1}{2}\%$		
4.	€150	$8\frac{1}{2}\%$		
5.	€80			€92
6.	€150			€177
7.	€2,500			€3,075
8.	€145		€11·60	

9. A radio costs €124. How much would it be sold for if the rate of VAT is 23%?

10. A magazine is advertised as €4·20 + VAT. If the VAT rate is 15%, what is the selling price of the magazine?

11. VAT at a rate of $12\frac{1}{2}\%$ is added to an electricity bill of €96. Calculate the bill including the VAT.

12. The price of a watch was €120 + VAT. If the price paid was €134·40, calculate the rate of VAT.

13. An article was priced at €180 + VAT. If a person paid €221·40 for the article, calculate the rate of VAT.

14. A tanker delivered oil to a school. Before the delivery, the meter reading showed 11,360 litres of oil in the tanker. After the delivery, the meter reading was 7,160 litres.

  (i) How many litres of oil were delivered to the school?

  (ii) Calculate the cost of oil delivered if 1 litre of oil costs 81c.

  (iii) When VAT was added to the price of the oil delivered, the bill to the school amounted to €4,116·42. Calculate the rate of VAT added.

15. A bill for €96·76 includes VAT at 18%. Calculate the amount of the bill before VAT is added.

16. A telephone bill, including VAT at 21%, came to €99·22. Calculate the bill before the VAT was added.

17. When a woman bought a television set in a shop, VAT at 21% was added on.

  (i) If the VAT on the cost of the set was €252, what was the price of the television set before VAT was added?

  (ii) What was the price including VAT?

18. A man bought a microwave oven in a shop. The rate of VAT was 18% and the VAT amounted to €75·60. How much in total did he pay for the microwave oven?

19. A boy bought a calculator for €74·75, which included VAT at 15%. Find the price of the calculator if VAT was reduced to 12%.

20. When the rate of VAT was increased from 18% to 23%, the price of a guitar increased by €40. Calculate the price of the guitar, inclusive of the VAT at 23%.

Household bills

Household utility bills are charged by the amount of electricity or gas used within a period of time. The usage is recorded by a meter which is read every month or every two months. The household is then charged for the units they have consumed during that period. A utility bill will show the present and previous meter readings, the rate per unit and any fixed (or standing) charge.

> Number of units used = present meter reading – previous meter reading

> Cost of units used = number of units used × rate per unit

EXAMPLE

Find the values of A, B, C, D and E on the following bill.

Electricity Supply Company

Bill no. 1579

Meter reading		Number of units used	Rate per unit	Description	Amount
Present	**Previous**				
55,347	53,291	A	€0·09	Cost of units used	B
				Standing charge	€4·71
				Total before VAT	C
				VAT at 12%	D
				Total due	E

Solution:

(i) Number of units used = present reading – previous reading

Number of units used = 55,347 – 53,291

Number of units used = 2,056 = A

(ii) Cost of units used = number of units used × rate per unit

Cost of units used = 2,056 × 0·09 = €185·04 = B

(iii) Total before VAT = cost of units used + standing charge

Total before VAT = €185·04 + €4·71 = €189·75 = C

(iv) VAT = 12% of €189·75 = $\frac{12}{100} \times 189·75 = €22·77 = D$

(v) Total due = total before VAT + VAT

Total due = €189·75 + €22·77 = €212·52 = E

Exercise 16.2

1. Find the values of *A*, *B*, *C*, *D* and *E* on the following bill.

Electricity Supply Company

Bill no. 2731

Meter reading		Number of units used	Rate per unit	Description	Amount
Present	Previous				
32,451	29,892	A	€0·08	Cost of units used	B
				Standing charge	€8·78
				Total before VAT	C
				VAT at 14%	D
				Total due	E

2. Find the values of *A*, *B*, *C*, *D* and *E* on the following bill.

Gas Supply Company

Bill no. 2731

Meter reading		Number of units used	Rate per unit	Description	Amount
Present	Previous				
69,751	63,466	A	€0·09	Cost of units used	B
				Standing charge	€11·35
				Total before VAT	C
				VAT at 14%	D
				Total due	E

3. A household electricity meter has a reading of 24,643 on March 1st and a reading of 27,378 on May 1st. The cost per unit is 11c. There is a standing charge of €7·55 and VAT is charged at $12\frac{1}{2}$ %. Calculate the following.

   (i) The number of units used during this two-month period
   (ii) The cost of the units used
   (iii) The total before VAT
   (iv) The total due including VAT

4. Paul has the following pay plan on his mobile phone. For €20 (excluding VAT) a month he gets 150 free minutes and 150 free texts. All additional calls are charged at 22c per minute and all additional texts are charged at 7c per text. VAT of 20% is then added to all charges.

   (i) In March, Paul makes 180 minutes of calls and sends 230 texts.
     Calculate the total of Paul's bill in March.

  (ii) In April, Paul makes 210 minutes of calls and sends 270 texts.
     Calculate the total of Paul's bill in April.

5. Colleen wants to change her mobile phone network. She researches her options and narrows it down to the following two plans.

	Option A	Option B
Standing charge	€18	€12
Free minutes	100	90
Free text messages	120	115
Additional minutes for calls	21c	23c
Additional texts	8c	10c

If Colleen were to make 125 minutes of calls and send 160 texts in a month, which option would work out cheaper for her?

Percentage profit and loss and selling price

Profit and loss are often given as a percentage of the cost price. This is useful when we need to compare profit or loss on different items. Percentage profit or loss is calculated with the following formulae:

$$\text{Percentage profit} = \frac{\text{profit}}{\text{cost price}} \times 100\%$$

$$\text{Percentage loss} = \frac{\text{loss}}{\text{cost price}} \times 100\%$$

Note: It is usual in the business world to express profit or loss as a percentage of the selling price. However, in solving problems in arithmetic, always give profit or loss as a percentage of the cost price, unless instructed to do otherwise.

EXAMPLE

A dealer bought a piano for €4,000 and sold it for €5,000.

(i) Calculate the amount of profit made.

(ii) Express the profit as a percentage of the cost price.

Solution:

(i) Profit = selling price − cost price

Profit = €5,000 − €4,000 = €1,000

(ii) Percentage profit = $\dfrac{\text{profit}}{\text{cost price}} \times 100\% = \dfrac{1{,}000}{4{,}000} \times 100\% = 25\%$

Exercise 16.3

Copy and complete the following table.

	Cost price	Selling price	Profit	Loss	Percentage profit or loss of the cost price
1.	€8	€10		−	
2.	€120	€108	−		
3.	€180	€153	−		
4.		€31·50	−	€3·50	
5.		€508	€108	−	
6.	€100		€24	−	
7.	€120	€114	−		
8.		€91·20	−	€28·80	
9.		€217	−	€31	
10.		€59	€9	−	

11. A dealer bought a table for €80 and sold it for €100. Express the profit as a percentage of the cost price.

12. A motorbike was bought for €1,224 and sold for €1,481·04. Express the profit as a percentage of the cost price.

13. A girl bought a watch for €80 and sold it for €89·60. Find her percentage profit.

14. By selling a car for €11,590 a dealer made a profit of 22%. Calculate how much the dealer paid for the car.

15. A dealer buys a car for €10,850 and marks it up by 18%. Calculate the price she sells the car for.

16. John buys an MP3 player and a year later he sells it, making a 12% loss of €30.

   (i) How much did he pay for the MP3 player?

   (ii) How much did he sell the MP3 player for?

17. A shop decides to sell off last year's stock. If they sell a coat for €72 at a 10% loss, calculate how much the coat cost the shop to buy last year.

18. A transition year mini company sells school calendars for €4·50 each. If this includes a mark-up of 20%, how much did the mini company pay for the calendars?

19. (i) A shopkeeper pays €240 for a bicycle and marks it up so that she makes a profit of 20%. Find the selling price.

   (ii) During a sale, the price of the bicycle is reduced by 15%. Calculate:

     (a) The sale price

     (b) The percentage profit on the bicycle during the sale

20. (i) A car dealer pays €12,500 for a car and marks it up so that he makes a profit of 24%. Find the selling price.

   (ii) After a month, he has still not sold the car, so he reduces its sale price by 8%. Calculate:

     (a) The selling price of the car now

     (b) The new percentage profit on the car, correct to the nearest per cent

Discounts (allowed and received)

A discount is a reduction in the selling price. A discount is typically given to encourage customers to buy a product or to pay for a product in advance or in cash.

$$\text{Percentage discount} = \frac{\text{discount}}{\text{selling price}} \times 100\%$$

EXAMPLE

A retailer is selling a wardrobe for €700.

(i) If he offers a 15% discount, calculate the price after the discount.

(ii) If he reduces the price by €140 instead, calculate the percentage discount in this case.

Solution:

(i) Discount = 15% of €700

Discount = $\frac{15}{100} \times 700 = €105$

Price after discount = €700 − €105 = €595

(ii) Selling price = €700   Discount = €140

Percentage discount = $\dfrac{\text{discount}}{\text{selling price}} \times 100\% = \frac{140}{700} \times 100\% = 20\%$

Exercise 16.4

1. Copy and complete the following table.

	Selling price	% discount	Discount	Price after discount
(i)	€150	6%		
(ii)	€2,300	14%		
(iii)	€420	5%		
(iv)	€12,300	12%		
(v)	€8,200	9·5%		
(vi)	€3,800	21%		

2) Copy and complete the following table.

	Selling price	Discount	% discount	Price after discount
(i)	€400	€80	20	320
(ii)	€1,200	€96	8	1104
(iii)	€130	€13	10	117
(iv)	€3,750	€600	16	3150
(v)	€15,600	€3,900	25	11700
(vi)	€8,250	€1,485	18	6765

3. A dealer is selling a car for €12,000. She offers an 8% discount if the buyer can pay with cash. How much would the car cost after the discount?

4. A clothes shop is having a sale where all the clothes are discounted by 15%. If a coat cost €120 before the discount, calculate its cost after the discount.

5. An electrical shop offers a €21 discount on a €420 television. Calculate the percentage discount.

6. A retailer offers a €35 discount on a €280 chair. Calculate the percentage discount.

7. A school purchases some stationery and gets invoiced as follows.

Stationery Supplies Ltd				
Invoice no. 1542				
Quantity	**Description**		**Unit price**	**Total**
6	Boxes of red pens		€0·90	€5·40
5	Boxes of whiteboard markers		€2·20	€11
7	Photocopy paper		€1·80	€12·60
			Total before VAT	€29
			VAT 20%	€5·80
			Total due	€34·8
Terms: Discount of 5% if total paid within a month				

  (i) Copy and complete the invoice.

  (ii) Calculate the discount received if the school pays within a month.

  (iii) Calculate the price to be paid after the discount.

Currency exchange

Currency is another name for money. In the European Union the unit of currency is called the euro (€).
The method of direct proportion is used to convert one currency into another currency.

Note: Write down the equation given in disguise, putting the currency we want to find on the
right-hand side.

EXAMPLE

On a certain day, €1 = $1·40. Find the value of:
(i) €120 in dollars   (ii) $84 in euro

Solution:

(i)   Given: €1 = $1·40   (dollars on the right because we want our answer to
                                                  be in dollars)

Therefore, €120 = $1·4 × 120   (multiply both sides by 120)

€120 = $168

(ii) Given: $1·40 = €1   (euro on the right because we want out answer in euro)

$1 = € $\frac{1}{1·40}$ (divide both sides by 1·40)

$84 = € $\frac{1}{1·40}$ × 84   (multiply both sides by 84)

$84 = €60   (simplify the right-hand side)

Exercise 16.5

1. If €1 = $1·50, find the value of: (i) €100 in dollars   (ii) $180 in euro

2. A train ticket costs €40. How much would the ticket cost in Canadian dollars if €1 = $2·25?

3. A ticket to a football game costs €25. How much does the ticket cost in US dollars if €1 = $1·60?

4. An airline ticket costs $416. If €1 = $1·30, calculate the cost of the ticket in euro.

5. If €1 = ¥320 (Japanese yen), convert ¥27,200 to euro.

6. If €1 = $1·20 (US), €1 = $2·76 (Canadian) and €1 = ¥331·2:

    (i) How many US dollars would you get for €40?

    (ii) How many Canadian dollars would you get for €350?

    (iii) How many Japanese yen would you get for €180?

    (iv) How many euro would you get for 90 US dollars?

    (v) How many euro would you get for 1,380 Canadian dollars?

    (vi) How many euro would you get for 238,464 Japanese yen?

7. Calculate the exchange rate for €1 in each case given the following transactions.

    (i) €80 for $112 (US)   (ii) €75 for $165 (Canadian)

8. A CD costs €28·50 in Ireland and the same CD costs ¥9,600 in Japan.

   If €1 = ¥320, in which country is it cheaper and by how much (in euro)?

9. A calculator costs $104 in the United States and $157·50 in Canada.

   If $1·30 (US) = €1 = $2·10 (Canadian), in which country is it cheaper and by how much (in euro)?

10. A part for a machine costs €750 in Germany and the same part costs R1,650 in South Africa. If €1 = R2·4, in which country is it cheaper and by how much (in euro)?

11. A tourist changed €800 on board a ship into South African rand at a rate of €1 = R2·4.

    (i) How many rand did she receive?

    (ii) When she came ashore she found that the rate was €1 = R2·48. How much did she lose, in rand, by not changing her money ashore?

Interest

Interest is the sum of money that you pay for borrowing money or that is paid to you for lending money. When dealing with interest, we use the following symbols.

P = the **principal**,
   the sum of money borrowed or invested at the beginning of the period.

t = the **time**,
   the number of weeks/months/years for which the sum of money is borrowed or invested.

i = the **interest rate**,
   the percentage rate per week/month/year expressed as a fraction or a decimal at which interest is charged.

A = the **amount**,
   the amount of money, including interest, at the end of a week/month/year.

F = the **final amount**,
   the final sum of money, including interest, at the end of the period.

Note: per annum = per year.

Compound interest

Very often when a sum of money earns interest, this interest is added to the principal to form a new principal. This new principal earns interest in the next year and so on. This is called **compound interest**.

When calculating compound interest, do the following.

Method 1:

Calculate the interest for the first year and add this to the principal to form the new principal for the next year. Calculate the interest for one year on this new principal and add it on to form the principal for the next year, and so on. The easiest way to calculate each stage is to multiply the principal at the beginning of each year by the factor:

$$(1 + i)$$

This will give the principal for the next year, and so on.

Method 2:

Sometimes using a formula and a calculator can be much quicker.

Use the formula $F = P(1 + i)^t$.

Note: The formula does not work if:

(i) The interest rate, i, is changed during the period.

(ii) Money is added or subtracted during the period.

Annual equivalent rate (AER) and annual percentage rate (APR)

Nowadays, if you put your money into a savings account or into an investment, you should be given the annual equivalent rate (AER). You may have invested your money for any period of time but the AER tells you how much your money would earn in **exactly one year**. For example, suppose a bank offers you a five-year deal: 4% interest for the first six months followed by 2% for each month of the remainder of the time. It will be much simpler to compare this deal with others if you can compare them on some common standard. The AER would, in this case, give you one simple annual percentage to use for comparison.

When borrowing money, there are often other costs involved, such as a set-up fee. Because these other costs can be significant, lenders are expected to tell the borrower the annual percentage rate (APR). This allows a potential borrower to compare different loans and see which is more expensive.

Note: AER is used when investing money in savings.

APR is used when borrowing money as a loan.

Both use the method of compound interest.

EXAMPLE

Calculate the compound interest on €2,500 for three years at 6% per annum.

Solution:

$1 + i = 1 + 0.06 = 1.06$

Method 1:

$P_1 = 2,500$

$A_1 = 2,500 \times 1.06 = 2,650$

$P_2 = 2,650$

$A_2 = 2,650 \times 1.06 = 2,809$

$P_3 = 2,809$

$A_3 = 2,809 \times 1.06 = 2,977.54$

Compound interest $= A_3 - P_1 = €2,977.54 - €2,500 = €477.54$

The working can also be shown using a table:

Year	Principal	Amount
1	2,500	$2,500 \times 1.06 = 2,650$
2	2,650	$2,650 \times 1.06 = 2,809$
3	2,809	$2,809 \times 1.06 = 2,977.54$
Compound interest $= A_3 - P_1 = €2,977.54 - €2,500 = €477.54$		

Method 2:

Given: $P = 2,500$, $i = \frac{6}{100} = 0.06$, $t = 3$. Find F.

$$F = P(1 + i)^t$$
$$F = 2,500(1 + 0.06)^3$$
$$F = 2,500(1.06)^3$$
$$F = 2,977.54$$

Compound interest $= F - P = 2,977.54 - 2,500 = €477.54$

Note: In this example, the final amount is $F = A_3$.

Exercise 16.6

Calculate the compound interest on each of the investments in questions 1–16.

1. €500 for two years at 6% per annum

2. €4,000 for two years at 5% per annum

3. €2,500 for two years at 8% per annum

4. €3,600 for two years at 7% per annum

5. €800 for two years at 4% per annum

6. €1,200 for two years at 3% per annum

7. €800 for two years at 10% per annum

8. €3,000 for two years at 8% per annum

9. €350 for three years at 10% per annum   10. €2,500 for three years at 8% per annum

11. €4,000 for three years at 5% per annum   12. €10,000 for three years at 6% per annum

13. €80 for three years at 5% per annum   14. €20,000 for three years at 4% per annum

15. €15,000 for three years at 12% per annum   16. €25,000 for three years at 6% per annum

17. A person invests €12,400 at 6·5% per annum compound interest for two years.

What does the investment amount to at the end of (i) one year (ii) two years?

18. A man borrowed €7,500 at an annual percentage rate (APR) of 8%. He agreed to pay back the entire loan, including interest, after three years. How much did he pay back?

19. (i) A woman invests €12,500 for three years at an annual equivalent rate (AER) of 6%.

Calculate the interest earned in (a) the first year (b) the second year (c) the third year.

(ii) How much is her investment worth at the end of the three years?

20. (i) €10,000 is invested for one year at an AER of 4%. Calculate the interest earned.

(ii) The initial €10,000 and the interest earned for the year are reinvested for another two years at an AER of 4%. Calculate the value of the investment at the end of the three years.

21. Post office savings certificates pay an AER of 3% if the money is invested for three years. How much would €20,000 amount to if invested with the post office for three years?

22. (i) €4,000 is invested for one year and amounts to €4,200. Calculate the annual rate of interest, *i*.

(ii) The €4,200 is then invested at *i*% per annum compound interest for two years. Calculate the total interest earned for the three years of the investment.

Compound interest when the rate changes

In some questions the annual interest rate changes each year. When this happens it is important to remember that the formula does not work. Consider the next example.

 EXAMPLE

€8,500 was invested for three years at compound interest. The rate for the first year was 6%, the rate for the second year was 8% and the rate for the third year was 5%.

Calculate the amount at the end of the third year and the compound interest earned.

Solution:

The rate changes every year, therefore we cannot use the formula.

$P_1 = 8{,}500$

$A_1 = 8{,}500 \times 1 \cdot 06 = 9{,}010$ $\qquad \left(1 + i_1 = 1 + \frac{6}{100} = 1 + 0 \cdot 06 = 1 \cdot 06\right)$

$P_2 = 9{,}010$

$A_2 = 9{,}010 \times 1 \cdot 08 = 9{,}730 \cdot 80$ $\qquad \left(1 + i_2 = 1 + \frac{8}{100} = 1 + 0 \cdot 08 = 1 \cdot 08\right)$

$P_3 = 9{,}730 \cdot 80$

$A_3 = 9{,}730 \cdot 80 \times 1 \cdot 05 = 10{,}217 \cdot 34$ $\qquad \left(1 + i_3 = 1 + \frac{5}{100} = 1 + 0 \cdot 05 = 1 \cdot 05\right)$

Therefore, the final amount after three years is $F = A_3 = €10{,}217 \cdot 34$.

Compound interest $= A_3 - P_1 = €10{,}217 \cdot 34 - €8{,}500 = €1{,}717 \cdot 34$.

The working can also be shown using a table.

Year	Principal	Amount
1	8,500	$8{,}500 \times 1 \cdot 06 = 9{,}010$
2	9,010	$9{,}010 \times 1 \cdot 08 = 9{,}730 \cdot 80$
3	9,730·80	$9{,}730 \cdot 80 \times 1 \cdot 05 = 10{,}217 \cdot 34$
Compound interest $= A_3 - P_1 = €10{,}217 \cdot 34 - €8{,}500 = €1{,}717 \cdot 34$		

Alternatively:

$F = A_3 = €8{,}500 \times 1 \cdot 06 \times 1 \cdot 08 \times 1 \cdot 05 = €10{,}217 \cdot 34$

Compound interest $= A_3 - P_1 = €10{,}217 \cdot 34 - €8{,}500 = €1{,}717 \cdot 34$

Exercise 16.7

1. €8,000 was invested for two years at compound interest. The interest rate for the first year was 4% and for the second was 5%. Calculate the total interest earned.

2. A person invested €3,500 at compound interest for two years. The interest rate for the first year was 5% and for the second was 7%. Calculate the total interest earned.

3. A man borrowed €10,000 at compound interest for two years. The interest rate for the first year was 8% and for the second was 6%. He agreed to pay off the loan, including the interest, after two years. Calculate how much he needed to pay to clear the loan.

4. A woman invested €5,000 at compound interest for two years. The interest rate for the first year was 3% and for the second was 4%. Calculate the value of her investment at the end of two years.

5. €6,500 was invested for three years at compound interest. The interest rate for the first year was 5%, for the second year 8% and for the third year 12%. Calculate the total interest earned.

6. €7,500 was invested for three years. The AER for the first year was 6%, the AER for the second year was 8% and the AER for the third year was 5%. Calculate the total interest earned.

7. €15,000 was invested for three years. The AER for the first year was 8%, the AER for the second year was 12% and the AER for the third year was 9%. Calculate the amount after three years.

8. €2,500 was invested for three years. The AER for the first year was 4%, the AER for the second year was 3% and the AER for the third year was $2\frac{1}{2}$%. Calculate the amount after three years.

Repayments

In some questions money is repaid at the end of a year. Again, it is important to remember that in this case the **formula does not work**.

Consider the next example, where r_1 = repayment at the end of year 1 and r_2 = repayment at the end of year 2.

EXAMPLE

A person borrowed €6,000 at 12% per annum compound interest. If they repay €2,000 at the end of each year, how much is outstanding after the second repayment?

Solution:

$1 + i = 1 + \frac{12}{100} = 1 + 0 \cdot 12 = 1 \cdot 12$

$P_1 = 6,000$

$A_1 = 6,000 \times 1 \cdot 12$

$\quad = 6,720$

$r_1 = 2,000$

$\overline{}$

$P_2 = 4,720 \qquad \text{(subtract } r_1\text{)}$

$A_2 = 4,720 \times 1 \cdot 12$

$\quad = 5,286 \cdot 40$

$r_2 = 2,000 \cdot 00$

$\overline{}$

$\quad = 3,286 \cdot 40 \qquad \text{(subtract } r_2\text{)}$

Therefore, the amount outstanding after two years is €3,286·40.

Exercise 16.8

1. A man borrowed €8,000 at 5% per annum compound interest. If he repays €2,000 at the end of each year, how much is outstanding after the second repayment?

2. A woman borrowed €5,000 at 8% per annum compound interest. If she repays €1,500 at the end of each year, how much is outstanding after the second repayment?

3. A man borrowed €7,500 at 6% per annum compound interest. If he repays €1,500 at the end of each year, how much is outstanding after the second repayment?

4. A man borrowed €10,000 at an APR of 3%. He agreed to repay €2,000 after one year and a further €3,000 at the end of two years. How much is outstanding after the second repayment?

5. A woman borrowed €4,000 at an APR of 8%. She agreed to repay €1,000 after one year and a further €1,500 at the end of two years. How much is outstanding after the second repayment?

Income tax

Income tax is a tax charged by the government on all employment-related income. Income tax is charged at two different rates. The standard rate is charged on income up to, and including, a standard cut-off point. Any income above this standard cut-off is charged at a higher rate.

Tax credits are a reduction in the tax you have to pay. The tax office will notify each individual of their standard cut-off point and their tax credits, which can vary each year. They will also be notified of the tax rates on gross income, which can also vary from year to year.

On our course, we will **only** be dealing with situations where the **income is below or equal to the standard cut-off point**.

The following is called the **income tax equation**:

$$\text{Gross tax} - \text{tax credits} = \text{tax payable}$$

Gross income is the amount of money earned before any deductions are made.

Net income (also called take-home pay) is the amount of money left after all deductions have been taken away.

$$\text{Net income} = \text{gross income} - \text{tax paid}$$

EXAMPLE

A man has a gross yearly income of €25,000. He has a standard rate cut-off point of €28,000 and a tax credit of €1,250. The standard rate of tax is 18% of income up to the standard rate cut-off point.

(i) Calculate the amount of gross tax for the year.

(ii) Calculate the amount of tax paid for the year.

(iii) Calculate the net income for the year.

(iv) Express tax paid for the year as a percentage of gross income for the year.

Solution:

(i) Gross tax = 18% of €25,000 = $\frac{18}{100} \times 25{,}000$ = €4,500

(ii) Income tax equation:

Gross tax − tax credits = tax payable

€4,500 − €1,250 = €3,250

Therefore, the amount of tax paid = €3,250.

(iii) Net income = gross income − tax paid

Net income = €25,000 − €3,250 = €21,750

(iv) Tax paid as a percentage of gross income = $\dfrac{\text{tax paid}}{\text{gross income}} \times 100\%$

$= \frac{3{,}250}{25{,}000} \times 100\% = 13\%$

Exercise 16.9

1. John has a gross yearly income of €15,000. He has a standard rate cut-off point of €18,000 and a tax credit of €2,000. The standard rate of tax is 20% of income up to the standard rate cut-off point. Use this information to copy and complete the following table.

Gross income	€15,000
Gross tax (tax at 20%)	
Tax credit	€2,000
Tax paid	
Net income (take-home pay)	

Copy and complete the following table, which shows the yearly income for nine people.

	Gross income	Standard rate cut-off point	Standard rate of tax	Gross tax	Tax credit	Tax paid	Net income
2.	€23,000	€25,800	20%		€2,600		
3.	€17,500	€21,200	18%		€2,250		
4.	€24,500	€26,800	19%		€2,155		
5.	€18,000	€21,700	22%		€1,890		
6.	€19,400	€20,300	17%		€2,728		
7.	€18,200	€19,700	16%		€1,852		
8.	€22,580	€25,300	20%		€2,813		
9.	€19,570	€22,000	21%		€2,082		
10.	€21,150	€23,450	22%		€1,194		

11. Kate has a gross yearly income of €22,000. She has a standard cut-off point of €25,000 and a tax credit of €3,300. The standard rate of tax is 20% of income up to the standard cut-off point.

   (i) Calculate the amount of gross tax per year.

   (ii) Calculate the amount of tax paid for the year.

   (iii) Calculate net income for the year.

   (iv) Express the tax paid for the year as a percentage of gross income for the year.

12. Brian has a gross yearly income of €19,000. He has a standard cut-off point of €23,400 and a tax credit of €2,090. The standard rate of tax is 18% of income up to the standard cut-off point.

   (i) Calculate the amount of gross tax per year.

   (ii) Calculate the amount of tax paid for the year.

   (iii) Calculate net income for the year.

   (iv) Express the tax paid for the year as a percentage of gross income for the year.

13. Clodagh has a gross yearly income of €25,400. She has a standard cut-off point of €28,320 and a tax credit of €3,302. The standard rate of tax is 17% of income up to the standard cut-off point.

   (i) Calculate the amount of gross tax per year.

   (ii) Calculate the amount of tax paid for the year.

   (iii) Calculate net income for the year.

   (iv) Clodagh's employer deducts her annual health insurance of €550 from her net income. Calculate her take-home pay after all deductions.

14. Sean has a gross yearly income of €29,500. He has a standard cut-off point of €30,000 and a tax credit of €3,100. The standard rate of tax is 21% of income up to the standard cut-off point. Each year Sean's union fees are €350, his health insurance is €520 and he puts €750 into savings.

   (i) Calculate the amount of gross tax per year.

   (ii) Calculate the amount of tax paid for the year.

   (iii) Calculate net income for the year after all deductions.

15. Laura has a gross yearly income of €21,720. She has a standard cut-off point of €24,500 and a tax credit of €1,840. The standard rate of tax is 18% of income up to the standard cut-off point. Each year Laura's union fees are €280, her health insurance is €490 and she puts €620 into savings.

   (i) Calculate the amount of gross tax per year.

   (ii) Calculate the amount of tax paid for the year.

   (iii) Calculate take-home pay after all deductions.

16. Helen's weekly wage is €750. The standard cut-off point is €800 and the standard rate of tax is 18%. If she has a weekly tax credit of €54, calculate how much tax Helen pays each week and hence her weekly gross income.

17. Damien's weekly wage is €620. The standard cut-off point is €700 and the standard rate of tax is 21%. If he has a weekly tax credit of €48, calculate how much tax Damien pays each week and hence his weekly gross income.

18. When the standard rate of tax is 18%, a woman with a tax credit of €2,348 pays €2,080 in tax. If her gross income for the year was below her standard cut-off point, calculate her gross income for the year.

19. When the standard rate of tax is 16%, a person with a tax credit of €1,992 pays €2,616 in tax. If their gross income for the year was below their standard cut-off point, calculate their gross income for the year.

Perimeter and area

> The **perimeter**, P, of a figure is the distance around its edges.

The perimeter is found by adding together the lengths of all the sides. It is measured in length units such as metres (m) or centimetres (cm).

> The **area**, A, of a figure is the amount of flat surface it contains.

Area is measured in square units such as square metres (m^2) or square centimetres (cm^2).

> When calculating perimeters or areas, make sure that all distances are in the same unit.

Area and perimeter are vital concepts to understand and apply in a wide variety of situations and careers, e.g. planning and designing a new shopping complex.

Rectangle, square and triangle

Formulas required (A = area, l = length, b = breadth):

Rectangle

$A = lb$
$P = 2l + 2b$

Square

$A = l^2$
$P = 4l$

Parallelogram

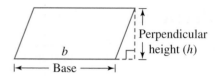

Area = base × perpendicular height
$= bh$

Triangle (three cases)

1.

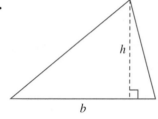

2.

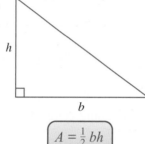

$$A = \tfrac{1}{2} bh$$

3.

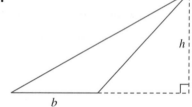

b = base h = perpendicular height

Notes: In case 1, the perpendicular height is inside the triangle.

In case 2, a right-angled triangle, the perpendicular height is one of the sides.

In case 3, the perpendicular height is outside the triangle.

EXAMPLE 1

(i) Find the area of the parallelogram *ABCD*.

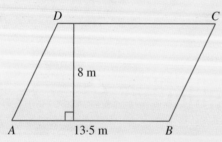

(ii) The area of parallelogram *PQRS* is 90 cm^2 and $|PQ| = 15$ cm.

Calculate the perpendicular height, *h* cm, of the parallelogram.

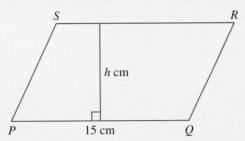

Solution:

(i) Area = (base)(perpendicular height) = $8 \times 13 \cdot 5 = 108$ m^2

(ii) Given: Area = 90   (equation given in disguise)

$b \times h = 90$

∴ $15\,h = 90$ (area = base × perpendicular height)

$h = 6$ (divide both sides by 15)

∴ The perpendicular height of the parallelogram is 6 cm.

EXAMPLE 2

Find the area of each of the following triangles (all dimensions are in centimetres).

(i)

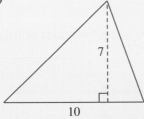

(ii)

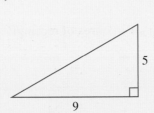

(iii)

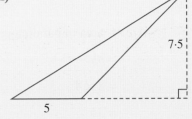

Solution:

(i) $A = \frac{1}{2}bh$

$= \frac{1}{2}(10)(7)$

$= 35$ cm^2

(ii) $A = \frac{1}{2}bh$

$= \frac{1}{2}(9)(5)$

$= 22 \cdot 5$ cm^2

(iii) $A = \frac{1}{2}bh$

$= \frac{1}{2}(5)(7 \cdot 5)$

$= 18 \cdot 75$ cm^2

When two or more shapes are joined together, these shapes are called compound shapes.

EXAMPLE 3

Find the area of the compound shape shown below, where all dimensions are in cm.

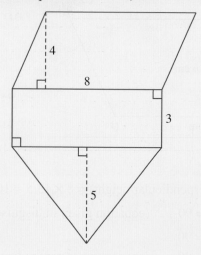

Solution:

Split the figure up into regular shapes, for which we have formulas to calculate the area.

Find the area of each shape separately and add these results together.

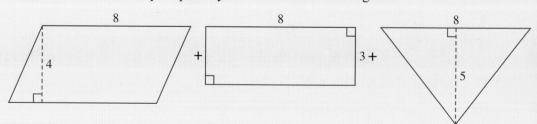

Area = area of parallelogram	+	area of rectangle	+	area of triangle
= bh	+	lb	+	$\frac{1}{2}bh$
= 8×4	+	8×3	+	$\frac{1}{2} \times 8 \times 5$
= 32	+	24	+	20
= 76 cm^2				

Exercise 17.1

Copy and complete the following table, which gives certain information for various rectangles.

	Length	Breadth	Area	Perimeter
1.	8 cm	4 cm	32 cm²	24 cm
2.	10 m	6 m	60 cm²	32 cm
3.	12 cm	8 cm	96 cm²	40 cm
4.	20 m	15 m	300 cm²	70 cm
5.	30 cm	20 cm	600 cm²	100 cm
6.	18 m	12 m	216 cm²	60 cm

In questions 7–12, find (i) the area and (ii) the perimeter of the squares whose sides are of the following length.

7. 5 cm 8. 8 m 9. 10 cm 10. 12 m 11. 2·5 cm 12. 4·5 m

In questions 13–15, find (i) the perimeter and (ii) the area of each of the following figures (all dimensions are in centimetres).

13.

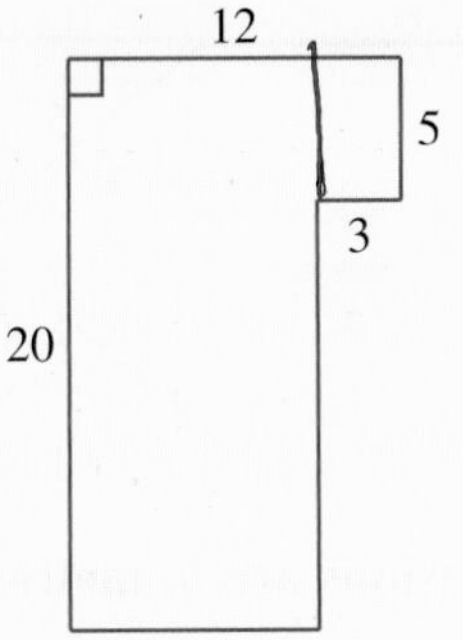

14.

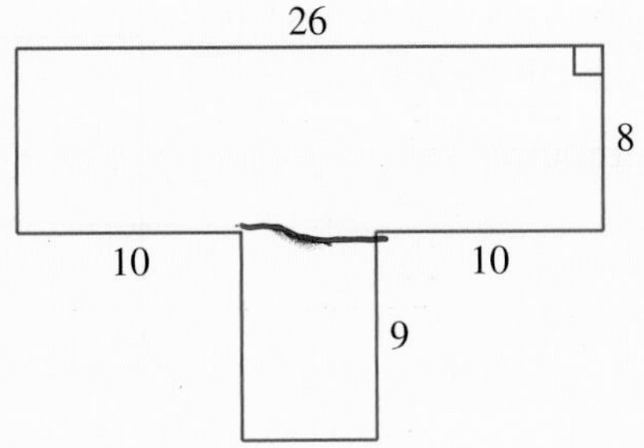

15.

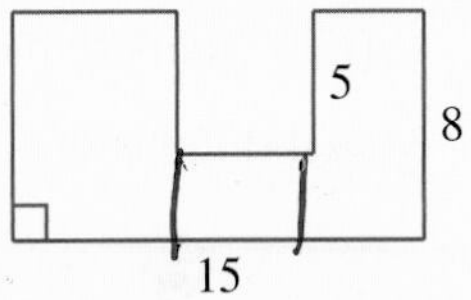

Calculate the area of each of the following in questions 16–21.

16.

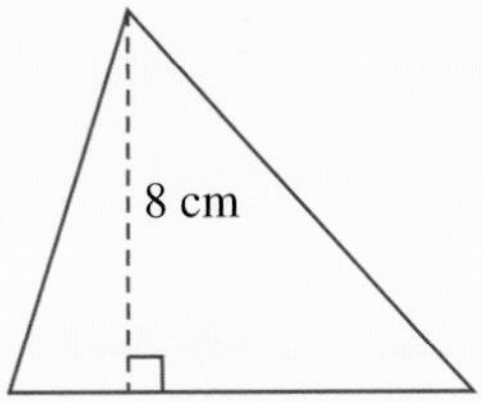

17.

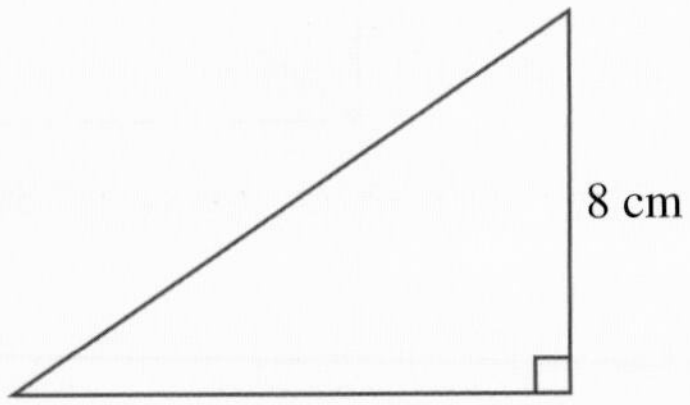

18.

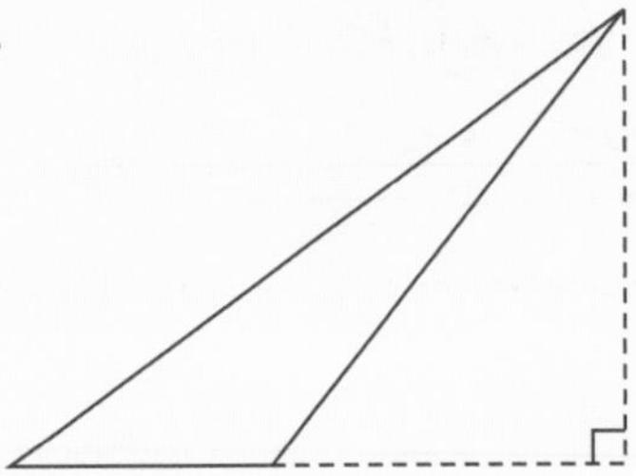

19.　　　　　　**20.**　　　　　　**21.**

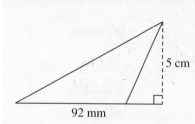 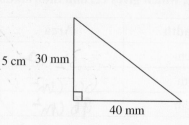 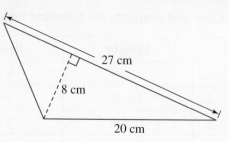

22. Find the area of each of the following parallelograms.

(i)　　　　　　**(ii)**　　　　　　　　　　**(iii)**

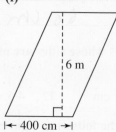 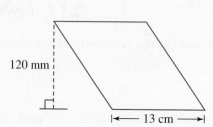 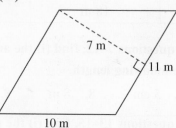

23. **(i)** Calculate the perimeter of the figure shown.

(ii) Calculate the area of the figure shown.

(All dimensions are in centimetres.)

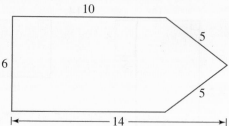

Calculate the area of the shaded regions in questions 24–30 (all dimensions are in metres).

24.　　　　　　　　　　　　　　**25.**

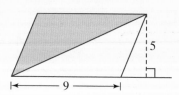 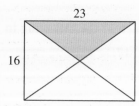

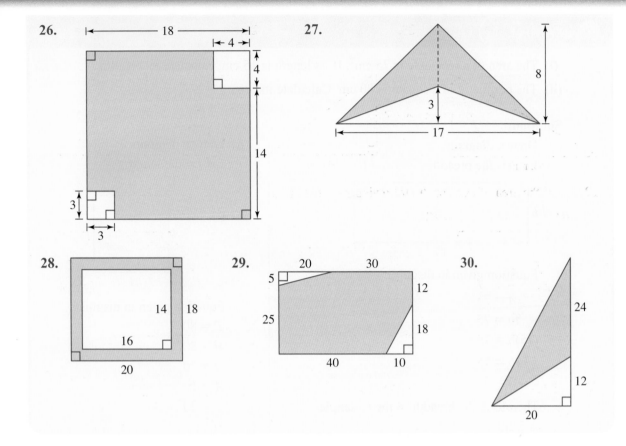

Given the perimeter of an area to find the missing lengths

In some questions we are given the perimeter or area and asked to find the missing lengths.

When solving this type of problem, do the following.

> **1.** Draw a diagram.
>
> **2.** Label the unknown length.
>
> **3.** Write down the equation given in disguise.
>
> **4.** Solve this equation.

EXAMPLE 1

(i) The area of a rectangle is 75 cm². If its length is 15 cm, calculate its breadth.

(ii) The perimeter of a square is 80 cm. Calculate its area.

Solution:

(i) Draw a diagram.

Let b = the breadth.

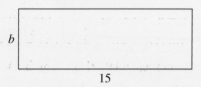

Equation given in disguise:

$$A = 75$$
$$lb = 75$$
$$(15)b = 75$$
$$15b = 75$$
$$b = 5$$

Therefore, the breadth of the rectangle is 5 cm.

(ii) Draw a diagram.

Let l = the length.

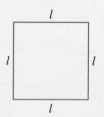

Equation given in disguise:

$$P = 80$$
$$4l = 80$$
$$l = 20$$
$$A = l^2$$
$$= 20^2 = 400$$

Therefore, the area of the square is 400 cm².

EXAMPLE 2

The area of a triangle is 44 cm².

If the base is 11 cm, calculate its perpendicular height, h.

Solution:

Equation given in disguise: $A = 44$

$$\tfrac{1}{2}bh = 44$$

$$\tfrac{1}{2}(11)h = 44 \quad \text{(put in 11 for } b\text{)}$$

$$11h = 88 \quad \text{(multiply both sides by 2)}$$

$$h = 8 \quad \text{(divide both sides by 11)}$$

∴ The height is 8 cm.

Exercise 17.2

The table shows certain information on rectangles for questions 1–4. In each case, write down the equation given in disguise and use the equation to find the missing dimensions.

	Length	Breadth	Area	Perimeter
1.		4 m	20 m^2	
2.	5 m		35 m^2	
3.		3 m		14 m
4.	10 m			32 m

5. The area of a rectangle is 96 cm^2. If its breadth is 8 cm, calculate **(i)** its length and **(ii)** its perimeter.

6. The perimeter of a rectangle is 28 cm. If its length is 9 cm, calculate its area.

7. The perimeter of a square is 20 cm. Calculate **(i)** its length and **(ii)** its area.

8. The area of a square is 36 m^2. Calculate **(i)** its length and **(ii)** its perimeter.

In questions 9–11, find the perpendicular height in each case where the base and area are given (all dimensions are in centimetres).

9.   **10.**   **11.**

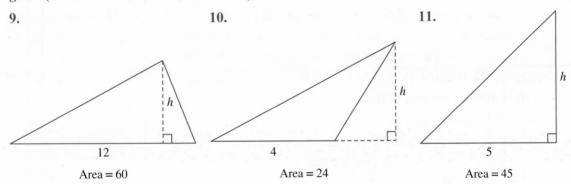

12	4	5
Area = 60	Area = 24	Area = 45

12. The area of a triangle with base 8 cm is 24 cm^2. Find its perpendicular height.

13. The area of a triangle with perpendicular height 3 cm is 18 cm^2. Find the length of its base.

14. The rectangle and the triangle have an equal area. Find h.

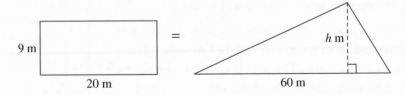

231

Solving problems in context

EXAMPLE

A rectangular patio is 8 m long and 5 m wide. The patio is covered with square paving slabs with sides of length 25 cm. Calculate the number of slabs required to cover the patio.

Solution:

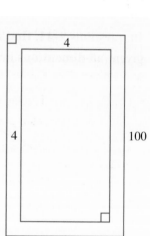

Change all dimensions to the smaller unit, centimetres.

8 m = 800 cm and 5 m = 500 cm

Area of patio = 800 × 500 = 400,000 cm²

Area of one slab = 25 × 25 = 625 cm²

Number of paving slabs = $\dfrac{\text{area of patio}}{\text{area of one slab}} = \dfrac{400,000}{625} = 640$

Exercise 17.3

(Remember: If necessary, change all lengths to the same unit.)

1. A rectangular plot of ground 100 m long and 60 m wide is surrounded by a fence. A path 4 m wide is laid around the edge, inside the fence. The path is covered with square paving slabs with side of length 2 m, costing €25 each.

   (i) Calculate the area of the plot of land.
   (ii) Calculate the area of the path.
   (iii) Calculate the number of paving slabs required to cover the path and the cost of the paving slabs.

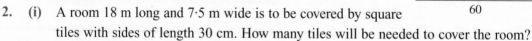

2. (i) A room 18 m long and 7·5 m wide is to be covered by square tiles with sides of length 30 cm. How many tiles will be needed to cover the room?

   (ii) The tiles are sold in boxes of 100 at a cost of €150 a box. Calculate the cost of the tiles.

3. A rectangular metal plate measuring 3 m by 1·5 m is cut up into small squares with sides of length 15 cm. How many squares will be cut?

4. A rectangular lawn is surrounded by a path. The lawn is 40 m long and 20 m wide. The path is 1 m wide. (The diagram is not to scale.) The path is covered with square paving slabs with sides of length 50 cm.

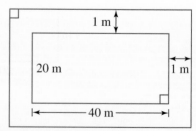

    (i)   Calculate the area of the lawn.

    (ii) Calculate the area of the path.

    (iii) Calculate the number of paving slabs required to cover the path.

5. The floor of a room 15 m long by 12 m wide is to be covered with tiles. Each tile is a square of length 20 cm.

    (i)   Find the number of tiles required to cover the floor.

    (ii) If each tile costs €2·80, find the cost of the tiles.

    (iii) If other materials and labour cost €1·10 per tile, find the cost of tiling the floor.

6. (i)   Paint is sold in litre tins costing €25·40 per litre. A wall is 60 m long and 2·5 m high. How many litres of paint are required to paint one side of the wall if one litre of paint will cover 7·5 m^2?

    (ii) Calculate the cost of the paint.

7. A rectangular bungalow measures 18 m long by 8·5 m wide. How much will it cost to put a concrete path measuring 1·5 m wide all round the bungalow at a cost of €30 per square metre?

8. Sheets of plywood measure 2·5 m × 1·2 m.

Shelves measuring 80 cm × 30 cm must be cut from sheets like this.

    (i) On the diagram, sketch out how a sheet can be cut so as to get as many shelves as possible.

    (ii) Write down the number of shelves.

    (iii) How many sheets must be bought if 30 shelves are needed? (Only full sheets can be bought.)

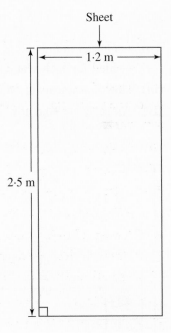

Sheet

1·2 m

2·5 m

9. A drama group is putting on a play in the local community hall. Below is a plan of the hall.

   (i) What is the area, in m², of seating area A and of seating area B?

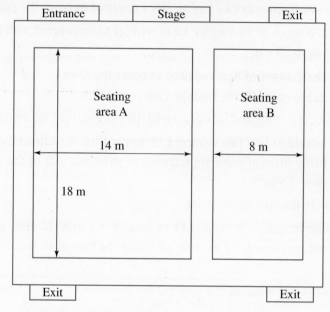

   (ii) Each seat in the hall needs a space of 80 cm × 50 cm. Calculate the area of space needed for each seat. Give your answer in m².

   (iii) How many seats in total fit into seating areas A and B?

   (iv) All seats are sold at €8·50 each. How much money does this raise?

10.

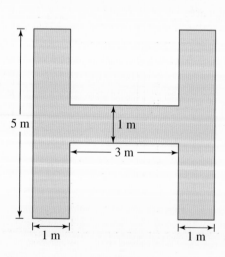

Design A

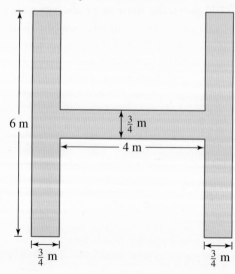

Design B

Nina, a health and safety officer, must choose one of the above designs for a helipad. She knows the bigger the coloured area, the more effective the design from a safety viewpoint.

Which design should she choose? Justify your answer.

11. **(i)** Five identical parallelograms are joined to make the shape shown in the diagram.

The perpendicular height of each parallelogram is 12 m.

If the total area of the shape is 795 m², find the length, a.

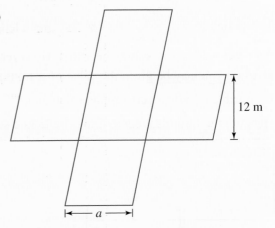

(ii) The diagram represents a flower garden with given dimensions as in part **(i)**. The shaded sections are planted with tulip bulbs. One tulip bulb is planted for every 0·04 m² of shaded area.

How many tulip bulbs are planted?

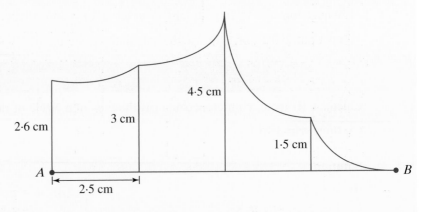

12. The diagram shows a flat piece of plastic produced by a factory (diagram not to scale).

The offsets of lengths 2·6 cm, 3 cm, 4·5 cm and 1·5 cm are measured at equal intervals of 2·5 cm along [AB].

Find, in cm², the area of the smallest rectangular sheet of plastic from which this piece can be cut.

Circumference and area of a circle

The length of the perimeter of a circle is called the **circumference**.

Part of the circumference is called an **arc**.

The value of $\dfrac{\text{circumference}}{\text{diameter}} = \pi$ (the Greek letter pi) and is the same value for all circles.

An exact value for π cannot be stated. However, the usual approximations are $\pi = 3\cdot14$ or $\pi = \frac{22}{7}$. In an exam you may be given the value of π to use.

If no value of pi is given, use the calculator.

Here are the formulas required for circles and sectors of circles.

Circle (area)	Sector of a circle
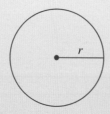	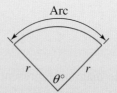
Area $= \pi r^2$	Area $= \dfrac{\theta}{360} \times \pi r^2$
Circumference $= 2\pi r$	
See these formulae in the formulae and tables booklet.	Length of arc $= \dfrac{\theta}{360} \times 2\pi r$
	(similar to circle with $\dfrac{\theta}{360}$ in front of formulas)

Notes: 1. When using $\pi = \frac{22}{7}$, it is good practice to write the radius as a fraction.

For example, $21 = \frac{21}{1}$ or $10\cdot5 = \frac{21}{2}$.

2. If a question says 'give your answer in terms of π', then leave π in the answer: do not put in $3\cdot14$ or $\frac{22}{7}$ or use the calculator value for π.

EXAMPLE 1

Calculate **(i)** the circumference and **(ii)** the area of a circle of radius 8 cm.
(Assume $\pi = 3\cdot14$.)

Solution:

(i) $C = 2\pi r$
$\qquad = 2 \times 3\cdot14 \times 8$
$\qquad = 50\cdot24$

Therefore, the circumference is 50·24 cm.

(ii) $A = \pi r^2$
$\qquad = 3\cdot14 \times 8 \times 8$
$\qquad = 200\cdot96$

Therefore, the area is 200·96 cm^2.

EXAMPLE 2

The diagram shows a sector of a circle.

(i) Calculate the area of the sector.

(ii) Calculate the length of the arc PQ.

(Assume $\pi = \frac{22}{7}$.)

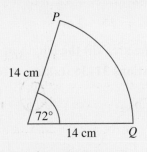

14 cm

72°

14 cm Q

Solution:

(i)   Area of sector

$= \dfrac{\theta}{360} \pi r^2$

$= \dfrac{72}{360} \times \dfrac{22}{7} \times \dfrac{14}{1} \times \dfrac{14}{1}$

↑   ↑

(fraction) × (area of full circle)

$= \dfrac{1}{5} \times \dfrac{22}{7} \times \dfrac{14}{1} \times \dfrac{14}{1}$

$= 123\frac{1}{5}$ or 123.2

Therefore, the area of the sector $= 123\frac{1}{5}$ cm^2 or 123.2 cm^2.

(ii)   Length of arc PQ

$= \dfrac{\theta}{360} \times 2\pi r$

$= \dfrac{72}{360} \times \dfrac{2}{1} \times \dfrac{22}{7} \times \dfrac{14}{1}$

↑   ↑

(fraction) × (full circumference)

$= \dfrac{1}{5} \times \dfrac{2}{1} \times \dfrac{22}{7} \times \dfrac{14}{1}$

$= 17\frac{3}{5}$ or 17.6

Therefore, the length of the arc PQ $= 17\frac{3}{5}$ cm or 17.6 cm.

Exercise 17.4

Taking π to be 3.14, calculate the circumference and area of a circle with the given radius in questions 1–10.

1. 5 cm   2. 10 m   3. 20 mm   4. 12 cm   5. 6 m

6. 4 mm   7. 13 cm   8. 30 cm   9. 8.5 m   10. 2.5 cm

Taking π to be $\frac{22}{7}$, calculate the circumference and area of a circle with the given radius in questions 11–20.

11. 14 cm   12. 7 cm   13. 21 mm   14. 28 cm   15. 35 mm

16. 2.1 m   17. 10.5 cm   18. 1.4 m   19. 3.5 cm   20. 4.9 cm

Taking π to be 3.14, calculate the circumference and area of a circle with the given diameter in questions 21–25.

21. 18 cm   22. 4 m   23. 6 cm   24. 1 m   25. 15 cm

Calculate, in terms of π, the circumference and area of a circle with the given radius in questions 26–30.

26. 3 cm   **27.** 2 m   **28.** 11 mm   **29.** 4·5 cm   **30.** 1·5 m

Calculate (i) the area (ii) the length of the arc and (iii) the perimeter of each of the following sectors in questions 31–36 (taking π to be 3·14; all dimensions are in centimetres).

31.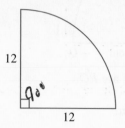

32.

33.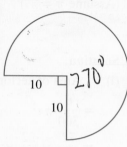

34.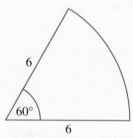

35.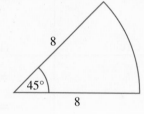

36.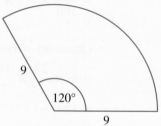

Calculate the areas of the following compound figures in questions 37–38 (taking π to be 3·14; all dimensions are in centimetres).

37.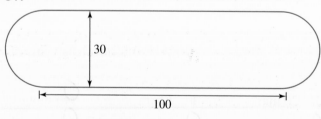

38.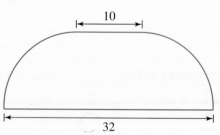

Find the area of each of the following shaded regions in questions 39–41 (taking π to be 3·14; all dimensions are in centimetres).

39.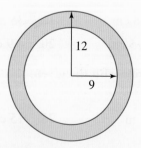

40.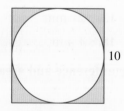

41.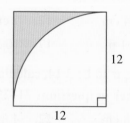

Find the area of the shaded regions in questions 42–43 (taking π to be $\frac{22}{7}$).

42.

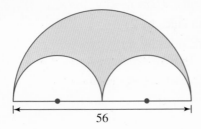

43.

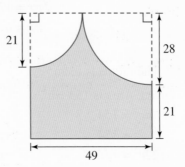

44. The diagram shows a disc inside a parallelogram. Calculate, correct to one decimal place, the area which is not shaded. Take $\pi = 3 \cdot 14$.

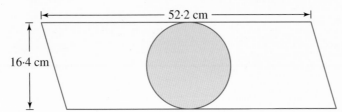

Given the circumference or area

In some questions we are given the circumference or area and asked to find the radius (or diameter). As before, write down the **equation given in disguise** and solve this equation to find the radius, r.

EXAMPLE

(i) If the area of a circle is 1,256 cm², calculate its radius (assume $\pi = 3 \cdot 14$).

(ii) The circumference of a circle is 12π cm. Calculate the radius.

(iii) The area of a circle is 154 cm². Calculate its diameter (assume $\pi = \frac{22}{7}$).

Solution:

(i) Given area: $\pi r^2 = 1{,}256 \text{ cm}^2$ (area $= \pi r^2$)

$\qquad\quad 3 \cdot 14 r^2 = 1{,}256$ (put in 3·14 for π)

$\qquad\qquad\quad r^2 = 400$ (divide both sides by 3·14)

$\qquad\qquad\quad r = \sqrt{400}$ (take the square root of both sides)

$\qquad\qquad\quad r = 20$

$\therefore$ The radius is 20 cm.

(ii) Given: Circumference is 12π cm

$$2\pi r = 12\pi \qquad \text{(circumference} = 2\pi r)$$
$$\pi r = 6\pi \qquad \text{(divide both sides by 2)}$$
$$r = 6 \qquad \text{(divide both sides by } \pi)$$

∴ The radius is 6 cm.

(iii) Given: Area is 154 cm²

$$\therefore \quad \pi r^2 = 154 \qquad \text{(area} = \pi r^2)$$
$$\tfrac{22}{7} r^2 = 154 \qquad \text{(put in } \tfrac{22}{7} \text{ for } \pi)$$
$$22r^2 = 1{,}078 \qquad \text{(multiply both sides by 7)}$$
$$r^2 = 49 \qquad \text{(divide both sides by 22)}$$
$$r = \sqrt{49} \qquad \text{(take the square root of both sides)}$$
$$r = 7$$
$$d = 2r = 2(7) = 14$$

∴ The diameter is 14 cm.

Exercise 17.5

The table below shows certain information on circles, including the value of π used. In each case write down the equation given in disguise and use this to find the radius.

	π	Circumference	Area	Radius
1.	π	8π cm		
2.	π	18π cm		
3.	3·14		314 cm²	
4.	3·14		706·5 m²	
5.	$\frac{22}{7}$	132 mm		
6.	$\frac{22}{7}$		616 cm²	
7.	π		16π cm²	
8.	3·14	78·5 m		

	π	Circumference	Area	Radius
9.	$\frac{22}{7}$		2,464 cm²	
10.	π		81π cm²	
11.	$\frac{22}{7}$	220 m		
12.	3·14		2,826 mm²	
13.	π		121π m²	
14.	3·14		5,024 cm²	
15.	$\frac{22}{7}$		38·5 m²	
16.	$\frac{22}{7}$	66 cm		

17. The area of a circle is 154 cm². Find its circumference (taking π to be $\frac{22}{7}$).

18. The circumference of a circle is 10π m. Find its area in terms of π.

19. The area of a circle is 12·56 cm². Find its circumference (taking π to be 3·14).

20. The area of a circle is $20·25\pi$ m². Find the radius of the circle.

Solving problems in context

EXAMPLE

A bicycle wheel, including the tyre, has a diameter of 56 cm. Find the number of turns the wheel must make in travelling 352 m without slipping. (Take π to be $\frac{22}{7}$.)

Solution:

Change all dimensions to the smaller unit, centimetres.

$352 \text{ m} = 352 \times 100 \text{ cm} = 35{,}200 \text{ cm}$

Number of turns of the wheel

$= \dfrac{\text{distance travelled}}{\text{circumference of the wheel}}$

$= \dfrac{35{,}200}{176}$

Therefore, the wheel will turn 200 times.

$\text{Radius} = r = \dfrac{56}{2} = 28$

Circumference of wheel

$= 2\pi r$

$= \dfrac{2}{1} \times \dfrac{22}{7} \times \dfrac{28}{1}$

$= 176 \text{ cm}$

Exercise 17.6

1. A bicycle wheel, including the tyre, has a diameter of 42 cm.

   (i) Calculate the length of the radius of the wheel.

   (ii) Find the distance moved by the bicycle if the wheel makes one full turn.

   (iii) How far, in metres, will the bike have travelled after 250 turns without slipping?

   (iv) Calculate how many turns the wheel makes when the bicycle moves 264 m without slipping. (Take $\pi = \frac{22}{7}$.)

2. A window is in the shape of a rectangle combined with a semi-circle, as shown. The rectangular part of the window is 70 cm long and 90 cm high. Find the area of the window in cm². (Take π to be $\frac{22}{7}$.)

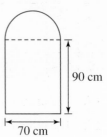

90 cm

70 cm

3. A circular lawn, centre Q and diameter 30 m, surrounds a square fountain with side of length 6 m, as shown. Assuming $\pi = 3 \cdot 14$, find:

    (i) The area covered by the lawn

    (ii) The cost of reseeding the lawn if reseeding costs €3·20 per m^2

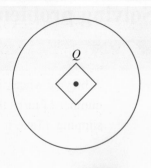

4. The diameter of a €1 coin is 23·25 mm. Taking $\pi = 3 \cdot 14$:

    (i) Calculate the circumference of the coin.

    If the coin is rolled along a desktop, find:

    (ii) The distance travelled if the coin makes five complete revolutions

    (iii) The number of complete revolutions the coin makes if it rolls 50 cm

5. **(i)** A student measures the circumference of a €2 coin and finds it to be 88 mm. Taking $\pi = \frac{22}{7}$, find its diameter.

    (ii) If the diameter of a €2 coin is 25·75 mm, find its circumference correct to one decimal place $\left(\text{assume } \pi = \frac{22}{7}\right)$.

    (iii) Hence, find the error in the calculation of:

    (a) The diameter

    (b) The circumference

6. The diameter of each wheel of a bicycle is 70 cm.

    (i) How far (in km) will the bicycle travel if each wheel turns 350 times? $\left(\text{Assume } \pi = \frac{22}{7}.\right)$

    (ii) How many times does each wheel complete a full turn if the bicycle travels a distance of 13,200 m?

7. A windscreen wiper blade rotates in a semi-circle, as in the diagram. The shaded region indicates the area that is wiped.

    Find the area of the shaded region. $\left(\text{Assume } \pi = \frac{22}{7}.\right)$

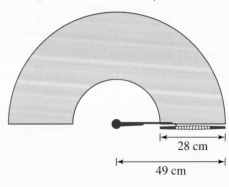

28 cm

49 cm

8. An athletics track is in the shape of a rectangle with semi-circular ends, as shown.

   (i) Write down the radius of the semi-circular ends.

   (ii) Calculate the length of both semi-circular ends. (Take π to be $\frac{22}{7}$.)

   (iii) Calculate the length of the track.

   (iv) Calculate the number of laps an athlete would have to complete in a 5·4 km race.

   (v) An athlete ran four laps in 10 minutes. Calculate his speed in kilometres per hour.

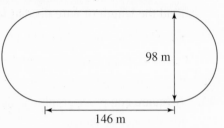

98 m

146 m

9. **(i)** If the diameter of a disc is 14 cm, calculate its area. (Take π to be $\frac{22}{7}$.)

   (ii) From a rectangular strip of tin 14 cm wide, five disks of radius 7 cm are cut out. Calculate l, the shortest length of strip required.

   (iii) Find the area of tin remaining from this latter strip after the five discs have been cut out.

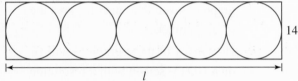

14

l

10. The diagram for one side of a stone bridge over a river is shown. Each arc is a semi-circle of radius 4·2 m.

    (i) Find l, the length of the bridge.

    (ii) It is decided to restore both sides of the stone bridge at a cost of €80 per m². Given that the sides of the bridge are symmetric, calculate the total cost of restoration. Take $\pi = \frac{22}{7}$.

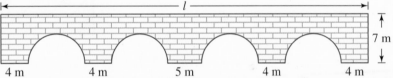

l

7 m

4 m   4 m   5 m   4 m   4 m

11. A plan for a wooden deck including a flowerbed and a water feature are shown.

    Taking $\pi = 3\cdot14$:

    (i) Find the area of the water feature.

    (ii) Find the area of the flowerbed.

    (iii) Find the area of the wooden deck.

    (iv) What percentage, to the nearest whole number, of the entire area will be wood?

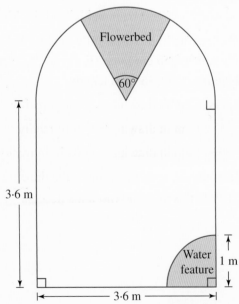

Flowerbed

60°

3·6 m

3·6 m

Water feature

1 m

12. A wire frame consists of a circle and a diameter. The diameter is 28 cm. Find the length of wire needed for a frame. (Take π to be $\frac{22}{7}$.)

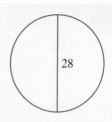

28

13. A square computer graphic is designed for a game, as shown.

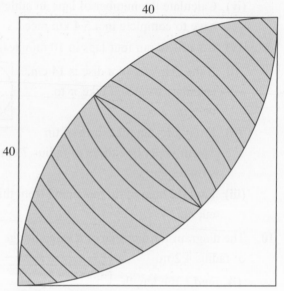

40

40

   (i) Find the area covered by this graphic, given that units for area are given in pixels.

   (ii) How many of these graphics will fit on a HDTV screen with a resolution of 1,280 × 720 pixels?

   (iii) Find the area of a quarter circle with a radius of 40, taking $\pi = 3{\cdot}14$.

   (iv) Hence, find the shaded area of the graphic.

Scale, drawings and diagrams

The world's largest mammal is the blue whale.

This drawing of a typical fully grown blue whale is approximately 6 cm long. However, the average adult blue whale measures 36 m in length.

That is, 6 cm in drawing = 36 m in reality

      1 cm in drawing = 6 m in reality

      1 cm in drawing = 600 cm in reality

We would then say the scale of the drawing is 1 to 600.
We write this as 1:600 (no units necessary).

EXAMPLE

The map shows the distance between two cities, Belfast and Cork. The map uses a scale of 1:7,500,000.

(i) Using the map, find the distance between Belfast and Cork to the nearest km.

(ii) If the distance between Dublin and Galway is 195 km, how far would this be on the map?

Solution:

(i) On the map:

1 cm = 7,500,000 cm

1 cm = 75,000 m   (divide by 100 to change cm to m)

1 cm = 75 km   (divide by 1,000 to change m to km)

We now know 1 cm = 75 km on the given map.

Using a ruler, we find that the distance from Belfast to Cork equals $4\frac{1}{2}$ cm.

Actual distance = $75 \times 4\frac{1}{2} = 337 \cdot 5 = 338$ to the nearest km.

(ii) 195 km from Galway to Dublin

The scale of the map is 1 cm = 75 km.

∴ The distance from Galway to Dublin on the map is given by $\frac{195}{75} = 2\cdot6$ cm.

Or you could simply measure the distance with a ruler.

Exercise 17.7

1. If a diagram has a scale of 1:40, calculate the actual lengths of lines in metres represented by:

   (i) 7 cm   (ii) 15 mm   (iii) $2\frac{1}{4}$ cm   (iv) 0·03 m

2. If a map has a scale of 1:50,000, calculate the scaled lengths that need to be drawn on the map to represent:

   (i) 4 km   (ii) 1 km   (iii) 5·5 km   (iv) 600 m

3. (i) This diagram of an adult African bush elephant is drawn to a scale of 1:175. Measure the diagram and hence estimate the height of the elephant.

(ii) Given that the height of the woman in the diagram is 1·6 m tall, estimate the height of the ape.

(iii) Find the scale of this illustration of a leatherback turtle (an endangered species) given that this turtle is 2·1 m long.

4. A model ship is made using a scale of 1:125.

   (i) If the model ship is 18 cm long, how long is the real ship?

   (ii) If the model ship is 3·2 cm wide, how wide is the real ship?

   (iii) If the real ship is 8·75 m high, how high is the model ship?

5. A map of three houses, A, B and C, is shown. Molly walked in a straight line from house A to house B. She then walked from house B to house C.

   (i) Draw a scaled diagram of her walk using a scale of 1:4,000.

   (ii) Use this scaled diagram to calculate the straight line distance between her start and finish points.

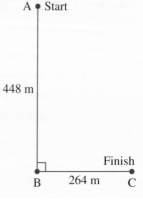

6. Copy each diagram using an appropriate scale. In each case, write down the scale.

(i)

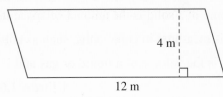

|← 3 m →|

(ii)

4 m

12 m

(iii)

500 m

400 m

(iv)

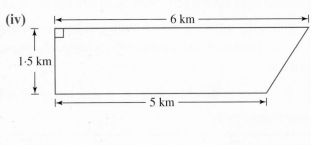

|← 6 km →|

1·5 km

|← 5 km →|

7. This is a scale drawing of a classroom.

(i) Find the actual perimeter of the room correct to the nearest m.

(ii) Find the actual area of the room correct to the nearest m².

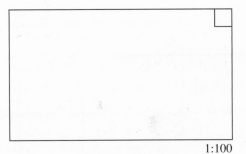

1:100

8. The plan of a soccer pitch is 10·5 cm long and 6·8 cm wide. The scale used is 1:1,000.

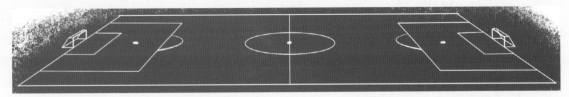

(i) Find the actual length of the pitch.

(ii) Find the actual width of the pitch.

(iii) Find the perimeter of the pitch.

(iv) Find the area of the pitch in m².

(v) Find the cost of reseeding the pitch at a cost of €28 per m².

(vi) If the goals are $3\frac{1}{2}$ m wide, how far is the corner flag from the near goal post?

247

Volume and surface area including nets

The volume of a solid is the amount of space it occupies.

Volume is measured in cubic units, such as cubic metres (m^3) or cubic centimetres (cm^3).

Capacity is the volume of a liquid or gas and is usually measured in litres.

$$1 \text{ litre} = 1,000 \text{ cm}^3 = 1,000 \text{ ml}$$

The surface area of a solid is the **total area of its outer surface**.

It is measured in square units such as square metres or square centimetres.

To calculate the surface area of a solid you have to find the area of each face and add them together (often called the total surface area). With some objects, such as a sphere, the surface area is called the curved surface area.

Note: It is usual to denote volume by V and surface area by SA.

Formulas required

1. Rectangular solid (cuboid) $$V = lbh$$ 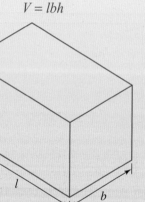 $$SA = 2lb + 2lh + 2bh$$	**2.** Cube $$V = l^3$$ 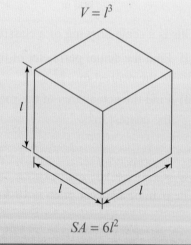 $$SA = 6l^2$$

EXAMPLE

Find **(i)** the volume and **(ii)** the surface area of a cube with sides of length 2 cm.

Solution:

(i) $V = l^3 = (2 \text{ cm})^3 = 8 \text{ cm}^3$

(ii) $SA = 6\, l^2$

$\qquad = 6(2 \text{ cm})^2$

$\qquad = 6(4 \text{ cm}^2)$

$\qquad = 24 \text{ cm}^2$

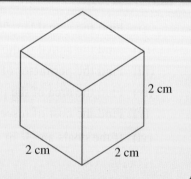

Nets of 3D shapes

A line has only one **dimension** – length (1D).

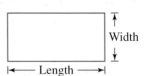

A flat shape has two dimensions – length and width (2D).

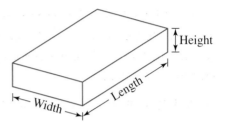

A **solid** shape has three dimensions – length, width and height (3D).

When a 3D shape is opened out, the flat shape is called the **net**.

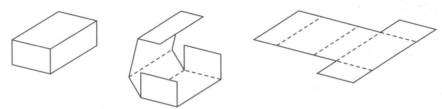

This is a **net** of a solid cube.

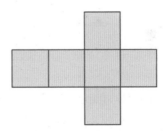

This is how it folds up to make the cube.

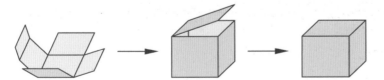

There can be many different nets for one rectangular solid. This is also a net of a solid cube.

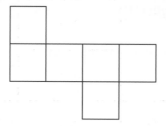

Here is a net for a cuboid that is 4 cm by 2 cm by 2 cm.

When you draw a net, you have to draw the lengths accurately. You may have to use a scale for your drawing. Choose a scale so that the net fits on your page and it's not too small.

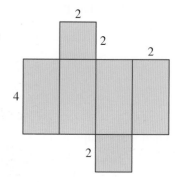

This is how the net folds up to make a cuboid.

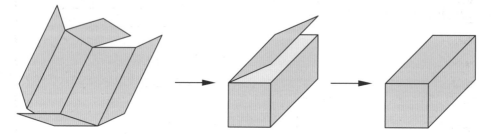

Naming parts of a 3D shape

Each flat surface is called a **face**. Two faces meet at an **edge**. Edges of a shape meet at a point called a **vertex** (corner). The plural of vertex is **vertices**.

The cuboid has eight vertices (each marked •).

The cuboid has 12 edges (count each line, including dotted lines).

The cuboid has six faces. They are the front and back plus two sides, plus a top and base.

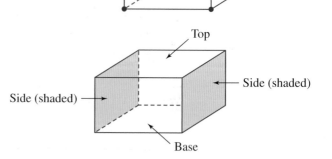

A net diagram indicates the faces clearly.

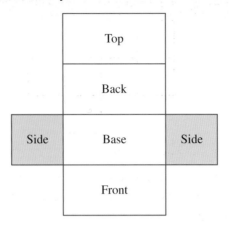

Using a net to determine the surface area of a 3D shape

EXAMPLE 1

Find the surface area of the cuboid with dimensions
height 7 cm, length 10 cm and width 6 cm.

Solution:

Surface area of a cuboid

= sum of the area of all six faces of the net

= area of (top + back + base + front + side + side)

= area of ((top + base) + (back + front) + (side + side))

= 2(top) + 2(back) + 2(side)

= 2(10 × 6) + 2(10 × 7) + 2(6 × 7)

= 120 + 140 + 84

= 344 cm²

Note: We can write a formula for the surface area
of a cuboid as

$2lb + 2lh + 2bh.$

3D shape ⇒

Net ⇒

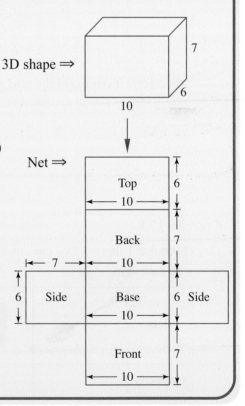

EXAMPLE 2

A rectangular glass tank has internal dimensions of length 1·2 m, breadth 80 cm and height 60 cm.

(i)   How many litres of water can it contain?

(ii)   If water is poured into the tank at the rate of 8 litres per minute, how long does it take to fill the tank?

Solution:

As 1 litre = 1,000 cm^3, we change all dimensions to centimetres.

Length = 1·2 m = 120 cm

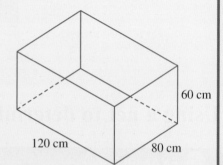

(i)   Volume of the tank = $l \times b \times h$

$\qquad\qquad\qquad = 120 \times 80 \times 60$

$\qquad\qquad\qquad = 576{,}000$ cm^3

$\qquad$ Number of litres $= \dfrac{\text{volume of the tank (in cm}^3)}{1{,}000 \text{ cm}^3}$

$\qquad\qquad\qquad\qquad = \dfrac{576{,}000}{1{,}000}$

$\qquad\qquad\qquad\qquad = 576$

(ii)   Time taken to fill the tank $= \dfrac{\text{volume of the tank (in litres)}}{\text{number of litres poured per minute}}$

$\qquad\qquad\qquad\qquad\qquad = \dfrac{576}{8}$

$\qquad\qquad\qquad\qquad\qquad = 72$ minutes, or 1 hour 12 minutes

Exercise 17.8

1.   Given that 1 litre = 1,000 cm^3, match the capacities 300 ml, 1 litre, 5 ml, 150 ml and 8 litres with each item.

Item					
Capacity					

2. Write the correct capacity below each item using the information given.

Item	Spoon 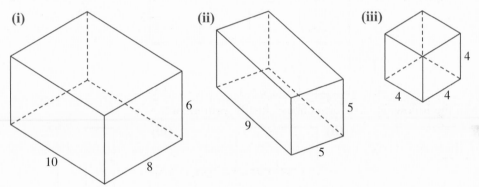	Cup	Mug	Jug	Bucket	Watering can
Capacity			360 ml			

- 20 spoonfulls will fill the mug.
- The cup holds 80 ml less than the mug.
- The jug holds $3\frac{1}{2}$ times as much as the cup.
- The bucket holds as much as the mug and two jugs.
- The watering can holds twice the total of the first five containers plus an extra 2·15 litres.

3. Calculate **(a)** the volume and **(b)** the surface area of each of the following solids (all dimensions are in cm).

(i)

10   8   6

(ii)

9   5   5

(iii)

4   4   4

Complete the following table, which gives certain information about various rectangular blocks (it may help to draw a diagram in each case).

	Length	Breadth	Height	Volume	Surface area
4.	10 cm	8 cm	6 cm		
5.	3 m	2 m	5 m		
6.	8 m	2 m	3 m		
7.	50 cm	40 cm	80 cm		
8.	25 mm	15 mm	12 mm		

9. Use the following nets of each rectangular solid to find their volume and surface area.

(i)

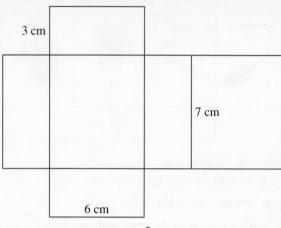

3 cm

7 cm

6 cm

(ii)

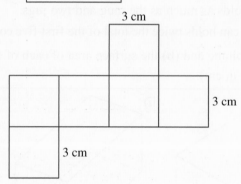

3 cm

3 cm

3 cm

10. Which of the following nets form cubes? Justify your answer.

(i) 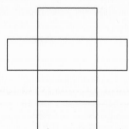 (ii) 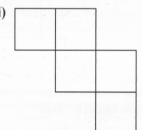 (iii)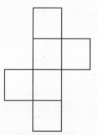

11. Sam made this shape using multilink cubes. Four cubes are purple. The other six are white.

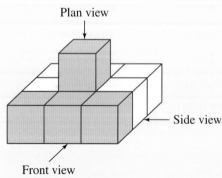

Plan view

Side view

Front view

Copy and complete each view of the shape by colouring in the squares that are purple.

(i)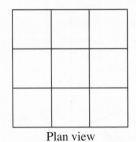

Plan view

(ii)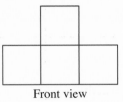

Front view

(iii)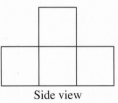

Side view

12. Draw an accurate net for each of these three-dimensional shapes.

(i)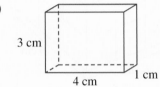

3 cm

4 cm   1 cm

(ii)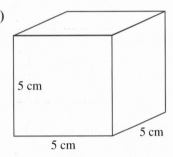

5 cm

5 cm   5 cm

13. Look at these diagrams of three-dimensional shapes. Dotted lines are used to show the edges that cannot be seen when you look at the shape from one side.

(i)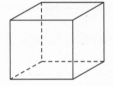

(ii)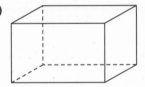

Copy and complete this table.

	Name of shape	Number of faces	Number of vertices	Number of edges
(i)				
(ii)				

14. **(i)** Calculate the volume of a cube with sides of length 2 cm.

    (ii) How many of these cubes will exactly
fill a rectangular box with a square base of
sides 6 cm and height 4 cm?

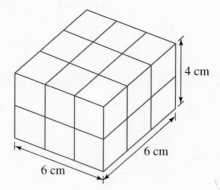

15. A box measures 6 cm by 6 cm by 15 cm. It has
seven cubes stacked tightly inside. Each cube
measures 3 cm by 3 cm by 3 cm. How many more
such cubes must be stacked inside to fill the box?

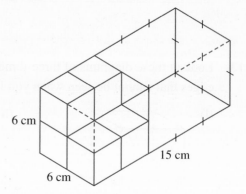

16. A metal box with no lid is shown. Draw a net of the box.
Hence or otherwise, find the area of the metal required to
make this box. Give your answers **(i)** in cm² **(ii)** in m².

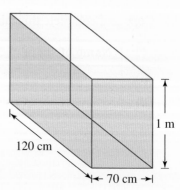

17. A rectangular sheet of metal measures 2 m by $1\frac{1}{2}$ m. A square of side 30 cm is removed from each corner. The remaining piece of metal is folded along the dotted lines to form an open box, as shown.

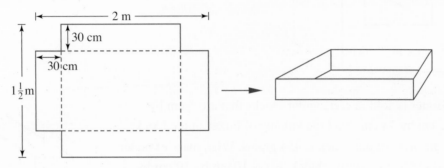

   (i) Find the surface area of the net used to construct the box.
   (ii) Find the volume of the box (a) in cm³ (b) in m³ (c) in litres.

18. How many cubes of side 4 cm will fit exactly into a rectangular box with dimensions 0·8 m by 0·4 m by 60 cm?

19. A rectangular block of metal has dimensions 48 cm by 24 cm by 16 cm. It is melted down and recast into cubes of length 8 cm, without loss of volume. How many cubes will be cast?

Calculate the volume of each of the following solids in questions 20–22 (all measurements in centimetres).

20.

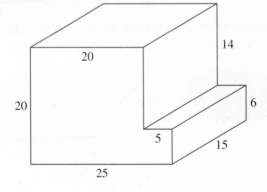

21.

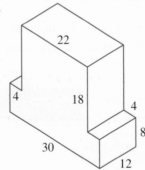

22.

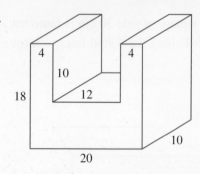

23. **(i)** Butter is sold in rectangular blocks that are 5 cm by 5 cm by 14 cm. Find the volume of butter in the block.

(ii) The mass of this block is 454 grams. What mass of butter would be in a similar block that is 10 cm by 10 cm by 28 cm?

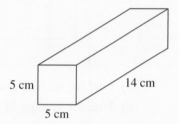

5 cm   14 cm

5 cm

24. A rectangular glass tank has internal dimensions of length 60 cm, breadth 30 cm and height 20 cm.

(i) Calculate its capacity (internal volume) in litres.

(ii) If water is poured into the tank at the rate of 3 litres per minute, how long does it take to fill the tank?

3 *l* per minute

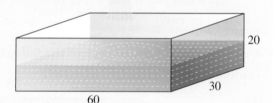

20

30

60

25. A rectangular tank full of oil has internal measurements of 1·8 m by 30 cm by 40 cm. If 4 litres are drained off every minute, how long will it take to empty the tank?

Oil tank   4 *l* per minute

26. Water is leaking from this tank at a speed of 0·5 litres per minute. How long would it take for a full tank of water to leak away?

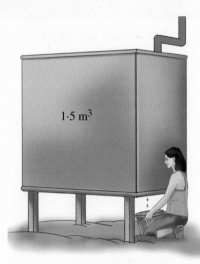

1·5 m³

Given the volume or surface area to find the missing lengths

In some questions we are given the volume or surface area and asked to find a missing dimension. As before, write down the **equation given in disguise** and solve this equation to find the missing dimension.

EXAMPLE 1

The volume of a rectangular block is 560 cm³.
If its length is 14 cm and its breadth is 8 cm,
find **(i)** its height and **(ii)** its surface area.

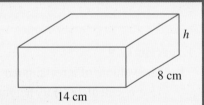

h

8 cm

14 cm

Solution:

(i) Equation given in disguise:

$$\text{volume} = 560 \text{ cm}^3$$
$$(14)(8)h = 560$$
$$112h = 560$$
$$h = \frac{560}{112} = 5 \text{ cm}$$

(ii)   Surface area
$$= 2lb + 2lh + 2bh$$
$$= 2(14)(8) + 2(14)(5) + 2(8)(5)$$
$$= 224 + 140 + 80$$
$$= 444 \text{ cm}^2$$

EXAMPLE 2

The surface area of a cube is 54 cm^2.

Calculate its volume.

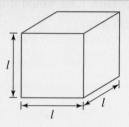

Solution:

Let the length of one side of the cube be l cm.

Equation given in disguise:

Surface area = 54 cm^2 Volume = l^3

$\therefore 6l^2 = 54$ = 3^3

$l^2 = 9$ = 27 cm^3

$l = 3$ cm   Therefore, the volume of the cube is 27 cm^3.

Note: In this example we could use a net to help us find l.

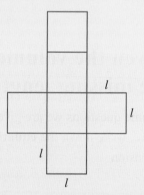

Exercise 17.9

1. The volume of a rectangular block is 2,400 cm^3. If its length is 20 cm and its breadth is 15 cm, calculate **(i)** its height and **(ii)** its surface area.

2. The volume of a cube is 64 cm^3. Calculate **(i)** the length of a side and **(ii)** its surface area.

3. The surface area of a cube is 24 cm^2. Calculate **(i)** the length of a side and **(ii)** its volume.

4. The volume of a rectangular block is 720 cm^3. If its breadth is 9 cm and its height is 8 cm, calculate **(i)** its length and **(ii)** its surface area.

5. The net of a rectangular container is given (all dimensions are in metres).

   (i) The volume of the container is 165 m^3. Find the length, l, of the container.

   (ii) Hence, calculate the surface area of the container.

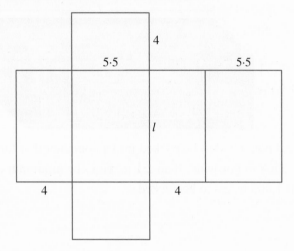

6. The net of an open (no lid) wooden box is given (all dimensions are in cm). The surface area of the box is 138 cm^2.

   (i) Find the breadth (b) of the box.

   (ii) Hence, write down the volume of the box in litres.

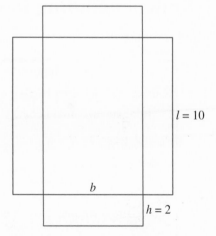

7. The volume of a cube is 125 cm^3. Calculate its surface area.

8. An oil storage tank is in the shape of a cuboid. Its rectangular base has dimensions 2·2 m by 80 cm and its height is 90 cm. When the tank is full, 704 litres are drawn off into another vessel. Calculate the drop in height (depth) of the oil.

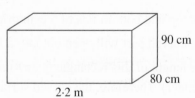

9. **(i)** 672 identical rectangular boxes, with dimensions 50 cm, 40 cm, 30 cm, are packed into a freight container with dimensions as shown. Find the minimum length, l, of the container required to contain all 672 boxes.

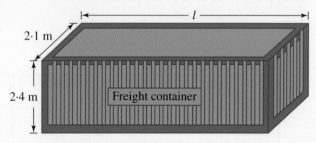

(ii) If 1,008 identical boxes had to be packed into a container that for safety reasons could not be longer than 8 m nor wider than 2·1 m, find the minimum height of container that would allow all 1,008 boxes to be packed.

Cylinder including in context questions

Formulas required

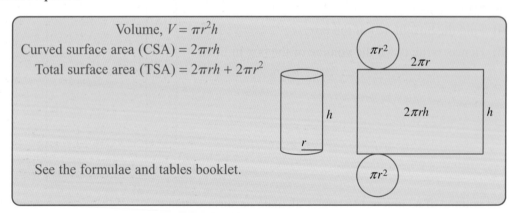

$$\text{Volume, } V = \pi r^2 h$$
$$\text{Curved surface area (CSA)} = 2\pi rh$$
$$\text{Total surface area (TSA)} = 2\pi rh + 2\pi r^2$$

See the formulae and tables booklet.

The top and bottom lids of a cylindrical can are circles, each of area πr^2.

The curved part will open out into a flat surface in the shape of a rectangle.

The length of this rectangle is $2\pi r$ (circumference of a lid) and its breadth will be h (height of the cylinder). Therefore, the curved surface area is $2\pi r \times h$ or simply $2\pi rh$.

EXAMPLE 1

Find **(i)** the volume and **(ii)** the total surface area of a closed cylindrical can of radius 7 cm and height 12 cm (taking π to be $\frac{22}{7}$).

Solution:

(i) $V = \pi r^2 h$

$= \dfrac{22}{7} \times \dfrac{7}{1} \times \dfrac{7}{1} \times \dfrac{12}{1}$

$= 1{,}848 \text{ cm}^3$

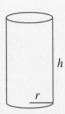

(ii) $\text{TSA} = 2\pi rh + 2\pi r^2$

$= \dfrac{2}{1} \times \dfrac{22}{7} \times \dfrac{7}{1} \times \dfrac{12}{1} + \dfrac{2}{1} \times \dfrac{22}{7} \times \dfrac{7}{1} \times \dfrac{7}{1}$

$= 528 + 308$

$= 836 \text{ cm}^2$

EXAMPLE 2

(i) A drinking trough is made from a half cylinder, as in the diagram. Its length is 1 m and its diameter is 20 cm. Find the capacity of the trough in litres. (Take $\pi = 3\cdot14$.)

(ii) If the trough is filled by a pipe at a rate of $392\cdot5 \text{ cm}^3$ every second, how long will it take to fill the trough?

Solution

(i)   Radius $= \frac{20}{2} = 10$ cm

Length $=$ height $= 1$ m $= 100$ cm

Volume of cylinder $= \pi r^2 h$

Volume of trough $= \frac{1}{2}(\pi r^2 h) = \frac{1}{2}(3\cdot14)(10)^2\, 100 = 15{,}700 \text{ cm}^3$

Number of litres $= \dfrac{15{,}700}{1{,}000} = 15\cdot7$

(ii) Time $= \dfrac{\text{capacity}}{\text{rate of flow}} = \dfrac{15{,}700}{392\cdot5}$ (notice both units are in cm^3)

$= 40$ seconds

EXAMPLE 3

A hollow concrete pipe has an external diameter of 20 cm and is 2 cm thick.
Calculate the volume of concrete in 50 cm of pipe. (Take π to be 3·14.)

Solution:

Volume of concrete = volume of outside cylinder − volume of inside cylinder

Outside cylinder	Inside cylinder
$V = \pi r^2 h$	$V = \pi r^2 h$
$\quad = 3·14 \times 10 \times 10 \times 50$	$\quad = 3·14 \times 8 \times 8 \times 50$
$\quad = 15{,}700 \text{ cm}^3$	$\quad = 10{,}048 \text{ cm}^3$

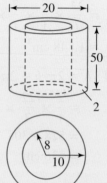

Volume of concrete $= 15{,}700 \text{ cm}^3 - 10{,}048 \text{ cm}^3$
$$= 5{,}652 \text{ cm}^3$$

Exercise 17.10

Copy and complete the following table, which gives certain information about various closed cylinders.

	π	Radius	Height	Volume	Curved surface area	Total surface area
1.	$\frac{22}{7}$	7 cm	10 cm			
2.	3·14	10 mm	5 mm			
3.	$\frac{22}{7}$	28 cm	20 cm			
4.	3·14	12 cm	50 cm			
5.	$\frac{22}{7}$	3·5 m	5 m			

6. A closed cylinder has a diameter of 42 cm and a height of 10 cm.
   Calculate **(i)** its volume and **(ii)** its curved surface area (assume $\pi = \frac{22}{7}$).

7. A rectangular box with a square base has
    dimensions as given in the diagram.
    A cylindrical birthday cake fits exactly into the box.
    (i)   Write down the height of the cake.
    (ii) Write down the radius of the cake.
    (iii) Calculate the volume of the cake to the nearest
          cm³ using the value of π from your calculator.

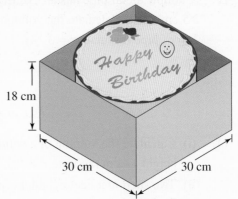

18 cm

30 cm   30 cm

8. (i)   A hot water cylinder in a café has dimensions as shown.
          Find, in terms of π, the volume of the cylinder.
    (ii) The café serves hot drinks in very large cylindrical mugs
          with dimensions of height 14 cm and radius 5 cm. They are
          filled to exactly 2 cm below the rim of the mug. Find, in
          terms of π, the volume of hot water in a mug.
    (iii) Hence, calculate how many mugs can be filled from the full
          hot water cylinder when each mug is filled as in part (ii).

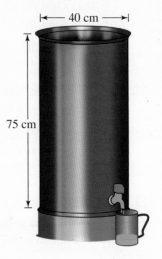

40 cm

75 cm

9. Which of the cylinders P, Q and R has the largest volume? Justify your answer.

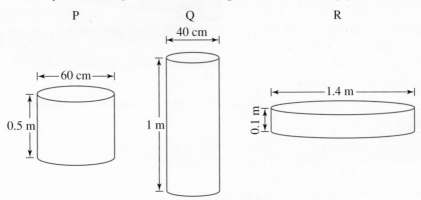

P

60 cm

0.5 m

Q

40 cm

1 m

R

1.4 m

0.1 m

10. A hollow metal pipe has an external diameter of 40 cm and its casing is 2·5 cm thick. Calculate the volume, in cubic centimetres, of metal in 2 m of pipe (assume $\pi = 3·14$).

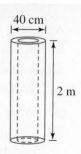

11. **(i)** Calculate the volume of a solid cylinder of diameter 10 cm and height 14 cm (assume $\pi = \frac{22}{7}$).

    (ii) Two such identical cylinders fit exactly into a rectangular box.

        (a) Find the dimensions of the box.

        (b) Find the internal volume of the box.

        (c) Find the volume of air in the box when the two cylinders are placed inside it.

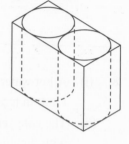

12. A semi-circular tunnel of height 5 m and length 600 m has been driven through a mountain. Calculate the volume, in cubic metres, of material that has been removed from the mountain. (Assume $\pi = 3·14$.)

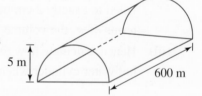

13. **(i)** A train passes through a semi-circular tunnel travelling at 72 km/hr. It takes the train $1\frac{1}{2}$ minutes to pass through the tunnel. Find the length of the tunnel in metres.

    (ii) The tunnel has been driven through a mountain. The volume, in cubic metres, of material that has been removed is 85,486·5 m³. Find the radius of the tunnel. (Assume $\pi = 3·14$.)

14. Find the missing dimension. In each case, the volumes are equal (all dimensions are in centimetres).

(i)

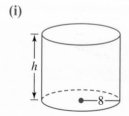 =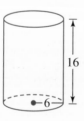

(ii)

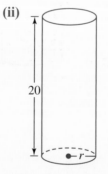 =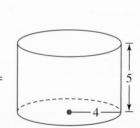

15. (i) Find the volume, in cubic centimetres, of a cylindrical carton with a radius of 5 cm and height of 7 cm, taking π to be $\frac{22}{7}$.

 (ii) Cartons of this type are filled with yoghurt. How many cartons must be filled so that the total amount of yoghurt contained in them is 22 litres? (1 litre = 1,000 cm^3)

 (iii) Larger cylindrical cartons are filled with ice cream. Each larger cylindrical carton has a height of 14 cm and a volume of 4·4 litres. Calculate the radius length of these larger cartons, taking $\pi = \frac{22}{7}$.

16. (i) Find the volume, in cubic centimetres, of a cylindrical cup of radius 3 cm and height 7 cm, taking π to be $\frac{22}{7}$.

 (ii) A fish tank has a square base measuring 30 cm by 30 cm. It has four rectangular sides, each 55 cm high. Find the volume of the tank in cubic centimetres.

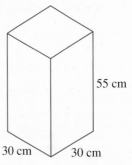

 (iii) The cylindrical cup is filled with water and then totally emptied into the fish tank. This is done 50 times. What is the total volume of water put into the fish tank?

 (iv) If the fish tank was empty at the start, what is the depth of water in it at the end?

17. (i) Jack has a cylindrical bucket with a height of 30 cm and a radius of 14 cm. Taking $\pi = \frac{22}{7}$, find the capacity of the bucket in litres.

 (ii) Jack is required to fill an empty metal cylinder of diameter 1·4 m to a height of 1 m. How many full buckets will Jack require to complete this task?

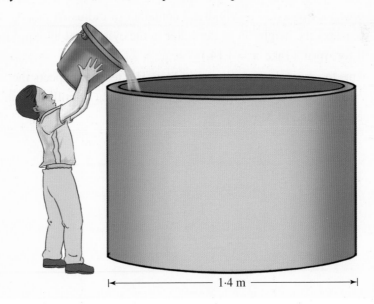

18. Two pieces of wire are the same length. One piece of wire is bent to form a right-angled triangle, as shown. The other is bent into a square. Calculate the difference in area between the square and the triangle.

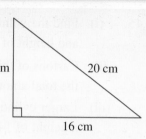

12 cm   20 cm

16 cm

19. Erin is working on a class project measuring rainfall during the month of April. Rainwater is collected using a rectangular tray of metal with dimensions 150 cm × 100 cm, as shown.

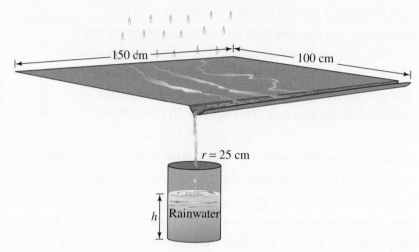

150 cm   100 cm

r = 25 cm

h   Rainwater

  (i) The rainwater flows into a cylindrical container of radius 25 cm. At the end of April, Erin measures the height, *h*, of the water in the cylinder at 84 cm. Find the amount of rainfall for April. (Take $\pi = 3\cdot14$.)

 (ii) Erin plans to repeat the experiment in May. Her teacher expects the amount of rainfall to be 7·85 cm for May. Calculate the expected height of collected rainwater in the cylinder at the end of May.

Repeated multiplication

We use a shorthand called **index notation** to indicate repeated multiplication.

For example, $(number)^3 = (number) \times (number) \times (number)$.

Thus, $4^3 = 4 \times 4 \times 4 = 64$

$4^3 \leftarrow$ power or index

The power or index simply tells you how many times a number is multiplied by itself.

For example, 3^5 means 3 is to be multiplied by itself five times.

$$3^5 = 3 \times 3 \times 3 \times 3 \times 3 = 243$$
$$2 \times 2 = 2^2 \qquad \text{read as '2 squared'}$$
$$2 \times 2 \times 2 = 2^3 \qquad \text{read as '2 cubed'}$$
$$2 \times 2 \times 2 \times 2 = 2^4 \qquad \text{read as '2 to the power of 4'}$$
$$2 \times 2 \times 2 \times 2 \times 2 = 2^5 \qquad \text{read as '2 to the power of 5' and so on.}$$

Note: The first power, or to the power of one, of a number is the number itself.
For example, $2^1 = 2$, $\quad 3^1 = 3$, $\quad 4^1 = 4$.

Powers with a calculator
You can find the value of a number in index form with a calculator by using repeated multiplication or by using the power key, $\boxed{y^x}$ or $\boxed{x^y}$ or $\boxed{\wedge}$.

To find 5^4 on your calculator, use either of the two ways:

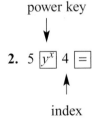

power key

1. $5 \boxed{\times} 5 \boxed{\times} 5 \boxed{\times} 5 \boxed{=}$

2. $5 \boxed{y^x} 4 \boxed{=}$

index

Exercise 18.1
Write questions 1–6 in index form (index notation), i.e. x^y.

1. $2 \times 2 \times 2$
2. $3 \times 3 \times 3 \times 3$
3. $4 \times 4 \times 4 \times 4 \times 4 \times 4$
4. $6 \times 6 \times 6 \times 6 \times 6 \times 6 \times 6$
5. $10 \times 10 \times 10 \times 10 \times 10$
6. $8 \times 8 \times 8 \times 8 \times 8 \times 8$

Using your calculator or otherwise, calculate questions 7–14.

7. 2^4
8. 3^4
9. 5^3
10. 10^5
11. 8^5
12. 2^{10}
13. 9^6
14. 7^7

Square roots

The square root of a number is the positive number that when multiplied by itself gives the original number. 4 is the square root of 16 because $4 \times 4 = 16$.

The symbol $\sqrt{}$ is used to denote square root, so $\sqrt{16} = 4$.

The easiest way to find the square root of a number is to use the $\boxed{\sqrt{}}$ button on your calculator.

> Square root as a power: $\sqrt{a} = a^{\frac{1}{2}}$

EXAMPLE

Using your calculator or otherwise, calculate each of the following.

(i) $\sqrt{25}$ (ii) $64^{\frac{1}{2}}$ (iii) $(6\cdot25)^{\frac{1}{2}}$

Solution:

(i) $\sqrt{25} = 5$ (ii) $64^{\frac{1}{2}} = \sqrt{64} = 8$ (iii) $(6\cdot25)^{\frac{1}{2}} = \sqrt{6\cdot25} = 2\cdot5$

Exercise 18.2

Find the value of each of the following in questions 1–15.

1. $\sqrt{9}$ 2. $\sqrt{49}$ 3. $\sqrt{81}$
4. $\sqrt{12\cdot25}$ 5. $4^{\frac{1}{2}}$ 6. $36^{\frac{1}{2}}$
7. $(20\cdot25)^{\frac{1}{2}}$ 8. $\sqrt{121}$ 9. $100^{\frac{1}{2}}$
10. $\sqrt{9} + \sqrt{16}$ 11. $\sqrt{64} \times \sqrt{81}$ 12. $\sqrt{144} \div \sqrt{4}$
13. $\sqrt{121} \times \sqrt{49}$ 14. $\sqrt{25} + \sqrt{1}$ 15. $\sqrt{100} \div \sqrt{6\cdot25}$

Using your calculator or otherwise, find the value of questions 16–21.

16. $(\sqrt{4})^2$ 17. $(\sqrt{144})^2$ 18. $(\sqrt{7})^2$
19. $(\sqrt{5})^2$ 20. $(\sqrt{11})^4$ 21. $(\sqrt{8})^4$

Using your calculator, evaluate each of the following in questions 22–27 (give your answer correct to two decimal places).

22. $\sqrt{28}$ 23. $41^{\frac{1}{2}}$ 24. $\sqrt{85}$
25. $54^{\frac{1}{2}}$ 26. $\sqrt{234}$ 27. $1{,}274^{\frac{1}{2}}$

Rules for powers or indices

Multiplication

Consider the following:

$3^3 \times 3^2 = (3 \times 3 \times 3) \times (3 \times 3) = 3 \times 3 \times 3 \times 3 \times 3 = 3^5$

or

$3^3 \times 3^2 = 3^{3+2} = 3^5$ (add the indices)

Similarly,

$2^4 \times 2^3 = (2 \times 2 \times 2 \times 2) \times (2 \times 2 \times 2) = 2 \times 2 \times 2 \times 2 \times 2 \times 2 \times 2 = 2^7$

or

$2^4 \times 2^3 = 2^{4+3} = 2^7$ (add the indices)

> When **multiplying** powers of the same number, **add** the indices.
> $$a^m \times a^n = a^{m+n}$$

Division

Consider the following:

$\dfrac{5^6}{5^4} = \dfrac{\cancel{5} \times \cancel{5} \times \cancel{5} \times \cancel{5} \times 5 \times 5}{\cancel{5} \times \cancel{5} \times \cancel{5} \times \cancel{5}} = 5 \times 5 = 5^2$

or

$\dfrac{5^6}{5^4} = 5^{6-4} = 5^2$ (subtract the index on the bottom from the index on the top)

Similarly,

$\dfrac{4^7}{4^2} = \dfrac{\cancel{4} \times \cancel{4} \times 4 \times 4 \times 4 \times 4 \times 4}{\cancel{4} \times \cancel{4}} = 4 \times 4 \times 4 \times 4 \times 4 = 4^5$

or

$\dfrac{4^7}{4^2} = 4^{7-2} = 4^5$ (subtract the index on the bottom from the index on the top)

> When **dividing** powers of the same number, **subtract** the index on the bottom from the index on the top.
> $$\frac{a^m}{a^n} = a^{m-n}$$

Power of a power

Consider the following:

$(4^2)^3 = 4^2 \times 4^2 \times 4^2 = 4^{2+2+2} = 4^6$

or

$(4^2)^3 = 4^{2 \times 3} = 4^6$ (multiply the indices)

Similarly,

$(3^4)^2 = 3^4 \times 3^4 = 3^{4+4} = 3^8$

or

$(3^4)^2 = 3^{4 \times 2} = 3^8$ (multiply the indices)

> When a power of a number is raised to a power, **multiply** the indices.
> $$(a^m)^n = a^{mn}$$

Remember: $mn = m \times n$

EXAMPLE

Express each of the following as a single power.

  (i) $5^3 \times 5^4 \times 5$ **(ii)** $\dfrac{4^7}{4^5}$ **(iii)** $(3^5)^2$

Solution:

(i) $5^3 \times 5^4 \times 5$

    $= 5^3 \times 5^4 \times 5^1$

    $= 5^{3+4+1}$

    $= 5^8$

(ii) $\dfrac{4^7}{4^5}$

    $= 4^{7-5}$

    $= 4^2$

(iii) $(3^5)^2$

    $= 3^{5 \times 2}$

    $= 3^{10}$

Exercise 18.3

Express questions 1–28 as a single power.

1. $2^3 \times 2^4$ 2. $3^2 \times 3^6$ 3. $4^3 \times 4^2$ 4. $5^3 \times 5^3$

5. $6^4 \times 6^5$ 6. $5^3 \times 5^4$ 7. 3×3^5 8. $2 \times 2^2 \times 2^4$

9. $4^3 \times 4^7$ 10. $6^2 \times 6^4$ 11. $4^{\frac{1}{2}} \times 4^{\frac{1}{2}}$ 12. $7^{\frac{3}{2}} \times 7^{\frac{1}{2}}$

13. $\dfrac{3^5}{3^2}$ 14. $\dfrac{4^7}{4^3}$ 15. $\dfrac{2^8}{2^5}$ 16. $\dfrac{10^5}{10^3}$

17. $\dfrac{9^6}{9^4}$ 18. $\dfrac{5^{10}}{5^6}$ 19. $\dfrac{6^9}{6^5}$ 20. $\dfrac{7^{10}}{7^8}$

21. $(2^2)^3$ 22. $(3^3)^4$ 23. $(5^4)^2$ 24. $(8^2)^5$

25. $(7^3)^5$ 26. $(6^4)^5$ 27. $(4^7)^2$ 28. $(9^3)^6$

In questions 29–36, calculate the value of a.

29. $2^4 \times 2^2 = 2^a$

30. $3^5 \times 3^2 = 3^a$

31. $4^3 \times 4^2 = 4^a$

32. $\dfrac{5^7}{5^4} = 5^a$

33. $\dfrac{6^8}{6^6} = 6^a$

34. $\dfrac{7^6}{7^2} = 7^a$

35. $(3^2)^5 = 3^a$

36. $(5^2)^3 = 5^a$

37. Simplify $\dfrac{4^6 \times 4^3}{4^2 \times 4^5}$, giving your answer in the form 4^n.

38. Simplify $\dfrac{3^5 \times 3^3}{3^2 \times 3^2}$, giving your answer in the form 3^n.

39. Simplify $\dfrac{2 \times 2^3 \times 2^7}{(2^2)^4}$, giving your answer in the form 2^n.

40. Simplify $\dfrac{9^{\frac{1}{2}} \times 3^7}{3^4 \times 3^2}$, giving your answer in the form 3^n.

Index notation

Very large numbers are difficult to use and many cannot be shown on your calculator display. For example, try this multiplication on your calculator: $8{,}000{,}000 \times 7{,}000{,}000$.

The answer is $56{,}000{,}000{,}000{,}000$.

It has 14 digits, which is too many to show on most calculator displays.

Your calculator will display your answer as $\boxed{5 \cdot 6 \ \text{E} \ 13}$ or $\boxed{5 \cdot 6 \times 10^{13}}$ or $\boxed{5 \cdot 6^{13}}$.

This tells you that the $5 \cdot 6$ is multiplied by 10^{13}.

This is written as:

$$5 \cdot 6 \times 10^{13}$$

This part is a number between 1 and 10 (but not including 10).

This part is written as a power of 10 (the power is always a whole number).

Another example to try on your calculator is $0 \cdot 000\ 000\ 23 \times 0 \cdot 000\ 000\ 04$.

The answer is $0 \cdot 000\ 000\ 000\ 000\ 009\ 2$.

Your calculator will display your answer as $\boxed{9 \cdot 2 \ \text{E} \ -15}$ or $\boxed{9 \cdot 2 \times 10^{-15}}$ or $\boxed{9 \cdot 2^{-15}}$.

This tells you that the $9 \cdot 2$ is multiplied by 10^{-15}.

This is written as:

$$9 \cdot 2 \times 10^{-15}$$

This way of writing a number is called **index notation** or **exponential notation** or sometimes **standard form**. (It was formerly called **scientific notation**.)

Index notation gives a number in two parts:

Number between 1 and 10 (but not 10)	×	power of 10

This is often written as $a \times 10^n$, where $1 \le a < 10$ and $n \in \mathbb{N}$.

EXAMPLE 1

Express the numbers **(i)** 8,000,000 and **(ii)** 25,800 in the form $a \times 10^n$, where $1 \le a < 10$ and $n \in \mathbb{N}$.

Solution:

To express a number in index notation, the value of a must be a number between 1 and 10.

(i)   8 000 000.   (put in the decimal point)

     8·000 000   (move the decimal point six places to give a number between 1 and 10)

     Therefore $8{,}000{,}000 = 8 \times 10^6$. ← (number of decimal places moved)

Alternatively, $8{,}000{,}000 = 8 \times 1{,}000{,}000 = 8 \times 10^6$

(ii)   25 800.   (put in the decimal point)

     2·5800   (move the decimal point four places to give a number between 1 and 10)

     Therefore, $25{,}800 = 2 \cdot 58 \times 10^4$.

Alternatively, $25{,}800 = 2 \cdot 5800 \times 10{,}000 = 2 \cdot 58 \times 10^4$.

EXAMPLE 2

Divide 1,506 by 0·3.

Express your answer in the form $a \times 10^n$, where $1 \le a < 10$ and $n \in \mathbb{N}$.

Solution:

     $1{,}506 \div 0 \cdot 3 = 5{,}020$

     5020.   (put in the decimal point)

     5·020   (move the decimal point three places to give a number between 1 and 10)

Therefore, $5{,}020 = 5 \cdot 02 \times 10^3$.

Alternatively, $5{,}020 = 5 \cdot 020 \times 1{,}000 = 5 \cdot 02 \times 10^3$.

Using a calculator

Most scientific calculators can be set to **display all answers** in index (scientific) notation. The procedure varies with different models and different manufacturers, so you are advised to read your calculator's manual. Furthermore, you will need to be able to return your calculator to its normal display settings.

Calculators which have a $\boxed{\text{SET UP}}$ button (which may need to be preceded with $\boxed{\text{SHIFT}}$) may either offer you an **FSE** option or take you to a list of display options. Selecting the **FSE** option may also take you to a list of display options.

The usual display options include **FIX**ed decimal place, **SCI**entific notation and **NORM**al. Using the **SCI** option will cause all answers to be displayed in index notation and the calculator screen should show **SCI** to confirm the display mode. You may continue to enter numbers in the usual manner.

To return your display to its usual state, you will need to go through the procedure again, this time choosing **NORM**al display. Most calculators have two versions of **NORM**al, so you may have to select **1** or **2**. The calculator screen will no longer show the **SCI** indicator.

Calculators which do not have a $\boxed{\text{SET UP}}$ button should have a $\boxed{\text{MODE}}$ button, which if pressed repeatedly will provide display options.

Notes: **1.** The display modes only refer to how the **answer** is displayed. You may enter numbers in any format at all times.

      2. Very large and very small numbers are always displayed in index notation.

      3. Remember to set your calculator back to **NORM**al display mode.

Exercise 18.4

Express each of the numbers in questions 1–16 in the form $a \times 10^n$, where $1 \leq a < 10$ and $n \in \mathbb{N}$.

1. 4,000	2. 50,000	3. 200,000	4. 3,000,000
5. 300	6. 7,500	7. 36,000	8. 650,000
9. 2,300,000	10. 2,080	11. 6,070	12. 30,500
13. 1,580,000	14. 20,400	15. 503,000	16. 8,532,000

In questions 17–31, write your answer in the form $a \times 10^n$, where $1 \leq a < 10$ and $n \in \mathbb{N}$.

17. $2,800 \times 0.5$	18. $48,000 \times 0.3$	19. $3,500 \times 1.2$
20. $58,000 \times 2.5$	21. $4.8 \times 25,000$	22. $1.4 \times 25,000$
23. $3,000 \div 1.2$	24. $7,200 \div 1.6$	25. $172,800 \div 5.4$
26. $67,500 \div 1.25$	27. $866,400 \div 3.8$	28. $1,118,000 \div 0.43$
29. $476,000 \div 2.8$	30. $12,000 \times (1.5)^2$	31. $61,920 \div (1.2)^2$

32. $45,000 \times 0.8 = a \times 10^n$, where $1 \leq a < 10$ and $n \in \mathbb{N}$. Write down the value of a and n.

33. $551,000 \times 2.9 = a \times 10^n$, where $1 \leq a < 10$ and $n \in \mathbb{N}$. Write down the value of a and n.

Addition and subtraction

To add or subtract two numbers in index notation, do the following.

> 1. Write each number as a natural number.
> 2. Add or subtract these numbers.
> 3. Write your answer in index notation.
>
> Alternatively, you can use your calculator by keying in the numbers in index notation.

Numbers given in index notation can be keyed into your calculator by using the **exponent key**.
It is marked $\boxed{\text{EXP}}$ or $\boxed{\text{EE}}$ or $\boxed{\times 10^x}$.

To key in a number in index notation, do the following.

> 1. Key in 'a', the 'number part', first.
> 2. Press the exponent key next.
> 3. Key in the index of the power of 10.

To enter $3{\cdot}4 \times 10^6$, for example, you key in $3{\cdot}4$ $\boxed{\text{EXP}}$ 6.

To enter negative powers, you need to find the **negative** button on your calculator. It is usually marked $\boxed{(-)}$ or $\boxed{+/-}$ and is used to enter negative numbers.

To enter $7{\cdot}1 \times 10^{-3}$, for example, you key in $7{\cdot}1$ $\boxed{\text{EXP}}$ $\boxed{(-)}$ 3.

Note: If you press $\boxed{-}$ at the end, the calculator will write the number as a decimal number, provided the index of the power of 10 is not too large.

EXAMPLE

Calculate **(i)** $2{\cdot}32 \times 10^4 + 3{\cdot}8 \times 10^3$ **(ii)** $8{\cdot}72 \times 10^3 - 5{\cdot}2 \times 10^2$.

Write your answers in the form $a \times 10^n$, where $1 \le a < 10$ and $n \in \mathbb{N}$.

Solution:

(i) $2{\cdot}32 \times 10^4 = 23{,}200$
$\phantom{2{\cdot}32 \times 10^4 =}$ $3{\cdot}8 \times 10^3 = \underline{3{,}800}$
$\phantom{2{\cdot}32 \times 10^4 =}$ $27{,}000$ (add)
$\phantom{2{\cdot}32 \times 10^4 ==} = 2{\cdot}7 \times 10^4$

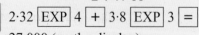 $2{\cdot}32$ $\boxed{\text{EXP}}$ 4 $\boxed{+}$ $3{\cdot}8$ $\boxed{\text{EXP}}$ 3 $\boxed{=}$

27,000 (on the display)

$= 2{\cdot}7 \times 10^4$

(ii) $8{\cdot}72 \times 10^3 = 8{,}720$
$\phantom{8{\cdot}72 \times 10^3 =}$ $5{\cdot}2 \times 10^2 = \underline{520}$
$\phantom{8{\cdot}72 \times 10^3 =}$ $8{,}200$ (subtract)
$\phantom{8{\cdot}72 \times 10^3 ==} = 8{\cdot}2 \times 10^3$

 $8{\cdot}72$ $\boxed{\text{EXP}}$ 3 $\boxed{-}$ $5{\cdot}2$ $\boxed{\text{EXP}}$ 2 $\boxed{=}$

8,200 (on the display)

$= 8{\cdot}2 \times 10^3$

Exercise 18.5

Calculate each of the following in questions 1–18 and write your answer in the form $a \times 10^n$, where $1 \leq a < 10$ and $n \in \mathbb{N}$.

1. $5{\cdot}6 \times 10^3 + 6 \times 10^2$
2. $5{\cdot}8 \times 10^4 + 2 \times 10^3$
3. $4{\cdot}36 \times 10^5 + 2{\cdot}4 \times 10^4$
4. $3{\cdot}53 \times 10^6 + 2{\cdot}7 \times 10^5$
5. $6{\cdot}57 \times 10^6 + 4{\cdot}3 \times 10^5$
6. $6{\cdot}468 \times 10^5 + 3{\cdot}2 \times 10^3$
7. $7{\cdot}569 \times 10^4 + 3{\cdot}1 \times 10^2$
8. $4{\cdot}276 \times 10^5 + 7{\cdot}24 \times 10^4$
9. $6{\cdot}4 \times 10^3 - 4 \times 10^2$
10. $7{\cdot}2 \times 10^4 - 2 \times 10^3$
11. $2{\cdot}84 \times 10^5 - 5{\cdot}4 \times 10^4$
12. $5{\cdot}49 \times 10^4 - 2{\cdot}9 \times 10^3$
13. $6{\cdot}4 \times 10^4 - 3{\cdot}6 \times 10^4$
14. $2{\cdot}58 \times 10^4 - 1{\cdot}8 \times 10^3$
15. $3{\cdot}74 \times 10^6 - 5{\cdot}4 \times 10^5$
16. $2{\cdot}348 \times 10^6 - 4{\cdot}8 \times 10^4$
17. $2{\cdot}43 \times 10^4 + 1{\cdot}5 \times 10^3 + 2 \times 10^2$
18. $5{\cdot}47 \times 10^5 + 3{\cdot}8 \times 10^4 - 2{\cdot}85 \times 10^5$

19. Calculate the value of a and n where $1 \leq a < 10$ and $n \in \mathbb{N}$.

    (i) $5{\cdot}24 \times 10^4 + 3{\cdot}6 \times 10^3 = a \times 10^n$

    (ii) $6{\cdot}45 \times 10^5 - 2{\cdot}5 \times 10^4 = a \times 10^n$

20. John is laying a patio and he orders 3×10^3 kg of sand. On the first day he uses 800 kg of the sand. What mass of sand is left after day one? (Give your answer in scientific notation.)

21. A swimming pool contains $2{\cdot}45 \times 10^3$ m^3 of water. Before cleaning the pool the water must be drained. The water drains out of the pool at a rate of 175 m^3 every 10 minutes.

    (i) Find how much water is left in the swimming pool after one hour. (Give your answer in scientific notation.)

    (ii) Find how many minutes it takes until the pool is completely empty.

Multiplication and division

To multiply or divide two numbers in index notation, do the following.

1. Multiply or divide the a parts (the number parts).
2. Multiply or divide the powers of 10 (add or subtract the indices).
3. Write your answer in index notation.

Alternatively, you can use your calculator by keying in the numbers in index notation.

EXAMPLE

Express **(i)** $(2{\cdot}25 \times 10^4) \times (1{\cdot}6 \times 10^3)$ **(ii)** $(3{\cdot}91 \times 10^5) \div (1{\cdot}7 \times 10^2)$

in the form $a \times 10^n$, where $1 \le a < 10$ and $n \in \mathbb{N}$.

Solution:

(i) $(2{\cdot}25 \times 10^4) \times (1{\cdot}6 \times 10^3)$

$= 2{\cdot}25 \times 10^4 \times 1{\cdot}6 \times 10^3$

$= 2{\cdot}25 \times 1{\cdot}6 \times 10^4 \times 10^3$

$= 3{\cdot}6 \times 10^{4+3}$ (add the indices)

$= 3{\cdot}6 \times 10^7$

2·25 $\boxed{\text{EXP}}$ 4 $\boxed{\times}$ 1·6 $\boxed{\text{EXP}}$ 3 $\boxed{=}$

36000000 (on the display)

$= 3{\cdot}6 \times 10^7$

(ii) $(3{\cdot}91 \times 10^5) \div (1{\cdot}7 \times 10^2)$

$= \dfrac{3{\cdot}91 \times 10^5}{1{\cdot}7 \times 10^2}$

$= \dfrac{3{\cdot}91}{1{\cdot}7} \times \dfrac{10^5}{10^2}$

$= 2{\cdot}3 \times 10^{5-2}$ (subtract the indices)

$= 2{\cdot}3 \times 10^3$

3·91 $\boxed{\text{EXP}}$ 5 $\boxed{\div}$ 1·7 $\boxed{\text{EXP}}$ 2 $\boxed{=}$

2300 (on the display)

$= 2{\cdot}3 \times 10^3$

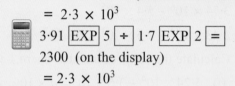

Exercise 18.6

Calculate questions 1–17 and write your answer in the form $a \times 10^n$, where $1 \le a < 10$ and $n \in \mathbb{N}$.

1. $(3 \times 10^4) \times (2 \times 10^2)$ 2. $(4 \times 10^5) \times (2 \times 10^3)$ 3. $(4 \times 10^3) \times (1{\cdot}3 \times 10^2)$

4. $(6 \times 10^3) \times (1{\cdot}4 \times 10^3)$ 5. $(1{\cdot}2 \times 10^2) \times (1{\cdot}5 \times 10^4)$ 6. $(2{\cdot}5 \times 10^4) \times (1{\cdot}8 \times 10^3)$

7. $(1{\cdot}6 \times 10^5) \times (4{\cdot}8 \times 10^3)$ 8. $(4{\cdot}5 \times 10^4) \times (2{\cdot}1 \times 10^2)$ 9. $(8 \times 10^5) \div (2 \times 10^3)$

10. $(6 \times 10^7) \div (3 \times 10^5)$ 11. $(8{\cdot}4 \times 10^6) \div (2{\cdot}1 \times 10^2)$ 12. $(8 \times 10^8) \div (3{\cdot}2 \times 10^5)$

13. $(5{\cdot}04 \times 10^7) \div (3{\cdot}6 \times 10^2)$ 14. $(8{\cdot}64 \times 10^5) \div (3{\cdot}6 \times 10^2)$ 15. $(9{\cdot}86 \times 10^5) \div (1{\cdot}7 \times 10^2)$

16. $(6{\cdot}72 \times 10^7) \div (5{\cdot}6 \times 10^5)$

17. $(2{\cdot}4 \times 10^4) \times (1{\cdot}5 \times 10^2) \div (1{\cdot}2 \times 10^3)$

18. Calculate the value of a and n where $1 \le a < 10$ and $n \in \mathbb{N}$.

   (i) $(3{\cdot}8 \times 10^4) \times (2{\cdot}5 \times 10^2) = a \times 10^n$

   (ii) $(9{\cdot}28 \times 10^8) \div (5{\cdot}8 \times 10^5) = a \times 10^n$

19. The mass of the moon is $7{\cdot}3 \times 10^{22}$ kg. If the mass of the earth is 82 times the mass of the moon, calculate the mass of the earth, correct to two decimal places.

20. 6,800 identical bricks are in a crate. If the total mass of the bricks is $8{\cdot}5 \times 10^3$ kg, calculate the mass of each brick.

21. Light travels at 3×10^5 km/sec. How many kilometres will light travel in 6 minutes? Express your answer in the form $a \times 10^n$, where $n \in \mathbb{Z}$ and $1 \leq a < 10$.

22. A packet of A4 paper contains 5×10^2 sheets of paper. The packet is 6 cm in height. Calculate the thickness of one sheet of paper. Express your answer in the form $a \times 10^n$, where $n \in \mathbb{Z}$ and $1 \leq a \leq 10$.

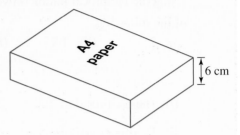

Reciprocals

If the product of two numbers is 1, then both numbers are the reciprocal of each other.
The reciprocal of 5 is $\frac{1}{5}$ and the reciprocal of $\frac{1}{5}$ is 5. Examples of reciprocals:

$5 \times \dfrac{1}{5} = 1$	$\dfrac{2}{3} \times \dfrac{3}{2} = 1$	$-\dfrac{7}{9} \times -\dfrac{9}{7} = 1$

To find the reciprocal of a number, do the following.

Method 1: Write the given number as a single fraction and turn it upside down.
Method 2: Use the reciprocal button, $\boxed{x^{-1}}$ or $\boxed{\frac{1}{x}}$, on your calculator.

EXAMPLE 1

Write out the reciprocal of each of the following numbers.
(i) 3   **(ii)** $-\frac{1}{4}$ **(iii)** $\frac{5}{7}$ **(iv)** $5\frac{1}{2}$

Solution:

(i) The reciprocal of 3 is $\frac{1}{3}$, since $3 \times \frac{1}{3} = 1$.

(ii) The reciprocal of $-\frac{1}{4}$ is $-\frac{4}{1}$, since $-\frac{1}{4} \times -\frac{4}{1} = 1$.

(iii) The reciprocal of $\frac{5}{7}$ is $\frac{7}{5}$, since $\frac{5}{7} \times \frac{7}{5} = 1$.

(iv) $5\frac{1}{2}$ as a single fraction $= \frac{11}{2}$.

The reciprocal of $\frac{11}{2}$ is $\frac{2}{11}$, since $\frac{11}{2} \times \frac{2}{11} = 1$.

EXAMPLE 2

Using the reciprocal button on your calculator, $\boxed{x^{-1}}$ or $\boxed{\frac{1}{x}}$, find the reciprocal of each of the following.

(i) $2 \cdot 5$ (ii) $1 \cdot 4$ (iii) $-3 \cdot 8$

Solution:

(i) The reciprocal of $2 \cdot 5$: $2 \cdot 5 \boxed{x^{-1}} = 0 \cdot 4$

(ii) The reciprocal of $1 \cdot 4$: $1 \cdot 4 \boxed{x^{-1}} = 0 \cdot 714$

(iii) The reciprocal of $-3 \cdot 8$: $-3 \cdot 8 \boxed{x^{-1}} = -0 \cdot 263$

Exercise 18.7

Write the reciprocal of questions 1–12 as a fraction.

1. 2 2. -8 3. 7 4. -6

5. $\dfrac{2}{3}$ 6. $\dfrac{5}{8}$ 7. $-\dfrac{1}{9}$ 8. $-\dfrac{4}{7}$

9. $\dfrac{1}{37}$ 10. $-\dfrac{7}{13}$ 11. $\dfrac{12}{11}$ 12. $-\dfrac{10}{7}$

Express questions 13–16 as single fractions and hence find their reciprocal as a fraction.

13. $2\dfrac{1}{3}$ 14. $3\dfrac{1}{4}$ 15. $5\dfrac{2}{7}$ 16. $3\dfrac{5}{9}$

Use your calculator to find the reciprocal of questions 17–20 correct to three decimal places.

17. $2 \cdot 55$ 18. $-3 \cdot 21$ 19. $0 \cdot 52$ 20. $1 \cdot 49$

CHAPTER 19

FACTORS

Factorising

> Factorising is the reverse procedure to removing brackets.

Expanding removes brackets.

Factorising does the opposite by putting in brackets.

For example:

> | | | |
> |---|---|---|
> | Expanding: | $5(2a + 3b) = 10a + 15b$ | Remove brackets. |
> | Factorising: | $10a + 15b = 5(2a + 3b)$ | Put in brackets. |

The process of finding the factors of an expression is called **factorisation**.

There are four types of factors that we will meet on our course.

	Type	Example	Factors
1.	Take out the HCF	$6pq + 3pr$	$3p(2q + r)$
2.	Factors by grouping	$ax + bx + ay + by$	$(a + b)(x + y)$
3.	Quadratic trinomials	$x^2 - 4x - 12$	$(x - 6)(x + 2)$
4.	Difference of two squares	$x^2 - 9$	$(x - 3)(x + 3)$

Note: It is good practice to check your answer by removing the brackets to make sure that the factors give the original expression you were asked to factorise.

Taking out the highest common factor (HCF)

> **1.** Find the HCF of all the terms making up the expression.
> **2.** Put the HCF outside the brackets.
> **3.** Divide each term by the HCF to find the factor inside the brackets.

● **EXAMPLE**

Factorise: **(i)** $5ab + 10ac$ **(ii)** $6xy - 3y^2$ **(iii)** $pq - pr + p$

Solution:

(i) $5ab + 10ac$

The HCF is $5a$.

Therefore, $5ab + 10ac$ (put $5a$ outside the bracket,

$= 5a(b + 2c)$ then divide each term by $5a$)

$$\frac{5ab}{5a} = b$$

$$\frac{10ac}{5a} = 2c$$

(ii) $6xy - 3y^2$

The HCF is $3y$.

Therefore, $6xy - 3y$ (put $3y$ outside the bracket,

$= 3y(2x - y)$ then divide each term by $3y$)

$$\frac{6xy}{3y} = 2x$$

$$\frac{-3y^2}{3y} = -y$$

(iii) $pq - pr + p$

The HCF is p.

Therefore, $pq - pr + p$ (put p outside the bracket,

$= p(q - r + 1)$ then divide each term by p)

↑

(There must be a 1 here)

Notice that the HCF is the same as one of the terms.

$$\frac{pq}{p} = q$$

$$\frac{-pr}{p} = -r$$

$$\frac{p}{p} = 1$$

Exercise 19.1

Simplify questions 1–15.

1. $\dfrac{8a}{2}$ **2.** $\dfrac{6p}{3}$ **3.** $\dfrac{4xy}{2x}$ **4.** $\dfrac{2q}{2q}$ **5.** $\dfrac{9ab}{3b}$

6. $\dfrac{-4p}{2}$ **7.** $\dfrac{3xy}{3y}$ **8.** $\dfrac{-20pq}{10q}$ **9.** $\dfrac{6x^2y}{2xy}$ **10.** $\dfrac{12pqr}{4pq}$

11. $\dfrac{5ab}{5a}$ **12.** $\dfrac{6ab}{3ab}$ **13.** $\dfrac{2x^2y}{2x^2y}$ **14.** $\dfrac{8ab}{2b}$ **15.** $\dfrac{6a^2b}{3ab}$

Copy questions 16–23 and fill in the missing terms in the brackets.

16. $2x + 4y = 2($ $)$ **17.** $5a + 15 = 5($ $)$

18. $x^2 + 3x = x($ $)$ **19.** $ac + ad = a($ $)$

20. $2pq - 6pr = 2p($ $)$ **21.** $4x^2 - 2xy = 2x($ $)$

22. $a^2 - a = a($ $)$ **23.** $5x - 10xy = 5x($ $)$

Factorise each of the following in questions 24–53.

24. $4x + 8$

25. $ab + ac$

26. $3a + 3b$

27. $2p + pq$

28. $12a + 8b$

29. $3m + 6n$

30. $x^2 + x$

31. $x^2 - 3x$

32. $2x + 4x^2$

33. $a^2 + 5a$

34. $4p + 2p^2$

35. $5x^2 + 10x$

36. $3ax + 6bx$

37. $4ab - 8a$

38. $2pq - 6pr$

39. $6xp - 6xq$

40. $5ab + 10ac$

41. $7x - 28xy$

42. $2a - 4a^2$

43. $3a + 6ab + 9ac$

44. $4a^2 - 20ab$

45. $pq + pr - p$

46. $6xy - 9xz$

47. $qr - 2qs$

48. $4ab - 3b^2$

49. $3x^2 - 9xy$

50. $18p^2q - 6pq$

51. $4x^2y + 8xy^2$

52. $2a^2b + 6ab^2$

53. $10abc - 15abd$

54. Simplify $3(a^2 + a - 2) + 2(3 - a^2)$ and then factorise your answer.

55. Factorise **(i)** $8ab + 12a$ **(ii)** $4b + 6$.

   (iii) Hence, simplify $\dfrac{8ab + 12a}{4b + 6}$.

Factors by grouping

An expression consisting of four terms with no common factor can be factorised with the following steps.

1. Group into pairs with a common factor.
2. Take out the common factor in each pair separately.
3. Take out the new common factor.

EXAMPLE

Factorise: **(i)** $ax + bx + ay + by$ **(ii)** $3ac - 3ad + bc - bd$ **(iii)** $pq + pr - q - r$

Solution:

(i) $ax + bx + ay + by$

$= (ax + bx) + (ay + by)$ (group into pairs with a common factor)

$= x(a + b) + y(a + b)$ (take out the common factor in each pair)

$= (a + b)(x + y)$ (take out the common factor $(a + b)$)

(ii) $3ac - 3ad + bc - bd$

$= (3ac - 3ad) + (bc - bd)$ (group into pairs with a common factor)

$= 3a(c - d) + b(c - d)$ (take out the common factor in each pair)

$= (c - d)(3a + b)$ (take out the common factor $(c - d)$)

(iii) **Method 1:**

$$pq + pr - q - r$$
$$= (pq + pr) - (q + r) \qquad \text{(group into pairs with a common factor)}$$
$$= p(q + r) - 1(q + r) \qquad \text{(take out the common factor in each pair)}$$
$$= (q + r)(p - 1) \qquad \text{(take out the common factor } (q + r))$$

Note: 1 or −1 is always a common factor.

Method 2:

$$pq + pr - q - r$$
$$= pq - q + pr - r \qquad \text{(rearrange order of the terms)}$$
$$= (pq - q) + (pr - r) \qquad \text{(group into pairs with a common factor)}$$
$$= q(p - 1) + r(p - 1) \qquad \text{(take out the common factor in each pair)}$$
$$= (p - 1)(q + r) \qquad \text{(take out the common factor } (p - 1))$$

Exercise 19.2

Factorise questions 1–34.

1. $c(a + b) + d(a + b)$
2. $r(p + q) + s(p + q)$
3. $p(x + a) + q(x + a)$
4. $m(x - y) + n(x - y)$
5. $2x(y - 3) + 5(y - 3)$
6. $2a(c - 3d) - b(c - 3d)$
7. $ax + bx + ay + by$
8. $pq + pr + xq + xr$
9. $mx + nx + my + ny$
10. $5a + 5b + xa + xb$
11. $4x + 4y + zx + zy$
12. $ab + ac + bd + cd$
13. $3p + 3q + pr + qr$
14. $ax + 4a + px + 4p$
15. $5x + 5y + ax + ay$
16. $ap + aq + bp + bq$
17. $ax - ay + 2x - 2y$
18. $3p - 3q + rp - rq$
19. $am - an + 4m - 4n$
20. $ac - bc + ad - bd$
21. $3a + 3b - ac - bc$
22. $pq + pr - 5q - 5r$
23. $px + qx - py - qy$
24. $pr + qr - 2ps - 2qs$
25. $a^2 + ab + 2a + 2b$
26. $x^2 - xy + xz - yz$
27. $x^2 + 2px + qx + 2pq$
28. $2x - x^2 + 2y - xy$
29. $m^2 + mn + 4m + 4n$
30. $p^2 - 3p + pq - 3q$
31. $ab + ac + b + c$
32. $pq + pr + q + r$
33. $ax + bx - a - b$
34. $xy + xz - y - z$

More difficult factors by grouping

Sometimes rearranging is necessary. We often have to take out a **negative** common factor from the second grouped pair.

For example:
$$-3a - 3b = -3(a + b) \qquad \text{(take out the common factor } -3)$$
$$-5ax + 5ay = -5a(x - y) \qquad \text{(take out the common factor } -5a)$$
$$\uparrow$$
(notice that this sign changes to a $-$)

> ## EXAMPLE
>
> Factorise: **(i)** $pq - 4r + pr - 4q$ **(ii)** $6xy + ab - 2by - 3ax$
>
> **Solution:**
>
> **(i)** $pq - 4r + pr - 4q$
>
> No common factors in the first two terms or in the last two terms, therefore rearrange.
> $$= pq + pr - 4q - 4r \qquad \text{(rearrange)}$$
> $$= (pq + pr) - (4q + 4r) \qquad \text{(group into pairs with a common factor)}$$
> $$= p(q + r) - 4(q + r) \qquad \text{(take out the common factor in each pair)}$$
> $$= (q + r)(p - 4) \qquad \text{(take out the common factor } (q + r))$$
>
> **(ii)** $6xy + ab - 2by - 3ax$
>
> No common factors in the first two terms or in the last two terms, therefore rearrange.
> $$= 6xy - 2by - 3ax + ab \qquad \text{(rearrange)}$$
> $$= (6xy - 2by) - (3ax - ab) \qquad \text{(group into pairs with a common factor)}$$
> $$= 2y(3x - b) - a(3x - b) \qquad \text{(take out the common factor in each pair)}$$
> $$= (3x - b)(2y - a) \qquad \text{(take out the common factor } (3x - b))$$

Exercise 19.3

Copy questions 1–8 and fill in the missing terms in the brackets.

1. $-5a - 5b = -5(\qquad)$
2. $-3ab - 3ac = -3a(\qquad)$
3. $-2pq - 2pr = -2p(\qquad)$
4. $-4ax - 4bx = -4x(\qquad)$
5. $-3a + 3b = -3(\qquad)$
6. $-qr + 3qs = -q(\qquad)$
7. $-5pq + 5pr = -5p(\qquad)$
8. $-x^2 + 2x = -x(\qquad)$

Factorise questions 9–24.

9. $ac + bd + ad + bc$
10. $pq + 3r + pr + 3q$
11. $ax + 2b + 2a + bx$
12. $3x + yz + 3y + xz$
13. $px - qy - qx + py$
14. $2ab - 5c - 5b + 2ac$

15. $ab - cd + bd - ac$
16. $2ap + bq - 2aq - bp$
17. $ax + 4p - 4a - px$
18. $3a + bq - 3b - aq$
19. $pq + rs - pr - qs$
20. $pa + bq - pb - aq$
21. $x(a + b) - a - b$
22. $p - q - 3ap + 3aq$
23. $p(a - b) - a + b$
24. $a - c(b - a) - b$

Quadratic trinomials

An expression of the form $x^2 + bx + c$, where b and c are numbers, is called a **quadratic trinomial**, since in the expression the highest power of x is 2 (quadratic) and it contains three terms (trinomial).

Factorising quadratic trinomials

Quadratic trinomials can be broken up into **two** types.

1. **Final term positive**

   When the final term is positive, the sign inside the middle of the brackets will be the **same**, either two pluses or two minuses. Keep the sign of the middle term given in the question.

Middle term plus:	$(x + number)(x + number)$	(two pluses)
Middle term minus:	$(x - number)(x - number)$	(two minuses)

2. **Final term negative**

   When the final term is negative, the signs inside the middle of the brackets will be **different**.

   $$(x + number)(x - number) \quad or \quad (x - number)(x + number)$$

In both cases the factors can be found by trial and improvement. The test is to multiply the inside terms, multiply the outside terms and add the results to see if you get the middle term of the original trinomial.

EXAMPLE

Factorise: **(i)** $x^2 + 8x + 15$ **(ii)** $x^2 - 7x + 10$ **(iii)** $x^2 + x - 12$ **(iv)** $x^2 - 2x - 8$

Solution:

(i) $x^2 + 8x + 15$

Factors of 15
1×15
3×15

Final term is + and middle term is +,

therefore the factors are $(x + \text{number})(x + \text{number})$.

$(x + 1)(x + 15)$ $\qquad x + 15x = 16x$ (no)

$(x + 3)(x + 5)$ $\qquad 3x + 5x = 8x$ (yes, this is the middle term)

Therefore, $x^2 + 8x + 15 = (x + 3)(x + 5)$.

(ii) $x^2 - 7x + 10$

Factors of 10
1×10
2×5

Final term is + and middle term is −,

therefore factors are $(x - \text{number})(x - \text{number})$.

$(x - 1)(x - 10)$ $\qquad -x - 10x = -11x$ (no)

$(x - 2)(x - 5)$ $\qquad -2x - 5x = -7x$ (yes, this is the middle term)

Therefore, $x^2 - 7x + 10 = (x - 2)(x - 5)$.

(iii) $x^2 + x - 12$

Factors of 12
1×12
2×6
3×4

Final term is −,

therefore the factors are $(x + \text{number})(x - \text{number})$

or

$(x - \text{number})(x + \text{number})$.

Note: It is good practice to begin the trial and improvement with $(x + \text{number})(x - \text{number})$.

$(x + 2)(x - 6)$ $\qquad 2x - 6x = -4x$ (no)

$(x + 3)(x - 4)$ $\qquad 3x - 4x = -x$ (no, wrong sign)

On our second trial we have the correct number in front of x but of the wrong sign.

So we just swap the signs:

$(x - 3)(x + 4)$ $\qquad -3x + 4x = x$ (yes, this is the middle term)

Therefore, $x^2 + x - 12 = (x - 3)(x + 4)$.

(iv) $x^2 - 2x - 8$

Factors of 8
1×8
2×4

Final term is −,

therefore the factors are $(x + \text{number})(x - \text{number})$

or

$(x - \text{number})(x + \text{number})$.

$(x + 1)(x - 8)$ $\qquad x - 8x = -7x$ (no)

$(x + 2)(x - 4)$ $\qquad 2x - 4x = -2x$ (yes, this is the middle term)

Therefore, $x^2 - 2x - 8 = (x + 2)(x - 4)$.

Exercise 19.4

Factorise each of the following in questions 1–48.

1. $x^2 + 3x + 2$
2. $x^2 + 4x + 3$
3. $x^2 + 6x + 5$
4. $x^2 + 8x + 7$
5. $x^2 + 12x + 11$
6. $x^2 + 6x + 8$
7. $x^2 + 5x + 4$
8. $x^2 + 7x + 12$
9. $x^2 + 7x + 10$
10. $x^2 + 11x + 10$
11. $x^2 + 8x + 12$
12. $x^2 + 13x + 12$
13. $x^2 - 9x + 14$
14. $x^2 - 10x + 21$
15. $x^2 - 8x + 12$
16. $x^2 - 2x - 8$
17. $x^2 + 8x - 20$
18. $x^2 - 4x - 12$
19. $x^2 + 2x - 15$
20. $x^2 - x - 12$
21. $x^2 + x - 30$
22. $x^2 + 6x + 9$
23. $x^2 + 4x + 4$
24. $x^2 + 10x + 24$
25. $x^2 + x - 2$
26. $x^2 - x - 6$
27. $x^2 - 5x - 24$
28. $x^2 - 2x - 3$
29. $x^2 + 5x - 6$
30. $x^2 - 29x + 100$
31. $x^2 + 19x + 48$
32. $x^2 + 3x - 4$
33. $x^2 + x - 20$
34. $x^2 - 2x - 24$
35. $x^2 - 3x - 10$
36. $x^2 + 17x - 60$
37. $x^2 - 2x - 35$
38. $x^2 - 9x + 20$
39. $x^2 - x - 42$
40. $x^2 + 3x - 18$
41. $x^2 + 14x + 45$
42. $x^2 - 3x - 28$
43. $x^2 - 5x - 14$
44. $x^2 + 3x - 40$
45. $x^2 - 6x - 27$
46. $x^2 - 14x - 72$
47. $x^2 + 28x - 60$
48. $x^2 - 11x - 80$

49. Simplify $5(x^2 - 3x + 4) - 4(x^2 - 6x)$ and then factorise your answer.
50. Simplify $2(2x - x^2) - 3(5 + 2x - x^2)$ and then factorise your answer.

Difference of two squares

An expression such as $a^2 - b^2$ is called the **difference of two squares**.

The product $(a - b)(a + b) = a^2 - b^2$.

In reverse, $a^2 - b^2 = (a - b)(a + b)$.

We use this to factorise any expression that can be written as the difference of two squares.

We factorise the difference of two squares with the following steps.

> 1. Write each term as a perfect square with brackets.
> 2. Use the rule $a^2 - b^2 = (a - b)(a + b)$.
>   In words: $(\text{first})^2 - (\text{second})^2 = (\text{first} - \text{second})(\text{first} + \text{second})$.

EXAMPLE 1

Factorise: **(i)** $x^2 - 4$ **(ii)** $y^2 - 1$

Solution:

(i) $x^2 - 4$

$= (x)^2 - (2)^2$ (write as perfect squares in brackets)

$= (x - 2)(x + 2)$ (apply the rule, (first − second)(first + second))

(ii) $y^2 - 1$

$= (y)^2 - (1)^2$ (write as perfect squares in brackets)

$= (y - 1)(y + 1)$ (apply the rule, (first − second)(first + second))

Note: $1 = 1^2$, i.e. 1 is a perfect square.

The factorisation of the difference of two squares can also be used to simplify some calculations.

EXAMPLE 2

By resolving into factors, evaluate the following.

(i) $101^2 - 99^2$ **(ii)** $(1{\cdot}02)^2 - (0{\cdot}98)^2$

Solution:

(i) $101^2 - 99^2$

$= (101 - 99)(101 + 99)$

$= (2)(200)$

$= 400$

(ii) $(1{\cdot}02)^2 - (0{\cdot}98)^2$

$= (1{\cdot}02 - 0{\cdot}98)(1{\cdot}02 + 0{\cdot}98)$

$= (0{\cdot}04)(2)$

$= 0{\cdot}08$

Exercise 19.5

Copy questions 1−6 and fill in the missing terms in the brackets.

1. $25 = (\quad)^2$ **2.** $4 = (\quad)^2$ **3.** $144 = (\quad)^2$

4. $81 = (\quad)^2$ **5.** $169 = (\quad)^2$ **6.** $625 = (\quad)^2$

Factorise each of the following in questions 7−15.

7. $x^2 - 16$ **8.** $x^2 - 64$ **9.** $x^2 - 121$

10. $x^2 - 9$ **11.** $x^2 - 36$ **12.** $a^2 - 100$

13. $p^2 - 81$ **14.** $49 - y^2$ **15.** $1 - x^2$

Factorise and hence evaluate each of the following in questions 16−24.

16. $5^2 - 3^2$ **17.** $8^2 - 4^2$ **18.** $10^2 - 7^2$

19. $11^2 - 10^2$ **20.** $15^2 - 5^2$ **21.** $103^2 - 97^2$

22. $(2{\cdot}75)^2 - (1{\cdot}25)^2$ **23.** $(5{\cdot}5)^2 - (4{\cdot}5)^2$ **24.** $(10{\cdot}01)^2 - (9{\cdot}99)^2$

25.   Simplify $5(x^2 - 1) - 4(x^2 + 1)$ and then factorise your answer.

Simultaneous linear equations

An equation such as $2x + 3y = 19$ is called a linear equation in two unknowns, x and y. Simultaneous linear equations are a pair of such equations. Two equations are necessary if we are to be able to find the values of x and y that satisfy both equations.

For example, consider the following pair of simultaneous linear equations:

$$5x + 2y = 20 \quad ①$$
$$4x + 3y = 23 \quad ②$$

The solution of this pair of simultaneous linear equations is $x = 2$ and $y = 5$.

This pair of values satisfies both equations simultaneously (at the same time).

We can check this by substituting $x = 2$ and $y = 5$ in both equations and showing that the left-hand side is equal to the right-hand side in each equation.

Check:

$5x + 2y = 20$ ①	$4x + 3y = 23$ ②
$\downarrow \quad \downarrow$	$\downarrow \quad \downarrow$
$5(2) + 2(5) = 20$	$4(2) + 3(5) = 23$
$10 + 10 = 20$	$8 + 15 = 23$
$20 = 20$ True	$23 = 23$ True

∴ Our solution $x = 2$ and $y = 5$ is correct.

Equations that are solved together are called simultaneous equations.

Solving a pair of simultaneous linear equations means finding the values of x and y that make both equations true at the same time.

Consider the following pair of simultaneous linear equations:

$p - 2q = 10$ and $3p + 5q = -22$.

Is $p = 0$ and $q = -5$ the correct solution for both?

To check, we proceed as in the previous example and substitute $p = 0$ and $q = -5$ into **both** equations.

$p - 2q = 10$	$3p + 5q = -22$
$\downarrow \quad \downarrow$	$\downarrow \quad \downarrow$
$(0) - 2(-5) = 10$	$3(0) + 5(-5) = -22$
$0 + 10 = 10$	$0 - 25 = -22$
$10 = 10$ True	$-25 = -22$ False

∴ $p = 0$ and $q = -5$ is not the correct solution for both equations.

Exercise 20.1

Check if the given solution in each case is correct for the simultaneous (both) linear equations.

1. $x - 4y = 3$
   $x + y = 13$
   Solution: $x = 11, y = 8$

2. $x + 3y = 2$
   $3x + y = 14$
   Solution: $x = 5, y = -1$

3. $3p - 3q = 48$
   $p + 2q = -5$
   Solution: $p = 9, q = -7$

4. $5a + 4b = 24$
   $a - 2b = 4$
   Solution: $a = 4, b = 1$

5. $p + q = 8$
   $4p - 3q = 11$
   Solution: $p = 5, q = -3$

6. $m + 9n = 14$
   $-2m + n = 10$
   Solution: $m = -4, n = 2$

7. $6x - y = 17$
   $3y + x = 1$
   Solution: $x = 2, y = -5$

8. $2x + 4y + 9 = 0$
   $x - 2y + 5 = 0$
   Solution: $x = 7, y = 6$

9. $x - 3y - 14 = 0$
   $y + 2x + 7 = 0$
   Solution: $x = -1, y = -5$

Simultaneous linear equations in two variables are solved with the following steps.

1. Write both equations in the form $ax + by = k$ and label the equations ① and ②.
2. Multiply one or both of the equations by a number in order to make the coefficients of x or y the same, but of opposite sign.
3. Add to remove the variable with equal coefficients but of opposite sign.
4. Solve the resultant equation to find the value of the remaining unknown (x or y).
5. Substitute this value in equation ① or ② to find the value of the other unknown.

EXAMPLE 1

Solve for x and y: $\quad x + y = 6$
$\quad\quad\quad\quad\quad\quad\quad x - y = 2$

Solution:

1. Both equations are in the form $ax + by = k$.
   Label the equations ① and ②.
   $$x + y = 6 \quad ①$$
   $$x - y = 2 \quad ②$$

2 and 3. Since the coefficients of y are equal but of opposite sign we add ① and ②.
$$2x = 8$$

4. Divide both sides by 2. $\quad x = 4$

5. Put $x = 4$ into ① or ②
   $$x + y = 6 \quad ①$$
   $$\downarrow$$
   $$4 + y = 6$$
   $$y = 2$$

∴ The solution is $x = 4$ and $y = 2$.

Here is the situation represented on a graph:

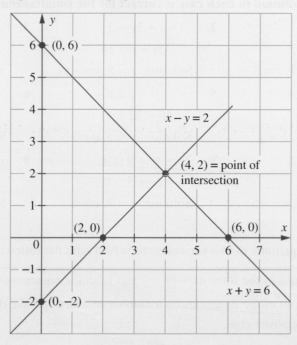

EXAMPLE 2

Solve for p and q: $\quad\quad 5p + 6q - 19 = 0$
$$p = 2q - 9$$

Solution:

1. Write both equations in the form $ap + bq = k$. $\quad$ $5p + 6q = 19$ ①
$$p - 2q = -9 \quad ②$$

2. Make the coefficients q the same, but of opposite sign.
   Multiply ② by 3. $\quad\quad\quad\quad\quad\quad\quad\quad\quad$ $5p + 6q = 19$ ①
$$3p - 6q = -27 \quad ② \times 3$$

3. Add these new equations. $\quad\quad\quad\quad\quad\quad\quad\quad$ $8p = -8$

4. Divide both sides by 8. $\quad\quad\quad\quad\quad\quad\quad\quad$ $p = -1$

5. Put $p = -1$ into ① or ②. $\quad\quad\quad\quad\quad\quad$ $p - 2q = -9$ ②
$$\downarrow$$
$$-1 - 2q = -9$$

Add 1 to both sides.	$-2q = -8$
Multiply both sides by -1.	$2q = 8$
Divide both sides by 2.	$q = 4$

$\therefore$ The solution is $p = -1$ and $q = 4$.

Exercise 20.2

Solve the following pairs of simultaneous equations in questions 1–15.

1. $x + y = 7$
   $x - y = 1$

2. $x + y = 10$
   $x - y = 2$

3. $p + q = 11$
   $p - q = 1$

4. $p + q = 28$
   $p - q = 6$

5. $2x + y = 14$
   $x + y = 9$

6. $2p + q = 20$
   $p + q = 18$

7. $2x + y = 12$
   $x - y = 3$

8. $3x + y = 13$
   $2x - y = 7$

9. $x + 3y = 11$
   $2x - 3y = 4$

10. $x + y = 3$
    $6x - 5y = 7$

11. $x - y = 4$
    $x + 2y = 1$

12. $3x + 2y = 13$
    $4x - 3y = 6$

13. $3p + 5q = 19$
    $7p = -14$

14. $3y = -12$
    $5x - 2y = 13$

15. $2x - y = 8$
    $3x + 2y = -16$

In questions 16–24, write both equations in the form $ax + by = k$ before attempting to solve.

16. $x + y - 10 = 0$
    $x - y - 4 = 0$

17. $x = y + 5$
    $3y = 15 - 2x$

18. $y = -3x + 13$
    $2x - y - 7 = 0$

19. $x = y$
    $2x + 3y = 25$

20. $x = -2y$
    $y + 9 - x = 0$

21. $x = y - 3$
    $2x = -y$

22. $3x + 2y - 7 = 0$
    $x - 3y + 5 = 0$

23. $2x = 5 - 3y$
    $x + 14 = 4y$

24. $3x = y + 2$
    $2y + 4 = x$

25. Ciana has some unknown weights labelled x and y and some 8 kg and 4 kg weights. She finds that the following combinations of weights balance.

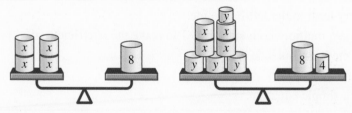

(i) Find the value of (a) x (b) y.

(ii) Ciana also has some unknown weights labelled z. She finds that $7z + 2y = 2z + 11x$. Find the value of z.

An equation such as $x^2 - 3x - 10 = 0$ is called a quadratic equation in x.

A quadratic equation has x^2 (x squared) as its highest power. In general, a quadratic equation has two different solutions (often called roots), but with some quadratic equations the two solutions are the same.

For example, consider the quadratic equation $x^2 - 5x - 14 = 0$.

The two solutions of the equation $x^2 - 5x - 14 = 0$ are $x = 7$ and $x = -2$.

We can check this by substituting $x = 7$ or $x = -2$ in the equation and showing that in each case the left-hand side is equal to the right-hand side.

Check $x = 7$:		Check $x = -2$:	
$x^2 - 5x - 14 = 0$		$x^2 - 5x - 14 = 0$	
$(7)^2 - 5(7) - 14 = 0$		$(-2)^2 - 5(-2) - 14 = 0$	
$49 - 35 - 14 = 0$		$4 + 10 - 14 = 0$	
$49 - 49 = 0$		$14 - 14 = 0$	
$0 = 0$	True	$0 = 0$	True

Therefore, our solutions $x = 7$ or $x = -2$ are correct.

There are three types of quadratic equations we will meet on our course:

1.	$x^2 - 2x - 15 = 0$	(three terms)
2.	$x^2 - 3x = 0$	(no constant)
3.	$x^2 - 9 = 0$	(no x term)

Solving a quadratic equation means finding the values of x that make the equation true.

Quadratic equations are solved with the following steps.

> **1.** Bring every term to the left-hand side.
>   (If necessary, multiply both sides by -1 to make the coefficient of x^2 positive.)
> **2.** Factorise the left-hand side.
> **3.** Let each factor $= 0$.
> **4.** Solve each simple equation.

Type 1

 EXAMPLE

Solve for x: $x^2 - 4x - 21 = 0$.

Solution:

1. $x^2 - 4x - 21 = 0$ (every term is on the left-hand side)
2. $(x + 3)(x - 7) = 0$ (factorise the left-hand side)
3. $x + 3 = 0$ or $x - 7 = 0$ (let each factor $= 0$)
4. $x = -3$ or $x = 7$ (solve each simple equation)

Therefore, $x = -3$ or $x = 7$.

Type 2

 EXAMPLE

Solve for x: $x^2 - 3x = 0$.

Solution:

1. $x^2 - 3x = 0$
2. $x(x - 3) = 0$ (factorise the left-hand side)
3. $x = 0$ or $x - 3 = 0$ (let each factor $= 0$)
4. $x = 0$ or $x = 3$ (solve each simple equation)

Therefore, $x = 0$ or $x = 3$.

Note: It is important not to divide both sides by x, otherwise the root $x = 0$ is lost.

Type 3

EXAMPLE

Solve for x: $x^2 - 25 = 0$.

Solution:

We will use two methods to solve this quadratic equation.

Method 1:

1. $\quad x^2 - 25 = 0$ (every term is on the left-hand side)
2. $\quad (x)^2 - (5)^2 = 0$ (difference of two squares)
   $\quad (x - 5)(x + 5) = 0$ (factorise the left-hand side)
3. $\quad x - 5 = 0$ or $x + 5 = 0$ (let each factor $= 0$)
4. $\quad\quad x = 5$ or $\quad x = -5$ (solve each simple equation)

Therefore, $x = 5$ or $x = -5$.

Method 2:

$\quad x^2 - 25 = 0$

$\quad\quad x^2 = 25$ (add 25 to both sides)

$\quad\quad x = \pm\sqrt{25}$ (take the square root of both sides)

$\quad\quad x = \pm 5$ ($\sqrt{25} = 5$)

Therefore, $x = 5$ or $x = -5$.

Exercise 21.1

Solve each of the equations in questions 1–36.

1. $(x - 1)(x + 3) = 0$
2. $(x - 8)(x - 3) = 0$
3. $(x + 5)(x + 4) = 0$
4. $x(x - 1) = 0$
5. $x(x + 4) = 0$
6. $x(x - 2) = 0$
7. $(x - 4)(x + 4) = 0$
8. $(x - 2)(x + 2) = 0$
9. $(x - 12)(x + 12) = 0$
10. $x^2 - 5x + 4 = 0$
11. $x^2 + 6x + 8 = 0$
12. $x^2 - 8x + 15 = 0$
13. $x^2 + 2x - 8 = 0$
14. $x^2 + x - 2 = 0$
15. $x^2 - 2x - 15 = 0$
16. $x^2 + 12x + 35 = 0$
17. $x^2 - x - 20 = 0$
18. $x^2 - 5x + 6 = 0$
19. $x^2 - 5x = 0$
20. $x^2 + 2x = 0$
21. $x^2 - 4x = 0$
22. $x^2 - 9 = 0$
23. $x^2 - 64 = 0$
24. $x^2 - 100 = 0$
25. $x^2 - 1 = 0$
26. $x^2 - 81 = 0$
27. $x^2 - 49 = 0$
28. $x^2 - 7x = 0$
29. $x^2 - 7x - 8 = 0$
30. $x^2 - 121 = 0$
31. $x^2 - 9x + 20 = 0$
32. $x^2 - 3x - 4 = 0$
33. $x^2 + 8x = 0$
34. $x^2 - 8x - 9 = 0$
35. $x^2 - 36 = 0$
36. $x^2 - 10x + 21 = 0$

In questions 37–45, write the question in the form $x^2 + bx + c = 0$ and then solve.

37. $x^2 - 12x + 35 = 15$
38. $x^2 = 4x + 12$
39. $x^2 + 12x = 7x$
40. $5x^2 + 2x = 4x^2 + 15$
41. $3x^2 - 8x + 4 = 2x^2 - 8$
42. $x(x - 6) - 16 = 0$
43. $x(x - 4) = 21$
44. $3(x^2 - 2x) = 2(x^2 - 3x + 8)$
45. $(x + 3)(x - 5) = 9$

Algebraic fractions

Arithmetic fractions

We often encounter fractions when working in algebra. As a first step it is vital that you can understand and handle fractions with numbers only (arithmetic).

EXAMPLE

Find the value of each of the following without using a calculator and write your answer in its simplest form $\dfrac{a}{b}$ where $a, b \in \mathbb{Z}$.

(i) $\dfrac{2}{3} + \dfrac{5}{8}$

(ii) $\dfrac{7}{10} - \dfrac{1}{2}$

(iii) $\dfrac{4}{x} + \dfrac{5}{y}$ where $x = 3$ and $y = 7$

Solution:

(i) Multiples of 3 = (3, 6, 9, 12, 15, 18, 21, 24, 27…)

Multiples of 8 = (8, 16, 24, 32, 40…)

The LCD of 3 and 8 is 24.

$$\therefore \frac{2}{3} + \frac{5}{8} = \frac{(8)(2) + (3)(5)}{24} = \frac{16 + 15}{24} = \frac{31}{24}$$

(ii) Multiples of 10 = (10, 20, 30, 40…)

Multiples of 2 = (2, 4, 6, 8, 10, 12…)

The LCD of 10 and 2 is 10.

$$\therefore \frac{7}{10} - \frac{1}{2} = \frac{(1)(7) - (5)(1)}{10} = \frac{7 - 5}{10} = \frac{2}{10} = \frac{1}{5}$$

We reduce $\dfrac{2}{10}$ to $\dfrac{1}{5}$ by dividing above and below by 2.

We know $\dfrac{1}{5} = \dfrac{2}{10}$, but $\dfrac{1}{5}$ is in its simplest form.

(iii) $\dfrac{4}{x} + \dfrac{5}{y}$ where $x = 3$ and $y = 7$ becomes $\dfrac{4}{3} + \dfrac{5}{7}$.

Multiples of $3 = (3, 6, 9, 12, 15, 18, 21, 24, 27\ldots)$

Multiples of $7 = (7, 14, 21, 28\ldots)$

The LCD of 3 and 7 is 21.

$$\therefore \frac{4}{3} + \frac{5}{7} = \frac{(7)(4) + (3)(5)}{21} = \frac{28 + 15}{21} = \frac{43}{21}$$

Exercise 22.1

1. Find the value of each of the following without using a calculator and write your answer in the form $\frac{a}{b}$ where $a, b \in \mathbb{Z}$.

   (i) $\dfrac{1}{3} + \dfrac{1}{7}$

   (ii) $\dfrac{3}{5} + \dfrac{5}{6}$

   (iii) $\dfrac{4}{7} - \dfrac{1}{8}$

   (iv) $\dfrac{2}{5} + \dfrac{3}{4} - \dfrac{7}{10}$

In questions 2–4, substitute the given values and evaluate each expression without using a calculator. Write each answer in its simplest form $\frac{a}{b}$ where $a, b \in \mathbb{Z}$.

2. If $p = 2$ and $q = 9$:

   (i) $\dfrac{1}{p} + \dfrac{1}{q}$

   (ii) $\dfrac{1}{q} - \dfrac{1}{p}$

   (iii) $\dfrac{3}{p} + \dfrac{2}{q}$

   (iv) $\dfrac{p}{q} + \dfrac{q}{p}$

3. If $x = 3$, $y = 4$ and $z = 5$:

   (i) $\dfrac{1}{x} + \dfrac{1}{y} + \dfrac{1}{z}$

   (ii) $\dfrac{x + y}{2} - \dfrac{z}{4}$

   (iii) $\dfrac{x}{y} + \dfrac{z}{y}$

   (iv) $\dfrac{3}{x} - \dfrac{3}{y} + \dfrac{3}{z}$

4. If $p = 2$, $q = \dfrac{1}{4}$ and $r = \dfrac{1}{3}$:

   (i) $p + q + r$

   (ii) $p + q - r$

   (iii) $2p + 3q + 4r$

   (iv) $\dfrac{p - r}{p + q}$

Addition and subtraction of algebraic fractions

Algebraic fractions that have numbers as denominators can be added or subtracted in exactly the same way as in arithmetic, i.e. we express the fractions with the lowest common denominator.

Algebraic fractions are added or subtracted with the following steps.

1. Put brackets on the top of each fraction.
2. Find the LCD of the numbers on the bottom.
3. Proceed in exactly the same way as in arithmetic.
4. Simplify the top (add and subtract terms that are the same).

EXAMPLE 1

Express the following as a single fraction.

(i) $\dfrac{p}{2} + \dfrac{p}{3}$ (ii) $\dfrac{2p}{5} - \dfrac{p}{8}$

Solution:

(i) $\dfrac{p}{2} + \dfrac{p}{3}$

$= \dfrac{(p)}{2} + \dfrac{(p)}{3}$ (put brackets on top)
(the LCD is 6)

$= \dfrac{3(p) + 2(p)}{6}$ (do the same as in arithmetic)

$= \dfrac{3p + 2p}{6}$ (remove the brackets on top)

$= \dfrac{5p}{6}$ (simplify the top)

(ii) $\dfrac{2p}{5} - \dfrac{p}{8}$

$= \dfrac{(2p)}{5} - \dfrac{(p)}{8}$ (put brackets on top)
(the LCD is 40)

$= \dfrac{8(2p) - 5(p)}{40}$ (do the same as in arithmetic)

$= \dfrac{16p - 5p}{40}$ (remove the brackets on top)

$= \dfrac{11p}{40}$ (simplify the top)

EXAMPLE 2

Express the following as a single fraction.

(i) $\dfrac{x+2}{3} + \dfrac{x+5}{4}$

(ii) $\dfrac{3x-4}{5} - \dfrac{2x-3}{4} - \dfrac{1}{2}$

Solution:

(i) $\dfrac{x+2}{3} + \dfrac{x+5}{4}$

$= \dfrac{(x+2)}{3} + \dfrac{(x+5)}{4}$ (put brackets on top)
    (the LCD is 12)

$= \dfrac{4(x+2) + 3(x+5)}{12}$ (do the same as in arithmetic)

$= \dfrac{4x + 8 + 3x + 15}{12}$ (remove the brackets on top)

$= \dfrac{7x + 23}{12}$ (simplify the top)

(ii) $\dfrac{3x-4}{5} - \dfrac{2x-3}{4} - \dfrac{1}{2}$

$= \dfrac{(3x-4)}{5} - \dfrac{(2x-3)}{4} - \dfrac{(1)}{2}$ (put brackets on top)
    (the LCD is 20)

$= \dfrac{4(3x-4) - 5(2x-3) - 10(1)}{20}$ (do the same as in arithmetic)

$= \dfrac{12x - 16 - 10x + 15 - 10}{20}$ (remove the brackets on top)

$= \dfrac{2x - 11}{20}$ (simplify the top)

Exercise 22.2

Express questions 1–6 as a single fraction.

1. $\dfrac{x}{2} + \dfrac{x}{3}$

2. $\dfrac{x}{4} + \dfrac{x}{3}$

3. $\dfrac{x}{5} + \dfrac{x}{4}$

4. $\dfrac{2x}{3} + \dfrac{x}{6} - \dfrac{4x}{9}$

5. $\dfrac{3x}{8} + \dfrac{x}{2} - \dfrac{3x}{4}$

6. $\dfrac{x}{2} + \dfrac{3x}{4} - \dfrac{5x}{3}$

7. (i) Express $\dfrac{2}{3} - \dfrac{1}{9}$ as a single fraction in its simplest form.

   (ii) Express $\dfrac{x+7}{3} - \dfrac{x}{9}$ as a single fraction in its simplest form.

8. (i) Express $\dfrac{3}{5} - \dfrac{3}{10}$ as a single fraction in its simplest form.

   (ii) Express $\dfrac{x+2}{5} - \dfrac{x+7}{10}$ as a single fraction in its simplest form.

Express questions 9–17 as a single fraction in its simplest form.

9. $\dfrac{x+4}{2} + \dfrac{x+5}{2}$

10. $\dfrac{2x+3}{6} + \dfrac{x+1}{4}$

11. $\dfrac{2x-3}{4} + \dfrac{3x+6}{2}$

12. $\dfrac{5x-3}{2} - \dfrac{3x-4}{3}$

13. $\dfrac{5x+1}{6} - \dfrac{2x-3}{4}$

14. $\dfrac{x+2}{3} + \dfrac{x+5}{2} + \dfrac{3}{4}$

15. $\dfrac{3x+2}{8} - \dfrac{x}{4} + \dfrac{x+1}{2}$

16. $\dfrac{5x-1}{4} + \dfrac{x}{3} - \dfrac{5}{6}$

17. $\dfrac{5x}{3} - \dfrac{1}{6} + \dfrac{2-3x}{2}$

18. Show that:

   (i) $\dfrac{3x+5}{6} - \dfrac{2x+3}{4} = \dfrac{1}{12}$

   (ii) $\dfrac{4x+3}{6} - \dfrac{6x+4}{9} = \dfrac{1}{18}$

19. (i) Express $\dfrac{2x-1}{5} + \dfrac{x+7}{2}$ as a single fraction in its simplest form.

   (ii) Verify your answer to part (i) by letting $x = 3$.

20. (i) Express $\dfrac{3x+2}{4} - \dfrac{x+4}{5}$ as a single fraction in its simplest form.

   (ii) Verify your answer to part (i) by letting $x = 6$.

Dividing terms

Dividing terms in algebra is similar to dividing numbers in arithmetic.

When dividing one term by another, do the following:

> Divide the top and bottom by common factors.

EXAMPLE

Simplify: (i) $\dfrac{10ab}{2b}$ (ii) $\dfrac{12x^2y}{3x}$

Solution:

(i) $\dfrac{10ab}{2b}$

$= 5a$ (divide top and bottom by $2b$)

(ii) $\dfrac{12x^2y}{3x}$

$= \dfrac{12xxy}{3x}$

$= 4xy$ (divide top and bottom by $3x$)

Exercise 22.3

Simplify each of the following.

1. $\dfrac{20ab}{5b}$ 2. $\dfrac{10xy}{2y}$ 3. $\dfrac{21pq}{7q}$ 4. $\dfrac{12ab}{6a}$ 5. $\dfrac{16a}{8}$

6. $\dfrac{28p}{7}$ 7. $\dfrac{15x}{5}$ 8. $\dfrac{6pq}{3pq}$ 9. $\dfrac{x^2}{x}$ 10. $\dfrac{x^2y}{xy}$

11. $\dfrac{a^2}{a^2}$ 12. $\dfrac{3pq}{3pq}$ 13. $\dfrac{5ab}{5ab}$ 14. $\dfrac{22a^2}{11a}$ 15. $\dfrac{6x^2y}{3xy}$

16. $\dfrac{18a^3b}{6a^2b}$ 17. $\dfrac{24ab^2}{8ab}$ 18. $\dfrac{30p^2q}{15p^2}$ 19. $\dfrac{12a^2b^2}{6b^2}$ 20. $\dfrac{25xy^2z}{5y^2z}$

Dividing more complex terms in algebra

The method is to factorise the top and bottom and then divide the top and bottom by common factors.

EXAMPLE 1

Simplify the following.

(i) $\dfrac{3x - 12}{x - 4}$ (ii) $\dfrac{x^2 + 5x}{x + 5}$ (iii) $\dfrac{4x}{x^2 - 7x}$

Solution:

(i) $\dfrac{3x - 12}{x - 4}$

$= \dfrac{3(x - 4)}{(x - 4)}$ (factorising top and bottom)

$= 3$ (dividing top and bottom by $(x - 4)$)

(ii) $\dfrac{x^2 + 5x}{x + 5}$

$= \dfrac{x(x + 5)}{(x + 5)}$ (factorising top and bottom)

$= x$ (dividing top and bottom by $(x + 5)$)

(iii) $\dfrac{4x}{x^2 - 7x}$

$= \dfrac{4x}{x(x - 7)}$ (factorising the bottom)

$= \dfrac{4}{x - 7}$ (dividing top and bottom by x)

EXAMPLE 2

(i) Factorise $x^2 + 8x + 15$.

(ii) Factorise $x^2 - x - 12$.

(iii) Hence, simplify $\dfrac{x^2 + 8x + 15}{x^2 - x - 12}$.

Solution:

(i) $x^2 + 8x + 15$

Final term is + and middle term is +,

therefore the factors are $(x + \text{number})(x + \text{number})$.

Factors of 15
1×15
3×5

$(x + 1)(x + 15)$ $x + 15x = 16x$ (no)

$(x + 3)(x + 5)$ $3x + 5x = 8x$ (yes, this is the middle term)

Therefore, $x^2 + 8x + 15 = (x + 3)(x + 5)$.

(ii) $x^2 - x - 12$

Final term is a negative number,

therefore factors are $(x + \text{number})(x - \text{number})$.

	Factors of 12
	1×12
	2×6
	3×4

$(x + 1)(x - 12)$ $\quad 1x - 12x = -11x$ (no)

$(x + 2)(x - 6)$ $\quad 2x - 6x = -4x$ (no)

$(x + 3)(x - 4)$ $\quad 3x - 4x = -1x$ (yes)

Therefore, $x^2 - x - 12 = (x + 3)(x - 4)$.

(iii) $\dfrac{x^2 + 8x + 15}{x^2 - x - 12} = \dfrac{(x + 3)(x + 5)}{(x - 4)(x + 3)}$

$= \dfrac{x + 5}{x - 4}$ $\qquad$ (divide top and bottom by $(x + 3)$)

Exercise 22.4

Simplify each of the following algebraic fractions.

1. $\dfrac{7x + 14}{x + 2}$

2. $\dfrac{5}{15 - 25x}$

3. $\dfrac{y^2 + 3y}{y + 3}$

4. $\dfrac{5w}{w^2 + 2w}$

5. $\dfrac{x^2 - 10x}{x - 10}$

6. $\dfrac{5x^2 + 35x}{x^2 + 7x}$

7. $\dfrac{2x^2 - 6x}{4x^2 - 12x}$

8. $\dfrac{4y^2 + 16y}{y + 4}$

9. $\dfrac{2x^2 - 8x}{x(x - 4)}$

10. $\dfrac{2w - 3w^2}{3w - 2}$

11. $\dfrac{x^2 - 64}{x + 8}$

12. $\dfrac{x - 3}{x^2 - 9}$

13. $\dfrac{x + 3}{x^2 + 6x + 9}$

14. $\dfrac{x^2 - 2x - 35}{x^2 - 7x}$

15. $\dfrac{x + 8}{x^2 + 13x + 40}$

16. $\dfrac{x^2 - 2x - 8}{x^2 + 9x + 14}$

17. $\dfrac{x^2 - 9x - 10}{x^2 - 8x - 9}$

18. $\dfrac{x^2 - 36}{x^2 - x - 30}$

19. Given the area of the triangle ABC is $\frac{1}{2}(x + 2)(x)$ and the area of the rectangle $PQRS$ is $(3x)(x + 2)$

Write in its simplest form $\dfrac{\text{Area of the rectangle } PQRS}{\text{Area of the triangle } ABC}$

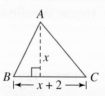

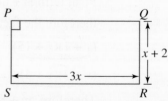

The four inequality symbols are:

1.	$>$	means	greater than
2.	$\geq$	means	greater than or equal to
3.	$<$	means	less than
4.	$\leq$	means	less than or equal to

Algebraic expressions that are linked by one of the four inequality symbols are called **inequalities**.

For example: $2x + 1 \geq 11$ is an inequality.

Note: Inequalities can be turned around. For example:

$8 > 5$ means the same as $5 < 8$.

$3 \leq x$ means the same as $x \geq 3$.

Number lines

The following rules apply to graphing inequalities on a number line.

Number line for $x \in \mathbb{N}$ or $x \in \mathbb{Z}$, use dots.

Number line for $x \in \mathbb{R}$, use a full heavy line.

EXAMPLE

Represent the following inequalities on a number line.

(i) $x < 4$ where $x \in \mathbb{N}$ (ii) $x > -2$ where $x \in \mathbb{Z}$ (iii) $x > -1$ where $x \in \mathbb{R}$

(iv) $x \geq 3$ where $x \in \mathbb{R}$

Solution:

(i) $x < 4$ where $x \in \mathbb{N}$ means that x represents all the natural numbers that are less than 4. The first natural number which is less than 4 is 3, so we put a dot on 3 and then on 2 and 1.

1 is the lowest natural number so we stop there and do not put an arrow on the number line.

(ii) $x > -2$ where $x \in \mathbb{Z}$ means that x represents all integers that are greater than -2. The first integer which is greater than -2 is -1, so we put a dot on -1 and then on $0, 1$, etc.

We draw an arrow to show that the number line continues on for all further integers.

(iii) $x < 5$ where $x \in \mathbb{R}$ means that x represents all real numbers that are less than 5. 5 is not included but all values below 5 are, so we draw an empty circle around 5 on the number line, then shade in the line and put an arrow at the end.

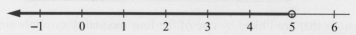

(iv) $x \geq 3$ where $x \in \mathbb{R}$ means that x represents all real numbers that are greater than or equal to 3. To show that 3 is included, we use a full circle to show this on the number line, then shade in the line and put an arrow at the end.

Exercise 23.1

Copy and write the correct inequality symbol, $<$ or $>$, between the pairs of numbers in questions 1–9.

1. 3   10
2. 5   4
3. -3 6
4. 0 -1
5. 3 -3
6. -4 -2
7. -1 -6
8. -5 0
9. 7   9

Write down the first five values of the inequalities in questions 10–15.

10. $x > 1$ where $x \in \mathbb{Z}$
11. $x > 2$ where $x \in \mathbb{N}$
12. $x < 2$ where $x \in \mathbb{Z}$
13. $x \geq 0$ where $x \in \mathbb{N}$
14. $x > 1$ where $x \in \mathbb{N}$
15. $x \leq -3$ where $x \in \mathbb{Z}$

Draw separate number lines to show the inequalities in questions 16–21.

16. $x > 1$ where $x \in \mathbb{N}$
17. $x < 3$ where $x \in \mathbb{Z}$
18. $x \geq -2$ where $x \in \mathbb{R}$
19. $x \leq 2$ where $x \in \mathbb{N}$
20. $x \leq 4$ where $x \in \mathbb{R}$
21. $x > -1$ where $x \in \mathbb{Z}$

Solving inequalities

Solving an inequality means finding the values of x that make the inequality true.
On our course we will only solve inequalities in the form $ax + b \leq k$, where $a \in \mathbb{N}$ and $b, k \in \mathbb{Z}$.
Solving inequalities is similar to solving equations.

**EXAMPLE 1**

(i) Solve $3x + 4 \geq 1$, where $x \in \mathbb{Z}$.

(ii) Graph your solution on the number line.

Solution:

(i)
$$3x + 4 \geq 1$$
$$3x + 4 - 4 \geq 1 - 4 \quad \text{(subtract 4 from both sides)}$$
$$3x \geq -3 \quad \text{(simplify the right-hand side)}$$
$$x \geq -1 \quad \text{(divide both sides by 3)}$$

This is the set of integers greater than -1, including -1.

(ii) Number line:

EXAMPLE 2

(i) Solve the inequality $2x - 4 < 6$, where $x \in \mathbb{N}$.

(ii) List the set of values for x.

(iii) Graph your solution on the number line.

Solution:

(i)
$$2x - 4 < 6$$
$$2x - 4 + 4 < 6 + 4 \quad \text{(add 4 to both sides)}$$
$$2x < 10 \quad \text{(simplify both sides)}$$
$$x < 5 \quad \text{(divide both sides by 2)}$$

(ii) This is the set of natural numbers less than 5 but not including 5.
$$x = 1, 2, 3, 4$$

(iii) Number line:

307

Exercise 23.2

Solve each of the following inequalities in questions 1–16. In each case, graph the solution set on the number line.

1. $x + 3 \geq 7$, where $x \in \mathbb{N}$ 2. $x - 2 \leq 1$, where $x \in \mathbb{Z}$ 3. $5x - 7 > 3$, where $x \in \mathbb{N}$

4. $2x + 5 < 11$, where $x \in \mathbb{Z}$ 5. $3x - 1 \geq -4$, where $x \in \mathbb{R}$ 6. $4x + 2 \leq -6$, where $x \in \mathbb{Z}$

7. $3x - 1 < 8$, where $x \in \mathbb{R}$ 8. $4x + 1 \geq 9$, where $x \in \mathbb{N}$ 9. $7x - 1 \leq -15$, where $x \in \mathbb{R}$

10. Find the values of x for which $2x - 3 \leq 7$, where $x \in \mathbb{N}$.

11. List the values of x which satisfy $3x - 1 < 11$, where $x \in \mathbb{N}$.

12. Find the smallest natural number that satisfies $x - 3 > 2$.

In questions 13–16, the solution contains a fraction.

13. $2x + 3 < 4$, where $x \in \mathbb{R}$ 14. $3x - 1 \geq 4$, where $x \in \mathbb{R}$ 15. $4x - 5 > 4$, where $x \in \mathbb{R}$

16. $5x + 2 \leq 8$, where $x \in \mathbb{R}$

17. Find the biggest natural number that satisfies $3x - 1 < 7$, where $x \in \mathbb{N}$.

18. The diagram shows a rectangle of length
    $(x + 3)$ cm and width $(x + 2)$ cm. Find the
    largest value of x for which the perimeter of
    the rectangle is less than or equal to 30 cm.

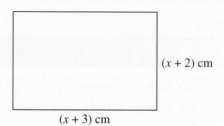

$(x + 2)$ cm

$(x + 3)$ cm

19. The diagram shows a map of an island.

    Treasure is buried at a point where the x and
    y coordinates are positive whole numbers.

    Use the clues to work out the coordinates
    where the treasure is buried.

    Clues:

    (a) $x > 5$
    (b) $y > 6$
    (c) $x + y = 13$

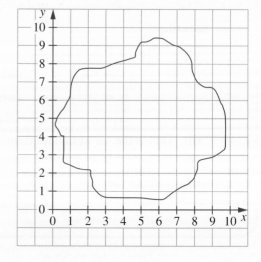

20. The diagram shows a map of an island.

Treasure is buried at a point where the x and y coordinates are positive whole numbers.

Use the clues to work out the coordinates of the **two** possible locations where the treasure is buried.

Clues:

(a) $x < 4$

(b) Product of x and y is 12

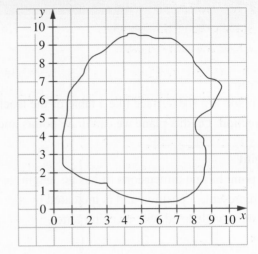

21. The entrance fee to a video game arcade is €3. Once inside, each game is 25c to play.

(i) Write an inequality that represents the possible number of games that can be played having no more than €10.

(ii) Find the maximum number of games you can play.

If each game was 30c instead of 25c:

(iii) Write a new inequality to represent the possible number of games that can be played now, having no more than €10.

(iv) Find the maximum number of games you can play in this case.

(v) If you play the maximum number of games, how much change will you have out of the €10?

Plane

A plane is a flat surface like a table or the teacher's board, except that it extends forever in every direction. On this plane we can draw points and lines.

Point

A point has no dimensions. It has no length, breadth or thickness.
It represents a position and is indicated by a dot.
A point is denoted with a capital letter.

A

B

Line

A line can be denoted in two ways:

1. By naming two points on it.   **2.** Using a lower case letter.

Here is a diagram of the line AB, or the line l.

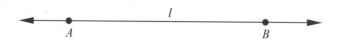

You may reverse the order of the letters and call it line BA.
A line extends indefinitely in both directions, as indicated by the arrows.

Note: There is one, and only one, line that can be drawn through any two points.

Ray or half-line

A ray, or half-line, is part of a line that begins at a certain point (called the starting point) and extends indefinitely in one direction. A ray is denoted on the direction in which it extends.

The diagram shows the ray $[AB$.
The square bracket indicates that it starts at A and extends towards B and beyond forever.

Note: We must be careful of the order in which a ray is denoted. Ray $[AB \neq$ Ray $[BA$.

Line segment

A part of a line is called a line segment. It has a beginning and an end.
The line segment AB is denoted by $[AB]$. The square brackets indicate that it begins at A and ends at B.

The length of the line segment [AB] is denoted by |AB|.

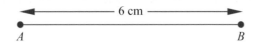

The diagram shows the line segment [AB] with |AB| = 6 cm.

Collinear points

Points that are on the same line are said to be collinear.

The points A, B, C and D are collinear, as they are all on the same line.

Distance from a point to a line

The distance, d, from a point to a line is defined as the **shortest** distance from the point to the line. This distance is often called the **perpendicular** distance.

Pairs of lines

Consider the lines l and k:

intersecting	**parallel**	**perpendicular**
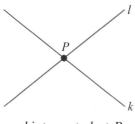	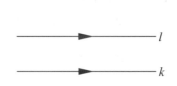	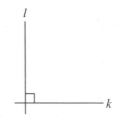
l intersects k at P	l is parallel to k	l is perpendicular to k
Written: l ∩ k = P	Written: l ‖ k	Written: l ⊥ k
	Parallel lines never meet and are often indicated by arrows.	The symbol ⌐ is placed where the two lines meet to show that they are perpendicular.

Note: Given any line l and a point P there is one, and only one, line that can be drawn through P that is parallel to l.

Exercise 24.1

Describe each of the following in questions 1–6 in words.

1.

2.

3.

4. $[MN]$ **5.** $|XY|$ **6.** $[CD$

7. $[PQ]$ is a line segment such that $|PQ| = 12$ cm.

S is the midpoint of $[PQ]$.

R is the midpoint of $[PS]$.

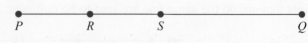

Calculate:

   (i) $|PS|$ **(ii)** $|RS|$ **(iii)** $|QR|$ **(iv)** $|PQ| + |QS|$

   (v) $|PQ| - |RQ|$ **(vi)** $|QR| + |RS| - |PS|$ **(vii)** $\frac{1}{2}|PS|$ **(viii)** $\frac{1}{3}|PQ|$

Name a line segment equal in length to:

   (ix) $|PS| + |SQ|$ **(x)** $|RS| + |SQ|$ **(xi)** $|PS| - |SR|$

   (xii) Name two line segments that are equal in length.

8. Draw a line segment $[AB]$ such that $|AB| = 6$ cm.

C is a point on $[AB]$ such that $|AC| = |CB|$. Describe, in words, the point C and indicate the point C on your diagram.

9. The diagram shows the rectangle $ABCD$.

   (i) Measure and write down, in cm, the following lengths.

      (a) $|AB|$ **(b)** $|BC|$ **(c)** $|AC|$

  (ii) Show that $|AB|^2 + |BC|^2 = |AC|^2$.

  (iii) State if each of the following are true or false, giving a reason in each case.

      (a) $|AC| > |BC|$

      (b) A, B and C are collinear

      (c) $|AB| = |DC|$

      (d) $|DB| > |CA|$

      (e) $AB \perp BC$

      (f) $DC \parallel AB$

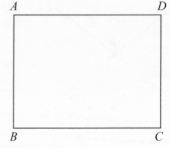

10. The diagram shows the line PQ, containing the points R, S and T.

   (i) Name the line using different letters.

  (ii) State if each of the following are true or false, giving a reason in each case.

      (a) P is on the line segment $[RS]$ **(b)** T is on the line segment $[SQ]$

      (c) S is on the ray $[RT$ **(d)** Q is on the ray $[SR$

11. Choose from: **Non-parallel Horizontal Parallel Perpendicular** to complete the sentences.

    (i) _____ lines never meet.   (ii) _____ lines meet at 90°.

    (iii) _____ lines have a slope of zero.   (iv) _____ lines meet at one point.

Angles

Angles are formed where rays, lines or line segments meet or intersect. The size of an angle is measured by the amount of turning or rotation in moving one ray to the other ray. The rays which form the angle are called the **arms** of the angle. The size of the angle depends only on the amount of turning and does not depend on the length of the arms. The point where they meet is called the **vertex** of the angle. Angles are measured in **degrees**, where there are 360° in a full revolution. An angle is denoted by the symbol ∠.

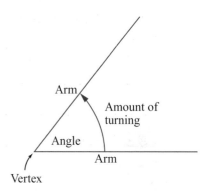

An angle can be denoted in four ways

1. Three capital letters	2. One capital letter	3. One lower case letter	4. A number
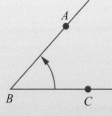	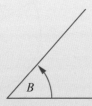	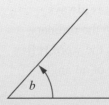	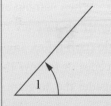
Using three capital letters, with the centre letter at the vertex. The angle is then denoted as: ∠ABC or ∠CBA	Putting a capital letter at the vertex of the angle. The angle is then denoted as: ∠B	Putting a lower case letter at the vertex of the angle. The angle is then denoted as: ∠b	Putting a number at the vertex of the angle. The angle is then denoted as: ∠1

The size, or measure, of $\angle ABC$ is written $|\angle ABC|$. In other words, $|\angle ABC|$ is the **number of degrees** in the $\angle ABC$.

Note: $|\angle ABC| = |\angle B| = |\angle b| = |\angle 1|$.

Types and names of angles

Angles are named according to the amount of turning, or rotation, measured in degrees.

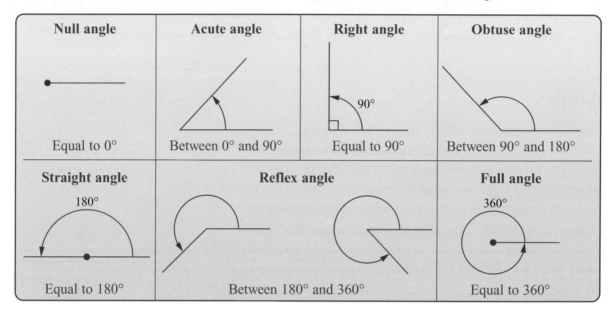

Null angle	Acute angle	Right angle	Obtuse angle
Equal to 0°	Between 0° and 90°	Equal to 90°	Between 90° and 180°

Straight angle	Reflex angle	Full angle
Equal to 180°	Between 180° and 360°	Equal to 360°

Ordinary angle

An **ordinary angle** is an angle between 0° and 180°. When naming an angle, it is **always** assumed that we are referring to the ordinary angle (non-reflex angle), unless the word **reflex** precedes or follows the naming of an angle. Consider the diagram.

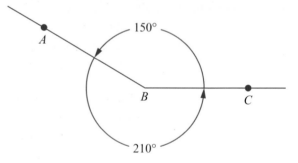

$$|\angle ABC| = 150° \quad \text{(ordinary angle)} \qquad |\text{reflex } \angle ABC| = 210° \quad \text{(reflex angle)}$$

Properties of angles

It is very important to know the following properties of angles.

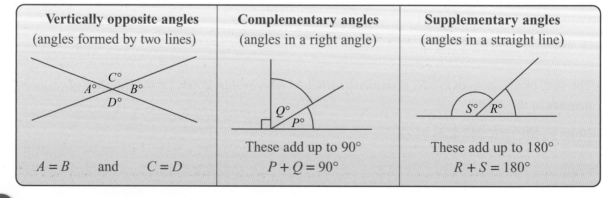

Vertically opposite angles (angles formed by two lines)	Complementary angles (angles in a right angle)	Supplementary angles (angles in a straight line)
$A = B$ and $C = D$	These add up to 90° $P + Q = 90°$	These add up to 180° $R + S = 180°$

EXAMPLE

Calculate the value of the letter representing the angle in each of the following diagrams. In each case, give a reason for your answer.

(i)

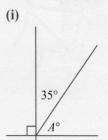

(ii)

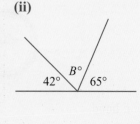

(iii)

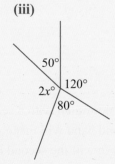

(iv)

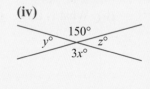

Solution:

(i)

$$A° + 35° = 90°$$ (angles in a right angle add up to 90°)

$$A + 35 = 90$$

$$A = 55$$ (subtract 35 from both sides)

(ii)

$$42° + B° + 65° = 180°$$ (angles in a straight angle add up to 180°)

$$42 + B + 65 = 180$$

$$B + 107 = 180$$

$$B = 73$$ (subtract 107 from both sides)

(iii)

$$2x° + 50° + 120° + 80° = 360°$$ (angles in a full angle add up to 360°)

$$2x + 50 + 120 + 80 = 360$$

$$2x + 250 = 360$$

$$2x = 110$$ (subtract 250 from both sides)

$$x = 55$$ (divide both sides by 2)

(iv)

$$3x° = 150°$$ (vertically opposite angles are equal)

$$3x = 150$$

$$x = 50$$ (divide both sides by 3)

$$y° + 150° = 180°$$ (angles in a straight angle add up to 180°)

$$y + 150 = 180$$

$$y = 30$$ (subtract 150 from both sides)

$$z° = y°$$ (vertically opposite angles are equal)

$$z = y$$

$$z = 30$$ ($y = 30$)

315

Exercise 24.2

1. The diagram shows a cyclist on a bike.

   (i) If the wheels make one complete turn, with no slipping, how many degrees is this?

   (ii) What is this angle called?

2. The diagram shows a stopwatch with a second hand.
   Every minute the second hand will make one complete revolution.

   (i) Through what angle will the second hand turn in:

(a) Half a minute	**(b)** Quarter of a minute
(c) 20 seconds	**(d)** 45 seconds
(e) 12 seconds	**(f)** 2 minutes

   (ii) The second hand starts at 0 and stops at 40. What fraction of a complete revolution has it travelled?

3. This clock shows 02:00.

   (i) What is the **(a)** acute angle **(b)** the reflex angle between the hands of the clock?

   (ii) Through what angle will the hour hand turn between 03:00 and 04:30?

   (iii) If the minute hand turns 450°, what time will the clock show?

4. Use a protractor to measure, correct to the nearest degree, each of the following angles and complete the table.

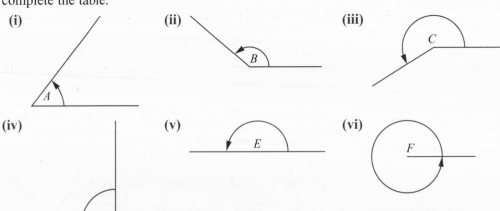

(i)   **(ii)**   **(iii)**

(iv)   **(v)**   **(vi)**

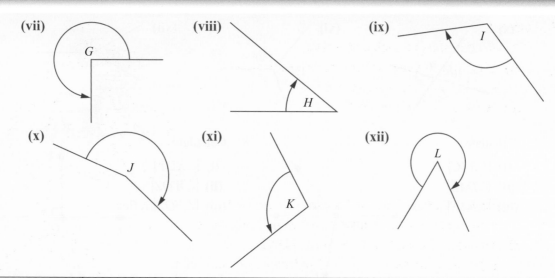

(vii)   (viii)   (ix)

(x)   (xi)   (xii)

Acute angle	Right angle	Obtuse angle	Straight angle	Reflex angle	Full angle
		B,			

5. Using a ruler and a protractor, construct angles with the following measure.
   (i) 40°   (ii) 75°   (iii) 120°   (iv) 150°
   (v) 240°   (vi) 215°   (vii) 270°   (viii) 340°

6. Calculate the value of the letter representing the angle in each of the following diagrams. In each case, give a reason.

(i)   (ii)   (iii)

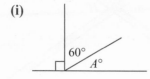

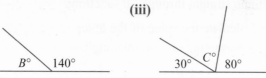

(iv)   (v)   (vi)

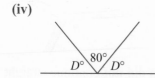
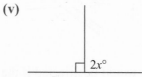
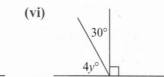

(vii)   (viii)   (ix)

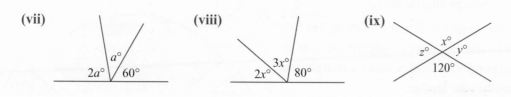

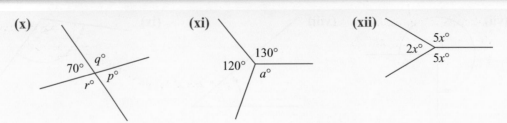

(x)

(xi)

(xii)

7. Calculate:

    (i) $|\angle BAC|$

    (ii) $|\angle DAE|$

    (iii) $|\angle BAC|$ reflex

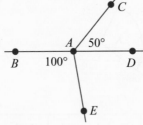

8. Calculate:

    (i) $|\angle XDY|$

    (ii) $|\angle WOZ|$

    (iii) $|\angle YOZ|$ reflex

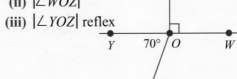

9.

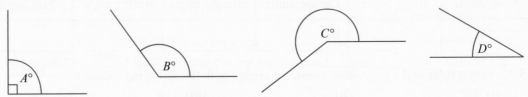

Complete the following: _____ is less than _____ is less than _____ is less than _____.

10. The map shows the main streets in the centre of a town where all streets continue straight through all junctions.

    (i) Calculate the value of the letter representing the missing angle.

$A =$	$B =$
$C =$	$D =$
$E =$	$F =$
$G =$	$H =$

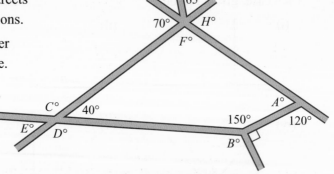

    (ii) Discuss how your answers would be affected if the streets did **not** continue straight through all junctions.

11. Three shapes A, B and C with angles $28°$, $101°$ and $49°$, respectively, fit together at the point P. Will they make a straight line? Justify your answer.

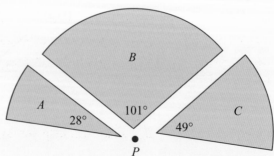

12. A plumber uses connectors as shown. Explain why the connector shown is called a 30° connector.

Angles and parallel lines

When a line cuts a pair of parallel lines, eight angles are formed in such a way that:

1. All the acute angles are equal.

2. All the obtuse angles are equal.

Some of these angles have special names.

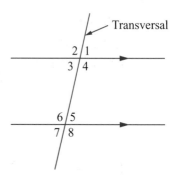

Transversal

Note: If you know one of these angles then you can work out all the others.

A line that intersects two or more lines is called a **transversal**, even if the lines are not parallel.

Corresponding angles

Corresponding angles are equal and occur in pairs. A pair of corresponding angles is marked on each of the diagrams. Corresponding angles are always on the **same** side of the transversal.

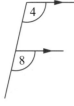   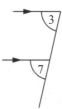   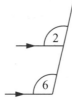   

$|\angle 4| = |\angle 8|$ $\qquad$ $|\angle 3| = |\angle 7|$ $\qquad$ $|\angle 2| = |\angle 6|$ $\qquad$ $|\angle 1| = |\angle 5|$

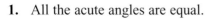

Looking for a $\mathsf{F}, \mathsf{7}, \mathsf{E}$ or J shape can help you to spot corresponding angles.

Alternate angles

Alternate angles are equal and occur in pairs. A pair of alternate angles is marked on each of the diagrams. Alternate angles are always on **opposite** sides of the transversal.

     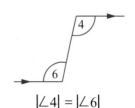

$|\angle 3| = |\angle 5|$ $\qquad$ $|\angle 4| = |\angle 6|$

Looking for a Z or $\mathsf{\rule{0pt}{1em}}$ shape can help you to spot alternate angles.

Interior angles

Interior angles add up to 180°. A pair of interior angles is marked on each of the diagrams. Interior angles are always on the **same** side of the transversal.

$$|\angle 4| + |\angle 5| = 180° \qquad |\angle 3| + |\angle 6| = 180°$$

Looking for a ⌐ or ⌐ shape can help you to spot interior angles.

In short:

Corresponding angles	Alternate angles	Interior angles
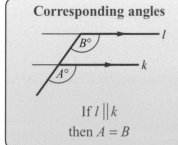	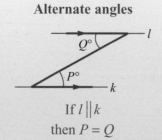	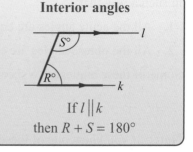
If $l \parallel k$ then $A = B$	If $l \parallel k$ then $P = Q$	If $l \parallel k$ then $R + S = 180°$

The converses are also true:

Corresponding angles	Alternate angles	Interior angles
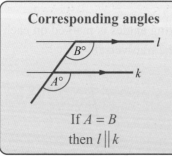	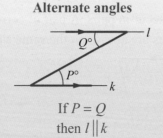	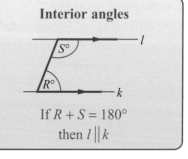
If $A = B$ then $l \parallel k$	If $P = Q$ then $l \parallel k$	If $R + S = 180°$ then $l \parallel k$

EXAMPLE

l and m are parallel lines.

Calculate the value of:

(i) A (ii) B (iii) C

In each case, give a reason for your answer.

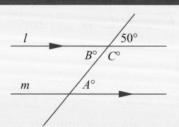

Solution:

(i)

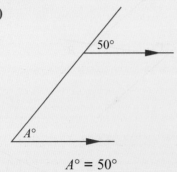

$A° = 50°$

Reason: Corresponding angles

$\therefore A = 50°$

(ii)

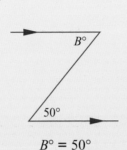

$B° = 50°$

Reason: Alternate angles

$\therefore B = 50°$

(iii)

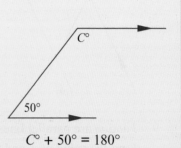

$C° + 50° = 180°$

Reason: Interior angles

$\therefore C = 130°$

Note: These show just one of the ways to calculate A, B and C. There are other ways.

Exercise 24.3

Calculate the value of the letter representing the angle in each of the following diagrams. In each case, give a reason for your answer (parallel lines are indicated by arrows).

1.

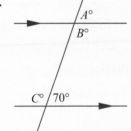

2.

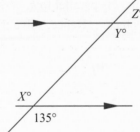

3.

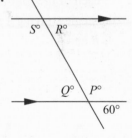

4.

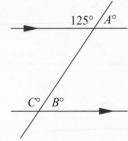

5.

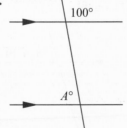

6.

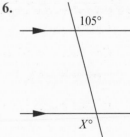

7.

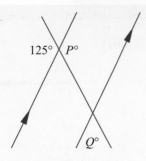

8.

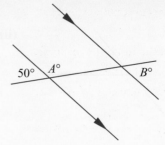

9. *l* and *m* are parallel lines.
Find the value of *X* and the value of *Y*.
In each case, give a reason for your answer.

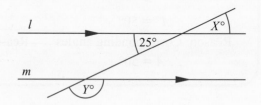

10. *l* and *k* are parallel lines.
Find the value of *A* and the value of *B*.
In each case, give a reason for your answer.

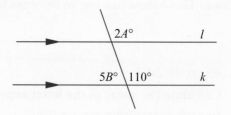

11. In each of the following diagrams, *l* is parallel to *k*. Write down an equation that connects the angles, giving a reason in each case. Hence, solve these equations to find the value of *A*, *B* and *C*.

(i)

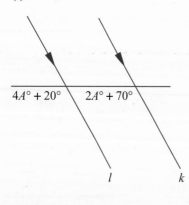

(ii)

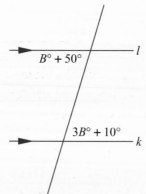

(iii)

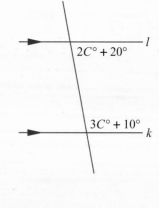

12. The diagram shows a boy on a swing.

   (i) Name an angle vertically opposite to R.

   (ii) Complete the following.

      (a) $|\angle P| = |\angle\quad|$

      (b) $|\angle P| + |\angle\quad| = 180°$

      (c) $P + Q + R + S =$

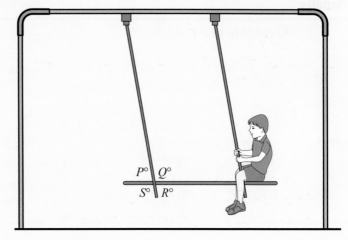

13. **(i)** In the diagram, $l \parallel k$. Name an angle which is:

     (a) Alternate to $\angle D$

     (b) Corresponds to $\angle A$

     (c) Vertically opposite to $\angle B$

     (d) Interior opposite to $\angle F$

     (e) Alternate to $\angle E$

     (f) Corresponds to $\angle G$

     (g) Vertically opposite to $\angle H$

     (h) Interior opposite to $\angle E$

     (i) Supplementary to $\angle F$

  (ii) Which line is the transversal?

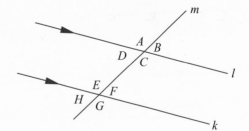

Triangles

Naming triangles

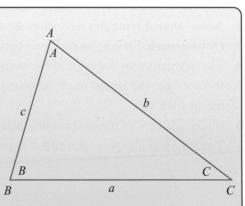

The symbol for a triangle is $\triangle$.

Each of the three corners of a triangle is called a **vertex**.

Triangles are named according to the letters at the vertices.

The triangle shown here could be named $\triangle ABC$.

It could also be named:

$\triangle ACB$ or $\triangle BAC$ or $\triangle BCA$ or $\triangle CAB$ or $\triangle CBA$.

The lengths of the sides are denoted with a lower case letter of the capital letter opposite the vertex, as shown.

Thus:

$a = |BC|$, $b = |AC|$ and $c = |AB|$.

The angles opposite the sides can be named with three letters or a single capital letter.

Thus, $\angle BAC = \angle A$, $\angle ABC = \angle B$ and $\angle BCA = \angle C$.

Triangles

Angle sum of a triangle	Exterior angle of a triangle
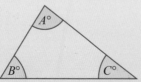	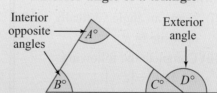
The three angles of a triangle add up to 180°. $$A° + B° + C° = 180°$$	If one side is produced, the exterior angle is equal to the sum of the two interior opposite angles. $$D° = A° + B°$$

Special triangles

Equilateral triangle	Isosceles triangle	Right-angled triangle
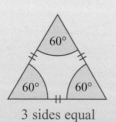	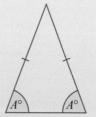	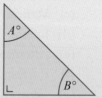
3 sides equal 3 equal angles All angles are equal to 60°	2 sides equal Base angles are equal (base angles are the angles opposite the equal sides)	One angle is 90° The other two angles add up to 90° $$A° + B° = 90°$$

Notes:
1. **Scalene triangles** have no equal sides and no equal angles.
2. **Acute-angled triangles** have three acute angles.
3. **Obtuse-angled triangles** have one obtuse angle and two acute angles.
4. The tick marks on the sides of the triangle indicate sides of equal length.
5. In a triangle, the largest angle is always opposite the largest side and the smallest angle is opposite the smallest side.
6. If two sides are of unequal length, then the angles opposite these sides are also unequal.
7. The length of any two sides added together is always greater than the length of the third side.

EXAMPLE

Using the diagram, calculate the value of:

(i) *A*   (ii) *B*

Give a reason in each case.

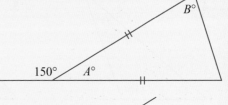

Solution:

(i) $A° + 150° = 180°$ (straight angle)

$A + 150 = 180$

$A = 30°$

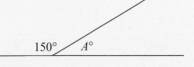

(ii) Redraw the triangle separately.

The tick marks indicate that the triangle is isosceles.

Therefore, the two base angles are equal.

$B° + B° + 30° = 180°$ (3 angles in a triangle)

$B + B + 30 = 180$

$2B + 30 = 180$

$2B = 150$

$B = 75°$

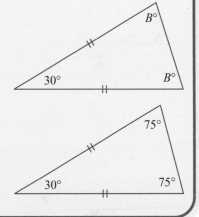

Exercise 24.4

Calculate the value of the letter representing the angle in each of the diagrams in questions 1–20. In each case, give a reason.

1.

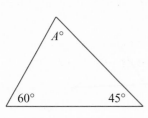

2.

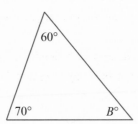

3.

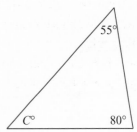

4.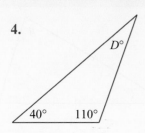

5.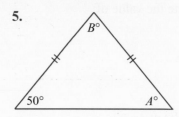

6.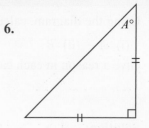

7.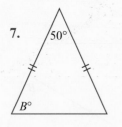

8.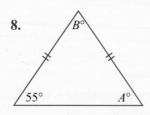

9.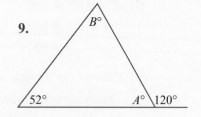

10.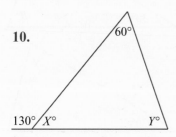

11.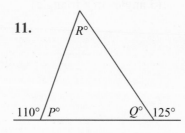

12.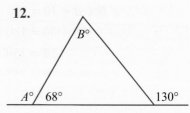

13.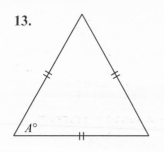

14.

15.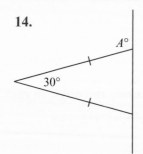

16.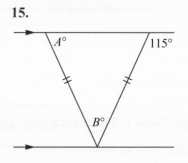

17.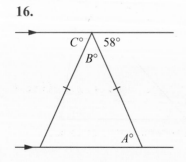

18.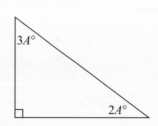

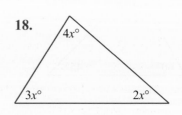

19.

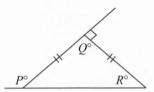

20.

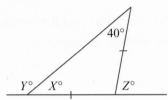

21. The diagram shows the beams in a roof.
Calculate the value of X and Y.

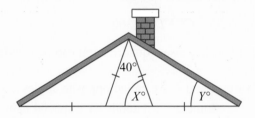

22. ABC is an isosceles triangle with $|CA| = |CB|$.
The side $[AB]$ is extended to D and $CE \perp AB$.
  (i) Name an angle equal in measure to $\angle ABC$.
     Give a reason for your answer.
  (ii) Given that $|\angle ABC| = 48°$, find $|\angle CBD|$.
     Give a reason for your answer.

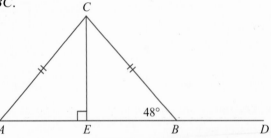

23. Explain why $\triangle PQR$ is isosceles.

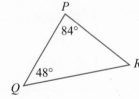

24. The diagram shows a side view of an ironing board
standing on horizontal ground.
The board is parallel to the floor.
$|\angle ABE| = 120°$ and $|\angle DCE| = 150°$
What type of triangle is triangle EFG?
Give a reason for your answer.

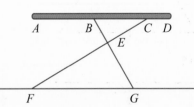

25. In a right-angled triangle, one of the angles is obtuse. Is this statement true or false? Give a
reason for your answer.

26. An equilateral triangle is also an acute-angled triangle. Is this statement true or false?
Justify your answer.

Quadrilaterals

A quadrilateral is a figure that has four sides and four vertices.
It has two diagonals that join the opposite vertices.

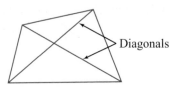

Diagonals

The four angles of a quadrilateral add up to 360°.

$A° + B° + C° + D° = 360°$

(This is because a quadrilateral can be divided up into two triangles.)

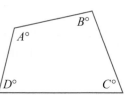

Note: A and C are called opposite angles and B and D are also called opposite angles.

Some quadrilaterals have special names and special properties.

Square properties

1. Opposite sides are parallel.   **2.** All sides are equal.   **3.** All angles are right angles.

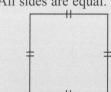

4. Diagonals are equal and bisect each other.   **5.** Diagonals intersect at right angles.   **6.** Diagonals bisect each angle.

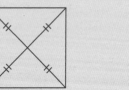

Rectangle properties

1. Opposite sides are parallel.   **2.** Opposite sides are equal.

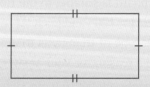

3. All angles are right angles.   **4.** Diagonals are equal and bisect each other.

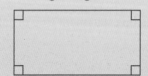
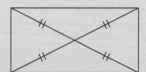

Parallelogram properties

1. Opposite sides are parallel.

2. Opposite sides are equal.

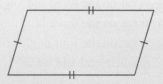

3. Opposite angles are equal.

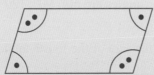

4. Diagonals bisect each other.

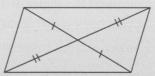

EXAMPLE

$ABCD$ is a parallelogram.
$|\angle BAD| = 125°$ and $|\angle CBD| = 25°$.

Find: **(i)** $|\angle BCD|$ **(ii)** $|\angle ADB|$ **(iii)** $|\angle ABD|$
(iv) $|\angle CDB|$

In each case, give a reason for your answer.

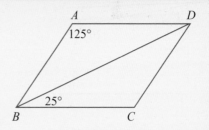

Solution:

(i)

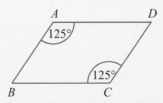

$$|\angle BCD| = |\angle BAD| = 125°$$

opposite angles of the parallelogram

(ii)

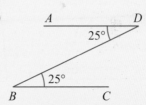

$$|\angle ADB| = |\angle CBD| = 25°$$

alternate angles

(iii)

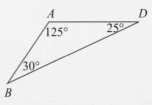

$$|\angle ABD| + |\angle BAD| + |\angle ADB| = 180°$$

Three angles in a triangle add to 180°.

$$|\angle ABD| + 125° + 25° = 180°$$
$$|\angle ABD| + 150° = 180°$$
$$|\angle ABD| = 30°$$

(iv)

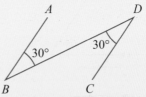

$$|\angle CDB| = |\angle ABD| = 30°$$

alternate angles

Exercise 24.5

1. *PQRS* is a quadrilateral with diagonal [*PR*].
   (i) What do the three red angles add up to?
   (ii) What do the three blue angles add up to?
   (iii) What do the four angles of the quadrilateral add up to?

   In each case, give a reason for your answer.

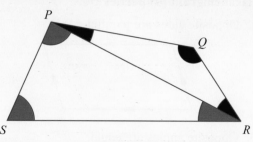

2. Colm measures the angles of a quadrilateral. He says the angles are 50°, 90°, 120° and 105°. Could he be right? Justify your answer.

3. Three angles of a quadrilateral are 65°, 70°, 100°. Find the size of the fourth angle.

Calculate the value of the letter representing the angle in each of the diagrams in questions 4–15 (arrows indicate parallel lines). In each case, give a reason.

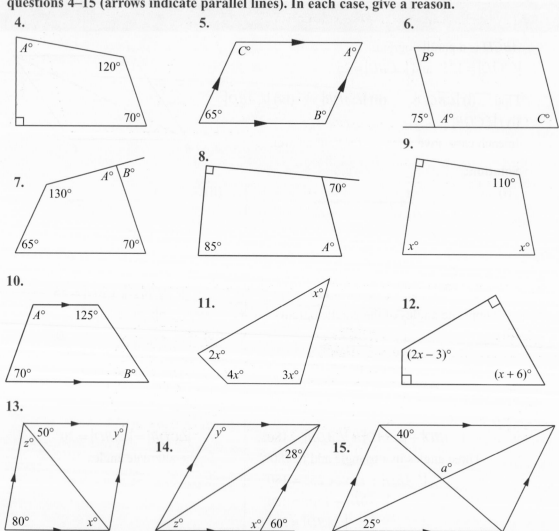

16. *ABCD* is a parallelogram.
    Calculate $|\angle BDC|$.
    Justify your answer.

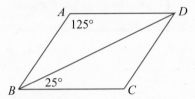

17. *WXYZ* is a parallelogram with
    $|\angle WXY| = 70°$ and $|WY| = |XY|$.
    Calculate (i) $|\angle WYX|$ (ii) $|\angle WYZ|$.
    In each case, give a reason for
    your answer.

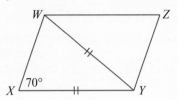

18. (i) Complete the statement: The four angles
    in the quadrilateral add up to _____ °.
    (ii) In the diagram, triangle *ABC* is isosceles
    and *FE* $\parallel$ *CA*. Calculate:
    (a) $|\angle BCA|$ (b) $|\angle ACD|$
    (c) $|\angle CDE|$ (d) $|\angle DEF|$
    In each case, give a reason for your answer.

19. (i) If all four angles of a quadrilateral are
    equal, what size is each angle?
    (ii) What sort of quadrilateral could it be?
    Justify your answer.

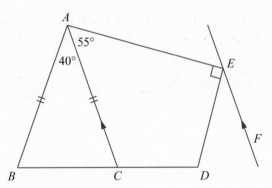

Circle

The diagrams below show some of the terms we use when dealing with a circle.

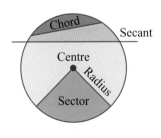

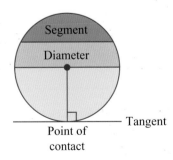

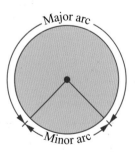

Angle in a semicircle

A **diameter** divides a circle into two **semi-circles**.

> Each angle in a semi-circle is a right angle.

The converse is also true.

> If the angle standing on a chord at a point on the
> circle is a right angle, then the chord is a diameter.

If $|\angle BAC| = 90°$, then $[BC]$ is a diameter and vice versa.

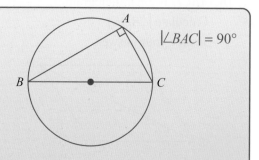

$|\angle BAC| = 90°$

Isosceles triangle

When dealing with a circle, look out for the isosceles and equilateral
triangle within the question. The isosceles triangle occurs when the
lengths of the sides are equal in length to the radius. The equilateral
triangle occurs when the length of the chord is equal to the radius.

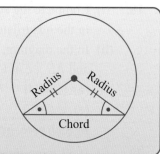

EXAMPLE

A, B and C are three points on a circle with centre O.
Calculate the value of:

(i) $|\angle COB|$ **(ii)** $|\angle OBC|$ **(iii)** $|\angle OBA|$

Justify your answer in each case.

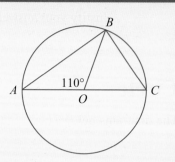

Solution:
Let
$x° = |\angle COB|$
$y° = |\angle OBC|$
$z° = |\angle OBA|$

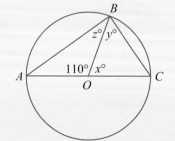

(i) $x° + 110° = 180°$ (straight angle)
$\quad\quad x + 110 = 180$
$\quad\quad\quad\quad\quad x = 70$ (subtract 70 from both sides)
$\therefore |\angle COB| = 70°$

(ii) $\triangle OBC$ is isosceles as $|OB| = |OC| =$ radius of the circle.
Therefore, the two base angles are equal to $y°$.

$y° + y° + 70° = 180°$ (three angles in a triangle add up to 180°)
$y + y + 70 = 180$
$2y + 70 = 180$
$2y = 110$ (subtract 70 from both sides)
$y = 55$ (divide both sides by 2)
$\therefore$ $|\angle OBC| = 55°$

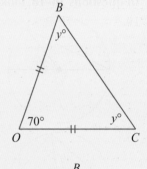

(iii) $z° + y° = 90°$ (angle in a semi-circle is 90°)
$z + y = 90$
$z + 55 = 90$ (put in $y = 55$)
$z = 35$ (subtract 55 from both sides)
$\therefore$ $|\angle OBA| = 35°$

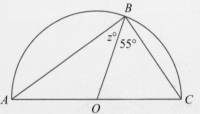

Exercise 24.6

Calculate the value of the letter representing the angle in each of the diagrams in questions 1–23, where O is the centre of the circle. In each case, give a reason for your answer.

1.

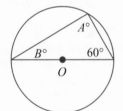

2.

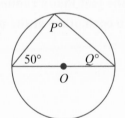

3.

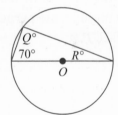

4.

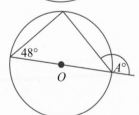

5.

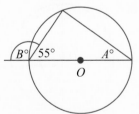

6.

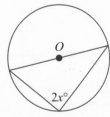

7.

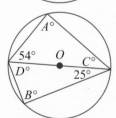

8.

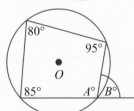

9.

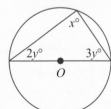

In questions 10–18, look for the isosceles triangles and equilateral triangles in the diagrams.

10.

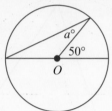

11.

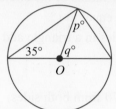

12.

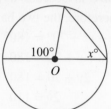

13.

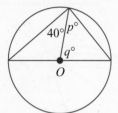

14.

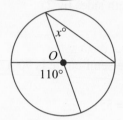

15.

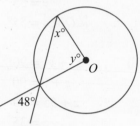

16.

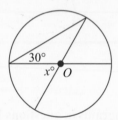

17.

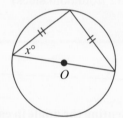

18.

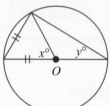

In questions 19–23, we make use of the fact that a radius, r, and a tangent, t, are perpendicular to each other at the point of contact, P.

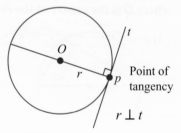

Point of tangency

$r \perp t$

19.

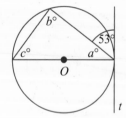

20.

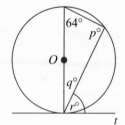

21.

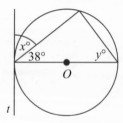

22.

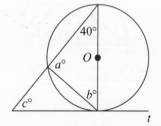

23.

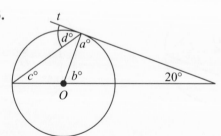

24. **(i)** *X*, *W* and *Y* are three points on the semi-circle with centre *O*.

$|\angle XWO| = 40°$. Describe [*XY*] and [*OW*].

(ii) Calculate:

(a) $|\angle WXO|$ **(b)** $|\angle XOW|$ **(c)** $|\angle WOY|$

(d) $|\angle OWY|$

In each case, give a reason for your answer.

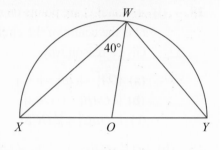

25. *k* is a circle with centre *O*.

PQRS are points on the circumference of *k*.

$|\angle QPR| = 30°$ and $|\angle PRS| = 40°$.

Calculate:

(i) $|\angle QRS|$ **(ii)** $|\angle QPS|$

Justify your answers.

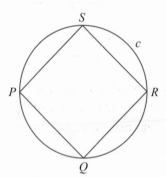

26. **(i)** *c* is a circle. *PQRS* is a square.

Each vertex is a point on the circle.

What can you say about [*PR*]?

(ii) Calculate:

(a) $|\angle PQR|$ **(b)** $|\angle PRS|$

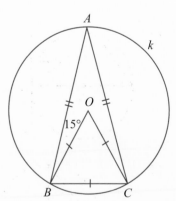

27. *A*, *B* and *C* are points on the circle *k*.

O is the centre of the circle and $|\angle OBA| = 15°$.

$|AB| = |AC|$ and $|OB| = |OC| = |BC|$.

(i) Write down $|\angle OBC|$. Give a reason for your answer.

(ii) Write down $|\angle ABC|$.

(iii) Prove that $|\angle BOC| = 2|\angle BAC|$.

28. (i) *A*, *B* and *C* are points on circle *k*.

O is the centre of the circle.

Give a reason why:

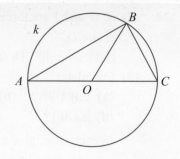

(a) $|OA| = |OB| = |OC|$

(b) $|\angle OAB| = |\angle OBA|$

(c) $|\angle OBC| = |\angle OCB|$

(ii) Let $|\angle OAB| = x°$ and $|\angle OBC| = y°$.

Complete the following, giving a reason for **(a)** and **(b)**.

(a) $2x + 2y =$

(b) $x + y =$

(c) $|\angle ABC| =$

(d) Therefore, the angle in a semicircle is a _____ angle.

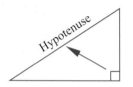

PYTHAGORAS' THEOREM

The longest side of a right-angled triangle is always opposite the right angle and is called the **hypotenuse**.

Pythagoras' theorem states that in a right-angled triangle:

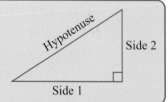

The square on the hypotenuse is equal to the sum of the squares on the other two sides.

$$(\text{hypotenuse})^2 = (\text{side 1})^2 + (\text{side 2})^2$$

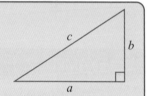

This equation can be written algebraically:

$$c^2 = a^2 + b^2$$

The converse (opposite) also applies:
If $c^2 = a^2 + b^2$, then the triangle must be right-angled.

Note: Pythagoras' theorem only applies to right-angled triangles.

We can use Pythagoras' theorem to find the missing length of a side in a right-angled triangle if we know the lengths of the other two sides.

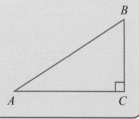

Pythagoras' theorem can also be written as:

$$|AB|^2 = |AC|^2 + |BC|^2$$

EXAMPLE 1

Find the value of **(i)** x and **(ii)** y, correct to two decimal places.

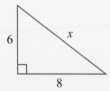

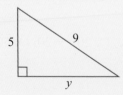

Solution:

(i)

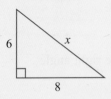

$$x^2 = 8^2 + 6^2$$
$$x^2 = 64 + 36$$
$$x^2 = 100$$
$$x = \sqrt{100}$$
$$x = 10$$

(ii)

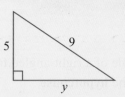

$$y^2 + 5^2 = 9^2$$
$$y^2 + 25 = 81$$
$$y^2 = 81 - 25$$
$$y^2 = 56$$
$$y = \sqrt{56} \text{ (exactly)}$$
$$y = 7 \cdot 48$$

(correct to two decimal places)

EXAMPLE 2

The diagonal of a square is $\sqrt{32}$. Calculate the length of the side.

Solution:
Draw a square.
Let x = the length of a side.
The diagonal bisects the square to create two right-angled triangles.
Therefore, we can apply Pythagoras' theorem.

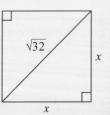

$$a^2 + b^2 = h^2 \qquad \text{(Pythagoras' theorem)}$$
$$x^2 + x^2 = (\sqrt{32})^2$$
$$2x^2 = 32$$
$$x^2 = 16 \qquad \text{(divide both sides by 2)}$$
$$x = \sqrt{16} \qquad \text{(take the square root of both sides)}$$
$$x = 4$$

Therefore, the length of a side of the square is 4.

Note: $(\sqrt{a})^2 = a$. For example, $(\sqrt{20})^2 = 20$; $(\sqrt{50})^2 = 50$.

Exercise 25.1

1. Copy and complete the table.

a	b	c	a^2	b^2	c^2
3	4				
	8	10			
8		17			
				64	100
			144		169
		50		900	
	7		576		
				2·25	6·25

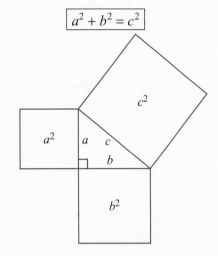

$$a^2 + b^2 = c^2$$

Use Pythagoras' theorem to find the length of the side indicated by a letter in each of the diagrams in questions 2–25.

2.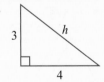

3.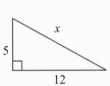

4.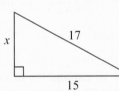

5.

6.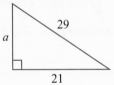

7.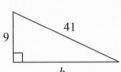

8.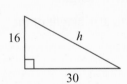

9.

10.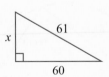

11.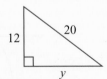

12.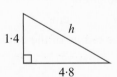

13.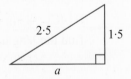

In questions 14–17, remember that $\left(\sqrt{x}\right)^2 = x$. For example, $\left(\sqrt{5}\right)^2 = 5$, $\left(\sqrt{8}\right)^2 = 8$.

14.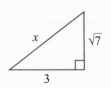

15.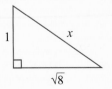

16.

17.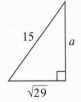

In questions 18–21, leave your answer in square root (surd) form.

18.

19.

20.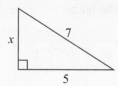

21.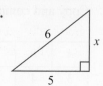

In questions 22–25, the diagrams represent squares.

22.

23.

24.

25.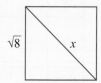

26. Prove that the triangle with sides of lengths 10 units, 24 units and 26 units is right-angled.

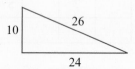

27. The lengths of the three sides of some triangles are given below. Using Pythagoras' theorem, investigate which triangles are right-angled and which are not.

   (i) 6, 8, 10   **(ii)** 5, 12, 14   **(iii)** 20, 21, 29   **(iv)** 6, 8, 9   **(v)** 2, 1, $\sqrt{5}$

28. The isosceles triangle shown in the diagram has a base of length 10 cm and the other two sides are each 13 cm in length.

   Find h, the perpendicular height of the triangle.

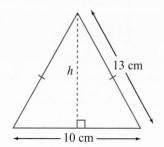

29. O is the centre of the circle.
   If $|AC| = 8$ cm and $|BC| = 6$ cm,
   find the length of the radius of the circle.

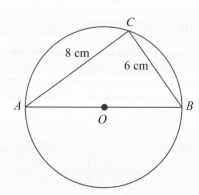

30. The diagram shows a ladder, 5 m in length, leaning against a vertical wall. The foot of the ladder is on horizontal ground, 1·4 m from the wall. Calculate how far up the wall the ladder reaches.

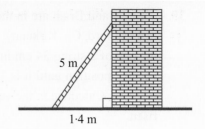

31. Find the area of the squares marked *A* and *B* in the following diagrams.

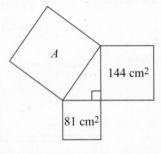
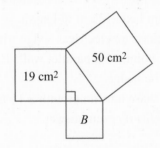

32. The diagram shows a circle *k* with centre *O*. *PQ* is a tangent and *P* is the point of contact. If $|OQ| = 12·5$ cm and $|PQ| = 10$ cm, calculate the radius of the circle.

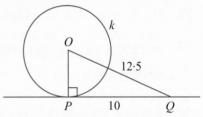

33. In the diagram, $AB \perp BC$ and $AC \perp CD$. $|AB| = 3$, $|BC| = 4$ and $|AD| = 13$. Using Pythagoras' theorem twice, calculate **(i)** $|AC|$ **(ii)** $|CD|$.

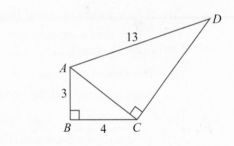

34. The diagram shows the side view of a wedge. The wedge is 112 mm long and 30 mm high. The top part of the wedge is 40 mm long. Calculate the length of the sloping part of the wedge.

35. Andrew and Brian are in the all-Ireland conkers competition in Freshford, Co. Kilkenny. Andrew's conker, C, is tied to the end of a string 34 cm in length. He pulls it back from its vertical position until it is 30 cm horizontal from its original position. Calculate h, the vertical distance that the conker has risen.

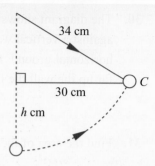

36. Sean has a straight hedge 26 m in length.
He wants to purchase an electrical hedge trimmer.
There is a power point, on a parallel wall, 10 m from the midpoint of the hedge.
Should Sean purchase a trimmer with a 15 m or a 20 m cable? Justify your answer.

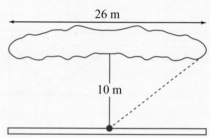

37. The diagram shows a rectangular field surrounded by a concrete path.
The length of the field is 432 m and the width is 126 m.
There are entrances to the field at A and B.
A person wants to get from A to B.

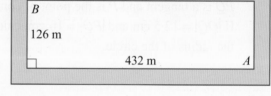

   (i) If they follow the path, how far will they walk?
   (ii) If they take a shortcut across the field, how far will they walk?
   (iii) Find the distance saved by taking the shortcut.
   (iv) The person can walk at 2 m/s on the path and 1·5 m/s across the field. Calculate the quickest route and the time saved.

38. The diagram shows a wedge $PQRSUV$.
$|RU| = 3$ cm, $|US| = 4$ cm and $|PS| = 12$ cm.
$RU \perp US$ and $RS \perp PS$.
Calculate (i) $|RS|$ (ii) $|PR|$.

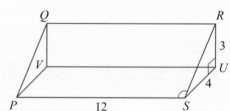

39. Consider the triangle $\triangle ABC$, using **acute angle**, **right-angle** or **obtuse angle**. Name the type of angle that $\angle ACB$ makes if:
   (i) $c^2 = a^2 + b^2$
   (ii) $c^2 > a^2 + b^2$
   (iii) $c^2 < a^2 + b^2$

In each case, explain your answer.

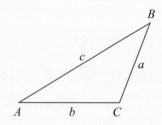

Area of a parallelogram

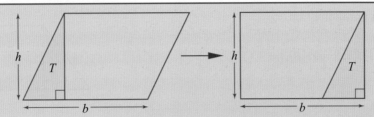

The area of a parallelogram of base b and height h has the same area as a rectangle of length b and width h. This can be seen by cutting out the triangle T in the parallelogram and placing it at the other end to form a rectangle. Thus, this parallelogram has the same area as the rectangle. The area of the rectangle is bh.

A parallelogram of base b and height h has area A given by $A = bh$.

Note: Unfortunately, the formulae and tables book on page 8 uses a instead of b.

Any side can be taken as the **base**. It does not need to be at the bottom of the parallelogram. The height must always be perpendicular to the side chosen as the base.

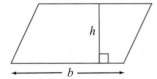
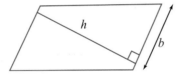

$b = $ length of base
$h = $ perpendicular height
$A = b \times h$

In a parallelogram, therefore, there are two possible values for its base. Each of these **base lengths** has a corresponding **perpendicular height**.

Therefore, there are two possible ways to calculate the area of a parallelogram. It depends on the base length and perpendicular height that is known. In some questions we have to use Pythagoras' theorem to find the perpendicular height.

Diagonals and area

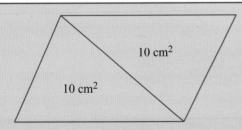
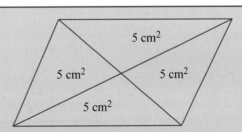

A diagonal divides a parallelogram into two triangles, each of equal area.
If the area of the parallelogram is 20 cm², then the area of each triangle is 10 cm².

Two diagonals divide a parallelogram into four triangles, each of equal area.
If the area of the parallelogram is 20 cm², then the area of each triangle is 5 cm².

EXAMPLE

ABCD is a parallelogram.
AE ⊥ *BC*,
$|AB| = 5, |AD| = 8$ and $|BE| = 3.$

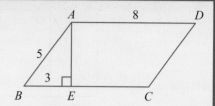

Calculate:

(i) $|AE|$

(ii) The area of the parallelogram *ABCD*

(iii) The length of the perpendicular from [*AB*] to [*CD*]

(iv) The perimeter of the parallelogram *ABCD*

Solution:

(i) △*ABE* is a right-angled triangle.

Using Pythagoras' theorem,

$$|AE|^2 + |BE|^2 = |AB|^2$$
$$|AE|^2 + 3^2 = 5^2$$
$$|AE|^2 + 9 = 25$$
$$|AE|^2 = 16$$
$$|AE| = \sqrt{16} = 4$$

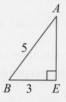

(ii) Area of parallelogram *ABCD*

$$= \text{base} \times \text{height}$$
$$= |AD| \times |AE|$$
$$= 8 \times 4$$
$$= 32$$

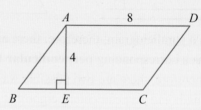

(iii) Let the length of the perpendicular from [*AB*] to [*CD*] = *h*.

Equation given in disguise:

area of parallelogram = 32

$$\text{base} \times \text{height} = 32$$
$$|AB| \times h = 32$$
$$5 \times h = 32$$
$$h = 6{\cdot}4$$

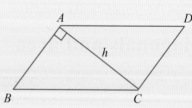

Therefore, the length of the perpendicular from [*AB*] to [*CD*] is 6·4.

(Notice that 8 × 4 = 5 × 6·4. Both are equal to 32.)

(iv) Perimeter of the parallelogram
(opposite sides are equal in length)
$$= 8 + 5 + 8 + 5$$
$$= 26$$

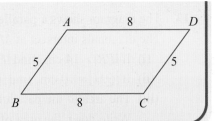

Exercise 25.2

In questions 1–6, calculate (i) the perimeter and (ii) the area of each of the following parallelograms (all dimensions are in cm).

1.

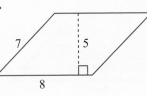

2.

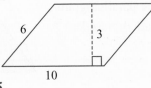

3.

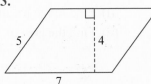

4.

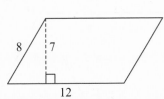

5.

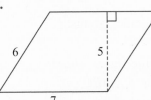

6.

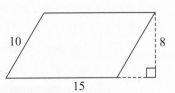

In questions 7–9, calculate the perpendicular height, h cm, where the area, A cm, is given.

7.

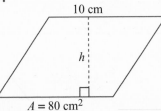

8.

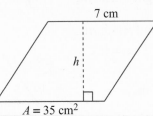

9.

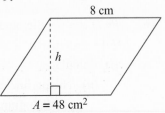

In questions 10–12, use Pythagoras' theorem (i) to find the perpendicular height, h cm, and then (ii) find the area of the parallelogram.

10.

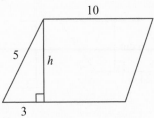

11.

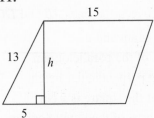

12.

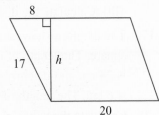

13. The diagram shows a parallelogram *PQRS*.
The diagonals intersect at *M*.

(i) If $|PR| = 14$ cm, find $|PM|$.

(ii) If $|QM| = 10$ cm, find $|QS|$.

(iii) The area of the parallelogram is 104 cm².
Write down the area of **(a)** △*PQR*
(b) △*PMS*. In each case, give a reason
for your answer.

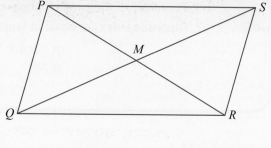

14. The diagram shows a parallelogram with base
length 20 cm.
The area of the parallelogram is 180 cm².

(i) Find *h*, the height of the parallelogram.

(ii) Find the area of the shaded triangle.

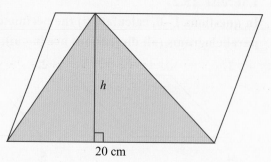

15. *ABCD* and *ACED* are two parallelograms.
$|BC| = 8$ cm.

(i) Given that the area of the figure *ABED*
is 60 cm², find the area of △*ABC*.
Justify your answer.

(ii) Taking [*BC*] as the base, calculate
the perpendicular height of △*ABC*.

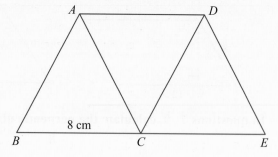

16. *ABCD* is a parallelogram and $AE \perp BC$.
$|AD| = 16$ cm and $|AB| = 10$ cm $= |EC|$.

(i) Calculate:

(a) The perimeter of the
parallelogram

(b) $|BE|$

(c) $|AE|$

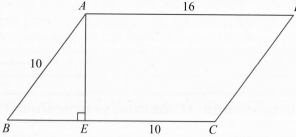

(ii) Calculate the area of **(a)** parallelogram *ABCD* **(b)** △*ACD* **(c)** △*AEC*.

(iii) Calculate the distance between the lines *AB* and *DC*.

17. The diagram shows a parallelogram and a
square. The length of one side of the parallelogram
is 24 cm and its corresponding perpendicular height
is 6 cm. The length of a side of the square is *x* cm.
Calculate the value of *x* if the area of the parallelogram
is equal to the area of the square.

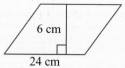

Transformations

The word '**transformation**' means change. The movement of a point or a shape from one position to another is called a **transformation**. In other words, a transformation changes the position of a shape.

Object and image

The original position of a shape is called the **object**. The new position of the shape is called the **image**. In other words, the image is where the object moves to. In mathematics we say that the object **maps onto** the image.

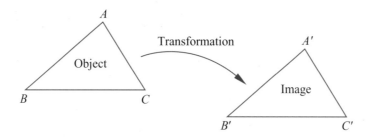

Often the images of points are indicated by primes. A' is pronounced 'A prime'. A and A' are called **corresponding** points, because the point A' is the image of the point A. Figures have **critical** points that define its shape, usually its vertices (corners). When constructing an image, we usually only find the image of the critical points. In the triangle above, the critical points are A, B and C and their images are A', B' and C', respectively. Then we join the image points to construct the image of the object.

On our course we will meet three types of transformations:

1. Translation   **2.** Axial symmetry   **3.** Central symmetry

> Each of these transformations changes the position of a shape but not its size or shape.

Translation

The diagram shows the movement of a child on a slide. She slides, in a straight line, from one position to another.	The diagram shows a person on an escalator. She moves, in a straight line, from one position to another.
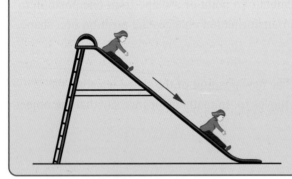	

In mathematics, movement in a straight line is called a **translation**.

Under a translation, every point in the shape is moved the same distance in the same direction. It is often called a **slide**, since the shape appears to slide from one position to another. The shape does not turn or flip over. The object and its image are congruent (identical).

To describe a translation, we need to give its direction and say by how much it has moved. A translation is often denoted by an arrow above two letters, for example $\overrightarrow{AB}$ or $\overrightarrow{AA'}$.

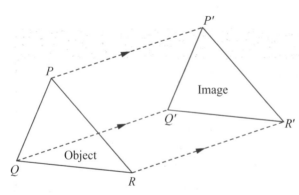

This translation could be described as $P \rightarrow P'$, written as $\overrightarrow{PP'}$.
The translation could also be written $\overrightarrow{QQ'}$ or $\overrightarrow{RR'}$.
Under a translation, lengths and angles are preserved.
$|PQ|=|P'Q'|$, $|PR|=|P'R'|$ and $|QR|=|Q'R'|$.
$PQ\|P'Q'$, $PR\|P'R'$ and $QR\|Q'R'$.

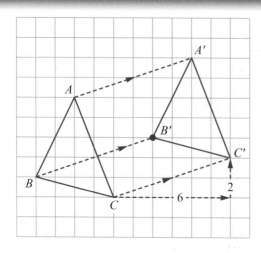

A translation is more easily described using a grid and indicating how far right (positive), left (negative) and how far up (positive) and down (negative) a figure is moved.

Each point on the object has moved 6 units to the right and 2 units up. To avoid using a sentence, this can also be described using a **column vector**. A column vector is written similar to coordinates, with the left or right (horizontal) displacement on top and the up or down (vertical) displacement on the bottom.

The translation can be written $\begin{pmatrix} 6 \\ 2 \end{pmatrix}$.

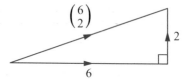

$\begin{pmatrix} 4 \\ -3 \end{pmatrix}$ is a translation of 4 units to the right and 3 units down.

$\begin{pmatrix} -2 \\ 5 \end{pmatrix}$ is a translation of 2 units to the left and 5 units up.

$\begin{pmatrix} -1 \\ -4 \end{pmatrix}$ is a translation of 1 unit to the left and 4 units down.

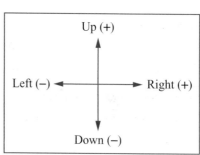

EXAMPLE 1

Construct the image of *ABCD* under the translation 5 units right and 1 unit down.

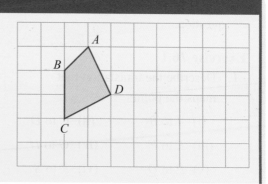

Solution:

Move the point *A* 5 units right and 1 unit down.
Label this point *A′*.
Construct *B′*, *C′* and *D′*, the images of *B*, *C* and
D, in the same way.
Join the points *A′*, *B′*, *C′* and *D′*.
A′B′C′D′ is the image of *ABCD* under the
translation 5 units right and 1 unit down.

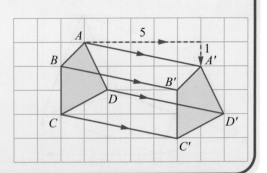

EXAMPLE 2

ABCD and *ACED* are parallelograms.
Under the translation $\vec{BC}$, write down the image of:

(i) △*ABC*   **(ii)** [*AC*]   **(iii)** ∠*BAC*

(iv) Name two other translations equal to $\vec{BC}$.

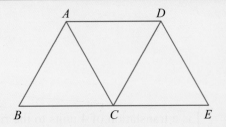

Solution:

The image of a point is where the point moves to after the transformation.

Under the translation $\vec{BC}$:

$A \rightarrow D$ (*A* moves to *D*)

$B \rightarrow C$ (*B* moves to *C*)

$C \rightarrow E$ (*C* moves to *E*)

(i) △*ABC* → △*DCE*

(ii) [*AC*] → [*DE*]

(iii) ∠*BAC* → ∠*CDE*

(iv) Two other translations equal to $\vec{BC}$ are $\vec{AD}$ and $\vec{CE}$ (same length and direction).

Note: It is good practice, but not necessary, to keep the order of the images of points asked in the
question.

Exercise 26.1

1. Describe the translation that
   maps the point:

   (i) *A* to *B*   **(ii)** *C* to *D*

   (iii) *E* to *F*   **(iv)** *G* to *H*

   (v) *P* to *Q*   **(vi)** *R* to *S*

   Write your answers as a sentence
   or a column vector.

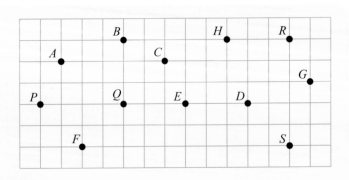

2. Describe the translation that maps the shape:

   (i) *A* to *B*

   (ii) *C* to *D*

   (iii) *E* to *F*

   (iv) *G* to *H*

Write each answer as a sentence or a
column vector.

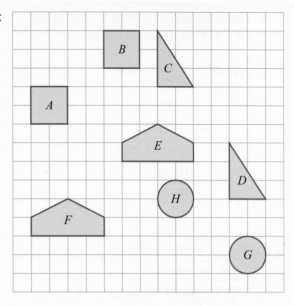

3. Copy the grid below and construct the image of the triangle *A* under the following translation.

   (i) 2 units right and 3 units up: label this *B*.   **(ii)** 4 units left and 1 unit up: label this *C*.

   (iii) 5 units right: label this *D*.   **(iv)** 4 units down: label this *E*.

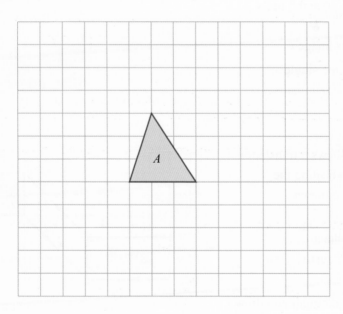

4. Copy the grid and construct the image of *ABCDE* under the translation $\overrightarrow{AA'}$.

   Describe the translation.

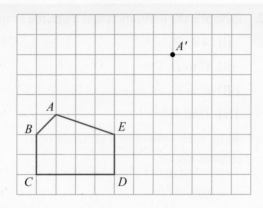

5. The diagram shows △*A*.
   Copy the diagram.

   (i) Construct the image of *A* under the translation 4 units right and 2 units up. Label this image *B*.

   (ii) Construct the image of *B* under the translation 3 units right and 5 units down. Label this image *C*.

   (iii) Describe the single translation that maps *A* onto *C*.

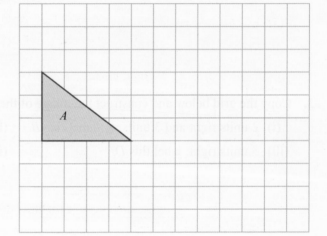

6. The diagram shows a translation. The arrows, indicating the translations, are drawn incorrectly.

   (i) Why are the arrows incorrect? Justify your answer.

   (ii) Copy the diagram and draw an arrow which correctly indicates the translation.

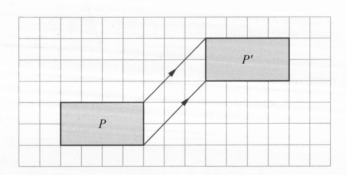

7. *PQRS* and *PRTS* are parallelograms.

    (i) Under the translation $\overrightarrow{PS}$, write down the image of:

    (a) △*PQR*   **(b)** [*QR*]   **(c)** ∠*QPR*

    (ii) Name two other translations equal to $\overrightarrow{PS}$.

    (iii) Find the image of *S* under the translation $\overrightarrow{RQ}$.

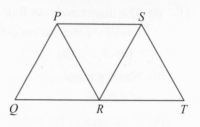

8. *RSTU* is a square and *USTV* is a parallelogram.

    (i) Under the translation $\overrightarrow{ST}$, write down the image of:

    (a) △*RSU*   **(b)** [*SU*]   **(c)** ∠*SRU*

    (ii) Under the translation $\overrightarrow{UR}$, write down the image of:

    (a) △*UVT*   **(b)** [*UT*]   **(c)** ∠*TVU*

    (iii) Name one translation equal to:

    (a) $\overrightarrow{SU}$ **(b)** $\overrightarrow{VT}$ **(c)** $\overrightarrow{TU}$

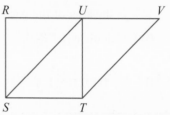

9. *PQRS* is a rectangle. The midpoint of [*QR*] is *Z*. $|QZ|=|XY|$ and $|PX|=|YS|$.

    (i) Under the translation $\overrightarrow{QZ}$, write down the image of:

    (a) △*XQZ*   **(b)** [*XZ*]   **(c)** ∠*QXZ*

    (ii) Name two parallelograms that are not rectangles.

    (iii) Name two angles equal to ∠*XQZ*.

    (iv) If $|PQ| = 5$ cm and $|PX| = 2$ cm, calculate the area of the rectangle *PQRS*.

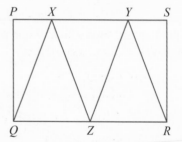

10. **(i)** The diagram shows two identical squares, *ABCD* and *DCEF*, with their diagonals intersecting at *X* and *Y*, respectively. Under the translation $\overrightarrow{AD}$, write down the image of:

    (a) *C*   **(b)** [*AB*]   **(c)** △*AXD*
    (d) [*BX*]   **(e)** [*XD*]   **(f)** ∠*XAD*

    (ii) Name another square.

    (iii) If the area of △*ABX* is 4 cm², find the area of:

    (a) △*BAD*   **(b)** △*ACF*   **(c)** The rectangle *ABEF*

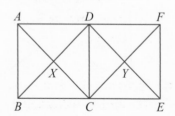

11. (i) The diagram shows four equilateral triangles.
Under the translation $\overrightarrow{QR}$, write down the image of:

   (a) S (b) $[QP]$ (c) $\triangle PSR$ (d) $\angle RPS$

   (ii) Name a translation under which $\triangle PRS$ is the image of $\triangle SUV$.

   (iii) If the area of the parallelogram $PQUV$ is 20 cm^2, what is the area of the parallelogram $PRUS$?

   (iv) Calculate $|\angle PRU|$.

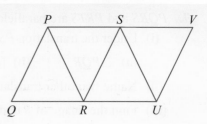

Axial symmetry

Axial symmetry is a reflection in a line. It involves reflecting points perpendicularly through a line.

The diagram shows an **L** shape reflected in a mirror.	We can also draw the reflection without a mirror. The **object** is reflected in the mirror to give the **image**. The mirror becomes a line of symmetry.

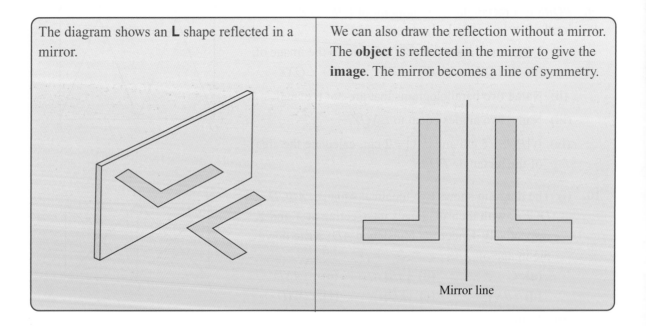

Mirror line

An object reflected in a mirror creates an image. A reflection in a line, an axial symmetry, gives an image that looks like a reflection in a mirror (sometimes called a mirror image). The line is called the **axis of reflection** or **line of reflection** or **mirror line**. The object and the image are symmetrical about the mirror line. In other words, any point and its image are the same perpendicular distance from the axis of symmetry. The object and the image are congruent. However, under a reflection in a line, a figure flips over.

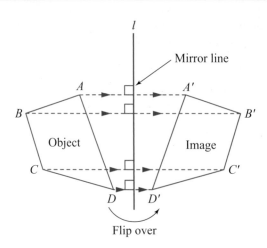

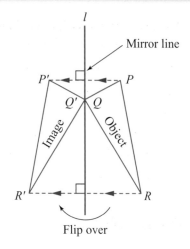

If a point is on the mirror line, its image is the same point. In the second diagram, the image of Q is still Q, i.e., $Q' = Q$. The line joining the corresponding points A and A' is perpendicular to the mirror line, i.e. $AA' \perp l$.

Note: Under an axial symmetry, the order of the letters are reversed.

S_l denotes 'the axial symmetry in the line l'.

EXAMPLE 1

Draw the image of $\triangle PQR$ under an axial symmetry in the line l.

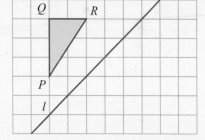

Solution

Draw a perpendicular broken line from P to the line l. Continue this broken line the same distance on the other side of l. Label this point P'.

Construct Q' and R', the images of Q and R, respectively, in the same way.
Join the points P', Q' and R'.

$\triangle P'Q'R'$ is the image of $\triangle PQR$ under an axial symmetry in the line l.

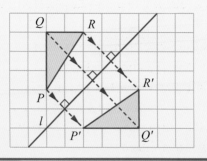

EXAMPLE 2

PQRS and *SRUV* are two squares with diagonals intersecting at *A* and *B*, respectively. Under the axial symmetry in *SR*, write down the image of:

(i) △*PQS*   (ii) [*PQ*]   (iii) ∠*APS*

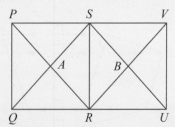

Solution:

Under the axial symmetry in *SR*:

$$P \rightarrow V$$
$$Q \rightarrow U$$
$$S \rightarrow S \quad \text{(own image)}$$
$$A \rightarrow B$$

(i) △*PQS* → △*VUS*

(ii) [*PQ*] → [*VU*]

(iii) ∠*APS* → ∠*BVS*

Exercise 26.2

1. Copy and construct the image of each figure under an axial symmetry in the mirror line, *l*.

(i)

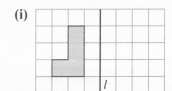

(ii)

(iii)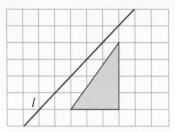

(iv)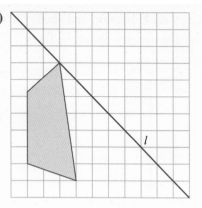

2. Each diagram shows an object and its image. Copy the diagram and in each case draw the line of reflection (mirror line).

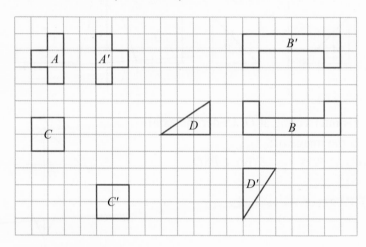

3. Copy and construct the image of *ABCD* under axial symmetry in:
   (i) *l*   **(ii)** *k*

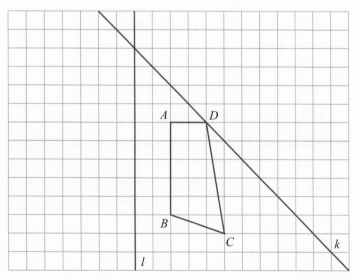

357

4. Copy each diagram and shade the minimum number of squares so that each pattern has axial symmetry about the lines.

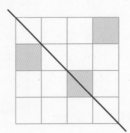
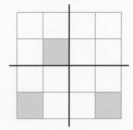

5. In each case, explain why A' is not the image of A under an axial symmetry in the line l.

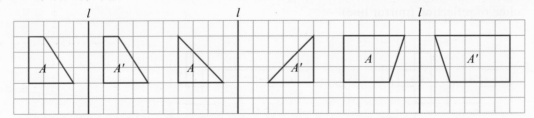

6. PQRS is a kite with diagonals intersecting at O. Under the axial symmetry in PR, write down the image of:

(i) Q (ii) S (iii) $\triangle POS$ (iv) $\angle PSO$

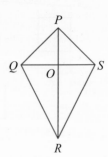

7. [PQ] and [RS] are two diameters of a circle that are perpendicular to each other. Write down the image of:

(i) P under the axial symmetry in RS

(ii) [PO] under the axial symmetry in RS

(iii) $\triangle QOR$ under the axial symmetry in PQ

8. ABCD and DCEF are squares with diagonals intersecting at X and Y, respectively.

(i) Under the axial symmetry in DC, write down the image of:

     (a) A (b) B (c) E

     (d) F (e) D (f) C

     (g) X (h) Y (i) [AB]

     (j) $\triangle DFY$ (k) $\angle XAD$ (l) $\angle YCD$

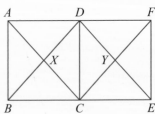

(ii) Under the axial symmetry in *AC*, write down the image of:

    (a) *B*   (b) *D*   (c) *A*   (d) *C*

    (e) *X*   (f) △*ABX*   (g) ∠*BXC*   (h) [*XD*]

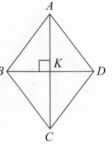

9. *ABCD* is a parallelogram with diagonals intersecting at *K* and *AC* ⊥ *BD*.

    (i) Find the image of △*BCK* under the axial symmetry in *BD*.

    (ii) What is the image of *ABCD* under the axial symmetry in *AC*?

    (iii) Name four isosceles triangles.

    (iv) Find the image of [*AB*] under the translation $\overrightarrow{BC}$.

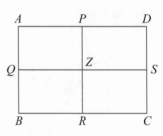

10. The diagram shows a rectangle *ABCD* divided into four smaller rectangles of equal size. The diagonals of the rectangle *ABCD* meet at *Z*.

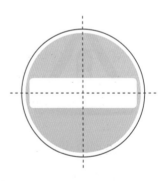

    (i) Under the axial symmetry in *PR*, write down the image of:

      (a) *A*   (b) *B*   (c) *S*   (d) △*CZS*   (e) ∠*ZPD*

    (ii) Under the axial symmetry in *QS*, write down the image of:

      (a) *B*   (b) *P*   (c) *C*   (d) △*QBR*   (e) The rectangle *RZSC*

    (iii) Find the image of [*QZ*] under the translation $\overrightarrow{DS}$.

    (iv) If the area of △*APQ* = 4 cm², what is the area of the rectangle *ABCD*?

Axis of symmetry

A shape has an **axis of symmetry** or a **line of symmetry** when one half of the shape fits exactly over the other half when the shape is folded along that line. Shapes which are evenly balanced are said to be **symmetrical**. Some shapes have no axis of symmetry, some have only one axis of symmetry and others have more than one axis of symmetry.

Parallelogram

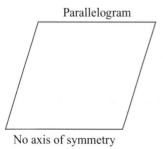

No axis of symmetry

Isosceles triangle

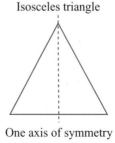

One axis of symmetry

Rectangle

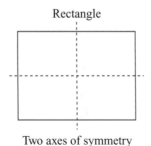

Two axes of symmetry

Equilateral triangle

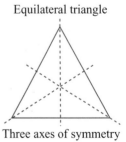

Three axes of symmetry

Exercise 26.3

How many axes of symmetry does each of the following shapes have?

1.

2.

3.

4.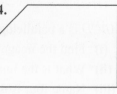

5.

6.

7.

8.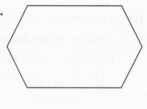

9.

10.

11.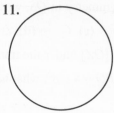

12.

13.

14.

15.

16.

17. On each diagram, shade in two more squares so that each pattern has one line of symmetry.

(i)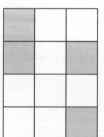

(ii)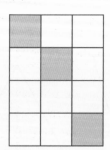

(iii)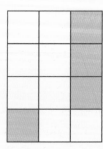

18.

Some words, written in upper case block form, have a horizontal line of symmetry. They also look the same after reflection at a horizontal line, e.g. **KICK**.	Some words, written in upper case block form, have a vertical line of symmetry. They also look the same after reflection at a vertical line, e.g. **TOT**.

KICK

KICK

TOT

T T
O O
T T

(i) Write down the four capital letters, in upper case block form, that have both horizontal and vertical symmetry.

(ii) How many words in the grid can you find with horizontal or vertical symmetry?

(iii) Make up some words of your own that have horizontal or vertical symmetry.

H	O	B	B	O	Y
A	C	O	D	D	O
M	A	M	A	T	U
A	T	A	T	A	B
T	E	T	O	X	O
T	H	O	O	D	O
A	I	O	T	O	T
W	M	X	H	T	H

Central symmetry

A pinhole camera has a small hole cut in it and the opposite side has a piece of photographic film attached to it. Rays of light, travelling in straight lines, enter through the pinhole and form an image on the photographic film. The image on the film will be upside-down.

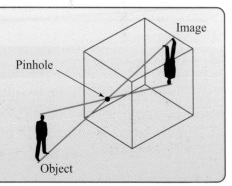

Central symmetry is a reflection in a point. The point is called the **centre of symmetry**. It involves reflecting points through the centre of symmetry to the same distance on the other side.

An object reflected in a point creates an image. Under a central symmetry, any point and its image are equidistant from the centre of symmetry. The object and the image are congruent. However, under a central symmetry, a shape is turned over. Central symmetry is exactly the same as a rotation of 180° about the centre of symmetry.

Note: S_O denotes 'the central symmetry in the point O'.

EXAMPLE 1

Construct the image of $\triangle PQR$ under the central symmetry in the point O.

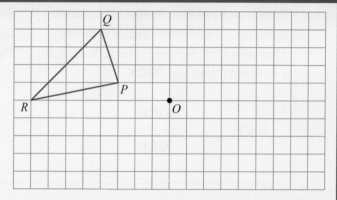

Solution:

Draw a straight line from P to O and continue the same distance on the other side of O. Label this point P'. Construct Q' and R', the images of Q and R, respectively, in the same way. Join the points P', Q' and R'.

$\triangle P'Q'R'$ is the image of $\triangle PQR$ under a central symmetry in O.

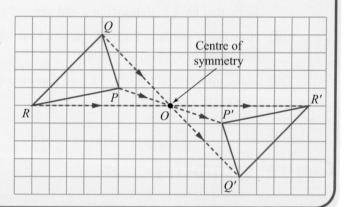

EXAMPLE 2

$ABCD$ and $EDGF$ are two identical parallelograms with diagonals intersecting at P and Q, respectively. Under the central symmetry in D, write down the image of:

(i) $\triangle APD$ **(ii)** $[AB]$ **(iii)** $\angle QFE$

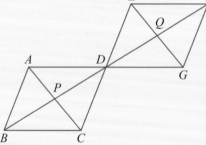

Solution:

Under the central symmetry in D:

$A \rightarrow G$

$P \rightarrow Q$

$D \rightarrow D$ (own image)

$B \rightarrow F$

$Q \rightarrow P$

$F \rightarrow B$

$E \rightarrow C$

(i) $\triangle APD \rightarrow \triangle GQD$

(ii) $[AB] \rightarrow [GF]$

(iii) $\angle QFE \rightarrow \angle PBC$

Exercise 26.4

1. Copy and construct the image of each figure under a central symmetry in the point *O*.

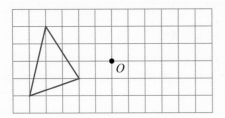 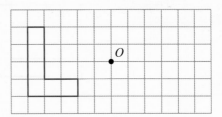

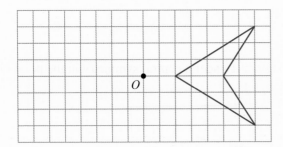 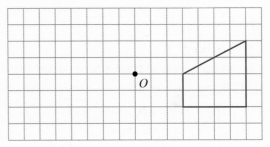

2. Each diagram shows an object and its image. Copy the diagram and in each case, indicate the centre of symmetry with a dot and label it *O*.

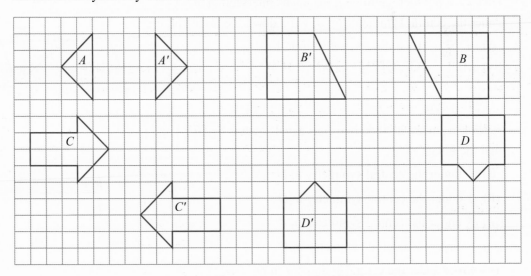

3. Copy and construct the image of *P* under a central symmetry in the point **(i)** *A* and **(ii)** *B*.

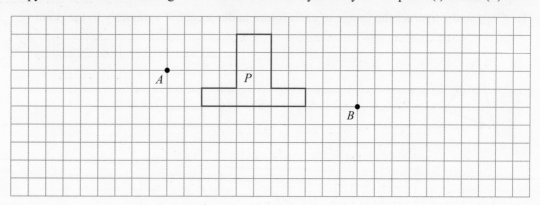

4. In each case, explain why *A'* is **not** the image of *A* under a central symmetry in the point *O*.

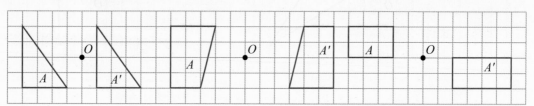

5. *ABCD* is a parallelogram with diagonals intersecting at *M*.
   Under the central symmetry in *M*, write down the image of:

   (i) *A*　　**(ii)** *B*　　　**(iii)** [*DC*]

   (iv) [*AD*]　**(v)** △*ABM*　　**(vi)** ∠*BCM*

6. *PQRS* is a square divided into four equal squares by [*WY*] and [*XZ*].
   Find the image of:

   (i) *P* under the central symmetry in *O*

   (ii) *Y* under the central symmetry in *O*

   (iii) *R* under the central symmetry in *Z*

   (iv) *S* under the central symmetry in *W*

   (v) [*SW*] under the central symmetry in *O*

   (vi) △*QXO* under the central symmetry in *O*

   (vii) △*XYQ* under the central symmetry in *O*

   (viii) The square *WSZO* under the central symmetry in *O*

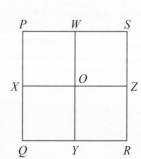

7. *PQRS* is a square and *SQRT* is a parallelogram with diagonals intersecting at *X* and *Y*, respectively.

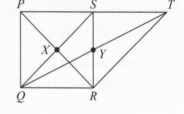

   (i) Name four line segments equal in length to [*PS*].

   (ii) Under the central symmetry in *X*, write down the image of:

       (a) *R*   **(b)** *Q*   **(c)** [*PQ*]   **(d)** △*PXS*

   (iii) Under the central symmetry in *Y*, write down the image of:

       (a) *R*   **(b)** *Q*   **(c)** [*SQ*]   **(d)** △*STY*   **(e)** ∠*QRT*

   (iv) What is the image of [*PS*] under the translation $\overrightarrow{QR}$?

   (v) What is the image of *P* under the axial symmetry in *SR*?

   (vi) If the area of △*PSQ* = 20 cm², what is the area of the parallelogram *SQRT*?

8. *ABCD* is a rectangle. *ABDX* and *BYCD* are parallelograms.

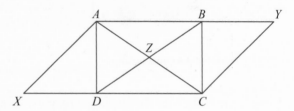

   (i) Name three line segments equal in length to [*DC*].

   (ii) What is the image of △*BCY* under the central symmetry in *Z*?

   (iii) What is the image of △*AXD* under the axial symmetry in the line *AD*?

   (iv) What is the image of [*AX*] under the translation $\overrightarrow{BY}$?

   (v) If |∠*AXD*| = 40°, write down the measure of |∠*ADZ*|.

   (vi) If the area of △*ADZ* = 8 cm², what is the area of the figure *AXCY*?

Centre of symmetry

Some shapes are symmetrical about a point. The point is called the **centre of symmetry** (sometimes called the point of symmetry). The following shapes have a centre of symmetry, indicated by *O*.

Circle

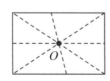

Rectangle

Square

Letter X

In each case, if any point is taken on the figure, its image under a central symmetry in the point O is **always** another point on the figure. To see if a figure has a centre of symmetry, rotate it by 180° (a half-turn). If the figure looks identical, then the figure has a centre of symmetry.

For example, consider the playing card, the 4 of clubs. Under a rotation of 180° (half-turn), the card looks identical. Every point P and Q on the card has a corresponding point P' and Q', respectively, on the card under a central symmetry in the point O. The point O is called the centre of symmetry. The centre of symmetry, point O, is the point of intersection of the lines PP' and QQ'.

Original position
(object)

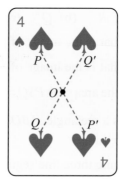

Rotation of 180°
(image)

Try the same thing with the playing card, the 5 of clubs. Does it have a centre of symmetry? Explain your answer.

Exercise 26.5

For each figure in questions 1–20, state whether it has a centre of symmetry and indicate where it is.

1.

2.

3.

4.

5.

6.

7.

8.

9.

10.

11.

12.

13.

14.

15.

16.

17.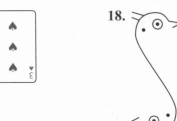

18.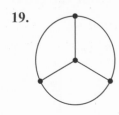

19.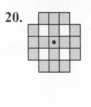

20.

21. On each diagram, shade in two squares so that each pattern has a centre of symmetry.

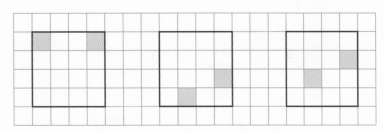

22. What letters, written in upper case block form, have a point of symmetry?

23. What letters, written in upper case block form, have a point of symmetry and have horizontal and vertical axes of symmetry?

24. No triangle has a centre of symmetry. Do you agree or disagree? Give a reason for your answer.

Instruments for constructions

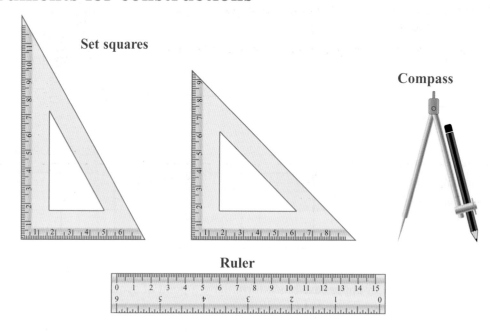

Set squares

Compass

Ruler

Protractor

A **protractor** is used to measure angles between
$0°$ and $180°$.

It has two scales, an **inner** scale and an **outer** scale.
These scales go in opposite directions.

The outer scale goes in a clockwise direction.

The inner scale goes in an anti-clockwise direction.

The centre of the protractor is always placed on the
vertex of the angle.

The base line is always placed on one arm of the angle.

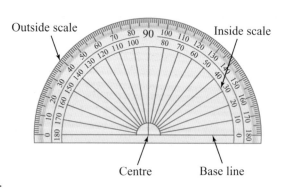

Never rub out any construction lines or marks. All construction lines or marks must be left on a diagram.

Note:

A straight edge is like a ruler without any numbers or markings.

A ruler is a straight edge but has numbers and markings on it.

When a question requires a straight edge, you can use your ruler but not the numbers or markings on it.

1. Perpendicular bisector of a given line segment

Given a line segment [AB].

A ——————————— B

Steps to bisect any line segment [AB] (using only a compass and straight edge).

1. Set the compass to a radius of about three-quarters of the length of the line segment AB. (Any radius above half the length of the line segment will do.)	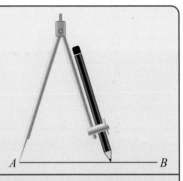
2. Place the compass point on A and draw arcs above and below the line segment.	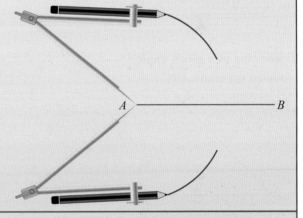
3. Keep the same radius as in step 2. Place the compass point on B and draw arcs above and below the line segment to intersect the other arcs. Where the arcs intersect, label the points X and Y.	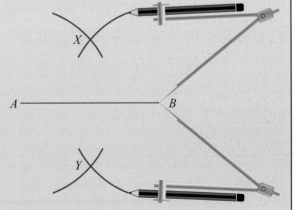

4. Draw the line through X and Y.
The line XY is the perpendicular bisector
of the line segment $[AB]$.

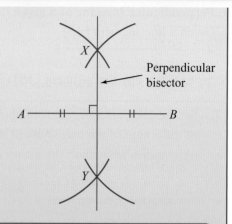

Perpendicular bisector

Any point on the perpendicular bisector of a line segment AB is equidistant (same distance) from the points A and B. The perpendicular bisector of the line segment AB is always at right angles to the line segment.

2. Bisector of a given angle

Given the angle ABC.

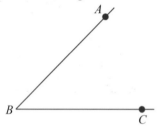

Steps to bisect any angle ABC (using only a compass and straight edge).

1. Set your compass to a sensible radius
(not too large). Place the compass point
on the vertex, B. Draw two arcs to intersect
the arms at X and Y.

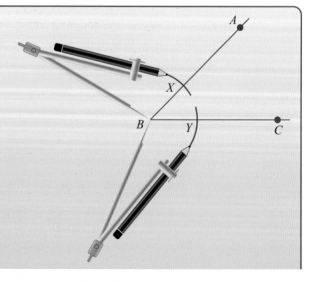

2. Place the compass point on *X* and draw an arc.
    Keep the same radius.
    Place the compass point on *Y* and draw an arc.
    Where the arcs intersect, label the point *Z*.

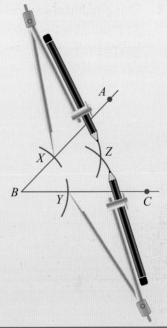

3. Draw a line from *B* through the point *Z*.
    The line *BZ* is the bisector of the angle *ABC*.

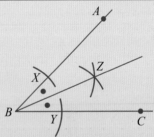

Any point on the bisector of an angle is equidistant (same distance) from the arms of the angle. The bisector of an acute or obtuse angle also bisects its related reflex angle.

3. Division of a line segment into three equal parts

Given a line segment [*AB*].

A ————————————— B

Steps to divide any line segment [*AB*] into three equal parts (using only a compass, straight edge and set square).

1. Draw the line *AC* at an acute angle to *AB*
    (any acute angle between 30° and 60° will do).

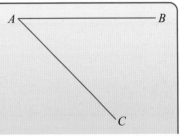

2. Using your compass, mark off three points
X, Y and Z on this line such that
$|AX|=|XY|=|YZ|$.

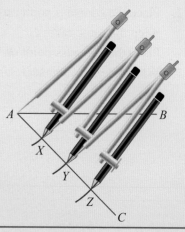

3. Draw the line ZB.

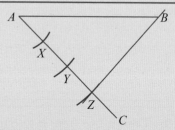

4. Place the edge of the set square on ZB.
Place the ruler under the set square.

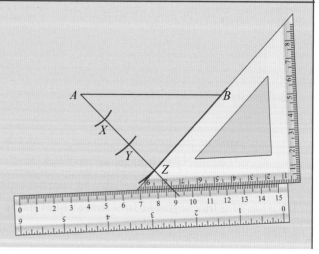

5. Keeping pressure on the ruler, slide the set square along the ruler until the edge meets the point Y.
   Through Y, draw a line parallel to ZB.
   Where this line meets the line AB, label the point N.

6. Keeping pressure on the ruler, slide the set square, again, along the ruler until the edge meets the point X.
   Through X, draw a line parallel to ZB.
   Where this line meets the line AB, label the point M.

7. The points M and N divide the line segment AB into three equal parts.

Note: This method can also be used to bisect a line segment or to divide a line segment into any number of parts.

4. Line perpendicular to a given line *l*, passing through a point on *l*

Given line *l* and a point *A* on *l*.

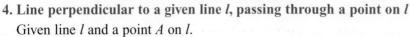

Steps in drawing a line perpendicular to a given line *l*, passing through a point on *l*.

Method 1 (using a set square and ruler)

1. Place one edge of the set square on the line *l* and the other edge directly over the point *A*. Toward *A*, draw a line perpendicular to the line *l*.	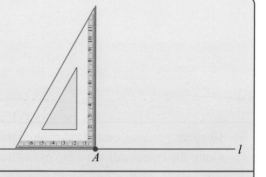
2. Using the ruler or set square, complete the line.	
3. This line is perpendicular to *l* at the point *A*.	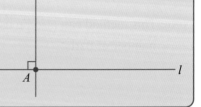

Method 2 (using a ruler and set square)

1. Place the edge of the ruler on the line *l*.
   Place the set square on the ruler.

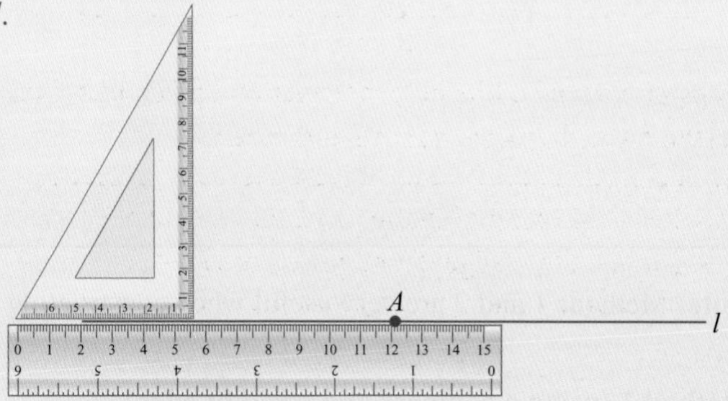

   A

   l

2. Keeping pressure on the ruler, slide the set square along
   the ruler until the edge meets the point *A*.
   Draw a line towards *A*.

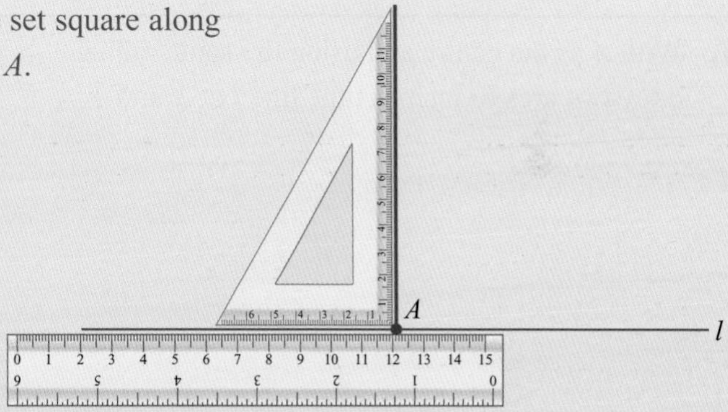

   A

   l

3. Using the ruler or set square, complete the line.

   A

   l

4. This line is perpendicular to *l* at the point *A*.

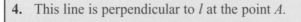

Note: Methods 1 and 2 are very useful when constructing rectangles and right-angled triangles.

Method 3 (using a compass and straight edge)

1. With *A* as the centre and using the same radius, draw two arcs to intersect the line *l* at *X* and *Y*.

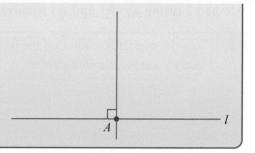

2. Place the compass point on *X* and draw arcs above and below the point *A*.

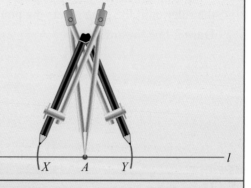

3. Keep the same radius as in part 2. Place the compass point on *Y* and draw arcs above and below the line at point *A* to intersect the other two arcs. Where the arcs intersect, label the points *P* and *Q*.

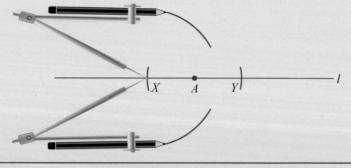

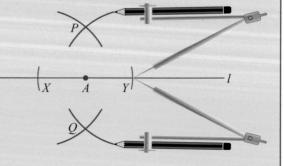

4. Draw the line through P and Q.

The line PQ is perpendicular to l at the point A.

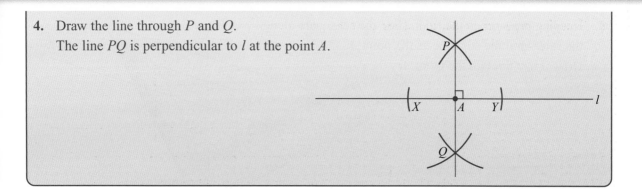

5. Line parallel to a given line l, through a point not on l

Given a line l and a point A not on l.

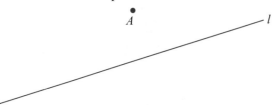

Steps in drawing a line parallel to a given line l, passing through a point A not on l (using only a straight edge and set square).

1. Place the edge of the set square on the line l.

Place the ruler under the set square.

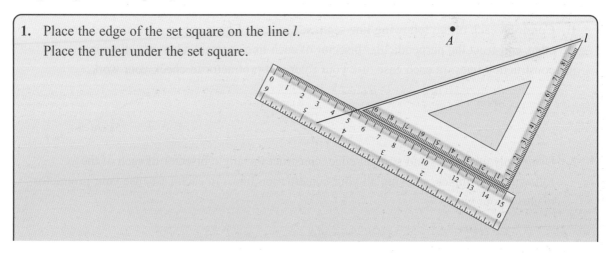

2. Keeping pressure on the ruler, slide the set square along
the ruler until the edge meets the point *A*.
Draw a line through the point *A*.

3. This line is parallel to the line *l* and contains the point *A*.

Exercise 27.1

1. Construct each of the following line segments exactly. Using only a compass and straight
edge, construct the perpendicular bisector of each line segment, showing all your
construction lines. In each case, use your ruler and protractor to check your work.

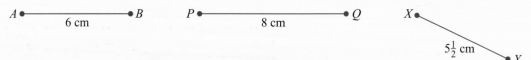

2. Using only a compass and straight edge, construct the angle bisector of each of the
following line angles, showing all your construction lines. In each case, use your protractor
to check your work.

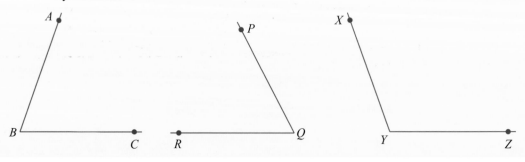

3. Construct each of the following line segments exactly. Using only a compass, straight edge and set square, show how to divide each of the line segments into three equal parts, showing all your construction lines. In each case, use your ruler to check your work.

A —————————— B P —————————— Q X —————————— Y
        9 cm $7\frac{1}{2}$ cm   63 mm

4. In each of the following, draw a line through the given point, perpendicular to the line that contains the point.

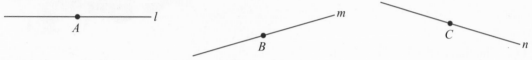

5. In each of the following, draw a line through the given point, not on the line, parallel to the line.

6. Construct a rectangle 12 cm long and 5 cm wide. Measure, in cm, the length of a diagonal of the rectangle.

7. Construct a square with each side of length 6 cm.

8. Using a compass and straight edge only, construct the perpendicular bisector of the line segment $|AB|$. Mark any point, C, on the perpendicular bisector. What is the relationship between the point C and the points A and B?

9. A boat sails from a harbour, H, on the mainland to a harbour, G, on an island. Throughout the journey the boat sails a course that remains at equal distances from the lighthouses R and S. Using only a compass and straight edge, draw the path of the boat and indicate on the diagram the locations of the harbours H and G.

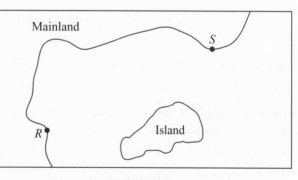

10. A man is about to sail his boat out to sea. He wants to set a course which keeps him as far away from the rocks as possible.
On the diagram, construct his course.

11. The diagram shows an island.
There is treasure buried at the point *T*.
T is equidistant from *A* and *B* and is also equidistant from *C* and *D*.
Using only a compass and straight edge, locate the point *T*.

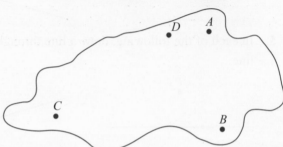

12. The diagram shows a snooker table.
A ball is hit in the direction shown. Using your ruler and protractor, find the position where the ball is going to hit after its first, second and third bounce (assume that the ball continues to bounce so that it forms equal angles). A player predicts that the ball will sink into the middle pocket after three bounces. Discuss.

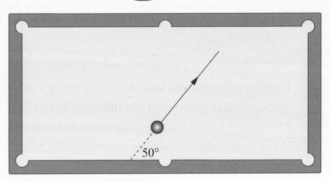

Constructing triangles

1. Given the length of the three sides (SSS)

Construct a triangle *ABC* with $|AB| = 7$ cm, $|AC| = 6$ cm and $|BC| = 5$ cm.

1. A rough sketch, with the given information, is shown on the right.

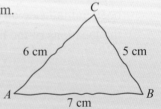

2. Using a ruler, draw a horizontal line segment 7 cm in length. Label the end points *A* and *B*.

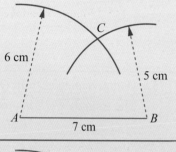

3. Set your compass to a radius of 6 cm.
Place the compass point on the point *A*.
Draw an arc above the line segment.
Set your compass to a radius of 5 cm.
Place the compass point on the point *B*.
Draw an arc above the line segment to meet the other arc.
Label the point *C* where the arcs meet.

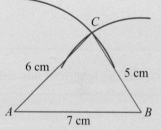

4. Using your ruler, join *A* to *C* and *B* to *C*.
The triangle *ABC* is now drawn as required.

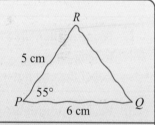

2. Given the length of two sides and the measure of the angle between them (SAS)

Construct the triangle *PQR* with $|PQ| = 6$ cm, $|PR| = 5$ cm and $|\angle QPR| = 55°$.

1. A rough sketch, with the given information, is shown on the right.

2. Using a ruler, draw a horizontal line segment 6 cm in length.
Label the end points *P* and *Q*.

3. Place your protractor on the point *P*.
Draw an angle of 55°.

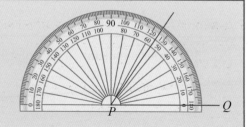

4. Use your ruler or compass to mark the point R such that $|PR| = 5$ cm.

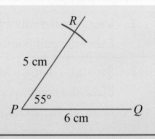

5. Using your ruler, join Q to R.
The triangle PQR is now drawn as required.

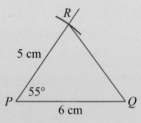

3. Given the length of one side and the measure of two angles (ASA)

Construct the triangle XYZ with $|XY| = 5$ cm, $|\angle YXZ| = 40°$ and $|\angle XYZ| = 70°$.

1. A rough sketch, with the given information, is shown on the right.

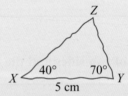

2. Using a ruler, draw a horizontal line segment 5 cm in length.
Label the end points X and Y.

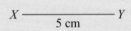

3. Place your protractor on the point X.
Draw an angle of $40°$.

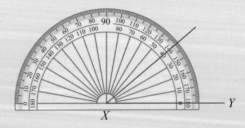

4. Place your protractor on the point Y.
Draw an angle of $70°$.

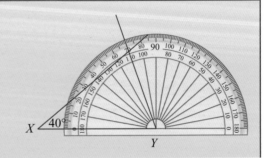

5. Where these two lines meet, label the point Z.
The triangle XYZ is now drawn as required.

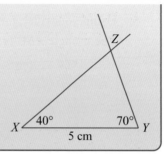

4. Given a right angle, length of the hypotenuse and the length of one other side (RHS)

Construct the triangle ABC with $|\angle BAC| = 90°$, $|AB| = 7$ cm and $|BC| = 8$ cm.

1. A rough sketch, with the given information, is shown on the right.

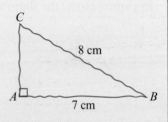

2. Using a ruler, draw a horizontal line segment 7 cm in length.
Label the end points A and B.

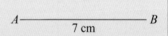

3. Using a set square or protractor, draw an angle of 90° at A.

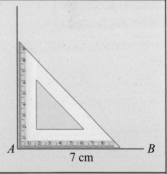

4. Set your compass to a radius of 8 cm.
Place the compass point on the point B.
Draw an arc to meet the vertical line.
Label this point C.

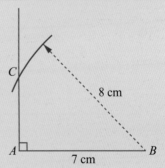

5. Using your ruler, join B to C.
The triangle ABC is now drawn as required.

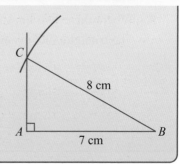

Exercise 27.2

Accurately construct each of the following triangles in questions 1–12, with all dimensions in centimetres (the diagrams are not drawn to scale).

1.

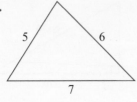

2.

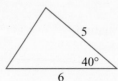

3.

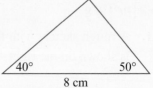

4.

5.

6.

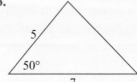

7.

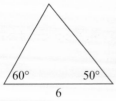

8.

9.

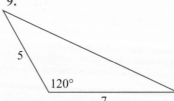

10.

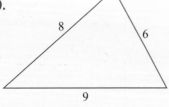

11.

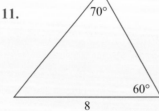

12.

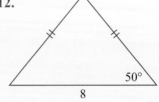

In questions 13–20, it is good practice to draw a rough sketch first and to draw one side as a horizontal base at the beginning.

13. Construct a triangle ABC with $|AB| = 9$ cm, $|AC| = 8$ cm and $|BC| = 7$ cm.

14. Construct a triangle PQR with $|PQ| = 8$ cm, $|QR| = 6$ cm and $|\angle PQR| = 30°$.

15. Construct a triangle PQR with $|PQ| = 5$ cm, $|\angle RPQ| = 60°$ and $|\angle RQP| = 45°$.

16. Construct a triangle XYZ with $|XY| = 8$ cm, $|XZ| = 6$ cm and $|\angle YXZ| = 90°$. Write down $|YZ|$.

17. Construct a triangle ABC with $|AB| = 6$ cm, $|AC| = 5$ cm and $|BC| = 4$ cm.

18. Construct a triangle PQR with $|PQ| = 7$ cm, $|\angle RPQ| = 80°$ and $|PR| = 6$ cm.

19. Construct a triangle XYZ with $|\angle YXZ| = 90°$, $|XZ| = 6$ cm and $|YZ| = 7$ cm.

20. Construct a triangle ABC with $|AB| = 8$ cm, $|\angle BAC| = 30°$ and $|\angle ABC| = 110°$.

21. Construct the following parallelograms.

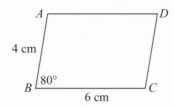
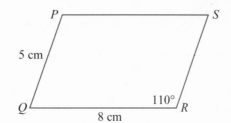

22. Construct triangle PQR.
    Then construct triangle PSR.
    Using your protractor, find:
    (i) $|\angle QPR|$ (ii) $|\angle PSR|$
    (All dimensions are in cm.)

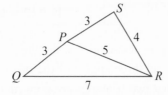

23. Patrick thinks that he can construct a triangle with sides of length 10 cm, 5 cm and 4 cm.

    (i) Try to construct Patrick's triangle.

    (ii) Explain why it is not possible to draw Patrick's triangle.

24. In $\triangle ABC$, the angles are $x°$, $(2x + 10)°$ and $(3x + 20)°$.

    (i) Write down an equation in x.

    (ii) By solving your equation, calculate the three angles.

    (iii) If $|AB| = 7$ cm, construct $\triangle ABC$.

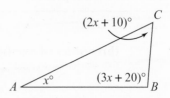

Congruent triangle

The word '**congruent**' means **identical**. Two triangles are said to be congruent if they have exactly the same size and shape. They have **equal length of sides**, **equal angles** and **equal areas**. One triangle could be placed on top of the other so as to cover it exactly. Sometimes it is necessary to turn one of the triangles over to get an exact copy. The symbol for congruence is ≡. The fact that △ABC is congruent to △PQR is written △ABC ≡ △PQR. When naming congruent triangles, it is important that the order of the letters is correct when stating whether two triangles are congruent. In other words, the points ABC correspond to the points PQR in that order.

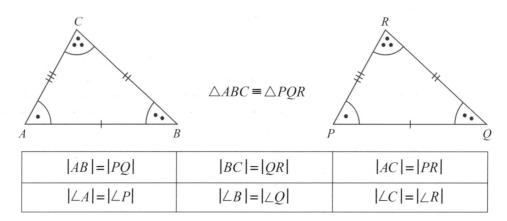

$$\triangle ABC \equiv \triangle PQR$$

$|AB|=|PQ|$	$|BC|=|QR|$	$|AC|=|PR|$
$|\angle A|=|\angle P|$	$|\angle B|=|\angle Q|$	$|\angle C|=|\angle R|$

For two triangles to be congruent (identical), the three sides and the three angles of one triangle must be equal to the three sides and three angles of the other triangle. However, it is not necessary to prove all six equalities to show that two triangles are congruent. There are four standard minimum tests that can be used to determine whether two triangles are congruent. Any one of the four tests is sufficient to prove that two triangles are congruent. However, each of these tests must include the fact that the length of at least one of the sides is equal in both triangles.

Four tests for congruency

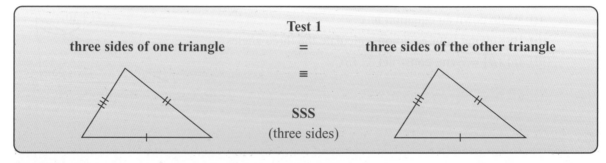

Test 1

three sides of one triangle = three sides of the other triangle

≡

SSS
(three sides)

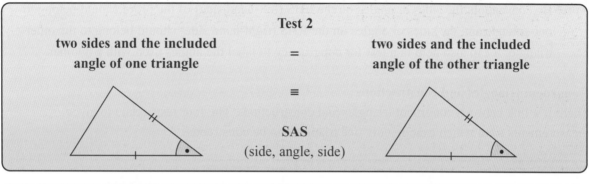

Test 2

two sides and the included
angle of one triangle

=

≡

two sides and the included
angle of the other triangle

SAS
(side, angle, side)

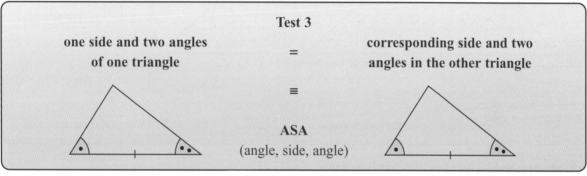

Test 3

one side and two angles
of one triangle

=

≡

corresponding side and two
angles in the other triangle

ASA
(angle, side, angle)

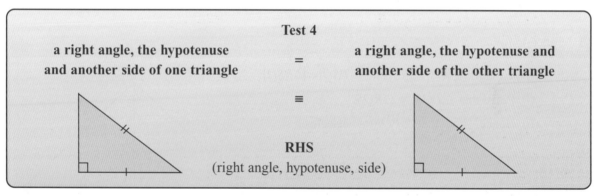

Test 4

a right angle, the hypotenuse
and another side of one triangle

=

≡

a right angle, the hypotenuse and
another side of the other triangle

RHS
(right angle, hypotenuse, side)

Note: Consider case 3. If any two pairs of angles are equal, then the third pair must also be equal.
What is essential is that the equal sides correspond to each other.

A proof using congruent triangles contains three steps.

1. Identify the two triangles that are being used in the proof.
2. Name the three pairs of equal sides and/or angles.
   Always give reasons why the angles used are equal, e.g. alternate angles.
   Always give reasons why the lengths of the sides used are equal, e.g. opposite sides of a parallelogram.
3. Name the congruent triangles, in matching order.
   State the congruence test used, i.e. whether SSS, SAS, ASA or RHS.

Note: By convention, the sides or angles on the LHS (left-hand side) of the proof should belong to one triangle and the sides or angles on the RHS (right-hand side) should belong to the other triangle. It can also help in a test for congruency to label the angles used with a number.

Congruent triangles and constructions

There is a link between congruent triangles and constructions. The four tests relate to given measurements from which exactly only one triangle can be constructed.

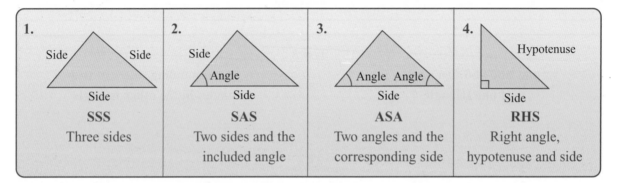

1.	2.	3.	4.
SSS	**SAS**	**ASA**	**RHS**
Three sides	Two sides and the included angle	Two angles and the corresponding side	Right angle, hypotenuse and side

See the note about case 3 on the previous page.

EXAMPLE 1

In the diagram, $|PS|=|RS|$ and $|\angle PSQ|=|\angle RSQ|$.

(i) Prove that $\triangle PQS \equiv \triangle RQS$.

(ii) Hence, show that $\triangle PQR$ is isosceles.

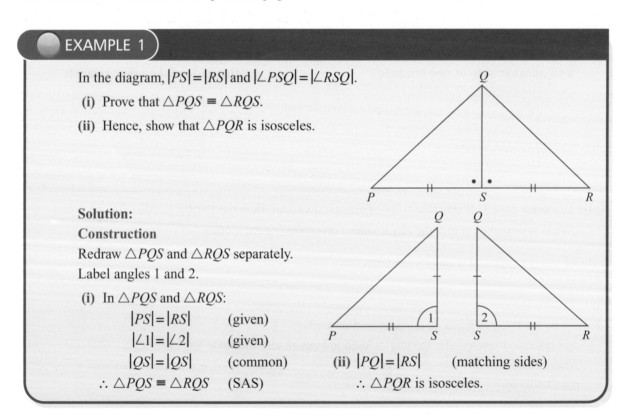

Solution:

Construction

Redraw $\triangle PQS$ and $\triangle RQS$ separately.
Label angles 1 and 2.

(i) In $\triangle PQS$ and $\triangle RQS$:

$|PS|=|RS|$	(given)
$|\angle 1|=|\angle 2|$	(given)
$|QS|=|QS|$	(common)
$\therefore \triangle PQS \equiv \triangle RQS$	(SAS)

(ii) $|PQ|=|RS|$ (matching sides)

$\therefore \triangle PQR$ is isosceles.

EXAMPLE 2

ABCD is a parallelogram, with diagonals intersecting at *M*.

(i) Prove that diagonal [*AC*] bisects the area of parallelogram *ABCD*.

(ii) Prove that $|BM| = |DM|$.

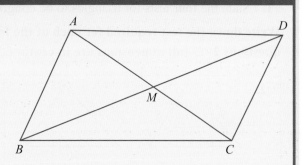

Solution:

(i) **Construction**

Redraw △*ABC* and △*ADC* separately.

In △*ABC* and △*ADC*:

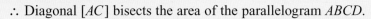

$\qquad |AB| = |CD| \qquad$ (opp. sides)

$\qquad |BC| = |DA| \qquad$ (opp. sides)

$\qquad |AC| = |AC| \qquad$ (common)

∴ $\qquad$ △*ABC* ≡ △*ADC* $\quad$ (SSS)

∴ Area △*ABC* = area of △*ADC*

∴ Diagonal [*AC*] bisects the area of the parallelogram *ABCD*.

(ii) **Construction**

Redraw △*AMD* and △*CMB* separately.

Label angles 1, 2, 3 and 4.

In △*AMD* and △*CMB*:

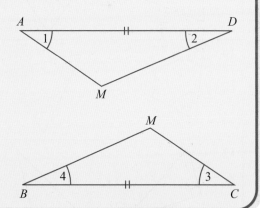

$\qquad |\angle 1| = |\angle 3| \qquad$ (alternate angles)

$\qquad |AD| = |CB| \qquad$ (opp. sides)

$\qquad |\angle 2| = |\angle 4| \qquad$ (alternate angles)

∴ △*AMD* ≡ △*CMB* $\quad$ (ASA)

∴ $\quad |BM| = |DM| \quad$ (matching sides)

Note: It should be noted that in many situations more than one test of congruency can be used. Under a translation, axial symmetry or central symmetry, the shape and size of a figure remain **exactly the same**. Therefore, when these transformations are applied to a figure, the image is **always congruent** to the original figure.

Exercise 28.1

1. State the four tests for triangles to be congruent.

Write down the test required for each of the following pairs of triangles to be congruent in questions 2–13 (all dimensions are in centimetres; diagrams are not drawn to scale).

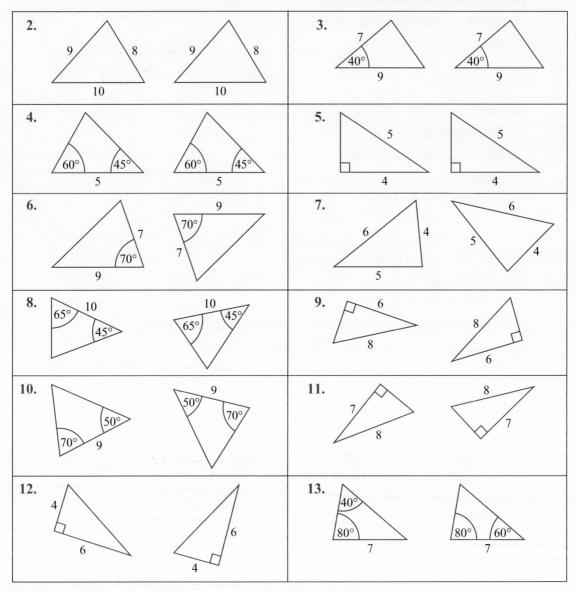

14.

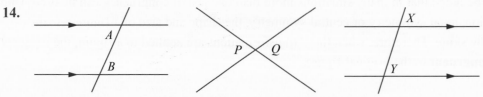

Choose from **corresponding**, **alternate** and **vertically opposite** to complete the sentences.

    (i) *A* and *B* are _____ angles.

    (ii) *P* and *Q* are _____ angles.

    (iii) *X* and *Y* are _____ angles.

15. In the diagram, [*AE*] and [*BD*] bisect each other at *C*.

    (i) Prove that △*ABC* ≡ △*EDC*.

    (ii) Prove that *AB* ∥ *DE*.

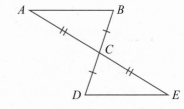

16. *ABCD* is a parallelogram.
Using a test for congruent triangles, show that the opposite angles are equal, i.e. prove that $|\angle ABC| = |\angle ADC|$.

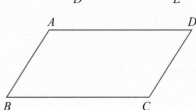

17. **(i)**

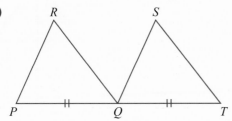

    (ii)

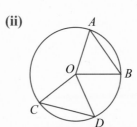

PR ∥ *QS*, *RQ* ∥ *ST* and $|PQ| = |QT|$.
Prove that $|PR| = |QS|$.

O is the centre of the circle and $|AB| = |CD|$.
Prove that $|\angle AOB| = |\angle COD|$

18. In the diagram,
PQ ∥ *ST* and $|PR| = |TR|$.
Prove that △*PQR* ≡ △*TSR*.

19. Lines *AD* and *CB* intersect at the point *E*.
$|AE| = |CE|$ and $|BE| = |DE|$.
Is △*ABE* ≡ △*CDE*?
Justify your answer.

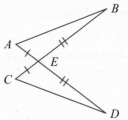

20. *ABCD* is a cyclic quadrilateral.
    $|AB| = |AD|$ and [*AC*] is a diameter
    of the circle.

    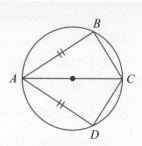

    (i) Prove $\triangle ABC \equiv \triangle ADC$.

    (ii) Hence, show that $|\angle BAC| = |\angle DAC|$.

21. *ABCD* is a parallelogram.
    [*AD*] is extended to *E*
    such that $|AD| = |DE|$.
    DC intersects *EB* at the point *F*.
    Prove that $|DF| = |FC|$.

    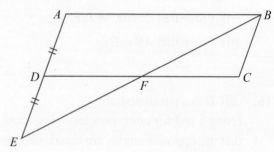

22. The diagram shows $\triangle XYZ$, in which
    $|XY| = |ZY|$ and *YW* bisects [*XZ*].

    (i) Prove $\triangle YXW \equiv \triangle YZW$.

    (ii) Hence, prove that $YW \perp XZ$.

    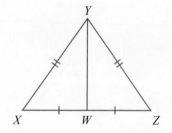

23. Construct the following triangles.

    (i) $|AB| = 4\cdot5$ cm, $|BC| = 6$ cm and $|AC| = 7\cdot5$ cm

    (ii) $|XY| = 4\cdot5$ cm, $XY \perp YZ$ and $|YZ| = 6$ cm

    (iii) Is $\triangle ABC \equiv \triangle XYZ$? Justify your answer.

24. (i) Is $\triangle ABC \equiv \triangle PQR$?
    Explain your answer.

    (ii) If the triangles are not
    congruent, write down one
    extra piece of information
    you would need to be
    given for the triangles to
    be congruent.

    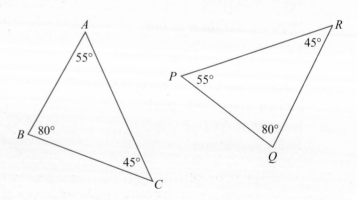

Similar triangles

Two triangles are similar if they have the same shape. One triangle can be obtained from the other by either an enlargement or a reduction (the reduction is also called an enlargement). The symbol for similarity is $|||$. The fact that $\triangle ABC$ is similar to $\triangle XYZ$ is written as $\triangle ABC \,|||\, \triangle XYZ$.

Four tests for similarity of triangles

1. If the lengths of matching sides are in proportion (same ratio), then the triangles are similar.

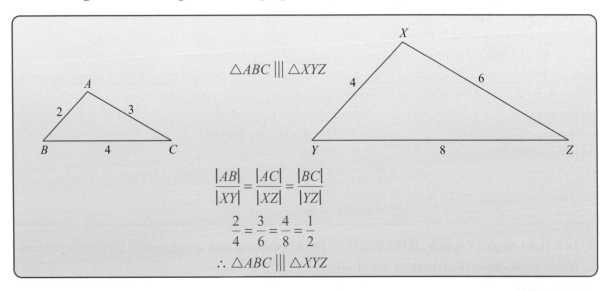

$$\frac{|AB|}{|XY|} = \frac{|AC|}{|XZ|} = \frac{|BC|}{|YZ|}$$

$$\frac{2}{4} = \frac{3}{6} = \frac{4}{8} = \frac{1}{2}$$

$$\therefore \triangle ABC \,|||\, \triangle XYZ$$

2. If two pairs of matching angles are equal, then the triangles are similar.

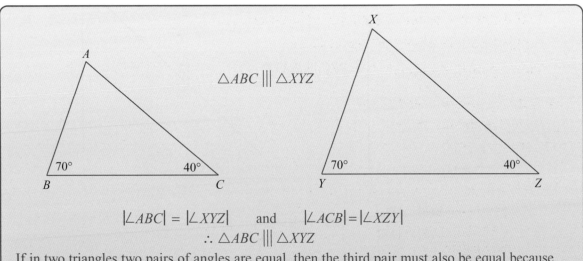

$$|\angle ABC| = |\angle XYZ| \quad \text{and} \quad |\angle ACB| = |\angle XZY|$$
$$\therefore \triangle ABC \,|||\, \triangle XYZ$$

If in two triangles two pairs of angles are equal, then the third pair must also be equal because the three angles in a triangle add up to $180°$. Therefore, to prove that two triangles are similar, it is sufficient to show that two pairs of angles are equal.

3. **If the lengths of two sides are in proportion (same ratio) and the included angles are equal, then the triangles are similar.**

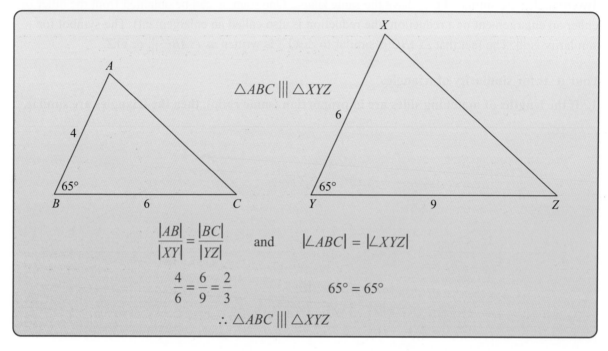

$\triangle ABC \;|||\; \triangle XYZ$

$$\frac{|AB|}{|XY|} = \frac{|BC|}{|YZ|} \quad \text{and} \quad |\angle ABC| = |\angle XYZ|$$

$$\frac{4}{6} = \frac{6}{9} = \frac{2}{3} \qquad\qquad 65° = 65°$$

$$\therefore \triangle ABC \;|||\; \triangle XYZ$$

4. **In a right-angled triangle, if the length of the hypotenuse and another side are in proportion (same ratio), then the triangles are similar.**

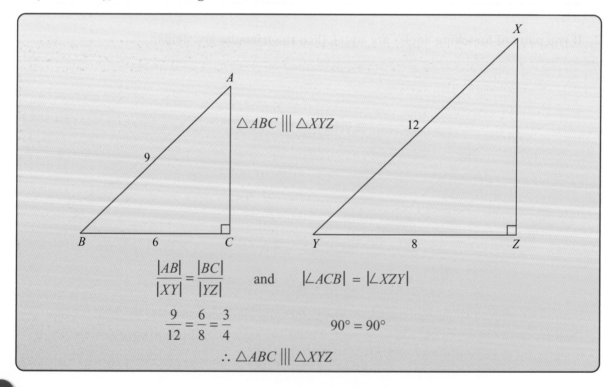

$\triangle ABC \;|||\; \triangle XYZ$

$$\frac{|AB|}{|XY|} = \frac{|BC|}{|YZ|} \quad \text{and} \quad |\angle ACB| = |\angle XZY|$$

$$\frac{9}{12} = \frac{6}{8} = \frac{3}{4} \qquad\qquad 90° = 90°$$

$$\therefore \triangle ABC \;|||\; \triangle XYZ$$

To prove that two triangles are similar, you only need to show one of the conditions for similarity. By convention, the abbreviations SSS, SAS, ASA and RHS are not used when tackling problems on similar triangles.

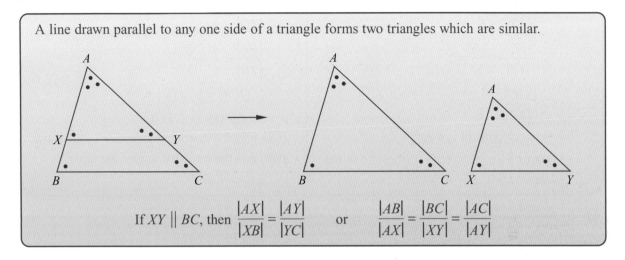

A line drawn parallel to any one side of a triangle forms two triangles which are similar.

If $XY \parallel BC$, then $\dfrac{|AX|}{|XB|} = \dfrac{|AY|}{|YC|}$ or $\dfrac{|AB|}{|AX|} = \dfrac{|BC|}{|XY|} = \dfrac{|AC|}{|AY|}$

Note: It helps in solving problems on similar triangles if the two triangles are redrawn so that the corresponding sides or angles match each other. It is good practice to put the unknown length on the top of the first fraction.

EXAMPLE 1

Show that each pair of triangles are similar.

(i)   (ii)

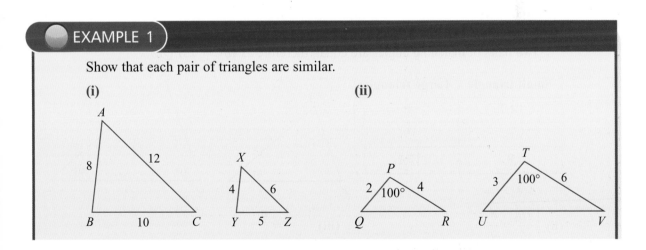

Solution:

(i) In $\triangle ABC$ and $\triangle XYZ$:

$$\frac{|AB|}{|XY|} = \frac{8}{4} = 2$$

$$\frac{|BC|}{|YZ|} = \frac{10}{5} = 2$$

$$\frac{|AC|}{|XZ|} = \frac{12}{6} = 2$$

$$\therefore \triangle ABC \,|||\, \triangle XYZ$$

(three pairs of matching sides are in the same ratio)

(ii) In $\triangle PQR$ and $\triangle TUV$:

$$\frac{|PQ|}{|TU|} = \frac{2}{3}$$

$$\frac{|PR|}{|TV|} = \frac{4}{6} = \frac{2}{3}$$

$$|\angle QPR| = |\angle UTV| = 100°$$

$$\therefore \triangle PQR \,|||\, \triangle TUV$$

(two pairs of matching sides are in the same ratio and the included angles are equal)

EXAMPLE 2

(i) Explain why $\triangle ABC$ and $\triangle PQR$ are similar.

Hence, calculate:

(ii) $|AB|$ **(iii)** $|PR|$.

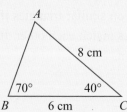
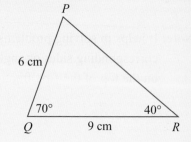

Solution:

(i) $|\angle ABC| = |\angle PQR| = 70°$ and $|\angle ACB| = |\angle PRQ| = 40°$.

Two pairs of matching angles are equal, therefore $\triangle ABC \,|||\, \triangle PQR$.

Small triangle	Large triangle
$|AB|$	6
6	9
8	$|PR|$

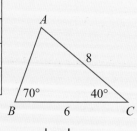
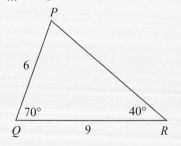

(ii)
$$\frac{|AB|}{6} = \frac{6}{9}$$

$$|AB| = \frac{6 \times 6}{9}$$

(multiply both sides by 6)

$$|AB| = \frac{36}{9} = 4 \text{ cm}$$

(iii)
$$\frac{|PR|}{8} = \frac{9}{6}$$

$$|PR| = \frac{8 \times 9}{6}$$

(multiply both sides by 8)

$$|PR| = \frac{72}{6} = 12 \text{ cm}$$

Exercise 28.2

1. State the four tests for triangles to be similar.

In questions 2–9, verify that the triangles are similar and state the test used (all dimensions are in centimetres and diagrams are not drawn to scale).

2.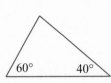

3.

4.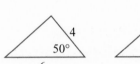

5.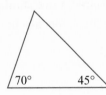

6.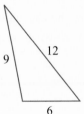

7.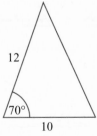

8.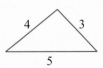

9.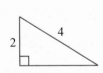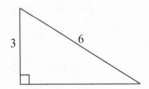

In questions 10–13, give one reason why each pair of triangles is not similar.

10.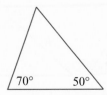

11.

12.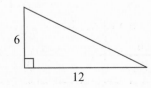

13.

14. In the diagram, $PQ \parallel BC$.
Redraw $\triangle APQ$ and $\triangle ABC$
separately.

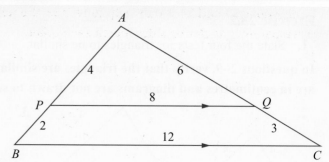

   (i) Are $\triangle APQ$ and $\triangle ABC$
   similar?
   Give a reason for your
   answer.

   (ii) Show that (a) $\dfrac{|AP|}{|AB|} = \dfrac{|AQ|}{|AC|} = \dfrac{|PQ|}{|BC|}$

   (b) $\dfrac{|AP|}{|PB|} = \dfrac{|AQ|}{|QC|}$

   (iii) Simplify: (a) $\dfrac{|CQ|}{|QA|}$ (b) $\dfrac{|BC|}{|PQ|}$ (c) $\dfrac{|AB|^2}{|AP|^2}$

In questions 15–24, the triangles are similar with equal angles marked. In each case, calculate the lengths p and q (all dimensions are in centimetres and diagrams are not drawn to scale).

15.

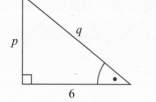

16.

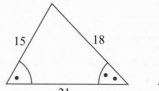

17.

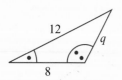

18.

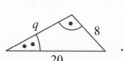

19.

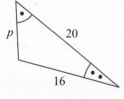

20.

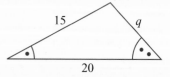

21.

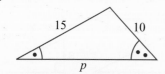

22.

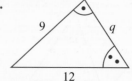
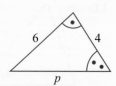

In questions 23 and 24 it may help to redraw the triangles so that the positions of corresponding angles or sides match each other.

23.

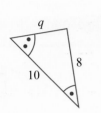 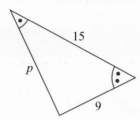

24.

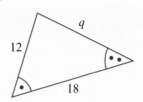

In questions 25–27, it may help to redraw the triangles separately.

25. In $\triangle PQR$, $ST \parallel QR$.

   (i) Are $\triangle PQR$ and $\triangle PST$ similar? Justify your answer.

   (ii) $|PS| = 3$ cm, $|PT| = 2$ cm, $|SQ| = 6$ cm, $|QR| = 12$ cm. Write down $|PQ|$.

   (iii) Calculate **(a)** $|PR|$ **(b)** $|TR|$ **(c)** $|ST|$.

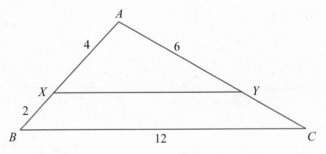

26. In $\triangle ABC$, $XY \parallel BC$.

   (i) Are $\triangle ABC$ and $\triangle AXY$ similar? Give a reason for your answer.

   (ii) $|AX| = 4$ cm, $|AY| = 6$ cm, $|XB| = 2$ cm, $|BC| = 12$ cm. Write down $|AB|$.

   (iii) Calculate **(a)** $|AC|$ **(b)** $|YC|$ **(c)** $|XY|$.

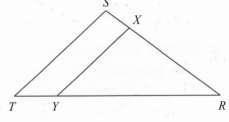

27. In $\triangle STR$, $XY \parallel ST$.

   (i) Explain why $\triangle STR$ and $\triangle XYR$ are similar

   (ii) $|SX| = 2$ cm, $|TY| = 3$ cm and $|SR| = 10$ cm. Write down $|XR|$.

   (iii) Calculate **(a)** $|TR|$ **(b)** $|YR|$.

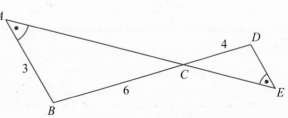

28. In the diagram, $|\angle BAC| = |\angle DEC|$, $|AB| = 3$ cm, $|BC| = 6$ cm and $|CD| = 4$ cm.

   (i) Explain why $\triangle ABC$ and $\triangle EDC$ are similar.

   (ii) Calculate $|DE|$.

Using similar triangles to solve real-life problems

Similar triangles can be used to solve practical or real-life problems.

EXAMPLE

A girl wants to calculate the height of a
building. From the bottom of the building she
walks 35 paces and places a pole in the ground
2 m vertically from the ground. She then walks
another 5 paces. She notices that from this
point on the ground, the top of the pole and the
top of the building are in line. Calculate the
height of the building.

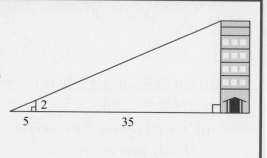

Solution:

Let the height of the building be h m and represent
the situation with two similar triangles.

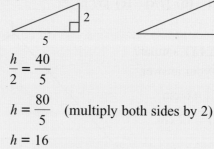

$$\frac{h}{2} = \frac{40}{5}$$

$$h = \frac{80}{5} \quad \text{(multiply both sides by 2)}$$

$$h = 16$$

Thus, the height of the building is 16 m.

Exercise 28.3

1. A stick 1 m long is placed vertically
   60 m from the base of a building so that
   the top of the building and top of the
   stick are in line with a point on the
   ground 10 m from the base of the stick.
   Calculate the height of the building.

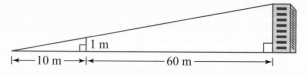

2. The shadow of a tree and the shadow of a
   golf flag coincide, as shown in the
   diagram.
   Calculate the height of the tree.

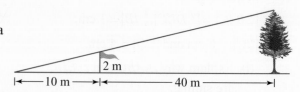

3. The diagram shows a building of height 48 m and another building of height h m. Paul paces out distances, as shown, so that the tops of each building are in line with each other. Calculate the height of the smaller building.

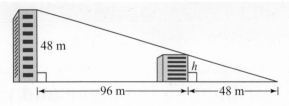

4. A conveyor belt of length 40 m carries bricks from the ground up to the top of a building. When the bricks have travelled a distance of 16 m on the conveyor belt they are 6 m above the ground. Calculate the height of the building.

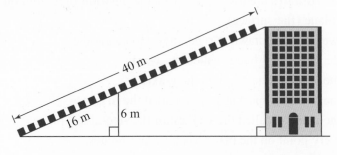

5. The rope on the pair of stepladders, as shown, stops the steps from opening too far.
Using similar triangles, find the length of the rope.

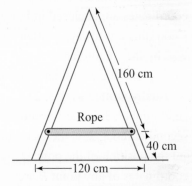

6. Frank needs to calculate the width, w m, of a river. He is unable to cross the river. He made the measurements as shown in the diagram. Calculate the width of the river.

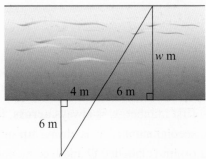

Coordinating the plane and plotting points

Coordinates are used to describe the **position** of a point on
a plane (flat surface).

Two lines are drawn at right angles to each other.

The horizontal line is called the **x-axis**.

The vertical line is called the **y-axis**.

The two axes meet at a point called the **origin**.

The plane is called the **Cartesian** (kar-tee-zi-an) plane.

Every point on the plane has two coordinates,

an **x coordinate** and a **y coordinate**.

The coordinates are enclosed in brackets.

The *x* coordinate is always written first, then a comma,

followed by the *y* coordinate.

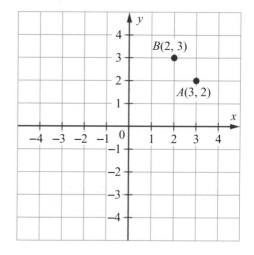

On the diagram, the coordinates of the point *A* are (3, 2).

This is usually written as *A*(3, 2).

The first number, 3, is the *x* coordinate of the point *A*.

The second number, 2, is the *y* coordinate of the point *A*.

To find the position of the point *A*, start at the origin, go 3 units right and then 2 units up.

The coordinates of any point *P* are:

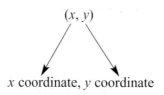

(*x*, *y*)

x coordinate, *y* coordinate

The first number, *x*, is always **across, left or right**.

The second number, *y*, is always **up or down**.

The origin is labelled *O* and has the coordinates (0, 0).

Order is very important. Notice that *A*(3, 2) ≠ *B*(2, 3).

The points *A*(3, 2) and *B*(2, 3) have different positions on the coordinated plane.

The word 'axis' means **line**. The plural of axis is **axes**.

Remember: x before y

The four quadrants

The intersecting x-axis and y-axis divide the plane into four regions called **quadrants** and are numbered 1, 2, 3 and 4, as shown on the right.

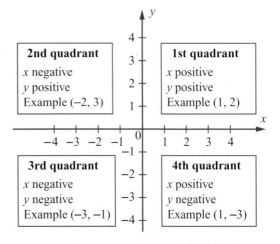

2nd quadrant
x negative
y positive
Example $(-2, 3)$

1st quadrant
x positive
y positive
Example $(1, 2)$

3rd quadrant
x negative
y negative
Example $(-3, -1)$

4th quadrant
x positive
y negative
Example $(1, -3)$

EXAMPLE

Draw the x-axis from -4 to 4 and the y-axis from -3 to 3. Plot the points $A(2, 3)$, $B(3, 2)$, $C(-4, 2)$, $D(-3, -1)$, $E(4, -3)$, $F(1, -1)$, $G(2, 0)$, and $H(0, -3)$.

Solution:

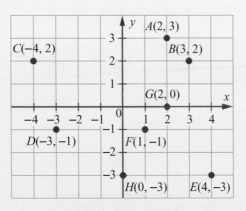

Exercise 29.1

1. Write down the coordinates of the points A to Z shown on the Cartesian plane.

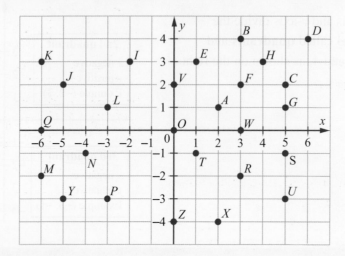

2. Plot each of the following points using the coordinates below:
   $A(3, 2)$, $B(1, 4)$, $C(5, 3)$, $D(4, 1)$, $E(1, 1)$, $F(-5, 4)$, $G(-2, 3)$, $H(-4, 1)$, $I(-2, 2)$,
   $J(-4, -2)$, $K(-3, -4)$, $L(-2, -2)$, $M(-5, -3)$, $N(2, -2)$, $O(0, 0)$, $P(4, -1)$, $Q(5, -3)$,
   $R(1, -4)$, $S(3, 0)$, $T(0, 3)$, $U(-2, 0)$, $V(0, -4)$, $W(5, 0)$, $Z(-4, 0)$.

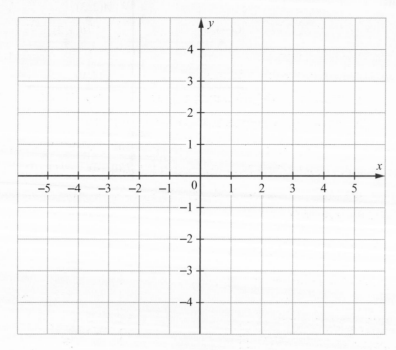

3. **(i)** Write down the coordinates of each of the following words.

(a) STAR

(b) MATHS

(c) MOBILE

(d) LEONARD

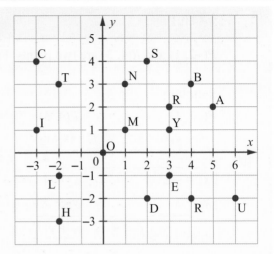

(ii) Mary sends a coded message to Damien. Her message reads:

(2, 4) (3, −1) (3, −1),   (3, 1) (0, 0) (6, −2),   (5, 2) (−2, 3),
(−2, −1) (6, −2) (1, 3) (−3, 4) (−2, −3).

What message did Mary send to Damien?

4. On graph paper, draw a set of axes. Draw the x-axis from −8 to 8 and the y-axis from −7 to 7. Plot each set of points on these axes. Join each point to the next one, with a straight line, and then join the first point to the last point. In each case, write down the shape you have constructed.

(i) (1, 1), (4, 1), (4, 4), (1, 4)

(ii) (−3, 2), (−7, 2), (5, 6)

(iii) (1, −1), (6, 2), (7, 5), (2, −4)

(iv) (−6, −1), (−6, −5), (−3, −5)

5. On which axis is each of the following points?

(i) $A(5, 0)$ (ii) $B(0, −2)$ (iii) $C(0, 0)$ (iv) $D(0, 7)$ (v) $E(−4, 0)$ (vi) $F(2, 0)$

6. Give the coordinates of any two points in the following.

(i) 1st quadrant   (ii) 2nd quadrant   (iii) 3rd quadrant   (iv) 4th quadrant

7. Which quadrant does each of the following points belong to?

(i) $A(4, 5)$ (ii) $B(3, −2)$ (iii) $C(−4, 6)$ (iv) $D(−3, 5)$ (v) $E(−1, −4)$
(vi) $F(−2, −5)$ (vii) $G(1, −3)$

Midpoint of a line segment

If (x_1, y_1) and (x_2, y_2) are two points, their midpoint is given by the formula:

$$\text{Midpoint} = \left(\frac{x_1 + x_2}{2}, \frac{y_1 + y_2}{2} \right)$$

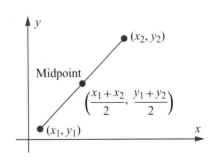

In words: $\left(\dfrac{\text{add the } x \text{ coordinates}}{2}, \dfrac{\text{add the } y \text{ coordinates}}{2} \right)$

405

EXAMPLE

$P(-2, 1)$ and $R(4, 3)$ are two points. Find the coordinates of Q, the midpoint of $[PR]$.

Solution:

$P(-2, 1)$ $\quad\quad\quad\quad R(4, 3)$

(x_1, y_1) $\quad\quad\quad\quad (x_2, y_2)$

$x_1 = -2$	$x_2 = 4$
$y_1 = 1$	$y_2 = 3$

Midpoint $= \left(\dfrac{x_1 + x_2}{2}, \dfrac{y_1 + y_2}{2} \right)$

$\quad\quad\quad = \left(\dfrac{-2 + 4}{2}, \dfrac{1 + 3}{2} \right)$

$\quad\quad\quad = \left(\dfrac{2}{2}, \dfrac{4}{2} \right) = Q(1, 2)$

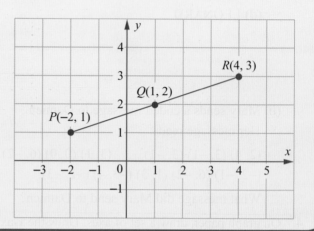

Exercise 29.2

Find the midpoint of the line segment joining each of the points in questions 1–12.

1. $P(4, 1)$ and $Q(6, 5)$
2. $M(1, 1)$ and $N(3, 7)$
3. $X(4, 1)$ and $Y(2, 3)$
4. $A(5, 4)$ and $B(7, 2)$
5. $C(3, 5)$ and $D(5, 7)$
6. $R(0, 2)$ and $S(6, 8)$
7. $U(8, 10)$ and $V(2, -4)$
8. $W(6, 7)$ and $Z(-2, 3)$
9. $E(10, 7)$ and $F(-8, -3)$
10. $G(4, -2)$ and $H(2, -6)$
11. $I(-1, -4)$ and $J(-3, -2)$
12. $K(-3, -1)$ and $L(-5, -7)$

13. The diagram shows a circle, s.
    The diameter of s is $[PR]$ and the centre is Q.
    Find the coordinates of Q.

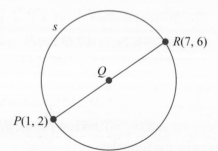

14. $A(1, 2)$, $B(9, 3)$, $C(11, 8)$ and $D(3, 7)$ are the coordinates of the vertices of the parallelogram $ABCD$. Plot the points on the diagram and join the points to construct the parallelogram.

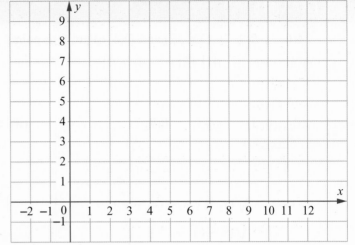

   (i) Find the coordinates of the midpoint of $[AC]$.

   (ii) Find the coordinates of the midpoint of $[BD]$.

   (iii) Give a reason why both answers are the same.

   (iv) Join A to C and B to D. What do you observe?

15. The diagram shows a hill. The bottom of the hill has coordinates $O(0, 0)$ and the top of the hill has coordinates $T(20, 12)$. Markers are placed at points A, B and C such that
B is the midpoint of $[OT]$,
A is the midpoint of $[OB]$, and
C is the midpoint of $[BT]$, as shown.
Find the coordinates of A, B and C.

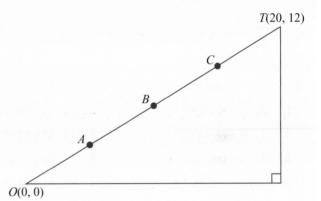

Distance between two points (length of a line segment)

If (x_1, y_1) and (x_2, y_2) are two points, the distance, d, between them is given by the formula:

$$d = \sqrt{(x_2 - x_1)^2 + (y_2 - y_1)^2}$$

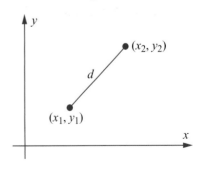

Note: Always decide which point is (x_1, y_1) and which point is (x_2, y_2) before you use the formula. The distance between the points A and B is written $|AB|$.

EXAMPLE

$A(6, 3)$, $B(9, 7)$, $C(5, -2)$ and $D(4, 6)$ are four points.

Calculate: (i) $|AB|$ (ii) $|CD|$

Solution:

(i) $A(6, 3)$ and $B(9, 7)$
  (x_1, y_1) (x_2, y_2)

$x_1 = 6, y_1 = 3$ $x_2 = 9, y_2 = 7$

$|AB| = \sqrt{(x_2 - x_1)^2 + (y_2 - y_1)^2}$

$= \sqrt{(9 - 6)^2 + (7 - 3)^2}$

$= \sqrt{(3)^2 + (4)^2}$

$= \sqrt{9 + 16}$

$= \sqrt{25} = 5$

(ii) $C(5, -2)$ and $B(4, 6)$
  (x_1, y_1) (x_2, y_2)

$x_1 = 5, y_1 = -2$ $x_2 = 4, y_2 = 6$

$|CD| = \sqrt{(x_2 - x_1)^2 + (y_2 - y_1)^2}$

$= \sqrt{(4 - 5)^2 + (6 + 2)^2}$

$= \sqrt{(-1)^2 + (8)^2}$

$= \sqrt{1 + 64}$

$= \sqrt{65}$

Exercise 29.3

Find the distance between each of the following pairs of points in questions 1–13.

1. $(5, 2)$ and $(8, 6)$
2. $(1, 1)$ and $(7, 9)$
3. $(1, 2)$ and $(6, 14)$
4. $(1, 0)$ and $(9, 5)$
5. $(3, 4)$ and $(5, 5)$
6. $(4, 3)$ and $(8, 1)$
7. $(1, -1)$ and $(2, 3)$
8. $(3, 0)$ and $(-2, 1)$
9. $(3, -4)$ and $(3, 2)$
10. $(-2, 2)$ and $(3, -1)$
11. $(2, 0)$ and $(5, 0)$
12. $(-7, -2)$ and $(-3, -6)$

13. $A(0, 2)$, $B(8, 8)$, $C(7, 9)$ and $D(4, 5)$ are four points. Show that $|AD| = |BD| = |CD|$.

14. The diagram shows a circle k with centre C.
    $[AB]$ is a diameter.
    The coordinates of A are $(2, 2)$ and the coordinates of B are $(8, 10)$.

    (i) Find the coordinates of C.

    (ii) Find the radius of k.

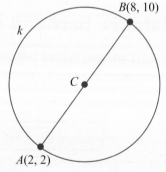

15. $A(1, 3)$, $B(2, 5)$ and $C(4, 7)$ are three points. Show that $|AB| < |BC|$.

16. A triangle has vertices $A(3, -2)$, $B(-2, 1)$ and $C(1, 6)$.
    Is the triangle isosceles? Give a reason for your answer.

17. $A(2, 1)$ and $B(6, 4)$ are two points, as shown.
C is a point such that $AC \perp CB$.

   (i) Find the coordinates of C.

   (ii) Write down **(a)** $|AC|$ and **(b)** $|BC|$.

   (iii) Using Pythagoras' theorem, calculate $|AB|$.

   (iv) Using the notation $A(x_1, y_1)$ and $B(x_2, y_2)$, calculate $|AB|$ using the formula
   $$\sqrt{(x_2 - x_1)^2 + (y_2 - y_1)^2}.$$

   (v) Comment on your results.

   (vi) Explain why the coordinates of C are (x_2, y_1).

   (vii) Express **(a)** $|AC|$ and **(b)** $|CB|$ in terms of x_1, y_1, x_2 and y_2.

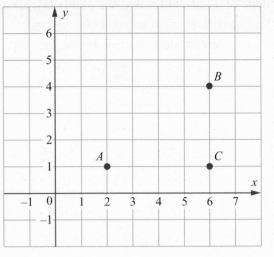

Slope of a line

All mathematical graphs are read from **left to right**.
The measure of the steepness of a line is called the **slope**.
The vertical distance, up or down, is called the **rise**.
The horizontal distance across is called the **run**.
The slope of a line is defined as:

$$\text{Slope} = \frac{\text{Rise}}{\text{Run}}$$

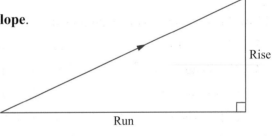

Note: This is also equal to the tangent ratio in trigonometry.
The rise can also be negative and in this case it is often called the **fall**.
If the rise is zero, then the slope is also zero.

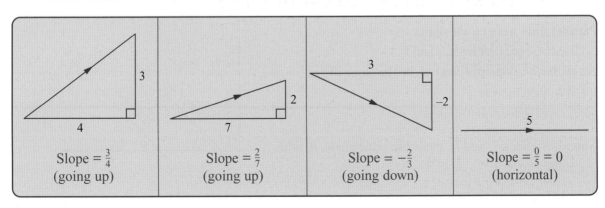

Slope $= \frac{3}{4}$
(going up)

Slope $= \frac{2}{7}$
(going up)

Slope $= -\frac{2}{3}$
(going down)

Slope $= \frac{0}{5} = 0$
(horizontal)

Slope of a line containing the points (x_1, y_1) and (x_2, y_2)

If a line contains the two points (x_1, y_1) and (x_2, y_2), then the slope is given by the formula:

$$m = \frac{y_2 - y_1}{x_2 - x_1}$$

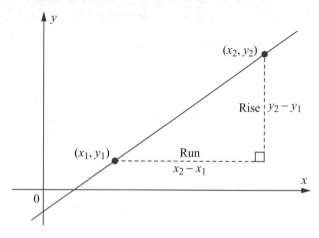

EXAMPLE

Find the slope of the line containing the points $(-1, 3)$ and $(4, 1)$.

Solution:

| $(-1, 3)$ | $(4, 1)$ | $x_1 = -1$ | $y_1 = 3$ |
| (x_1, y_1) | (x_2, y_2) | $x_2 = 4$ | $y_2 = 1$ |

Slope $= m = \dfrac{y_2 - y_1}{x_2 - x_1} = \dfrac{1 - 3}{4 + 1} = \dfrac{-2}{5} = -\dfrac{2}{5}$

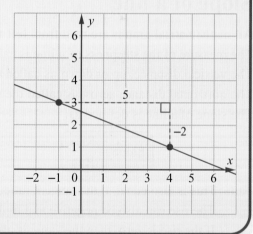

Parallel lines have equal slopes

Consider the parallel lines l_1 and l_2.

Let m_1 be the slope of l_1 and m_2 be the slope of l_2.

If $l_1 \parallel l_2$, then $m_1 = m_2$,

i.e. l_1 and l_2 have equal slopes.

Note: Both lines, l_1 and l_2, make the same angle, θ, with the x-axis.

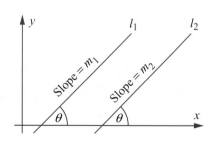

EXAMPLE

$A(2, 4)$, $B(7, 8)$, $C(2, 0)$ and $D(7, 4)$ are four points. Show that $AB \parallel CD$.

Solution:

Let $m_1 =$ the slope of AB and $m_2 =$ the slope of CD.

$A(2, 4)$ $B(7, 8)$
(x_1, y_1) (x_2, y_2)

$$\begin{array}{|c|}
\hline
x_1 = 2 \\
y_1 = 4 \\
x_2 = 7 \\
y_2 = 8 \\
\hline
\end{array}$$

$C(2, 0)$ $D(7, 4)$
(x_1, y_1) (x_2, y_2)

$$\begin{array}{|c|}
\hline
x_1 = 2 \\
y_1 = 0 \\
x_2 = 7 \\
y_2 = 4 \\
\hline
\end{array}$$

$$m_1 = \frac{y_2 - y_1}{x_2 - x_1} \qquad\qquad m_2 = \frac{y_2 - y_1}{x_2 - x_1}$$

$$= \frac{8 - 4}{7 - 2} \qquad\qquad\qquad = \frac{4 - 0}{7 - 2}$$

$$= \frac{4}{5} \qquad\qquad\qquad\qquad = \frac{4}{5}$$

$$m_1 = m_2$$

Therefore, $AB \parallel CD$.

Exercise 29.4

1. Write down the slope of each of the following.

   (i)   (ii)   (iii)

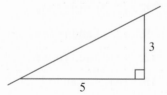

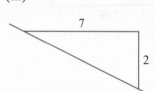

2. Find the slope of each of the following lines.

   (i)   (ii)   (iii)   (iv)

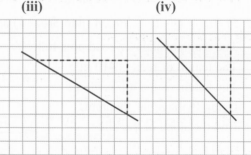

3. For each of the following graphs, state whether the slope of the line t is positive, negative or zero. In each case, give a reason for your answer.

(i)

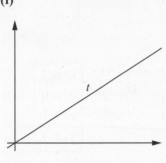

(ii)

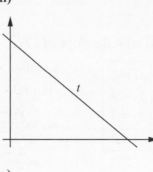

(iii)

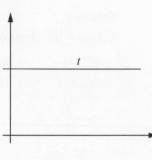

(iv)

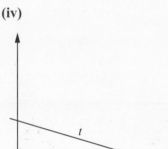

(v)

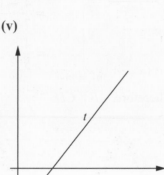

(vi)

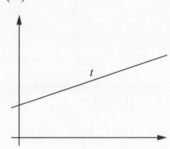

Find the slope of the line containing each of the given pairs of points in questions 4–18.

4. (1, 4) and (5, 7)   5. (3, 2) and (5, 3)   6. (2, 2) and (7, 4)

7. (3, 2) and (8, 6)   8. (4, 8) and (7, 9)   9. (2, 1) and (7, 8)

10. (4, 3) and (7, 5)   11. (1, 1) and (5, 2)   12. (2, 3) and (6, 8)

13. (3, 2) and (7, 8)   14. (2, 3) and (5, 1)   15. (−1, −2) and (3, 2)

16. (−7, 3) and (−5, 1)   17. (−3, −6) and (−5, −6)   18. (2, 3) and (−3, −7)

19. $A(-2, -1)$, $B(1, 3)$, $C(1, 1)$ and $D(4, 5)$ are four points. Show that $AB \parallel CD$.

20. $P(-6, 6)$, $Q(-1, 4)$, $R(1, 1)$ and $S(6, -1)$ are four points. Show that $PQ \parallel RS$.

21. The diagram shows a road up a hill.
    The length of road is 410 m.
    The height of the hill is 90 m.
    Using Pythagoras' theorem,
    find the slope of the hill.

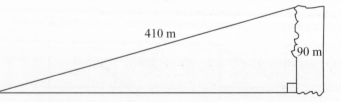

410 m

90 m

22. By calculating the slope, find the average speed, in each case, on the distance-speed graphs.

(i)

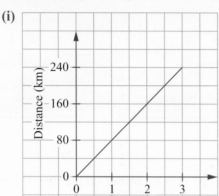

(ii)

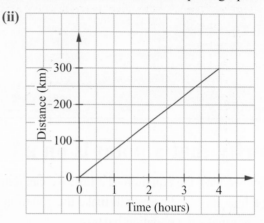

23. In a certain country, the slope of a hill is defined as $\dfrac{\text{rise}}{\text{run}}$.

In this country, what do these road signs mean? Which hill is the steepest? Which hill is the least steep? Justify your answer.

(i)

(ii)

(iii)

(iv)

Equation of a line 1

Plot the points $(-1, -1)$, $(0, 1)$, $(1, 3)$, $(2, 5)$, $(3, 7)$, $(4, 9)$.
The points all lie on the same straight line. When points lie on
the same straight line there is a relationship (connection, link)
between the x coordinate and the y coordinate for each point.
The relationship remains the same for each point on the line.
In this case, the relationship for each point is given by:

$$y = 2x + 1$$

This result will hold for every point on the line.
We say '$y = 2x + 1$' is the equation of the line.
In words:
'the y coordinate is **always** double the x coordinate plus 1'.
Consider the points $(-1, -1)$, $(1, 3)$ and $(4, 9)$ on the line.

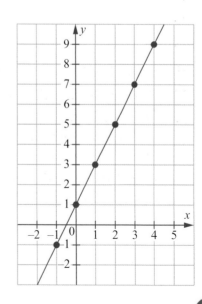

$(-1, -1); x = -1, y = -1$	$(1, 3); x = 1, y = 3$	$(4, 9); x = 4, y = 9$
$y = 2x + 1$	$y = 2x + 1$	$y = 2x + 1$
$-1 = 2(-1) + 1$	$3 = 2(1) + 1$	$9 = 2(4) + 1$
$-1 = -2 + 1$	$3 = 2 + 1$	$9 = 8 + 1$
$-1 = -1$ (balances)	$3 = 3$ (balances)	$9 = 9$ (balances)

In each case, the equation balances.

Verify that a point is on a line

Once we have the equation of a line, we can determine if a point is **on** or **not on** the line. If a point is on a line, its coordinates will make the equation balance. If a point is not on a line, its coordinates will not make the equation balance.

> ### EXAMPLE
>
> Investigate if the points $(2, 8)$ and $(-1, -2)$ are on the line $y = 3x + 2$.
>
> **Solution:**
>
> | $(2, 8)$ | $(-1, -2)$ |
> |---|---|
> | $y = 3x + 2$ | $y = 3x + 2$ |
> | $8 = 3(2) + 2$ | $-2 = 3(-1) + 2$ |
> | (put in $x = 2$ and $y = 8$) | (put in $x = -1$ and $y = -2$) |
> | $8 = 6 + 2$ | $-2 = -3 + 2$ |
> | $8 = 8$ (balances) | $-2 \neq -1$ (does not balance) |
> | $\therefore (2, 8)$ is **on** the line. | $\therefore (-1, -2)$ is **not on** the line. |

Exercise 29.5

1. Verify that the point $(1, 7)$ is **on** the line $y = 2x + 5$.

2. Verify that the point $(4, 11)$ is **on** the line $y = 3x - 1$.

3. Verify that the point $(2, 5)$ is **on** the line $y = \frac{1}{2}x + 4$.

4. Verify that the point $(1, 5)$ is **not on** the line $y = x + 3$.

5. Verify that the point $(-1, 7)$ is **on** the line $y = -5x + 2$.

6. Verify that the point $(8, 6)$ is **not on** the line $y = \frac{3}{4}x + 1$.

7. Verify that the point $(-4, 3)$ is **on** the line $y = -\frac{1}{2}x + 1$.

8. Verify that the point $(6, 1)$ is **not on** the line $y = -\frac{2}{3}x + 4$.

9. The point $(2, k)$ is on the line $y = x + 5$. Find the value of k.

10. The point $(t, 11)$ is on the line $y = 2x + 3$. Find the value of t.

Equation of a line 2

To find the equation of a line we need:

    1. The slope of the line, m.   **2.** A point on the line, (x_1, y_1).

        Then use the formula: $\boxed{(y - y_1) = m(x - x_1)}$

In short, we need the **slope** and a **point**.

EXAMPLE

Find the equation of the following lines
  (i) Containing the point $(2, -3)$ with slope 3
  (ii) Containing the point $(-6, 2)$ with slope $-\frac{2}{3}$

Solution:

(i) Containing $(2, -3)$ with slope 3

$$\boxed{x_1 = 2, \quad y_1 = -3, \quad m = 3}$$
$$(y - y_1) = m(x - x_1)$$
$$(y + 3) = 3(x - 2)$$
$$y + 3 = 3x - 6$$
$$y = 3x - 9$$

(subtract 3 from both sides)

(ii) Containing $(-6, 2)$ with slope $-\frac{2}{3}$

$$\boxed{x_1 = -6, \quad y_1 = 2, \quad m = -\frac{2}{3}}$$
$$(y - y_1) = m(x - x_1)$$
$$(y - 2) = -\frac{2}{3}(x + 6)$$
$$y - 2 = -\frac{2}{3}x - 4$$
$$y = -\frac{2}{3}x - 2$$

(add 2 to both sides)

Exercise 29.6

Find the equation of each of the following lines in questions 1–12.

1. Containing $(2, 3)$ with slope 4
2. Containing $(1, 2)$ with slope 3
3. Containing $(-1, 2)$ with slope 2
4. Containing $(-2, 3)$ with slope 1
5. Containing $(-2, 5)$ with slope -2
6. Containing $(0, 1)$ with slope -3
7. Containing $(-3, -2)$ with slope -5
8. Containing $(0, 0)$ with slope -4
9. Containing $(4, 3)$ with slope $\frac{1}{2}$
10. Containing $(6, -2)$ with slope $\frac{1}{3}$
11. Containing $(10, -1)$ with slope $-\frac{2}{5}$
12. Containing $(-8, -3)$ with slope $-\frac{5}{4}$
13. $A(1, 2)$ and $B(7, 8)$ are two points. M is the midpoint of the line segment $[AB]$. Find the coordinates of M. Find the equation of the line with slope 3 which contains the point M.
14. $P(1, 3)$ and $R(11, 7)$ are two points. Q is the midpoint of the line segment $[PR]$. Find the coordinates of Q. Find the equation of the line with slope $\frac{1}{2}$ which contains the point Q.

Equation of a line 3

To find the equation of a line, we need the **slope** and **one** point on the line.
However, in many questions one or both of these are missing.

EXAMPLE

Find the equation of the line which contains the points $(1, 3)$ and $(2, 1)$.

Solution:
The slope is missing. We first find the slope and use either one of the two points to find the equation.

$$(1, 3) \qquad (2, 1)$$
$$(x_1, y_1) \qquad (x_2, y_2)$$
$$m = \frac{y_2 - y_1}{x_2 - x_1}$$
$$m = \frac{1 - 3}{2 - 1}$$
$$m = \frac{-2}{1} = -2$$

$$x_1 = 1$$
$$y_1 = 3$$
$$x_2 = 2$$
$$y_2 = 1$$

Containing $(1, 3)$ with slope -2

$$x_1 = 1 \qquad y_1 = 3 \qquad m = -2$$
$$(y - y_1) = m(x - x_1)$$
$$(y - 3) = -2(x - 1)$$
$$y - 3 = -2x + 2$$
$$y = -2x + 5$$
(add 3 to both sides)

Exercise 29.7

1. $A(4, 4)$ and $B(5, 7)$ are two points. Find **(i)** the slope of AB and **(ii)** the equation of the line AB.

2. $P(2, 3)$ and $Q(4, 7)$ are two points. Find **(i)** the slope of PQ and **(ii)** the equation of the line PQ.

3. $R(2, 2)$ and $S(6, 4)$ are two points. Find **(i)** the slope of RS and **(ii)** the equation of the line RS.

4. $U(6, 2)$ and $V(9, 1)$ are two points. Find **(i)** the slope of UV and **(ii)** the equation of the line UV.

Find the equation of the line containing the given pair of points in questions 5–10.

5. $(0, 4)$ and $(3, 1)$ 6. $(2, 2)$ and $(3, -1)$ 7. $(1, 6)$ and $(3, 4)$

8. $(2, 1)$ and $(4, 9)$ 9. $(-2, 3)$ and $(6, -1)$ 10. $(-5, 0)$ and $(5, 6)$

11. $P(3, 4)$, $Q(7, 2)$ and $R(7, 7)$ are three points. S is the midpoint of the line segment $[PQ]$.

    (i) Find the coordinates of S.

    (ii) Find the equation of the line RS.

Slope-intercept

The diagram shows part of the graph of the line $y = 3x - 2$.

If we take any two points on the line we will find that the slope is 3 (the number in front of x).

Also notice that the line meets the y-axis at $y = -2$ (the constant in the equation).

In mathematical notation:

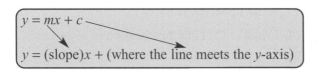

$y = mx + c$

$y = (\text{slope})x + (\text{where the line meets the } y\text{-axis})$

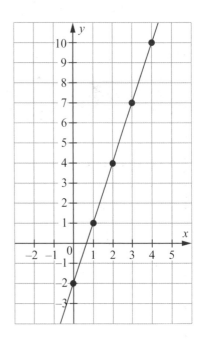

This is known as the **slope-intercept** form of the equation of a line as it shows the slope, m, and the y intercept, c (where the line meets the y-axis).

417

Find the slope of each of the following lines: **(i)** $y = -5x + 2$ **(ii)** $y = \frac{3}{4}x - 1$
In each case, state the coordinates of the point where the line meets the y-axis.

Solution:

(i) $y = -5x + 2$

$y = mx + c$

slope $= m = -5$

meets the y-axis at $(0, c) = (0, 2)$

(ii) $y = \frac{3}{4}x - 1$

$y = mx + c$

slope $= m = \frac{3}{4}$

meets the y-axis at $(0, c) = (0, -1)$

Exercise 29.8

Find the slope of each of the following lines in questions 1–12. In each case, state the coordinates of the point where the line meets the y-axis.

1. $y = 2x + 3$

2. $y = 3x + 4$

3. $y = 5x - 1$

4. $y = -4x + 1$

5. $y = -2x + 7$

6. $y = -7x - 3$

7. $y = \frac{1}{2}x - 2$

8. $y = \frac{1}{3}x - 5$

9. $y = -\frac{3}{4}x + 2$

10. $y = -\frac{1}{2}x - 4$

11. $y = -\frac{5}{4}x + 6$

12. $y = -\frac{7}{6}x - 8$

13.   **(i)** $y = 3x + 2$ is the equation of the line l. Write down the slope of l.

   (ii) The line k passes through the point $(-1, 5)$ and $k \parallel l$. Find the equation of k.

14.   **(i)** $y = \frac{1}{2}x + 5$ is the equation of the line t. Write down the slope of t.

   (ii) The line r passes through the point $(4, 1)$ and $r \parallel t$. Find the equation of r.

Graphing lines 1

Lines parallel to the axes

Some lines are parallel to the *x*- or *y*-axis.

Consider the line $x = 3$.

What is relationship between the points on the line $x = 3$?

The *x* coordinate is **always equal to 3**.

That is why its equation is $x = 3$.

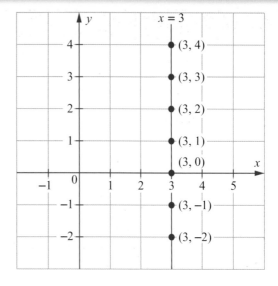

Consider the line $y = 2$.

What is the relationship between the points on the line $y = 2$?

The *y* coordinate is **always equal to 2**.

That is why its equation is $y = 2$.

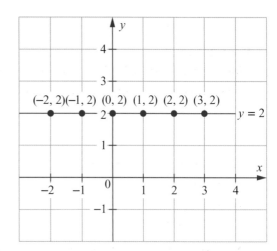

> On the *x*-axis, **y is always equal to 0**.
> Thus, the equation of the *x*-axis is $y = 0$.
> On the *y*-axis, **x is always equal to 0**.
> Thus, the equation of the *y*-axis is $x = 0$.

Exercise 29.9

Draw a diagram of the coordinated plane, with *x* from −5 to 5 and *y* from −4 to 4. On this diagram, graph each of the following lines.

1. $x = 1$
2. $y = 3$
3. $x = 4$
4. $y = 1$
5. $x = -2$
6. $y = -2$
7. $x = -5$
8. $y = -4$

Graphing lines 2

To draw a line, only two points are needed. The easiest points to find are those where lines cut the x and y axes.

This is known as the **intercept method**. We use the following fact:

On the x-axis, $y = 0$.   On the y-axis, $x = 0$.

To draw a line, do the following.

1. Let $y = 0$ and find x.   2. Let $x = 0$ and find y.

3. Plot these two points.   4. Draw the line through these points.

EXAMPLE

t is the line $y = -2x + 4$. t cuts the x-axis at P and the y-axis at Q.
Find the coordinates of P and Q and hence graph the line t.

Solution:

1. and 2.

$$y = -2x + 4$$

x-axis	y-axis
$y = 0$	$x = 0$
$-2x + 4 = 0$	$y = 4$
$-2x = -4$	$Q(0, 4)$
$2x = 4$	
$x = 2$	
$P(2, 0)$	

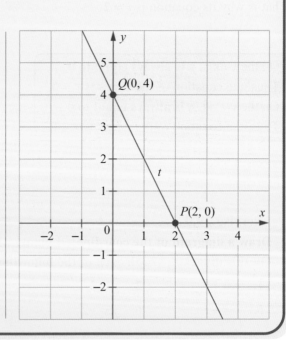

3. Plot the points $P(2, 0)$ and $Q(0, 4)$.

4. Draw the line through the points $P(2, 0)$ and $Q(0, 4)$.

Exercise 29.10

Find the coordinates of the points where each of the following lines cut the *x*- and *y*-axis in questions 1–9. In each case, plot these points and draw a graph of the line.

1. $y = -x + 1$
2. $y = x - 3$
3. $y = 2x - 4$
4. $y = 3x + 3$
5. $y = -4x + 8$
6. $y = 5x + 10$
7. $y = -2x + 8$
8. $y = -3x + 12$
9. $y = -6x + 6$

10. The point $P(2, 1)$ is shown on the diagram.

    (i) Plot the point $Q(4, 5)$ on the diagram.

    (ii) Find the coordinates of M, the midpoint of $[PQ]$. Plot the point M on the diagram.

    (iii) Show that $|PQ| = \sqrt{20}$.

    (iv) Find the slope of PQ.

    (v) Find the equation of the line PQ.

    (vi) The line PQ cuts the *y*-axis at R. By letting $x = 0$, find the coordinates of R.

    (vii) Confirm your answer to part (vi) by drawing the line PQ on the diagram.

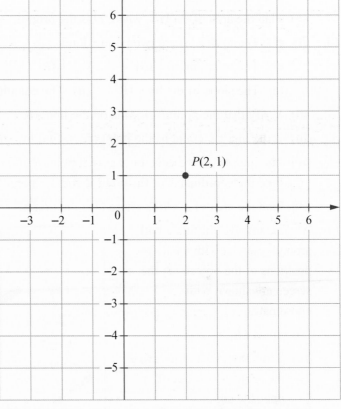

    (viii) The point $S(1, k)$ is on the line PQ. By letting $x = 1$, find the value of k. Confirm your answer by plotting the point S.

11. (i) The line k contains the point $(-1, 6)$. k has slope 2. Find the equation of k.

    (ii) By letting $x = 0$, find the coordinates of A, the point of intersection of the line k and the *y*-axis. Graph the line k.

12. **(i)** $P(1, 10)$ and $Q(5, 2)$ are two points. Find:

      (a) The midpoint of $[PQ]$ **(b)** $|PQ|$

      (c) The slope of the line PQ **(d)** The equation of the line PQ

  (ii) Verify that the point $R(7, -2)$ is on the line PQ.

  (iii) If the line PQ contains the point $(k, 8)$, find the value of k.

  (iv) The line PQ intersects the x-axis at point A and the y-axis at B. Find the coordinates of the point A and the point B.

  (v) Find the area of $\triangle OAB$, where O is the origin.

13. **(i)** $A(1, 7)$ and $B(3, 5)$ are two points. Find:

      (a) The midpoint of $[AB]$ **(b)** $|AB|$

      (c) The slope of the line AB **(d)** The equation of the line AB

  (ii) Verify that the point $C(4, 4)$ is on the line AB.

  (iii) If the line AB contains the point $(6, t)$, find the value of t.

  (iv) The line AB interesects the x-axis at point R and the y-axis at point S. Find the coordinates of the point R and the point S.

  (v) Find the area of $\triangle ORS$, where O is the origin.

14. A game involves hitting a ball around a screen with a bat. The positions of the objects on the screen are shown with coordinates.

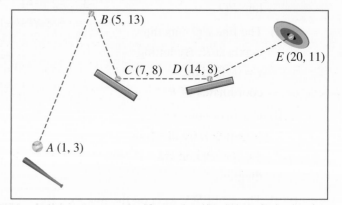

  (i) Find $|AB|$.

  (ii) Show that AB and BC have the same slopes but of opposite signs.

  (iii) Find the equation of the line DE.

  (iv) Show that A is **not** on the line DE.

CHAPTER 30

FUNCTIONS

Terminology

Number machine: Input to output

You can think of a function as a number machine that changes one number (input) into another number (output) according to some rule.

When the numbers (inputs) are entered, the machine works on them and produces other numbers (outputs).

Input

Output

> A function does exactly the same to each input number and produces only one output number for each input number.

The set of numbers that are put into a function is called the **domain**.

The set of total possible outputs is called the **co-domain**.

The set of numbers that comes out of a function is called the **range**.

A function connects **every** input in the domain to an output in the range.

A function is another way of writing an algebraic formula that links input to output.

Everyday examples of functions

This idea of a function has many everyday applications. Below are some examples of such applications.

1. **Bar codes:** In a supermarket checkout machine, the bar code on an item (the input) is transformed by the machine (the function) into a price (the output).
2. **Calculator:** If one of the function keys is chosen, e.g. $\sqrt{\ }$, the number keyed in (input) is transformed by the $\sqrt{\ }$ key (function) into the answer (output), i.e. the square root of the number.
3. **Internet:** When a webpage is required, the website's address (input) is converted by the worldwide web (function) into the relevant website (output).

Consider the number machine that applies the rule:

double the input and then add on 3,

i.e. 2(input) + 3 = output.

Look at what happens when we put in the numbers 0, 1, 2, 3, 4 and 5.

We set up the number machine in the form of a table.

Input (numbers put in)	Rule 2(input) + 3	Output (numbers that come out)
0	0 + 3	3
1	2 + 3	5
2	4 + 3	7
3	6 + 3	9
4	8 + 3	11
5	10 + 3	13

A function can be represented by a set of ordered pairs of couples (input, output),

i.e. {(0, 3), (1, 5), (2, 7), (3, 9), (4, 11), (5, 13)}.

A function can also be represented by a table:

Input	0	1	2	3	4	5
Output	3	5	7	9	11	13

We can also see that:

Domain = {0, 1, 2, 3, 4, 5}, the set of inputs.

Range = {3, 5, 7, 9, 11, 13}, the set of outputs.

The co-domain is the set of all possible outputs. In this case, the co-domain would be all natural numbers.

Exercise 30.1

In questions 1–10, copy and complete the table by working out the outputs. Write out each function as a set of ordered pairs (input, output). Write down the domain and range in each case.

1.

Input	3(input) + 2	Output
1		
2		
3		
4		
5		

2.

Input	4(input) + 1	Output
0		
2		
4		
6		
8		

3.

Input	2(input) + 1	Output
−3		
−2		
−1		
0		
1		
2		

4.

Input	(input) + 3	Output
−2		
−1		
0		
1		
2		
3		

5.

Input	5(input) + 3	Output
−5		
−4		
−3		
−2		
−1		
0		
1		
2		

6.

Input	3(input) − 4	Output
−2		
−1		
0		
1		
2		
3		
4		
5		

7.

Input	2(input) − 5	Output
−3		
−2		
−1		
0		
1		
2		

8.

Input	(input) − 3	Output
−1		
0		
1		
2		
3		
4		

9.

Input	$(input)^2 + 3$	Output
0		
1		
2		
3		
4		
5		
6		

10.

Input	$(input)^2 + 3(input)$	Output
−2		
−1		
0		
1		
2		
3		
4		

11. Input ⟶ ×5 ⟶ +7 ⟶ Output

    (i) What is the output if the input is 3?

    (ii) What is the input if the output is 27?

12. Input ⟶ −8 ⟶ ×12 ⟶ Output

    (i) What is the output if the input is 10?

    (ii) What is the input if the output is 84?

13. Input ⟶ ×8 ⟶ −6 ⟶ Output

    (i) What is the output if the input is 5?

    (ii) What is the input if the output is 50?

14. A function triples the input and then subtracts 2 from this value.

    (i) Write down this function.

    (ii) If the domain is {0, 1, 2, 3, 4, 5}, find the range.

15. A function squares the input and then adds twice the input to this value.

    (i) Write down this function.

    (ii) If the domain is the list of integers from −3 to 3 (inclusive), find the range.

16. Multiply the first digit of your age by 5, add 3, double this figure and now add on the second digit of your age. The answer should be 6 years more than your current age!

17. Take your age, multiply it by 7, then multiply again by 1,443.

    (i) What do you notice about your answer?

    (ii) Write down this function.

    (iii) Could you simplify this function so that it only involves one calculation?

18. Niamh is arranging a school play. She asks two companies for their prices to print the programmes. The total price is €y and the number of programmes printed is x.

    (i) Company A charges a basic fee of €150 plus an amount for each programme printed. The formula for Company A is $y = 150 + 0.6x$. What is the amount charged for each programme printed?

    (ii) Company B does not charge a basic fee, but charges €1·30 for each programme printed. Write down a formula for y in terms of x for Company B.

    (iii) If 100 people come to the play, which company will be cheaper?

    (iv) If 200 people come to the play, which company will be cheaper?

    (v) If 300 people come to the play, which company will be cheaper?

    (vi) Based on your answers for parts **(iii)**, **(iv)** and **(v)**, what do you think Niamh should do before ordering the programmes to ensure that she goes with the cheapest company?

Notation

A function changes input into output according to some rule.

Functions are often represented by the letter f.

For example, let's represent the function 'double input and then add one' by the letter f.

Then f is the rule that 'doubles input and then adds one.'

Let's look at this rule on a mapping diagram:

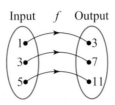

A mapping diagram is a diagram showing the linkage between inputs and outputs.

Generally, f changes x into $2x + 1$,

which can be written as: $\quad f: x \rightarrow 2x + 1 \quad$ or $\quad f(x) = 2x + 1$

$$(\text{input, output}) = (x, f(x)) = (x, 2x + 1)$$

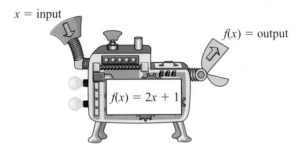

$f(x)$, which denotes the output, is read as 'f of x'.

Note: A **function** is also called a **mapping** or simply a **map**.

One number is mapped onto another number. In the above example, x is mapped onto $2x + 1$, written $f: x \rightarrow 2x + 1$.

Input number

If $f(x) = 3x + 2$, then $f(1)$ means input 1 into the function,

i.e. 'it is the result of applying f to the number 1'.

$$f(x) = 3x + 2$$
$$f(1) = 3(1) + 2 \quad (\text{put in 1 for } x)$$
$$= 3 + 2$$
$$= 5 \qquad (\text{output})$$

$(\text{input, output}) = (1, f(1)) = (1, 5)$

EXAMPLE 1

A function f is defined as $f: x \to 3x + 4$.

Find the value of $f(2) + f(-3)$

Solution:

$f(x) = 3x + 4$

$f(2) = 3(2) + 4$

$\quad = 6 + 4$

$\quad = 10$

$f(-3) = 3(-3) + 4$

$\quad\quad = -9 + 4$

$\quad\quad = -5$

Thus, $f(2) + f(-3)$

$\quad\quad = 10 - 5$

$\quad\quad = 5$

 EXAMPLE 2

A function f is defined as $f: x \to 2x^2 + 3$.

Find: **(i)** $f(1)$ **(ii)** $f(-2)$ **(iii)** $f(3)$

Solution:

$f(x) = 2x^2 + 3$

(i) $f(1) = 2(1)^2 + 3$

$\quad\quad = 2(1) + 3$

$\quad\quad = 2 + 3$

$\quad\quad = 5$

(ii) $f(-2) = 2(-2)^2 + 3$

$\quad\quad\quad = 2(4) + 3$

$\quad\quad\quad = 8 + 3$

$\quad\quad\quad = 11$

(iii) $f(3) = 2(3)^2 + 3$

$\quad\quad\quad = 2(9) + 3$

$\quad\quad\quad = 18 + 3$

$\quad\quad\quad = 21$

Exercise 30.2

1. A function f is defined as $f: x \to 2x + 5$.
   Find: **(i)** $f(1)$ **(ii)** $f(2)$ **(iii)** $f(3)$ **(iv)** $f(4)$

2. A function f is defined as $f: x \to 3x + 4$.
   Find: **(i)** $f(0)$ **(ii)** $f(2)$ **(iii)** $f(4)$ **(iv)** $f(6)$

3. A function f is defined as $f: x \to 4x + 3$.
   Find: **(i)** $f(5)$ **(ii)** $f(1)$ **(iii)** $f(3)$ **(iv)** $f(2)$

4. A function f is defined as $f: x \to 2x - 3$.
   Find: **(i)** $f(2)$ **(ii)** $f(0)$ **(iii)** $f(3)$ **(iv)** $f(6)$

5. A function f is defined as $f: x \to 3x - 1$.
   Find: **(i)** $f(0)$ **(ii)** $f(-1)$ **(iii)** $f(1)$ **(iv)** $f(-2)$

6. A function f is defined as $f: x \rightarrow 5x - 2$
   Find: **(i)** $f(1)$ **(ii)** $f(2)$ **(iii)** $f(-1)$ **(iv)** $f(-2)$

7. A function f is defined as $f: x \rightarrow x + 2$
   Find: **(i)** $f(3)$ **(ii)** $f(5)$ **(iii)** $f(1) + f(-3)$ **(iv)** $2f(4)$

8. A function f is defined as $f: x \rightarrow 3x$.
   Find: **(i)** $f(-2)$ **(ii)** $f(-1)$ **(iii)** $f(1) + f(2)$ **(iv)** $5f(2)$

9. A function f is defined as $f: x \rightarrow 1 - x$.
   Find: **(i)** $f(1)$ **(ii)** $f(-1)$ **(iii)** $f(-3) + f(2)$ **(iv)** $4f(-2)$ **(v)** Verify that $f(3) < 0$.

10. A function f is defined as $f: x \rightarrow 3 - 2x$.
    Find: **(i)** $f(0)$ **(ii)** $f(1)$ **(iii)** $f(2)$ **(iv)** $f(-1) - f(0)$ **(v)** Verify that $f(-2) > 0$.

11. A function f is defined as $f: x \rightarrow 2x^2 + 5$.
    Find: **(i)** $f(1)$ **(ii)** $f(2)$ **(iii)** $f(-1)$ **(iv)** $f(-2)$ **(v)** Verify that $f(3) = f(-3)$.

12. A function f is defined as $f: x \rightarrow \sqrt{x}$.
    Find: **(i)** $f(4)$ **(ii)** $f(9)$ **(iii)** $f(16)$ **(iv)** $f(1)$ **(v)** $f(0)$
    (vi) Verify that $f(36) > f(25)$.

13. A function f is defined as $f: x \rightarrow x^2 + 2x$.
    Find: **(i)** $f(1)$ **(ii)** $f(2)$ **(iii)** $f(-1)$ **(iv)** $f(-3)$
    (v) Find two values of x for which $f(x) = 8$.

14. A function f is defined as $f: x \rightarrow x^2 - 3x - 4$.
    Find: **(i)** $f(1)$ **(ii)** $f(2)$ **(iii)** $f(3)$
    (iv) Find two values of x for which $f(x) = 0$.

Representing functions with mapping diagrams and sets of couples

Functions can also be represented by mapping diagrams or sets of couples, or both. Consider the next example.

EXAMPLE

A function f is defined as $f: x \rightarrow 3x + 5$. The domain of f is $\{-2, -1, 0, 1, 2, 3, 4\}$.

Represent f **(i)** with a mapping diagram   **(ii)** as a set of couples.

(iii) Write down the range of f.

Solution:

A table is used to work out the couples. The domain = $\{-2, -1, 0, 1, 2, 3, 4\}$.

(i)

x	$3x + 5$	$f(x)$
-2	-6 + 5	-1
-1	-3 + 5	2
0	0 + 5	5
1	3 + 5	8
2	6 + 5	11
3	9 + 5	14
4	12 + 5	17

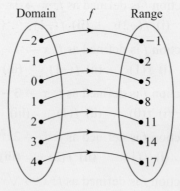

Mapping diagram

(ii) $f = \{(-2, -1), (-1, 2), (0, 5), (1, 8), (2, 11), (3, 14), (4, 17)\}$

(iii) Range = $\{-1, 2, 5, 8, 11, 14, 17\}$

Exercise 30.3

1. A function f is defined as $f: x \rightarrow 2x + 5$. The domain of f is $\{1, 2, 3, 4, 5\}$.
   (i) Find the range of f.   (ii) Write f as a set of couples.

2. A function f is defined as $f: x \rightarrow 3x + 2$. The domain of f is $\{2, 4, 6, 8\}$.
   (i) Find the range of f.   (ii) Write f as a set of couples.

3. A function f is defined as $f: x \rightarrow 4x - 3$. The domain of f is $\{0, 1, 2, 3, 4\}$.
   (i) Find the range of f.   (ii) Write f as a set of couples.

4. A function f is defined as $f: x \rightarrow 2x - 1$. The domain of f is $\{-2, -1, 0, 1, 2, 3\}$.
   (i) Find the range of f.   (ii) Write f as a set of couples.

5. A function f is defined as $f: x \rightarrow x + 4$. The domain of f is $\{-3, -2, -1, 0, 1, 2\}$.
   (i) Find the range of f.   (ii) Write f as a set of couples.

6. $f: x \rightarrow 3x + 4$ is a function. The domain of f is $\{1, 2, 3\}$. Find the range of f.

7. $f: x \rightarrow 5x - 2$ is a function. The domain of f is $\{0, 1, 2\}$. Find the range of f.

8. $f: x \rightarrow 2x + 5$ is a function. The domain of f is $\{-2, -1, 0, 1, 2\}$. Find the range of f.

9. $f: x \rightarrow 3x - 5$ is a function. The domain of f is $\{-1, 0, 1, 2\}$. Find the range of f.

10. $f: x \rightarrow 1 - 2x$ is a function. The domain of f is $\{-2, 0, 2, 4\}$. Find the range of f.

Mapping diagrams with numbers missing

Sometimes we have to solve problems where parts of the domain and the range are missing. Consider the next example.

EXAMPLE

A function f is defined as $f: x \rightarrow 3x - 2$.
Copy the mapping diagram and fill in the missing numbers a, b and c.

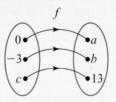

Solution:

$f(x) = 3x - 2$

$f(0) = 3(0) - 2 = 0 - 2 = -2$

$\therefore a = -2$

$f(-3) = 3(-3) - 2 = -9 - 2 = -11$

$\therefore b = -11$

To find c we are given an equation in disguise.

Given: Output = 13.   Find input, c.

$$f(x) = 13$$
$$3x - 2 = 13$$
$$3x = 15$$
$$x = 5$$

Therefore, $c = 5$.

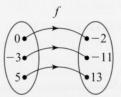

Exercise 30.4

1. A function f is defined as $f: x \rightarrow 2x + 3$.
    Copy the mapping diagram and fill in the missing numbers, a, b and c.

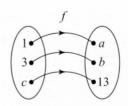

2. A function f is defined as $f: x \rightarrow 3x + 1$.
    Copy the mapping diagram and fill in the missing numbers, p, q and r.

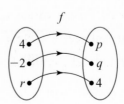

3. A function f is defined as $f: x \rightarrow 5x - 3$.
Copy the mapping diagram and fill in the
missing numbers, a, b and c.

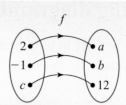

4. A function f is defined as $f: x \rightarrow 4x - 3$.
Copy the mapping diagram and fill in the
missing numbers, r, s and t.

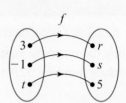

5. A function f is defined as $f: x \rightarrow 1 - x$.
Copy the mapping diagram and fill in the
missing numbers, x, y and z.

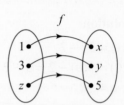

6. A function f is defined as $f: x \rightarrow 3x$.
Copy the mapping diagram and fill in the
missing numbers, a, b and c in the domain.

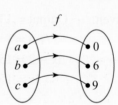

7. A function f is defined as $f: x \rightarrow x + 3$.
Fill in the missing numbers, p, q, r and s, of
the following four couples of f.
   (i) $(2, p)$ **(ii)** $(-2, q)$
   (iii) $(r, 6)$ **(iv)** $(s, 0)$

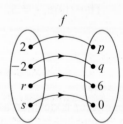

8. A function f is defined as $f: x \rightarrow 2x - 1$.
Fill in the missing numbers, a, b, c and d, of the following four couples of f.
(i) $(5, a)$ **(ii)** $(-2, b)$ **(iii)** $(c, 5)$ **(iv)** $(d, 1)$

9. A function f is defined as $f: x \rightarrow 4x + 1$. Complete the following four couples.
(i) $(2, \ )$ **(ii)** $(0, \ )$ **(iii)** $(\ ,5)$ **(iv)** $(\ ,-3)$

10. A function f is defined as $f: x \rightarrow 2x - 5$. Complete the following four couples.
(i) $(3, \ )$ **(ii)** $(-3, \ )$ **(iii)** $(\ ,3)$ **(iv)** $(\ ,-7)$

GRAPHING FUNCTIONS

Graphs

A function can be written as a set of couples, (input, output), (x, y) or $(x, f(x))$. When the couples are plotted and joined by a line or curve, we get the graph of the function. When graphing functions, always put the inputs, x, on the horizontal axis and the outputs, y or $f(x)$, on the vertical axis. A graph of a function is a diagram or picture showing the relationship (link) between the inputs and the outputs.

Note: It is very important not to draw a graph outside the given inputs (the given values of x).

Notation

The notation $y = f(x)$ means 'the value of the output y depends on the value of the input x, according to some rule called f'. Hence, y and $f(x)$ are interchangeable and the y-axis can also be called the $f(x)$-axis.

Graphing linear functions

The first four letters in the word '**linear**' spell **line**. Therefore, the graph of a linear function will be a straight line. A linear function is usually given in the form $f: x \rightarrow ax + b$, where $a \neq 0$ and a, b are constants. For example, $f: x \rightarrow 2x + 5$. As the graph is a straight line, two points are all that are needed to graph it. In the question, you will always be given a set of inputs, x, called the domain.

To graph a linear function, do the following.

1. Choose two suitable values of x in the given domain.

    (Two suitable values are the smallest and largest values of x.)

2. Substitute these in the function to find the two corresponding value of y.

3. Plot the points and draw the line through them.

Note: $-3 \leq x \leq 2$ means 'x is between -3 and 2, including -3 and 2'.

EXAMPLE

Graph the function $f : x \to 2x + 1$ in the domain $-3 \le x \le 2$, $x \in \mathbb{R}$.

Solution:

Let $y = f(x) \Rightarrow y = 2x + 1$

1. Let $x = -3$ and $x = 2$

2.

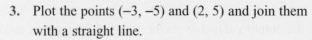

$y = 2x + 1$	
$x = -3$	$x = 2$
$y = 2(-3) + 1$	$y = 2(2) + 1$
$y = -6 + 1$	$y = 4 + 1$
$y = -5$	$y = 5$
$(-3, -5)$	$(2, 5)$

3. Plot the points $(-3, -5)$ and $(2, 5)$ and join them with a straight line.

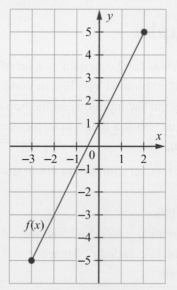

Exercise 31.1

Graph each of the following functions in the given domain.

1. $f : x \to 2x + 3$ in the domain $-4 \le x \le 2$, $x \in \mathbb{R}$.

2. $g : x \to 3x + 1$ in the domain $-2 \le x \le 3$, $x \in \mathbb{R}$.

3. $f : x \to 4x + 3$ in the domain $-2 \le x \le 2$, $x \in \mathbb{R}$.

4. $g : x \to 5x + 1$ in the domain $-1 \le x \le 4$, $x \in \mathbb{R}$.

5. $f : x \to 2x - 3$ in the domain $-1 \le x \le 4$, $x \in \mathbb{R}$.

6. $g : x \to 3x - 5$ in the domain $-2 \le x \le 4$, $x \in \mathbb{R}$.

7. $f : x \to x + 4$ in the domain $-5 \le x \le 2$, $x \in \mathbb{R}$.

8. $g : x \to 2x$ in the domain $-3 \le x \le 3$, $x \in \mathbb{R}$.

9. $f : x \to 3x$ in the domain $-2 \le x \le 4$, $x \in \mathbb{R}$.

10. $g : x \to x - 2$ in the domain $-3 \le x \le 4$, $x \in \mathbb{R}$.

11. $f : x \to 1 - x$ in the domain $-1 \le x \le 5$, $x \in \mathbb{R}$.

12. $g : x \to 3 - 2x$ in the domain $-1 \le x \le 4$, $x \in \mathbb{R}$.

13. $f : x \to 2 - 3x$ in the domain $-2 \le x \le 4$, $x \in \mathbb{R}$.

14. $g : x \to -1 - x$ in the domain $-3 \le x \le 4$, $x \in \mathbb{R}$.

15. $f : x \to 4 - 3x$ in the domain $-2 \le x \le 4$, $x \in \mathbb{R}$.

16. $g : x \to -1 - 2x$ in the domain $-3 \le x \le 3$, $x \in \mathbb{R}$.

Graphing quadratic functions

A **quadratic function** is usually given in the form $f : x \rightarrow ax^2 + bx + c$, $a \neq 0$, and a, b, c are constants. For example, $f : x \rightarrow 2x^2 - x + 3$. Because of its shape, quite a few points are needed to plot the graph of a quadratic function. In the question, you will always be given a set of inputs, x, called the domain. With these inputs, a table is used to find the corresponding set of outputs, y or $f(x)$, called the range. When the table is completed, plot the points and join them with a **smooth curve**.

Notes on making out the table

1. Work out each column separately, i.e. all the x^2 values first, then all the x values and finally the constant. (Watch for patterns in the numbers.)
2. Work out each corresponding value of y.
3. The **only** column that changes sign is the x term (middle) column.
   If the given values of x contain 0, then the x term column will make **one** sign change, either from + to − or from − to +, where $x = 0$.
4. The other two columns **never** change sign. They remain either all pluses or all minuses. These columns keep the sign given in the question.

Note: Decide where to draw the x- and y-axes by looking at the table to see what the largest and smallest values of x and y are. In general, the units on the x-axis are larger than the units on the y-axis. Try to make sure that the graph extends almost the whole width and length of the page.

EXAMPLE

Graph the function $f : x \rightarrow x^2 + 3x - 2$ in the domain $-5 \leq x \leq 2$, $x \in \mathbb{R}$.

Solution:
A table is drawn with the given values of x, from −5 to 2, to find the corresponding values of y.

$$\text{Let } y = f(x) \quad \Rightarrow \quad y = x^2 + 3x - 2$$

x	$x^2 + 3x - 2$	y
−5	$25 - 15 - 2$	8
−4	$16 - 12 - 2$	2
−3	$9 - 9 - 2$	−2
−2	$4 - 6 - 2$	−4
−1	$1 - 3 - 2$	−4
0	$0 + 0 - 2$	−2
1	$1 + 3 - 2$	2
2	$4 + 6 - 2$	8

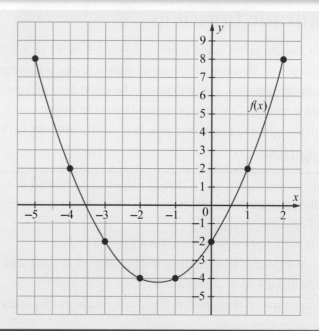

Exercise 31.2

Graph each of the following functions in the given domain.

1. $f: x \to x^2 + 2x - 8$ in the domain $-5 \le x \le 3$, $x \in \mathbb{R}$.
2. $f: x \to x^2 - 3x + 2$ in the domain $-2 \le x \le 5$, $x \in \mathbb{R}$.
3. $f: x \to x^2 - 2x - 3$ in the domain $-2 \le x \le 4$, $x \in \mathbb{R}$.
4. $f: x \to x^2 + 3x - 4$ in the domain $-5 \le x \le 2$, $x \in \mathbb{R}$.
5. $f: x \to x^2 + x - 6$ in the domain $-4 \le x \le 3$, $x \in \mathbb{R}$.
6. $f: x \to x^2 - x - 2$ in the domain $-2 \le x \le 3$, $x \in \mathbb{R}$.
7. $f: x \to x^2 - 7x + 6$ in the domain $0 \le x \le 7$, $x \in \mathbb{R}$.
8. $f: x \to x^2 - 4x + 3$ in the domain $-1 \le x \le 5$, $x \in \mathbb{R}$.
9. $f: x \to x^2 - 3x - 4$ in the domain $-2 \le x \le 5$, $x \in \mathbb{R}$.
10. $f: x \to x^2 - 6x + 5$ in the domain $-1 \le x \le 7$, $x \in \mathbb{R}$.
11. $f: x \to x^2 + 2x$ in the domain $-4 \le x \le 2$, $x \in \mathbb{R}$.
12. $f: x \to x^2 - 3x$ in the domain $-2 \le x \le 5$, $x \in \mathbb{R}$.
13. $f: x \to x^2 + 3$ in the domain $-3 \le x \le 3$, $x \in \mathbb{R}$.
14. $f: x \to x^2 - 2$ in the domain $-4 \le x \le 4$, $x \in \mathbb{R}$.
15. $f: x \to 2x^2 + 5x - 3$ in the domain $-4 \le x \le 2$, $x \in \mathbb{R}$.
16. $f: x \to 2x^2 + 3x - 2$ in the domain $-2 \le x \le 3$, $x \in \mathbb{R}$.
17. $f: x \to 2x^2 - x - 1$ in the domain $-2 \le x \le 3$, $x \in \mathbb{R}$.
18. $f: x \to 2x^2 - 5x$ in the domain $-2 \le x \le 4$, $x \in \mathbb{R}$.
19. On the same axis and scales, graph the functions
   $f: x \to x^2 - 2x - 4$, $g: x \to 2x + 5$ in the domain $-4 \le x \le 6$, $x \in \mathbb{R}$.

Using graphs

Once we have drawn the graph, we are usually asked to use the graph to answer some questions.
Below are examples of the general type of problems where graphs are used.

Notes: 1. $y = f(x)$, so $f(x)$ can be replaced by y.

2. In general, if given x, find y and vice versa.

Examples of the main problems, once the graph is drawn:

1. **Find the values of x for which $f(x) = 0$.**

   This question is asking:

   'Where does the curve meet the x-axis?'

   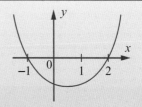

   Solution:
   Write down the values of x where the graph meets the x-axis (where $y = 0$).
   From the graph: $x = -1$ or $x = 2$.

2. **Find the values of x for which $f(x) = 2$.**

   This question is asking:

   'When $y = 2$, what are the values of x?'

   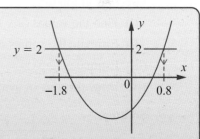

   Solution:
   Draw the line $y = 2$. Where this line meets the curve,
   draw broken perpendicular lines onto the x-axis.
   Write down the values of x where these broken lines meet the x-axis.
   From the graph:
   When $y = 2$, $x = -1{\cdot}8$, or $x = 0{\cdot}8$.

3. **Find the value of $f(-1{\cdot}5)$.**

   This question is asking:

   'When $x = -1{\cdot}5$, what is the value of y?'

   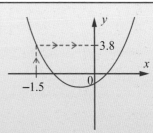

   Solution:
   From $x = -1{\cdot}5$ on the x-axis, draw a broken perpendicular
   line to meet the curve. From this, draw a broken horizontal line to
   meet the y-axis. Write down the value of y where this line meets the y-axis.
   From the graph:
   $f(-1{\cdot}5) = 3{\cdot}8$.

4. Axis of symmetry

Graphs of quadratic functions are symmetrical about a line that passes through the middle of the curve (and also through the minimum point). The line is called the axis of symmetry.

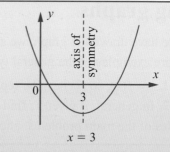

$$x = 3$$

Solution:

From the graph:

The equation of the axis of symmetry is $x = 3$.

3 is where the line meets the x-axis.

EXAMPLE

Draw the graph of the function $f : x \rightarrow x^2 - 2x - 3$ in the domain $-2 \leq x \leq 4$, $x \in \mathbb{R}$.

Use your graph to:

   (i) Find the values of x for which $f(x) = 0$

   (ii) Estimate the values of x for which $5f(x) = f(4)$

   (iii) Estimate $f(2 \cdot 5)$

   (iv) Draw the axis of symmetry of the graph of $f(x)$ and write down its equation.

Solution:

x	$x^2 - 2x - 3$	y
-2	$4 + 4 - 3$	5
-1	$1 + 2 - 3$	0
0	$0 + 0 - 3$	-3
1	$1 - 2 - 3$	-4
2	$4 - 4 - 3$	-3
3	$9 - 6 - 3$	0
4	$16 - 8 - 3$	5

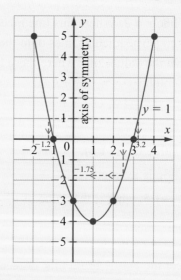

   (i) The values of x for which $f(x) = 0$

   This question is asking, 'Where does the graph cut the x-axis?'

   The graph cuts the x-axis at -1 and 3.

   Therefore, $f(x) = 0$ for $x = -1$ and $x = 3$.

   Note: Another way of asking the same question is,

   'Find the values of x for which $x^2 - 2x - 3 = 0$.'

(ii) The values of x for which $5f(x) = f(4)$

From the table, $f(4) = 5$ (i.e. when $x = 4$, $y = 5$).

Given: $5f(x) = f(4)$

$\qquad 5f(x) = 5 \qquad$ (put in 5 for $f(4)$)

$\qquad f(x) = 1 \qquad$ (divide both sides by 5)

$\qquad y = 1 \qquad$ (replace $f(x)$ with y)

This question is asking, 'When $y = 1$, what are the values of x?'

Draw the line $y = 1$. Where this line meets the curve, drop broken perpendicular lines to meet the x-axis. These lines meet the x-axis at $-1\cdot2$ and $3\cdot2$.

Therefore, $5f(x) = f(4)$ for $x = -1\cdot2$ and $x = 3\cdot2$.

Note: Another way of asking the same question is,

'Find the values of x for which $x^2 - 2x - 3 = 1$.'

(iii) $f(2\cdot5)$

This question is asking, 'When $x = 2\cdot5$, what is the value of y?'

From $x = 2\cdot5$ on the x-axis, draw a broken perpendicular line to meet the curve.

From this, a broken horizontal line is drawn to meet the y-axis.

This line meets the y-axis at $-1\cdot75$.

Therefore, $f(2\cdot5) = -1\cdot75$.

(iv) Axis of symmetry of the graph of $f(x)$

Through the minimum point $(1, -4)$, draw a line parallel to the y-axis.

This is the axis of symmetry.

As can be seen from the graph, the axis of symmetry meets the x-axis at 1.

Therefore, $x = 1$ is the equation of the axis of symmetry of the graph of $f(x)$.

Exercise 31.3

1. Below is a graph of the function $f : x \to x^2 + 2x - 3$ in the domain $-4 \le x \le 2, \quad x \in \mathbb{R}$.

   Use the graph to:

   (i) Find the values of x for which $f(x) = 0$

   (ii) Find the values of x for which $f(x) = 5$

   (iii) Estimate the value of $f(0\cdot5)$

   (iv) Estimate the values of x for which $f(x) = f(-4) + f(-2)$

   (v) Find two points on the axis of symmetry of the graph of $f(x)$ and write down the equation of the axis of symmetry

   (vi) Find the area of the smallest rectangle that encloses the graph

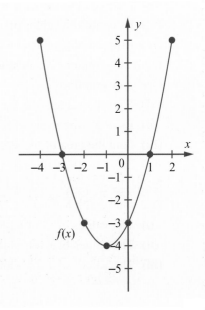

2. Below is a graph of the function $f : x \rightarrow x^2 - 3x - 4$ in the domain $-2 \leq x \leq 5, \quad x \in \mathbb{R}$.

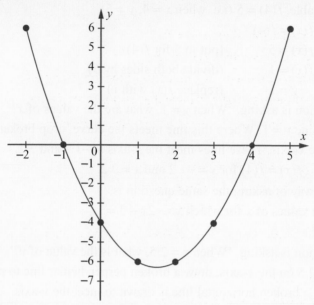

Use the graph to:
   (i) Find the values of x for which $f(x) = 0$
   (ii) Estimate the value of $f(3.5)$
   (iii) Find the values of x for which $f(x) = -4$
   (iv) Estimate the values of x for which $f(x) = f(5) + f(0)$

3. Draw the graph of the function $f : x \rightarrow x^2 - 3x + 2$ in the domain $-1 \leq x \leq 4, \quad x \in \mathbb{R}$.
   Use your graph to
   (i) Find the values of x for which $f(x) = 0$
   (ii) Estimate the value of $f(2.6)$
   (iii) Estimate the values of x for which $f(x) = 5$
   (iv) Estimate the values of x for which $f(x) = f(4) - f(0) - f(3)$

4. Draw the graph of the function $f : x \rightarrow x^2 - 6x + 5$ in the domain $0 \leq x \leq 6, \quad x \in \mathbb{R}$.
   Use your graph to:
   (i) Find the values of x for which $f(x) = 0$
   (ii) Estimate the value of $f(2.5)$
   (iii) Find the area of the smallest rectangle that encloses the graph
   (iv) Estimate the values of x for which $f(x) = f(1) + f(3) - f(4)$

5. Draw the graph of the function $f : x \rightarrow x^2 - x - 2$ in the domain $-3 \leq x \leq 4, \quad x \in \mathbb{R}$.
   Use your graph to find:
   (i) The values of x for which $f(x) = 0$
   (ii) The values of x for which $f(x) = 4$
   (iii) The values of x for which $f(x) = 2f(3) - f(4)$

6. Draw the graph of the function $f : x \to x^2 + 2x - 8$ in the domain $-5 \le x \le 3$, $x \in \mathbb{R}$.
   Use your graph to:

   (i) Find the values of x for which $f(x) = 0$

   (ii) Find the values of x for which $f(x) = -5$

   (iii) Find the equation of the axis of symmetry of the graph of $f(x)$

   (iv) Find the area of the smallest rectangle that encloses the graph.

7. Draw the graph of the function $f : x \to x^2 + x - 6$ in the domain $-4 \le x \le 3$, $x \in \mathbb{R}$.
   Use your graph to:

   (i) Find the values of x for which $f(x) = 0$

   (ii) Find the values of x for which $f(x) = -4$

   (iii) Estimate the values of x for which $f(x) = 4$

8. Draw the graph of the function $f : x \to x^2 - 4x - 5$ in the domain $-2 \le x \le 6$, $x \in \mathbb{R}$.
   Use your graph to:

   (i) Find the values of x for which $f(x) = 0$

   (ii) Find the values of x for which $f(x) = -8$

   (iii) Find the equation of the axis of symmetry of the graph of $f(x)$.

   (iv) Draw the axis of symmetry of the graph.

9. Draw the graph of the function $f : x \to x^2 - 2x - 3$ in the domain $-3 \le x \le 5$, $x \in \mathbb{R}$.
   Use your graph to find:

   (i) The values of x for which $f(x) = f(3)$

   (ii) The values of x for which $f(x) = 2 - f(0)$

   (iii) The area of the smallest rectangle that encloses the graph

   (iv) The estimate of $f(-2 \cdot 5)$

10. Draw the graph of the function $f : x \to x^2 - 4x + 2$ in the domain $-1 \le x \le 5$, $x \in \mathbb{R}$.
    Use your graph to find:

    (i) The two values of x for which $f(x) = -1$

    (ii) The estimate of $f(4 \cdot 5)$

    (iii) The two values of x for which $f(x) = 0$

11. Complete the following table and draw the graph of the function
    $f : x \to x^2 + x - 2$ in the domain $-3 \le x \le 2$, $x \in \mathbb{R}$.

x	-3	-2	-1	0	1	2
$f(x)$	4			-2		

   (i) Use your graph to find the values of x for which $f(x) = 0$.

   (ii) Use your graph to estimate the value of $f(0 \cdot 5)$.

    (iii) Construct the axis of symmetry of the graph of $f(x)$.

    (iv) Estimate the values of x for which $f(x) = f(0) + f(2)$.

12. Draw the graph of the function $f : x \rightarrow x^2 - 5x + 4$ in the domain $-1 \le x \le 6, \quad x \in \mathbb{R}$.
Use your graph to:

    (i) Find the values of x for which $x^2 - 5x + 4 = 0$

    (ii) Find the values of x for which $x^2 - 5x + 4 = -2$

    (iii) Estimate the value of $x^2 - 5x + 4$ when $x = 4 \cdot 5$

    (iv) Draw the axis of symmetry of the graph of $f(x)$.

13. Draw the graph of the function $f : x \rightarrow x^2 + 3x - 4$ in the domain $-5 \le x \le 2, \quad x \in \mathbb{R}$.
Use your graph to:

    (i) Find the values of x for which $x^2 + 3x - 4 = 0$

    (ii) Estimate the values of x for which $x^2 + 3x - 4 = 2$

    (iii) Estimate the value of $x^2 + 3x - 4$ when $x = -2 \cdot 2$

    (iv) Draw the axis of symmetry of the graph of $f(x)$.

14. Draw the x-axis from -2 to 4 and the y-axis from -5 to 5.
Graph the function $f : x \rightarrow x^2 - 2x - 3$ in the domain $-2 \le x \le 4, \quad x \in \mathbb{R}$.
Construct the image of the graph of $f(x)$ under an axial symmetry in the x-axis.

15. Draw the graph of the function $f : x \rightarrow 2x^2 - x - 3$ in the domain $-2 \le x \le 3, \quad x \in \mathbb{R}$.
Use your graph to estimate:

    (i) The two values of x for which $f(x) = 0$

    (ii) The two values of x for which $f(x) = 3$

16. Draw the graph of the function $f : x \rightarrow 2x^2 + 3x - 2$ in the domain $-3 \le x \le 1, \quad x \in \mathbb{R}$.
Use your graph to estimate:

    (i) The value of $f(-2 \cdot 8)$

    (ii) The two values of x for which $f(x) = 0$

    (iii) The two values of x for which $f(x) = -2$

17. On the same axis and scales, graph the functions
$f(x) \rightarrow x^2 - x - 6$, $g(x) \rightarrow x + 2$ in the domain $-3 \le x \le 4, \quad x \in \mathbb{R}$.
For what values of x does $f(x) = g(x)$?

18. On the same axis and scales, graph the functions
$f(x) \rightarrow x^2 - 5x + 4$, $g(x) \rightarrow -2x + 4$ in the domain $0 \le x \le 5, \quad x \in \mathbb{R}$.
Find the coordinates of the points where $f(x) = g(x)$.

19. On the same axis and scales, graph the functions
$f(x) \rightarrow x^2 + 3x - 4$, $g(x) \rightarrow 3x$ in the domain $-5 \le x \le 2, \quad x \in \mathbb{R}$.
Find the coordinates of the points where $f(x) = g(x)$.

Directly proportional graphs

If two quantities are in direct proportion, as one increases, the other increases by the same percentage. For example, if one doubles, the other quantity doubles.

Examples of situations where two values are directly proportional:

- The more hours you work, the more money you earn.
- The more bags of crisps you buy, the more money you will pay.

Characteristics of directly proportional graphs

- The graph is a straight line, which passes through the origin, (0, 0).
- The equation of the line in a directly proportional graph is in the form $y = mx$.

Note: In this case, the slope of the graph, m, can also be known as the constant of proportionality.

EXAMPLE

The graph shows the relationship between the hours that Sally worked babysitting and the money she earned as a result.

Use the graph to find the following.

(i) The amount that Sally will get paid if the parents come home after 2 hours.

(ii) How many hours Sally will have to babysit in order to earn €15.

(iii) The hourly rate that Sally is getting paid.

(iv) Form an equation which represents this relationship.

Solution:

(i) From the graph, 2 hours corresponds to €10.

(ii) From the graph, €15 corresponds to 3 hours.

(iii) From the graph, 1 hour corresponds to €5, so Sally is getting paid €5 per hour.

(iv) Equation of a line: $y = mx + c$

Use the points (0, 0) and (3, 15): $\quad m = \dfrac{y_2 - y_1}{x_2 - x_1} = \dfrac{15 - 0}{3 - 0} = \dfrac{15}{3} = 5$

$c = y\text{-intercept} = 0$

$y = mx + c$

$y = 5x + 0$

$y = 5x$

Exercise 32.1

1. The following graph is used for converting euro into New Zealand dollars. Use the graph to:

   (i) Convert €2 into dollars.

   (ii) Convert $10 into euros.

   (iii) Find the equation which represents this relationship.

   (iv) Explain how you know that the relationship between the euro and the New Zealand dollar is directly proportional.

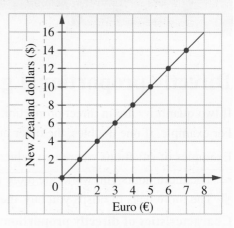

2. The graph shows the relationship between the hours Harry worked doing chores around the house and the money he earned as a result.

   Use the graph to find the following.

   (i) Estimate the amount that Harry will get paid for doing chores for two and a half hours.

   (ii) How many hours will Harry have to work in order to earn €16?

   (iii) Form an equation which represents the relationship between how much Harry earns and the number of hours he works.

   (iv) Harry wants to upgrade his mobile phone. To do this, he needs €60. How many hours will he have to work to earn this amount?

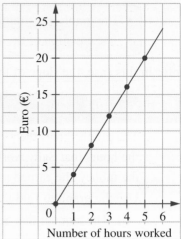

3. The graph shows the relationship between the hours Etta worked at her part-time job and the money she earned as a result.

   Use the graph to answer the following.

   (i) Estimate the amount that Etta will get paid for working a 4-hour shift.

   (ii) How many hours will Etta have to work in order to earn €63?

   (iii) Calculate the hourly rate that Etta is getting paid.

   (iv) Form an equation which represents the relationship between how much Etta earns and the number of hours she works.

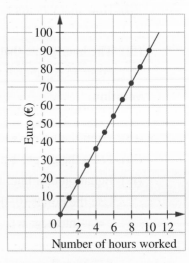

   (v) Etta wants to buy a new games console and needs to save €252. How many hours will she have to work to earn this amount?

4. An average body will burn 60 calories for every kilometre walked. Use this information to complete the following table.

Kilometres	0	1	2	3		5	
Calories	0	60			240		360

    (i) Graph this data, putting kilometres on the *x*-axis and calories on the *y*-axis.

    (ii) Use your graph to estimate how far a person would need to walk in order to burn 210 calories.

    (iii) Find the equation which represents the relationship between the kilometres walked and the calories burned.

    (iv) How far would Niamh need to walk in order to burn 450 calories?

5. On average, Joe's car can travel for 12 km on one litre of petrol. Use this information to complete the following table.

Litres	0	5	10	15	20	25	30
Kilometres	0		120				

    (i) Graph this data, putting litres on the *x*-axis and kilometres on the *y*-axis.

    (ii) Use your graph to estimate how far Joe could drive with 18 litres of petrol.

Joe needs to drive from Dublin to Waterford, a distance of 160 km, and back again.

    (iii) How many litres of petrol will he need in the tank of his car to make the return journey? Give your answer correct to the nearest litre.

    (iv) If a litre of petrol costs €1·52, how much will it cost Joe to make the journey?

6. Ohm's Law is a famous example of a directly proportional relationship. It states that in an electrical circuit, as the voltage increases across a resistor, the current flowing through it increases.

The following table shows the results a student obtained when performing an experiment to prove Ohm's Law.

Current (amps)	0	1	2	3	4	5	6
Voltage (volts)	0	1·5	3	4·5	6	7·5	9

    (i) Graph these results, putting current on the *x*-axis and voltage on the *y*-axis.

    (ii) Explain how we know that the voltage is directly proportional to the current.

    (iii) Use your graph to estimate the voltage value for a current of 4·5 amps.

    (iv) Use your graph to estimate the current value for a voltage of 5·25 volts.

    (v) Find the equation which represents the relationship between voltage and current.

    (vi) Use the equation of the graph to find the current when the voltage is 45 V.

7. Newton's second law states that the acceleration a body undergoes is directly proportional to the force applied to the body. A student performed an experiment in which she applied a variety of forces to an object and recorded its resulting acceleration in each case.

The results she obtained are as follows.

Acceleration (m/s²)	1	2	3	4	5	6
Force (N)	2·5	5	7·5	10	12·5	15

   (i) Graph these results, putting acceleration on the x-axis and force on the y-axis.

  (ii) Explain how we know that the acceleration is directly proportional to the force.

 (iii) Use your graph to find the force when the acceleration is 4 m/s².

 (iv) Use your graph to estimate the acceleration when a force of 6 N is applied.

  (v) Find the equation which represents the relationship between force and acceleration.

 (vi) In this experiment, the constant of proportionality (i.e. the slope of the line) represents the mass of the moving body. What is the mass of the body?

(vii) Use the equation of the graph to find the acceleration of the body when the applied force is 40 N.

8. This graph shows the conversion between centimetres and inches.

   (i) What is 13 cm in inches?

  (ii) What is 3 inches in cm?

 (iii) Find an equation which represents this relationship.

 (iv) A foot is 12 inches. Use the graph to estimate how many cm are in a foot.

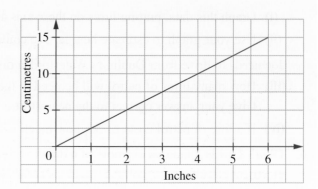

Proportional graphs

In exercise 32.2, the graphs do not begin at the origin.

Exercise 32.2

1. A cold object is placed in a warm room.
    Its temperature °C after time t minutes is
    shown in the graph.

    (i) After what time interval is the
        temperature 9°C?

    (ii) What is the temperature of the
        object at the beginning ($t = 0$)?

    (iii) What is the rise in temperature
        per minute?

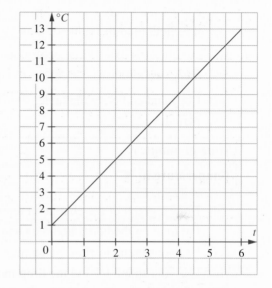

2. Jane receives a gift of a money box with €5 in it for her birthday. Jane decides she will
    save a further €2 a week for each week after her birthday.

    (i) How much money will Jane have in her money box 10 weeks after her birthday?

    (ii) Copy and complete the following table.

Number of weeks after Jane's birthday	0	1	2	3	4	5
Amount of money in € in Jane's money box	5				13	

    (iii) Using the completed table, draw a graph of the amount of money in Jane's money box
        for five weeks after her birthday. Put the number of weeks on the horizontal axis and
        the amount of money on the vertical axis.

    (iv) Jane wants to buy a new mobile phone, which will cost €75. How many weeks will
        it take for her to have enough money in her money box to buy this phone?

3. A taxi company charges as follows for a taxi journey:
    €4 for hiring the taxi plus €3 for each kilometre travelled.

    (i) William hired a taxi from this company and travelled 4 kilometres.
        Copy and complete the following table.

Distance in km	0	1	2	3	4
Cost in euro	4		10		

(ii) Draw a graph of the cost of William's journey. Put the distance on the horizontal axis and the cost on the vertical axis.

(iii) Use your graph to find out how far William could travel if he only had €11·50.

(iv) The cost of hiring a taxi from this company is given by the equation
$c = a + bk$, where c is the cost in euros and k is the number of kilometres travelled. Find the value of a and the value of b.

4. A warm object is placed in a cool room. Its initial temperature is 35°C and it drops by 5°C every two minutes.

(i) Copy and complete the table, showing the change in temperature over a 12-minute period.

Time in minutes	0	2	4	6	8	10	12
Temperature in °C			25				

(ii) Draw a graph of the change in temperature of the object over this 12-minute period. Put time on the horizontal axis and temperature on the vertical axis.

(iii) Use your graph to find the temperature of the object after 9 minutes.

(iv) Use your graph to find the drop in temperature in the first 8 minutes.

5. A pink plant measured 6 cm high at the beginning of a week and grew 3 cm each week afterwards.
A green plant measured 2 cm high at the beginning of a week and grew 4 cm each week afterwards.

(i) Calculate the heights of each plant for the first five weeks and plot your results on a graph.

(ii) After five weeks, which plant will be the tallest? Justify your answer.

(iii) Will the plants ever be the exact same height? If the answer is yes, when will they be the same height?

Distance-time graphs

Distance-time graphs are used to illustrate a journey. Always represent time on the horizontal axis (x-axis) and distance on the vertical axis (y-axis).

To find the speed of any part of the journey, we find the slope of the line segment representing that part of the journey.

On a distance-time graph:

Line going up (positive slope) — moving further away from where we started

Line horizontal (zero slope) — stopped

Line going down (negative slope) — moving back towards where we started

The **steeper** the slope, the **faster** the speed.

The **less steep** the slope, the **slower** the speed.

The distance-time graph below represents the journey of a bus leaving a terminus and returning there later.

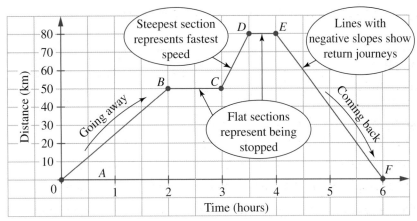

Section AB: The bus left the terminus and travelled 50 km in 2 hours.

$$\text{Speed} = \frac{\text{Distance}}{\text{Time}} = \frac{50}{2} = 25 \text{ km/h}$$

Section BC: The bus stopped for 1 hour.

$$\text{Speed} = \frac{\text{Distance}}{\text{Time}} = \frac{0}{1} = 0 \text{ km/h}$$

Section CD: The bus travelled 30 km in half an hour.

$$\text{Speed} = \frac{\text{Distance}}{\text{Time}} = \frac{30}{0\cdot5} = 60 \text{ km/h}$$

Section DE: The bus stopped for half an hour.

$$\text{Speed} = \frac{\text{Distance}}{\text{Time}} = \frac{0}{0\cdot5} = 0 \text{ km/h}$$

Section EF: The bus travelled 80 km in 2 hours (return journey).

$$\text{Speed} = \frac{\text{Distance}}{\text{Time}} = \frac{80}{2} = 40 \text{ km/h}$$

Notes: 1. By looking at the vertical axis, distance, the total distance travelled = 80 km + 80 km = 160 km.

2. By looking at the horizontal axis, time, the total time was 6 hours.

3. The points A and F represent the same position (in this case, the terminus).

Exercise 32.3

1. The graph shows Fintan's journey between the towns of Ardee and Monaghan.

   (i) How far did Fintan travel in the first two hours?

   (ii) For how many minutes did Fintan stop during the journey?

   (iii) Calculate Fintan's speed for the last part of his journey.

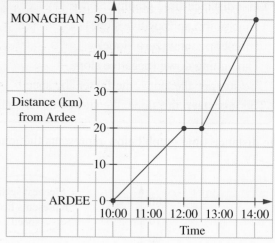

2. The graph shows the distance travelled by a bus and also the time taken on a completed journey.

   Distance, in kilometres, is shown on the vertical axis. The time of day is shown on the horizontal axis.

   For example, at 12:00 hours the bus had travelled zero kilometres, but at 13:00 hours it had travelled 20 kilometres.

   (i) What distance did the bus travel between 13:00 and 13:30?

   (ii) At what time was the bus 40 km from the start?

   (iii) What distance did the bus travel between 13:30 and 15:00?

   (iv) Calculate the average speed of the bus between 13:30 and 15:00.

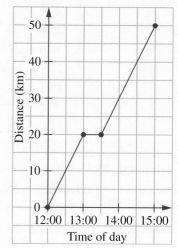

3. Tom was travelling in his car to meet his friend. He set off from home at 08:00 and stopped on the way for a break. This distance-time graph illustrates his journey.

   (i) At what time did he:
      (a) Stop for his break   (b) Set off after his break
      (c) Get to his meeting place

   (ii) At what average speed was he travelling:
      (a) Over the first hour   (b) Over the last hour
      (c) For the whole of his journey, including when he stopped

   (iii) Tom was 10 minutes late arriving. If he had stopped for half as long, would he have been on time?

4. Deirdre cycles to the post office to post a small parcel. On her journey to the post office she stops at a traffic light. When the light goes green she continues her journey, arrives at the post office and posts her parcel. She then returns home.

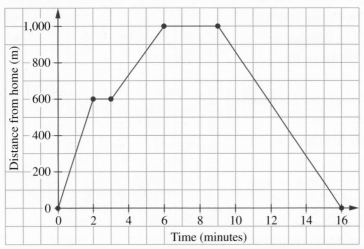

The distance-time graph shows Deirdre's journey.

   (i) How far is the post office from Deirdre's home?

   (ii) Calculate her average speed (in m/s) from her home to the traffic light.

   (iii) For how long does she stop at the post office?

   (iv) How far does she cycle altogether?

   (v) Calculate her average speed (in m/min) for the entire journey, including stopping.

5.

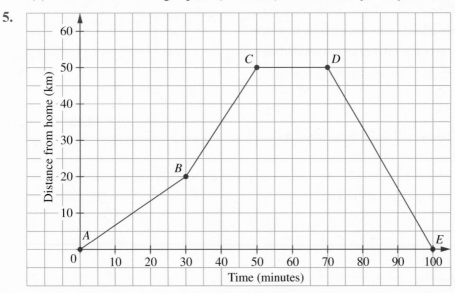

Cathy travelled by car to visit her grandparents. The graph represents her journey.

   (i) How far did she travel in the first 30 minutes?

   (ii) How long did she stay at her grandparents' house?

   (iii) What does section DE of the graph represent?

6. Alan, a salesman, leaves home at 09:00 and returns at 15:00. The distance he travels from home is shown on this graph.

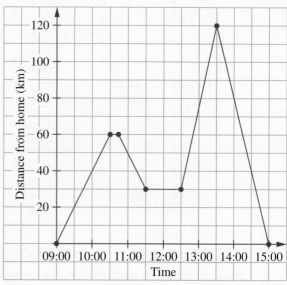

   (i) Calculate his average speed between 09:00 and 10:30.

   (ii) Calculate how far Alan travels during the day.

   (iii) Explain what Alan might have done between 11:30 and 12:30.

   (iv) How many times during the day does he travel towards his home?

   (v) Find his average speed for the whole day (including stopping).

7. Tim was waiting at a bus stop and he saw the bus 800 m away. The distance-time graph shows its journey.

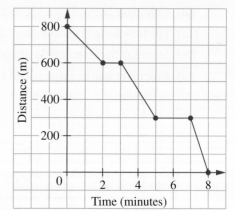

   (i) How many times does the bus stop before it reaches Tim?

   (ii) How long does it take to reach its first stop?

   (iii) How far apart are the first and second stops?

   (iv) How long does it spend at its first stop?

8. The distance-time graph shows the distance from the starting position of a swimmer who completed a race in a swimming pool.

    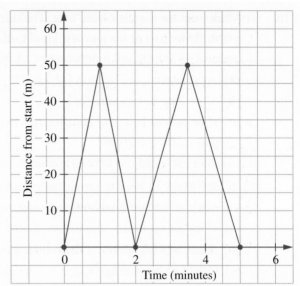

    (i)   What is the length of the pool?
    (ii) How many lengths of the pool is the race?
    (iii) What is the distance of the race?
    (iv) How long did the swimmer take to complete the race?
    (v)   Calculate the average speed of the swimmer, for the entire race, in m/s. Give your answer correct to two decimal places.

9. The distance-time graph shows the movement of a rabbit from its burrow.

    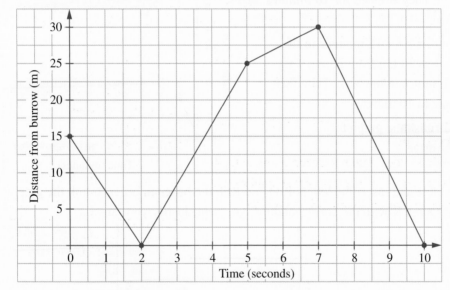

    (i)   Did the rabbit begin its journey from its burrow? Justify your answer.
    (ii) Did the rabbit rest at any point during its journey? Justify your answer.
    (iii) How often did the rabbit visit its burrow?
    (iv) What was the rabbit's speed during the **(a)** first two seconds **(b)** final second?
    (v)   What was the rabbit's average speed during the entire journey?

10. **(i)** Mark went for a cycle on his bike. The distance-time graph shows part of his journey. He set off from his home at 11:00. He got a puncture at 13:00.

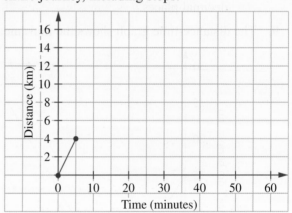

(a) At what time did he stop for a rest?

(b) How long did he stop for?

(c) How far did he travel after his rest before getting the puncture?

(d) At what speed did Mark travel after his rest?

(ii) It took Mark an hour to repair the puncture and then he cycled home without stopping, to arrive at 15:00.

(a) Copy and complete the distance-time graph to show this information.

(b) What was his speed on the return journey?

(c) Calculate his average speed for the entire journey, including stops.

11. Lucy and her mother took 5 minutes to drive 4 km. They stopped for 10 minutes to buy food.

They then drove for 15 minutes to the park, which is 14 km from home. They spent 20 minutes in the park. They then drove home in 10 minutes.

Copy and finish the graph to show their drive.

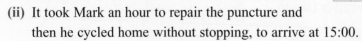

12. Copy the table and insert the letters P, Q and R in the boxes in order to link the graphs marked P, Q and R with the corresponding statement. Justify your answers.

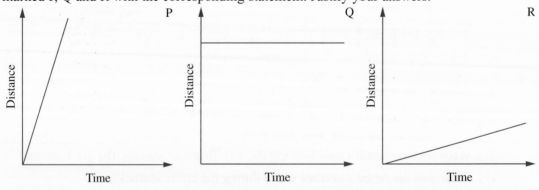

Statement	Slow average speed	Fast average speed	Not moving
Graph			

13. Emma entered a competition. It involved a race with three sections: running, cycling and swimming. The distance-time graph shows Emma's race.

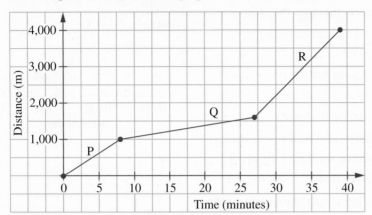

Identify the part of the graph which shows her:

(i) Running **(ii)** Cycling **(iii)** swimming.

Justify your answers.

14. Sinéad and her brother Cathal leave their home in Portlaoise at the same time. Sinéad drives her car but stops on the way to do some shopping. Cathal cycles, without stopping, on the same road as Sinéad. Sinéad and Cathal reach Dublin at the same time.

  (i) How far is it from their home to Dublin?

 (ii) For how long does Sinéad stop?

(iii) How far from Dublin is the shop?

(iv) Estimate the time when Cathal passes Sinéad, correct to the nearest minute.

  (v) At what speed does:

    (a) Cathal cycle?

    (b) Sinéad drive to the shop?

    (c) Sinéad drive from the shop to Dublin?

(vi) How far apart are Cathal and Sinéad at 12:00?

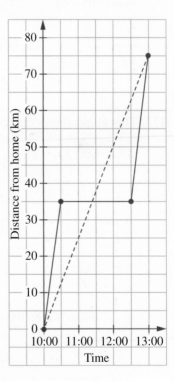

15. Larry sets off from Wicklow at 09:00 and travels to a town 150 km away to meet his girlfriend, Aoife. He stops for a rest on the way. Once he gets to Aoife's, he turns around and drives straight home because he discovers that Aoife set off for Wicklow some time ago to see Larry.

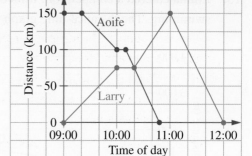

   (i) Describe Larry's journey in detail.

   (ii) Describe Aoife's journey in detail.

   (iii) At what time did Larry and Aoife pass each other and what distance were they from Wicklow when it happened?

16. James had a bath. The graph shows the height of the water over a 28-minute period.

   At A, James turned on both hot and cold taps.

   Between A and B the height of the water rose by 20 cm in 4 minutes.

   Describe what happened on the sections BC, CD, DE, EF, FG and GH.

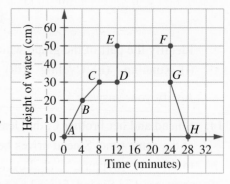

17. This graph shows the temperature of the water in a domestic hot water tank.

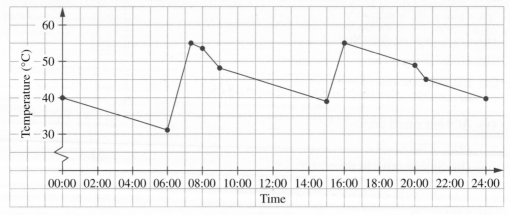

   (i) What was the water temperature at 10 p.m.?

   (ii) At what times was the temperature 35°C?

   (iii) The water heater switched on at 6 a.m. When did it turn off again?

   (iv) What was the rise in temperature when the water heater switched on in the afternoon?

   (v) For how long was the water heater switched on during the morning and afternoon?

18. Cans of drink can be bought from a vending machine in the school canteen. The graph shows the number of cans in the machine between 10:00 and 15:00 one day.

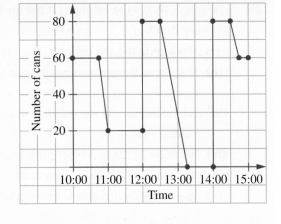

    (i) At 10:00 the machine is three-quarters full. How many cans does the machine hold when it is full?

    (ii) How many drinks were sold between 10:45 and 11:00?

    (iii) The machine was filled up twice during the day. At what times was the machine filled up?

    (iv) Between what times was the machine empty?

    (v) How many cans of drink were sold altogether between 10:00 and 15:00?

19. The graph shows the temperature on a certain day.

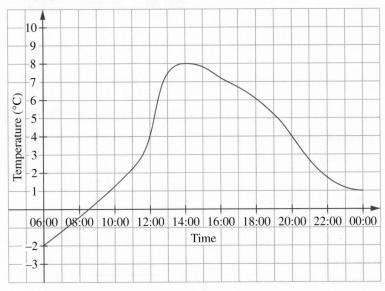

    (i) At what time did the temperature first go above freezing point (0°C)?

    (ii) What was the maximum temperature?

    (iii) For how many hours was the temperature above 6°C?

20. The graph shows the height of a hot air balloon during a morning flight.

   (i) What time did the balloon take off?

   (ii) What was the greatest height that the balloon reached?

   (iii) For how long did the balloon stay at its maximum height?

   (iv) Between 11:00 and 11:15, how many metres per minute did the balloon descend?

   (v) How long did the whole flight last?

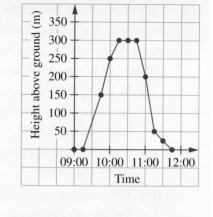

21. A chimpanzee escapes from a zoo.

   (i) At what time did the chimpanzee escape?

   (ii) At what time did the search party set off?

   (iii) How far from the zoo was the chimpanzee at this time?

   (iv) At what time was the chimpanzee recaptured?

   (v) How far from the zoo was the chimpanzee when it was recaptured?

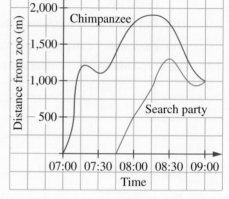

22. Grandad planted a tree when he was young and measured it every 10 years.

   (i) How tall was the tree in 1980?

   (ii) What happened during the 1980s?

   (iii) Use your line graph to find when the tree was exactly 12 m tall.

   (iv) What was the height of the tree in 2005?

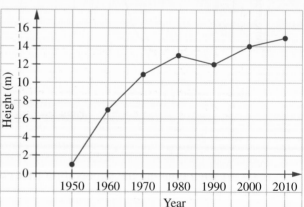

Quadratic graphs

 EXAMPLE

The depth of water in a harbour after t hours is given by $h = t^2 - 6t + 11$ where h is in metres.

(i) Draw the graph of the function $h = t^2 - 4t + 6$ in the domain $0 \le t \le 6$, where $t \in \mathbb{R}$.

(ii) Use your graph to find:

(a) The lowest depth of the water in the harbour and after how many hours this occurs.

(b) After how many hours the depth of the water was 6 m.

Solution:

(i) **Draw the graph of the function $h = t^2 - 4t + 6$ in the domain $0 \le t \le 6$, where $t \in \mathbb{R}$.**

t	$t^2 - 6t + 11$	h
0	$0 - 0 + 11$	11
1	$1 - 6 + 11$	6
2	$4 - 12 + 11$	3
3	$9 - 18 + 11$	2
4	$16 - 24 + 11$	3
5	$25 - 30 + 11$	6
6	$36 - 36 + 11$	11

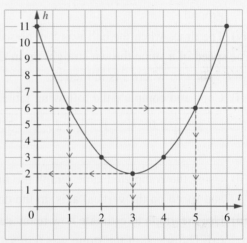

Note: If we are given the time, we are required to find the depth.

If we are given the depth, we are required to find the time.

(ii) **The lowest depth of the water in the harbour and after how many hours this occurs.** From the lowest point on the graph, draw a broken horizontal line to meet the depth axis.

This line meets the depth axis at 2.

Thus, the lowest depth of the water in the harbour is 2 m.

From the lowest point on the graph, draw a broken vertical line to meet the time axis.

This line meets the time axis at 3.

Thus, the lowest depth of 2 m occurs after 3 hours.

(iii) **After how many hours the depth of the water was 6 m.**

From 6 on the depth axis, draw a broken horizontal line to meet the curve at two places. Where this line meets the curve, draw broken perpendicular lines to meet the time axis. These lines meet the time axis at 1 and 5.

Thus, the depth of water was 6 m after 1 hour and 5 hours.

Exercise 32.4

1. The graph represents the flight of a ball kicked on level ground. The height in metres is shown on the vertical axis and the time in seconds is shown on the horizontal axis, where $h = 6t - t^2$ and $t \in \mathbb{R}$.

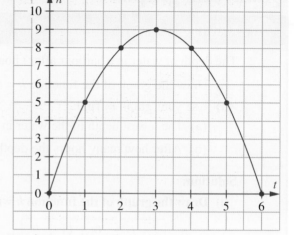

   Use the graph to find:
   - **(i)** The greatest height reached by the ball
   - **(ii)** The time taken to reach this height
   - **(iii)** The time taken for the ball to hit the ground
   - **(iv)** The times when the ball was 8 m above the ground

2. The speed of a stone thrown straight up in the air after t seconds is given by $s = t^2 - 6t + 9$, where s is in metres.
   - **(i)** Copy and complete the following table.

s	0	1	2	3	4	5	6
t		4					9

   - **(ii)** Using the completed table, graph the function with time on the horizontal axis and speed on the vertical axis, in the domain $0 \le t \le 6$, when $t \in \mathbb{R}$.
   - **(iii)** Use the graph to estimate how many seconds after the throw:
     - **(a)** The speed of the stone was 6 m/s   **(b)** The stone began to fall back down

3. A car starts from rest at the point A.

   The distance of the car from A after t seconds is given by $d = t^2 + t$, where d is in metres.
   - **(i)** Find the distance of the car from A after 3 seconds.
   - **(ii)** Copy and complete the following table.

t	0	1	2	3	4	5
d		2				

   - **(iii)** Graph the function of distance against time for the first 5 seconds, where $t \in \mathbb{R}$.
   - **(iv)** The distance from A to B is 16 m. Use your graph to estimate the time taken for the car to reach B.

4. A car begins to slow down at A in order to stop at a red traffic light at B.

The speed of the car after passing A is given by $s = t^2 - 10t + 25$, where t is in seconds and s is in metres per seconds.

(i) Find the speed of the car after 2 seconds.

(ii) Complete the following table.

t	0	1	2	3	4	5
s						

(iii) Graph the function of speed against time for the first 5 seconds, where $t \in \mathbb{R}$.

(iv) Use your graph to estimate speed of the car after 3·5 seconds.

5. Draw the graph of the function $f: x \to x^2 - 8x + 12$ in the domain $0 \le x \le 5$.

Let the graph represent a science experiment that lowers the temperature of an object from room temperature to below freezing over a period of five hours.

The time, in hours, is shown on the x-axis.

The temperature at any given time (in degrees Celsius) is shown on the y-axis.

Use the graph to:

(i) Find room temperature at the start of the experiment

(ii) Find the temperature of the object after $1\frac{1}{2}$ hours

(iii) Find the time taken for the temperature of the object to fall to freezing point

(iv) Find the time taken for the temperature of the object to be at its lowest

(v) Find the lowest temperature reached by the object in the experiment

6. The speed of the wind in a village after t hours is given by $s = t^2 - 5t + 8$, where s is in kilometres per hour.

   (i) Copy and complete the following table.

s	0	1	2	3	4	5
t				2		

   (ii) $t = 0$ means 12:00, $t = 1$ means 13:00, $t = 2$ means 14:00, etc.
   $s = 0$ means 0 km/h, $s = 1$ means 10 km/h, $s = 2$ means 20 km/h, etc.
   Using the completed table, graph the function with time on the horizontal axis and speed on the vertical axis, in the domain $0 \le t \le 5$, where $t \in \mathbb{R}$.

   (iii) Use your graph to estimate:
   (a) The times when the wind speed was 33 km/h
   (b) The speed of the wind at 16:45
   (c) The time when the wind speed was at its lowest

7. Draw the graph of the function $f: x \rightarrow 4 + x^2$ in the domain $-2 \le x \le 2$, $x \in \mathbb{R}$.
   Assume the graph shows the time of sunset from October until February.
   Take -2 on the x-axis to be 1 October.
   Take -1 on the x-axis to be 1 November, etc.
   On the other axis, take 4 to be 16:00, 5 to be 17:00, etc.
   Using the graph, estimate:
   (i) The time of sunset in mid-December
   (ii) The months in which sunset occurs at 18:30

Patterns

Much of mathematics is about patterns. Some are simple and numeric:

$$2, 4, 6, 8, 10, \ldots \qquad \frac{1}{2}, \frac{2}{3}, \frac{3}{4}, \frac{4}{5}, \ldots \qquad 10, 21, 32, 43, 54, \ldots$$

You should be able to write down the next three numbers in the list. You may even be able to predict the 10th number in the list *without* having to write out all the terms.

Even if you see a pattern and can write out the next number, it is much more difficult to predict what the 20th number or the 100th number in the list would be. If those numbers represented the population of the planet or the number of cancerous cells in a patient, then it would be very important to be able to predict future values.

Not all patterns are numeric. For example:

Is it possible to predict the number of green discs in the 10th diagram?

EXAMPLE 1

A pattern of repeating coloured blocks is shown.
What is the colour of the 25th block?

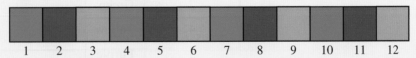

Solution:

The pattern repeats every three tiles. To find the colour of the 25th block, we need to find how many groups of three to skip over.

$25 \div 3 = 8\frac{1}{3}$. This tells us that we can skip over 8 groups or $8 \times 3 = 24$ blocks.

After 24 blocks, we are at the beginning of the sequence, so the colour of the 25th block is green.

EXAMPLE 2

A repeating pattern consists of blocks coloured yellow, purple, green, yellow, . . . and so on.

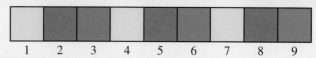

1	2	3	4	5	6	7	8	9

(i) Complete the table.

Block position	Colour
1	Yellow
2	
	Green
⋮	⋮

(ii) List the positions of the first three yellow blocks. Is there a pattern?

(iii) List the positions of the first three purple blocks. Is there a pattern?

(iv) List the positions of the first three green blocks. Is there a pattern?

(v) What is the colour of the 48th block?

(vi) What is the colour of the 50th block?

(vii) What is the colour of the 100th block?

Solution:

(i) The completed table:

Block position	Colour
1	Yellow
2	Purple
3	Green
4	Yellow
5	Purple
6	Green
7	Yellow
8	Purple
9	Green

(ii) Yellow blocks: 1, 4, 7, . . .

Yes. Starting with 1 and adding 3 each time, the other positions can be found.

(iii) Purple blocks: 2, 5, 8, . . .

Yes. Starting with 2 and adding 3 each time, the other positions can be found.

(iv) Green blocks: 3, 6, 9, . . .

Yes. Starting with 3 and adding 3 each time, the other positions can be found. Alternatively, the positions are multiples of 3, so the first green is at position $3 \times 1 = 3$, the second green is at position $3 \times 2 = 6$, the third green is at position $3 \times 3 = 9$ and so on.

(v) The colour of the 48th block:

As 48 is a multiple of 3 (48 can be divided exactly by 3), it must be a green block.

(vi) The colour of the 50th block:

Since the 48th block is green, the 50th must be purple.

(vii) The colour of the 100th block:

Using a calculator, 100 is not a multiple of 3 (it divides in just over 33 times). $3 \times 33 = 99$, which <u>is</u> a multiple of 3. So the 99th block must be green. The 100th block is therefore yellow.

Exercise 33.1

1. A repeating pattern consists of blocks coloured green, yellow, green, yellow, . . . and so on.

| | 1 | 2 | 3 | 4 | 5 | 6 | 7 | 8 | ... |

(i) Complete the table.

Block position	Colour
1	Green
2	
⋮	⋮

(ii) List the positions of the first three green blocks. Is there a pattern?

(iii) List the positions of the first three yellow blocks. Is there a pattern?

(iv) What is the colour of the 20th block?

(v) What is the colour of the 33rd block?

(vi) What is the colour of the 1,001st block?

2. A repeating pattern consists of blocks coloured red, white, blue, red, . . . and so on.

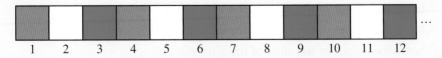

| | 1 | 2 | 3 | 4 | 5 | 6 | 7 | 8 | 9 | 10 | 11 | 12 | ... |

(i) List the positions of the first three red blocks. Is there a pattern?

(ii) List the positions of the first three white blocks. Is there a pattern?

(iii) List the positions of the first three blue blocks. Is there a pattern?

(iv) What is the colour of the 48th block?

(v) What is the colour of the 50th block?

(vi) What is the colour of the 100th block?

3. A collection of racing cars is lined up in the following repeating sequence.

    ...

(i) List the positions of the first three yellow racing cars.

(ii) List the positions of the first three blue racing cars.

(iii) List the positions of the first three silver racing cars.

(iv) What is the colour of the 10th racing car?

(v) What is the colour of the 17th racing car?

(vi) Where in the line-up is the 5th silver racing car?

(vii) Where in the line-up is the 8th yellow racing car?

4. A pattern of symbols is as follows.

(i) Explain why this pattern does not repeat every two symbols.

(ii) List the positions of the ♡ symbols. Describe the type of numbers in your list.

(iii) List the positions of the ⊙ symbols. Is there a pattern?

(iv) Is there a ⊙ symbol at position 50 in the list? Explain your answer.

(v) Find the symbol which appears at position **(a)** 16   **(b)** 21   **(c)** 31   **(d)** 99.

5. As part of the opening ceremony of a hockey competition, the hockey players parade in the following repeating sequence.

(i) List the positions of the first three players in each colour.

(ii) What is the colour of the shirt of the 12th player?

(iii) What is the colour of the shirt of the 22nd player?

(iv) What is the colour of the shirt of the 23rd player?

(v) Where in the line-up is the 8th player with a green shirt?

(vi) Where in the line-up is the 10th player with a yellow shirt?

Sequences

> A **sequence** is a set of numbers, separated by commas, in which each number after the first is formed by some definite rule.

3, 7, 11, 15, . . .
Each number after the first is obtained by adding 4 to the previous number. In this example, 3 is called the **first term**, 7 is the **second term** and so on.

1, 3, 9, 27, . . .
Each number after the first is obtained by multiplying the previous number by 3. In this example, 1 is called the **first term**, 3 is the **second term** and so on.

Linear sequences

If a sequence of numbers is formed by adding the same amount to any term to get the next term, then it is a **linear sequence**. For example, the sequence

$$2, 5, 8, 11, 14, . . .$$

is formed by starting with 2 and then adding 3 each time to get the other terms.

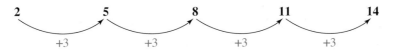

The **common difference** is +3. The **term-to-term** rule for this sequence is to add 3.

The sequence

$$7, 5, 3, 1, . . .$$

starts with 7 and the other terms are found by subtracting 2 each time.

The common difference is −2 and the term-to-term rule for this sequence is to subtract 2.

These types of sequences are called linear because when the terms are graphed, the sequence forms a **line**.

Note: To find the common difference, we subtract 'backwards'. The gap from 2 to 5 is 5 − 2 = 3.

EXAMPLE

(i) Find the next three terms of the sequence 2, 6, 10, 14, ...

(ii) Describe the sequence in words.

(iii) Is this a linear sequence? Explain.

Solution:

(i) By subtracting terms, there is a constant gap of +4.

Thus, the next three terms are

14 + 4 = 18,   18 + 4 = 22   and   22 + 4 = 26.

(ii) The sequence begins with 2 and the other terms are found by adding 4 each time.

(iii) It **is** a linear sequence because there is a common difference (of +4).

Exercise 33.2

In questions 1–10, write down the next four terms and describe the sequence in words.

1. 2, 4, 6, 8, . . .
2. 1, 4, 7, 10, . . .
3. 1, 5, 9, 13, . . .
4. 40, 35, 30, 25, . . .
5. 10, 9, 8, 7, . . .
6. 3, 6, 9, 12, . . .
7. −11, −9, −7, −5, . . .
8. 13, 10, 7, 4, . . .
9. 2·5, 2·9, 3·3, 3·7, . . .
10. 2·8, 2·2, 1·6, 1, . . .

In questions 11–20, write down the first four terms of the sequence described in words.

11. Start with 2, add 3 each time
12. Start with 1, add 4 each time
13. Start with 10, add 5 each time
14. Start with 5, add 2 each time
15. Start with 12, subtract 3 each time
16. Start with 18, subtract 2 each time
17. Start with 41, add 7 each time
18. Start with 36, add 8 each time
19. Start with 87, subtract 9 each time
20. Start with 54, subtract 11 each time

21. Joe is making a series of patterns from matchsticks.

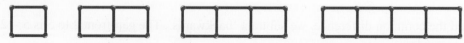

(i) Write down the number of matchsticks used in each of the first four patterns.

(ii) Is this a linear sequence? Explain.

(iii) Calculate the number of matchsticks needed in the 6th pattern.

22. Fergal has some coloured L-shaped tiles 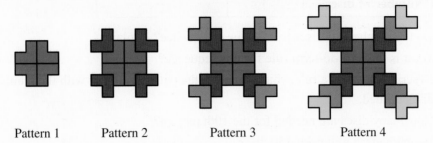 which he uses to make a set of patterns.

Pattern 1   Pattern 2   Pattern 3   Pattern 4

  (i) Write down the number of tiles used in each of the first four patterns.
 (ii) Is this a linear sequence? Explain.
(iii) What is the term-to-term rule for this sequence?
 (iv) What is the connection between the pattern number and the amount of tiles used?
  (v) Calculate the number of matchsticks needed in the sixth pattern.
 (vi) Which pattern will need 40 tiles?

23. Olivia makes a sequence of patterns using gold and purple triangular tiles.

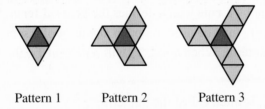

Pattern 1   Pattern 2   Pattern 3

  (i) Write down the number of gold tiles used in each of the first three patterns.
 (ii) Is this a linear sequence? Explain.
(iii) What is the term-to-term rule for this sequence?
 (iv) Write out the total number of tiles used in each of the first three patterns.
      Is this a linear sequence? If so, what is the term-to-term rule for this sequence?
  (v) How many tiles are needed in total for the 6th pattern?
 (vi) Which pattern will need a total of 52 tiles?

24. Elliot is making a series of triangles using green discs.

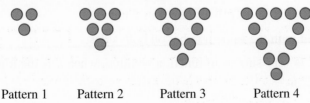

Pattern 1   Pattern 2   Pattern 3   Pattern 4

(i) Copy and complete the following table.

Pattern	1	2	3	4
Number of discs	3			

(ii) Do the numbers of discs form a linear sequence? Explain.

(iii) What is the term-to-term rule for this sequence?

(iv) Describe in words a rule which connects the pattern number with the number of green discs needed.

(v) How many discs are needed for the 10th pattern?

(vi) Which pattern will need 150 discs?

Sequence defined by a formula

Each number in a sequence is a **term** of that sequence. The first number is the **first term** and is denoted by T_1. Similarly, the second term is denoted by T_2 and so on.

Very often a sequence is given by a **rule** which defines the **general term**. We use T_n to denote the general term of the sequence. T_n may be used to obtain any term of a sequence. When $n = 1$, T_n will represent T_1, which is the first term. When $n = 2$, T_n will represent T_2, the second term, and so on.

Notes:

1. The general term, T_n, is often called the nth term.
2. n used with this meaning must always be positive, a whole number.
   It can never be fractional or negative.

Consider the sequence whose general term is $T_n = 3n + 2$.

We can find the value of any term of the sequence by putting in the appropriate value for n on both sides.

$T_n = 3n + 2$
$T_1 = 3(1) + 2 = 3 + 2 = 5$ (first term, put in 1 for n)
$T_2 = 3(2) + 2 = 6 + 2 = 8$ (second term, put in 2 for n)
$T_5 = 3(5) + 2 = 15 + 2 = 17$ (fifth term, put in 5 for n)

In each case, n is replaced with the same number on both sides.

The notation $T_n = 3n + 2$ is very similar to function notation, when n is the input and T_n is the output, i.e. (input, output) $= (n, T_n)$.

EXAMPLE

The nth term of a sequence is given by $T_n = n^2 + 3$.

(i) Write down the first three terms of the sequence.

(ii) Show that   (a) $\dfrac{T_5}{T_2} = T_1$ (b) $2T_4 = T_6 - 1$.

Solution:

(i) $T_n = n^2 + 3$

$T_1 = 1^2 + 3 = 1 + 3 = 4$ (put in 1 for n)

$T_2 = 2^2 + 3 = 4 + 3 = 7$ (put in 2 for n)

$T_3 = 3^2 + 3 = 9 + 3 = 12$ (put in 3 for n)

Thus, the first three terms are 4, 7, 12.

(ii) (a) From (i), $T_1 = 4$ and $T_2 = 7$.

$T_5 = 5^2 + 3 = 25 + 3 = 28$

LHS	RHS
$\dfrac{T_5}{T_2} = \dfrac{28}{7}$	$T_1 = 4$
$= 4$	

$\therefore \dfrac{T_5}{T_2} = T_1$

(b) $T_4 = 4^2 + 3 = 16 + 3 = 19$

$T_6 = 6^2 + 3 = 36 + 3 = 39$

LHS	RHS
$2T_4 = 2(19)$	$T_6 - 1 = 39 - 1$
$= 38$	$= 38$

$\therefore 2T_4 = T_6 - 1$

Exercise 33.3

In questions 1–12, write down the first four terms of the sequence defined by the given nth term and say whether it is a linear sequence or not.

1. $T_n = 2n + 3$

2. $T_n = 3n + 1$

3. $T_n = 4n - 1$

4. $T_n = 5n - 3$

5. $T_n = 1 - 2n$

6. $T_n = 3 - 4n$

7. $T_n = n^2 + 5$

8. $T_n = n^2 + 2n$

9. $T_n = \dfrac{n + 1}{n}$

10. $T_n = \dfrac{2n}{n + 1}$

11. $T_n = 2^n$

12. $T_n = 3^n$

13. (i) Write out the first four terms of the sequence defined by $T_n = 3n - 1$.

    (ii) Show that $T_2 + T_4 = 2T_6$.

14. (i) Write out the first four terms of the sequence defined by $T_n = 5n + 4$.

    (ii) Show that $2T_3 - T_4 = T_2$.

Viewing the sequence as a graph

The patterns we look for are based on the relationship between two sets of values – the positions in a sequence and the values or terms in the sequence.

For example, the sequence

$$1, 3, 5, 7, 9, \ldots$$

can be represented in this table:

Position	1	2	3	4	5
Terms	1	3	5	7	9

We can interpret the pairs (position, term) as points and plot (1, 1), (2, 3), (3, 5), (4, 7) and (5, 9).

The graph shows a line.

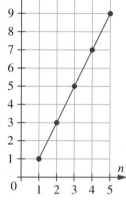

Note: The first four letters of the word **'linear'** spell line. A graph is linear if all the points can be joined by one straight line.

Exercise 33.4

In questions 1–8, find the first five terms and show your results on a graph. State whether the graph is linear or not. Put the position along the horizontal axis.

1. $T_n = 2n$
2. $T_n = 3n - 1$
3. $T_n = 4n + 1$
4. $T_n = n^2$
5. $T_n = n^2 - n$
6. $T_n = n(n + 2)$
7. $T_n = 2^n$
8. $T_n = n^3 - n^2$

9. (i) Find the first four terms in the sequence defined by $T_n = 2n + 3$.
   (ii) By forming pairs of the form (position, term), plot the sequence on a graph.

10. (i) Find the first four terms in the sequence defined by $T_n = 3n - 2$.
    (ii) By forming pairs of the form (position, term), plot the sequence on a graph.

11. John receives a gift of a money box with €4 in it for his birthday. John decides he will save a further €2 a day each day after his birthday.

    (i) Draw a table showing the amount of money John saves for the first five days (his birthday being the first day).
    (ii) Draw a graph using points on the form (day, money).
    (iii) How much money will John have in his money box on the **(a)** 10th **(b)** 25th day?
    (iv) By looking at the pattern in this question, can you explain why the amount of money John has on day 10 is not twice the amount he has on day 5?
    (v) How much money does John have in his money box on day 100?

(vi) How much money has John actually put in his money box after 10 days? Explain how you arrived at this amount.

(vii) John wants to buy a new computer game. The game costs €39·99. What is the minimum number of days John will have to save so that he has enough money to buy the computer game?

12. Owen has a money box. He starts with €1 and adds €3 each day.

(i) Draw a table showing the amount of money Owen has for the first 10 days.

(ii) Draw a graph to show the amount of money Owen has saved over 10 days. Put the number of days along the horizontal axis.

(iii) Why will the scale for the number of days be different to the scale for the amount of money?

13. Amy and Bill are discussing phone network offers. Bill says that on his network he begins each month with 30 free texts and receives three additional free texts each night. Amy says that she gets no free texts at the beginning of the month but that she receives five free texts each night.

(i) Draw a table showing the starting number of texts and the number of texts available for the first six days.

Day	Amy's texts	Bill's texts
Start (1)	0	30
Day 2	5	33
⋮		
Day 6		

(ii) Who has the most free texts after six days?

(iii) Using graph paper, draw a graph showing the number of texts for both Amy and Bill for the first 20 days. You should allow the vertical axis to reach 150 texts.

(iv) Are the two graphs linear or something else?

(v) At what point does Amy seem to have a better offer than Bill?

(vi) Will Amy and Bill ever have the same number of texts on a particular day? If so, which day? If not, why not?

14. Lenny begins the month with 20 free texts and receives two additional free texts each night. Jane does not have any free texts at the beginning of the month but receives three free texts each night.

(i) Draw a table showing the number of free texts for both Lenny and Jane for the first 10 days.

(ii) Represent both sets of results on a graph.

(iii) Will Lenny and Jane ever have the same number of free texts on a certain day? If so, which day? If not, why not?

(iv) Who in your opinion has the better deal for free texts each month? Give a reason for your answer.

15. Paula is creating triangular patterns from rods.

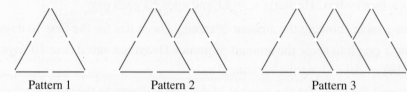

Pattern 1   Pattern 2   Pattern 3

  (i) Write the number of rods for each pattern as a sequence.

 (ii) Draw a table showing the pattern number and the number of rods used.

(iii) Represent your results on a graph.

16. As an 8-year-old, Freddie was 1 metre tall. By 9 he was 1·25 metres tall and by 10 he had reached 1·5 metres.

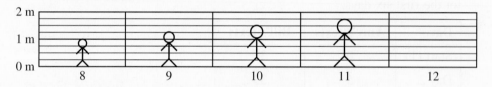

  (i) Write out Freddie's heights from when he was 8 years old until he is 12.

 (ii) Is this a linear sequence? Why?

(iii) If Freddie's growth continues as before, how tall will Freddie be when he is 21?

(iv) Why is this sequence (and graph) unsuitable to model how Freddie's height changes with age?

17. A yellow flower measured 5 cm high at the beginning of the week and grew 2 cm each week afterwards.

A red flower measured 8 cm high at the beginning of the same week but grew only 1·5 cm each week afterwards.

  (i) Calculate the heights of each plant for the first five weeks and plot your results on a graph.

 (ii) Which plant will grow taller?

(iii) Will the plants ever be the exact same height?

(iv) Give some reasons why the growth suggested by the graph may be unreliable.

Differences 1

Some sequences can be understood better by investigating the differences between the terms. For example, the sequence 2, 5, 8, 11, 14, . . . has the same difference between consecutive terms. We can say that the difference between the terms is constant.

The differences are equal to 3 (which is a constant). This means that the sequence is linear and we can now look at finding the relationship between the term number (or position) and the value in the sequence. If the difference is 3, then each term can be approximated by multiplying the term number by 3.

Term number	1	2	3	4	5
Value	2	5	8	11	14

If we multiply each term number by 3, we get:

Term number	1	2	3	4	5
Difference × term number	$3 \times 1 = 3$	$3 \times 2 = 6$	$3 \times 3 = 9$	$3 \times 4 = 12$	$3 \times 5 = 15$

This gives us the sequence 3, 6, 9, 12, 15, . . . but we want to arrive at 2, 5, 8, 11, 14, . . .

By inspection, we can see that if we subtracted 1 from each term in our new sequence, then we would have our original list.

Thus, the numbers in the sequence 2, 5, 8, 11, 14, . . . can be found by multiplying the term number by 3 and subtracting 1.

EXAMPLE

(i) Describe in words the relationship between the positions and the values in the sequence 5, 9, 13, 17, . . .

(ii) Use this to find T_{50}.

(iii) Write an expression for T_n in the form $dn + v$.

Solution:

(i) First, we need to find the common difference.

As the difference is 4, we need to multiply each position by 4 and then, by inspection, add or subtract a number.

Term number	1	2	3	4
Difference × position	$4 \times 1 = 4$	$4 \times 2 = 8$	$4 \times 3 = 12$	$4 \times 4 = 16$

Original sequence	5	9	13	17

By inspection, we can see we need to add 1.

Thus, the numbers in the sequence 5, 9, 13, 17, . . . can be found by multiplying the position by 4 and adding 1.

(ii) $T_{50} = 4(50) + 1 = 200 + 1 = 201$

(iii) $T_n = 4n + 1$

Exercise 33.5

In questions 1–6, describe in words the relationship between the term numbers (positions) and the values in the sequence.

1. 5, 7, 9, 11, . . .
2. 4, 6, 8, 10, . . .
3. 4, 7, 10, 13, . . .
4. 5, 8, 11, 14, . . .
5. 4, 9, 14, 19, . . .
6. 1, 7, 13, 19, . . .

7. (i) Describe the rule which connects the position and the number in the sequence 5, 13, 21, 29, . . .

   (ii) Use your rule to find T_{20}, the 20th number in the sequence.

8. (i) Describe the rule which connects the term number and the value in the sequence 10, 22, 34, 46, . . .

   (ii) Use your rule to find T_{10}, the 10th number in the sequence.

   (iii) Write out a rule for T_n.

9. A taxi charges €5 for a journey of 1 km, €8 for 2 km, €11 for 3 km and so on.

   (i) Write out a table showing the cost of journeys up to 6 km.

   (ii) The taxi fare is a fixed charge plus a rate per kilometre. What is (a) the fixed charge and (b) the rate per kilometre?

10. These three diagrams were made using matches.

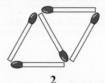

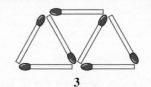

1   2   3

   (i) If the pattern is continued, how many matches will be needed for the 4th, 5th and 6th diagrams?

   (ii) The amount of matches used in the diagrams form which type of sequence?

   (iii) Find a formula, in terms of n, for the nth diagram.

   (iv) How many matches will be needed for the 50th diagram?

   (v) Explain why there is no diagram with this pattern needing 200 matches.

11. The instructions for cooking a chicken are 15 minutes per kg plus 20 minutes.

   (i) How long is needed to cook a 1 kg chicken?

   (ii) Write out a table showing the time needed to cook chickens weighing 1 kg, 2 kg, . . . , 6 kg.

   (iii) Show your results on a graph, putting *Weight* on the horizontal axis.

   (iv) Use your graph, or otherwise, to find out how long it will take to cook an 8 kg chicken.

12. A series of shapes are made using matches.

  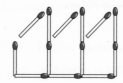

   (i) How many matches will be needed for the 4th and 5th shapes?

   (ii) Find a formula, in terms of n, for the nth shape.

   (iii) Which shape will need 49 matches?

Differences 2

Earlier, we investigated differences between terms in a sequence. When there was a common difference, the sequence was linear. If the differences vary, we can calculate the differences between the differences to see if *they* are the same.

When the differences between the differences are constant, then the sequence is a quadratic one.

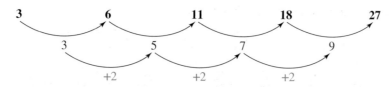

In this case, the differences between the differences is 2.

When the differences between the differences are negative, the graph will look like this:

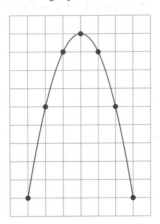

When the differences between the differences are positive, the graph will look like this:

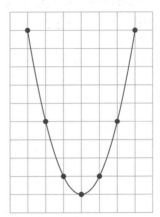

These are examples of quadratic graphs.

EXAMPLE

(i) Find the differences between the differences in the sequence 0, 5, 8, 9, 8, 5, 0.

(ii) What type of relationship is there between the position in the list and the corresponding value in the list?

(iii) Show this relationship on a graph.

Solution:

(i)

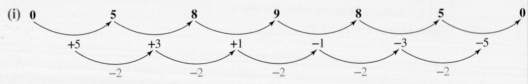

(ii) Because the second difference is −2 each time, the relationship is quadratic.

(iii)

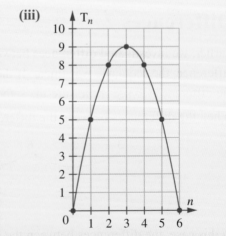

Exercise 33.6

In questions 1–6, find the first four terms and show that the difference between the differences is constant.

1. $T_n = n^2 + 1$ 2. $T_n = n^2 - 2$ 3. $T_n = n^2 + n$

4. $T_n = n^2 + 4$ 5. $T_n = n^2 + 3n - 2$ 6. $T_n = n^2 + 5n - 6$

7. Continue the diagram to find the next three terms in the sequence.

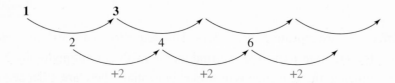

8. Continue the diagram to find the next three terms in the sequence.

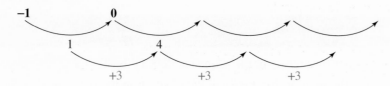

9. Continue the diagram to find the next four terms in the sequence.

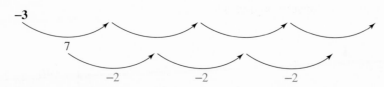

10. A rocket is launched and its path is described by the formula $h = 10t - t^2$, where h is the height of the rocket in metres and t is the time in seconds after blast-off.

  (i)   Find the height of the rocket after $t = 1, 2, \ldots, 6$ seconds.

  (ii) Is this a linear sequence? Explain.

 (iii) Show the path of the rocket on a graph, putting t on the horizontal axis.

 (iv) By finding the differences between the differences, confirm that the graph is quadratic.

  (v) Can you tell if the rocket has reached its maximum height? If so, what is this maximum height?

Differences 3

Sometimes, the method of calculating differences does not work. Take the following sequence and its differences:

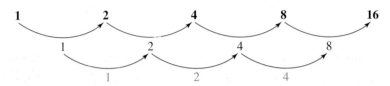

In this case, the differences are repeating themselves. This sequence is a new type – an exponential sequence. If we look for a term-to-term rule, we find that it involves multiplying by 2. When terms are calculated by multiplying, the sequence is always exponential. There are other sequences which are also exponential.

EXAMPLE

(i) Find the first four terms in the sequence defined by $T_n = 2^n$.

(ii) Show that the relationship between the position in the list is neither linear nor quadratic.

(iii) Show this relationship on a graph.

Solution:

(i) $T_n = 2^n$

$T_1 = 2^1 = 2$

$T_2 = 2^2 = 4$

$T_3 = 2^3 = 8$

$T_4 = 2^4 = 16$

(iii)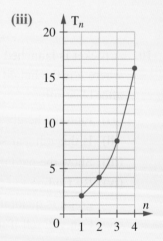

(ii) 2   4   8   16

    2   4   8

      2   4

The first differences are not equal, so the sequence is not linear.

The second differences are not equal, so the sequence in not quadratic.

Exercise 33.7

In questions 1–6, find the first four terms and show that the differences are not constant and that the differences between the differences are also not constant.

1. $T_n = 3^n$

2. $T_n = 3^n + 1$

3. $T_n = 3 + 2^n$

4. $T_n = 2(3^n)$

5. $T_n = 3(2^n)$

6. $T_n = 2(2^n + 1)$

7. A survey in a forest showed that there were eight pairs of red squirrels and three pairs of the larger grey variety. Further regular surveys showed that the number of red squirrels doubled each year, while the grey squirrels trebled in number.

   (i) Show the sequence of the numbers of each type of squirrel for the first four years.

   (ii) Draw a graph showing the numbers of each type over the four years.

   (iii) What notable event occurred after the third year?

Trigonometric ratios and right-angled triangles

In a right-angled triangle, special ratios exist between the angles and the lengths of the sides. We look at three of these ratios.

Consider the right-angled triangle below with the acute angle θ.

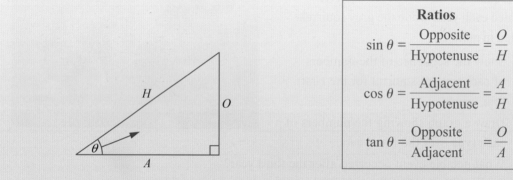

Ratios

$$\sin \theta = \frac{\text{Opposite}}{\text{Hypotenuse}} = \frac{O}{H}$$

$$\cos \theta = \frac{\text{Adjacent}}{\text{Hypotenuse}} = \frac{A}{H}$$

$$\tan \theta = \frac{\text{Opposite}}{\text{Adjacent}} = \frac{O}{A}$$

Memory aid: <u>O</u>, <u>H</u>ell, <u>A</u>nother <u>H</u>our <u>O</u>f <u>A</u>lgebra, <u>s</u>in, <u>c</u>os and <u>t</u>an.
Each trigonometric ratio links two sides and an angle in a right-angled triangle.

Notes:

1. The side opposite the right angle is called the **hypotenuse, *H***. The side opposite the angle θ is called the **opposite, *O***. The other side near the angle θ is called the **adjacent, *A***.

2. If the lengths of any two sides are known, the third side can be found using Pythagoras' theorem: $A^2 + O^2 = H^2$, where A, O and H are the lengths of the sides.

3. The three angles of a triangle add up to $180°$.

4. sin, cos and tan are short for sine, cosine and tangent, respectively.

5. The arrow points to the side opposite the angle under consideration.

6. θ is a Greek letter, pronounced theta, often used to indicate an angle.

We can write trigonometric ratios for the two acute angles in a right-angled triangle. Make sure you know which angle you are using and which sides are the opposite and adjacent (the hypotenuse is always opposite the right angle). A good idea is to draw an arrow from the angle under consideration to indicate the opposite side to the angle. If we are given one trigonometric ratio, we can find the other two trigonometric ratios by representing the situation with a right-angled triangle and using Pythagoras' theorem to find the missing side.

EXAMPLE 1

Consider the right-angled triangle with sides of 5, 12 and 13 and angles P and Q, as shown.
Write down the following ratios.

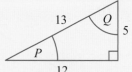

(i) $\sin P$ (ii) $\cos P$ (iii) $\tan P$

(iv) $\sin Q$ (v) $\cos Q$ (vi) $\tan Q$

Solution:

Angle P
(indicate opposite with an arrow)

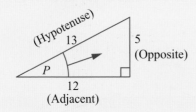

Angle Q
(indicate opposite with an arrow)

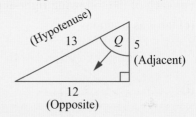

(i) $\sin P = \dfrac{O}{H} = \dfrac{5}{13}$

(ii) $\cos P = \dfrac{A}{H} = \dfrac{12}{13}$

(iii) $\tan P = \dfrac{O}{A} = \dfrac{5}{12}$

(iv) $\sin Q = \dfrac{O}{H} = \dfrac{12}{13}$

(v) $\cos Q = \dfrac{A}{H} = \dfrac{5}{13}$

(vi) $\tan Q = \dfrac{O}{A} = \dfrac{12}{5}$

EXAMPLE 2

(i)   Use Pythagoras' theorem to find the value of $|PQ|$.

(ii)   Hence, write down the value of $\cos \angle QPR$.

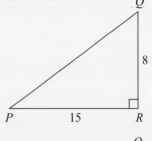

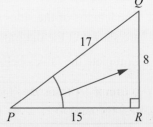

Solution:

(i)   Using Pythagoras' theorem:

$$|PQ|^2 = |PR|^2 + |RQ|^2$$
$$|PQ|^2 = 15^2 + 8^2$$
$$|PQ|^2 = 225 + 64$$
$$|PQ|^2 = 289$$
$$|PQ| = \sqrt{289} = 17$$

(ii) $\cos \angle QPR = \dfrac{A}{H} = \dfrac{|PR|}{|PQ|} = \dfrac{15}{17}$

Exercise 34.1

1. In each triangle, name the hypotenuse, the opposite side and adjacent side to the angle θ. It may help to draw an arrow from the angle θ to identify the opposite side.

(i)

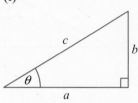

(ii)

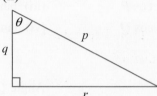

(iii)

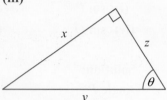

2. For each of the following right-angled triangles, write the value of **(a)** $\sin\theta$ **(b)** $\cos\theta$ and **(c)** $\tan\theta$ as fractions.

(i)

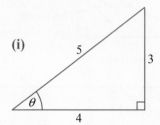

(ii)

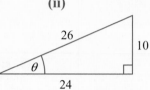

(iii)

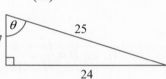

(iv)

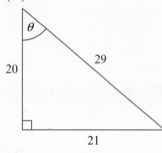

(v)

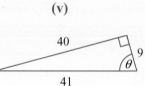

(vi)

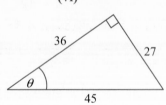

3. Complete each of the following with A or B.

   (i) $\tan$ ____ $= \frac{8}{15}$ **(ii)** $\sin$ ____ $= \frac{15}{17}$ **(iii)** $\cos$ ____ $= \frac{8}{17}$

   Complete each of the following with sin, cos or tan.

   (iv) ____ $A = \frac{15}{17}$ **(v)** ____ $B = \frac{15}{8}$ **(vi)** ____ $B = \frac{8}{17}$

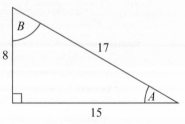

4. The lengths of the sides of a right-angled triangle are shown in the diagram and the angles are labelled.

   Complete the tables below, writing the answers as fractions.

sin A	cos A	tan A

sin B	cos B	tan B

5. **(i)** Using Pythagoras' theorem, find the value of x.

    (ii) Hence, find the following as fractions.

    (a) $\sin \theta$ **(b)** $\cos \theta$ **(c)** $\tan \theta$

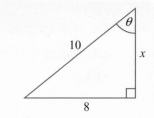

6. **(i)** Use Pythagoras' theorem to find the value of x.

    (ii) Find, as fractions, the values of:

         (a) $\sin \theta$ **(b)** $\cos \theta$ **(c)** $\tan \theta$

    (iii) Show that:

         (a) $\cos \theta + \sin \theta > \tan \theta$ **(b)** $\cos^2 \theta + \sin^2 \theta = 1$

    (Note: $\cos^2 \theta = (\cos \theta)^2$)

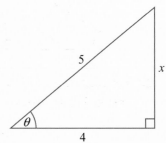

Calculating angles

Trigonometry can also be used to calculate the size of angles in a triangle.

Given a value of $\sin \theta$, $\cos \theta$ or $\tan \theta$, we can find the value of the angle θ using the $\boxed{\sin^{-1}}$, $\boxed{\cos^{-1}}$ or $\boxed{\tan^{-1}}$ key, respectively. On most calculators, $\boxed{\sin^{-1}}$, $\boxed{\cos^{-1}}$ and $\boxed{\tan^{-1}}$ are obtained by first pressing $\boxed{\text{INV}}$ or $\boxed{\text{2nd F}}$ and then pressing $\boxed{\sin}$, $\boxed{\cos}$ or $\boxed{\tan}$, as the case may be.

Summary of the trigonometric ratio to use when calculating an angle

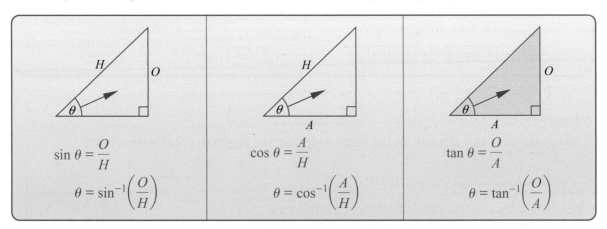

As before, we can use the memory aid: **O**, **H**ell, **A**nother **H**our **O**f **A**lgebra, **s**in, **c**os and **t**an.

Note: $\sin^{-1} x$ is pronounced 'sine inverse x', $\cos^{-1} x$ is pronounced 'cos inverse x' and $\tan^{-1} x$ is pronounced 'tan inverse x'.

EXAMPLE

In each case, find the size of the angle θ, correct to the nearest degree.

(i)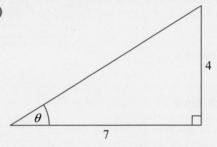

(ii)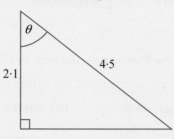

Solution:

(i)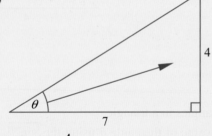

$$\tan \theta = \frac{4}{7}$$

$$\theta = \tan^{-1}\left(\frac{4}{7}\right)$$

$$\theta = 29{\cdot}7448813°$$

$$\theta = 30° \text{ (nearest degree)}$$

(▦ 2nd F tan (4 ÷ 7) =)

(ii)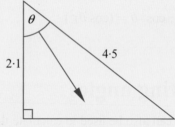

$$\cos \theta = \frac{2{\cdot}1}{4{\cdot}5}$$

$$\theta = \cos^{-1}\left(\frac{2{\cdot}1}{4{\cdot}5}\right)$$

$$\theta = 62{\cdot}18186072°$$

$$\theta = 62° \text{ (nearest degree)}$$

(▦ 2nd F cos (2·1 ÷ 4·5) =)

Exercise 34.2

In questions 1–12, calculate, to the nearest degree, the angles marked with a letter.

1.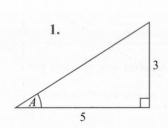

2.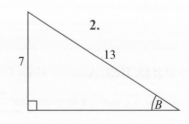

3.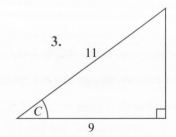

4.

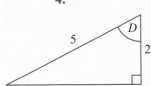

5.

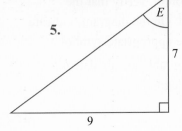

6.

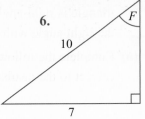

7.

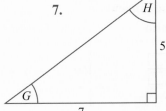

8.

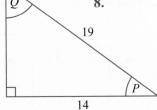

9.

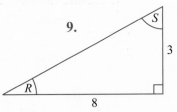

10.

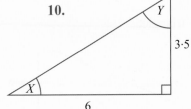

11.

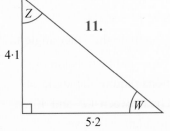

12.

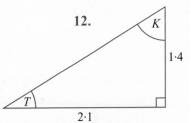

13. In $\triangle ABC$, $|\angle ABC| = 90°$,
$|AB| = 18$ cm and $|BC| = 12$ cm.
Find, to the nearest degree:

  (i) $|\angle BAC|$ **(ii)** $|\angle ACB|$

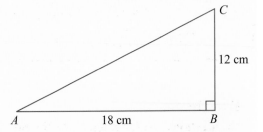

14. In $\triangle XYZ$, $|\angle XYZ| = 90°$,
$|XZ| = 200$ cm and $|YZ| = 100$ cm.

  (i) Write down the ratio $\sin \angle YXZ$
    in its simplest form.

  (ii) Calculate **(a)** $|\angle YXZ|$ and **(b)** $|\angle XZY|$.

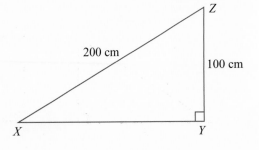

15. **(i)** Using Pythagoras' theorem, verify that the triangle is right-angled. On the diagram, indicate the right angle with the appropriate symbol.

(ii) Complete the following table to calculate θ, correct to the nearest degree.

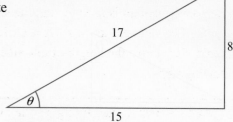

Using the sine ratio	Using the cosine ratio	Using the tangent ratio
$\sin \theta = \dfrac{\square}{\square}$	$\cos \theta = \dfrac{\square}{\square}$	$\tan \theta = \dfrac{\square}{\square}$
$\theta =$	$\theta =$	$\theta =$

(iii) What is your conclusion about the number of sides required to find an angle in a right-angled triangle?

(iv) Explain how you would calculate the other angle in the triangle.

16. The diagram shows the side view of an extension on a house. The building regulations require the angle of the roof, to the horizontal, to be between 17° and 40°. Does this extension pass the regulations? Give a reason why this regulation applies.

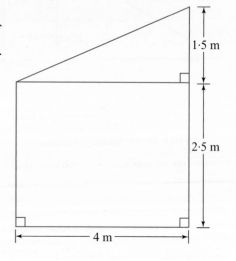

Finding the length of a short side

Pythagoras' theorem is used to find the length of a side in a right-angled triangle when the lengths of the other two sides are known. We use trigonometry to calculate the length of a side in a right-angled triangle if we know the length of one side and one angle (other than the right angle) with the following steps.

1. Draw a right-angled triangle (if not given), indicating the known angle and known side.
2. Choose the trigonometric ratio that links the required side with the known angle and known side.
3. Write down this equation (the ratio).
4. Put in the known values.
5. Solve the equation to find the required length.

EXAMPLE 1

From the right-angled triangle, calculate the value of x, correct to two decimal places.

Solution:
We know the **hypotenuse** and we require the length of the side **opposite** to the angle of 32°.
Therefore, use the sine ratio:

$$\sin \theta = \frac{\text{Opposite}}{\text{Hypotenuse}}$$

$$\sin 32° = \frac{x}{8} \qquad \text{(put in known values)}$$

$$8 \sin 32° = x \qquad \text{(multiply both sides by 8)}$$

$$4{\cdot}239354114 = x \qquad (\text{} 8 \; \boxed{\sin} \; 32 \; \boxed{=})$$

$$4{\cdot}24 = x \qquad \text{(correct to two decimal places)}$$

EXAMPLE 2

In $\triangle ABC$, $|\angle BCA| = 90°$,
$|\angle ABC| = 34°$ and $|AC| = 20$ m.
Calculate $|BC|$, correct to two decimal places.

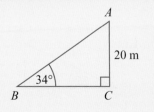

Solution:

Method 1

Using the angle 34°, the opposite is 20 m and the adjacent is [*BC*].

Therefore, use the tangent ratio:

$$\tan\theta = \frac{\text{Opposite}}{\text{Adjacent}}$$

$$\tan 34° = \frac{20}{|BC|} \qquad \text{(put in known values)}$$

$$|BC|\tan 34° = 20 \qquad \text{(multiply both sides by } |BC|)$$

$$|BC| = \frac{20}{\tan 34°} \qquad \text{(divide both sides by tan 34°)}$$

$$|BC| = 29\cdot65121937 \qquad (\boxed{}\,20\,\boxed{\div}\,\boxed{\tan}\,34\,\boxed{=})$$

$$|BC| = 29\cdot65 \qquad \text{(correct to two decimal places)}$$

Method 2

First calculate |∠*BAC*| and use the tan ratio.

|∠*BAC*| = 90° − 34° = 56°

Using the tangent ratio:

$$\tan\theta = \frac{\text{Opposite}}{\text{Adjacent}}$$

$$\tan 56° = \frac{|BC|}{20} \qquad \text{(put in known values)}$$

$$20\tan 56° = |BC| \qquad \text{(multiply both sides by 20)}$$

$$29\cdot65121937 = |BC| \qquad (\boxed{}\,20\,\boxed{\tan}\,56\,\boxed{=})$$

$$29\cdot65 = |BC| \qquad \text{(correct to two decimal places)}$$

(Same answer as in method 1 above.)

Exercise 34.3

Calculate the length of the sides marked *x* in each of the triangles in questions 1–18 (Where necessary, give answers correct to two decimal places. All dimensions are in centimetres.)

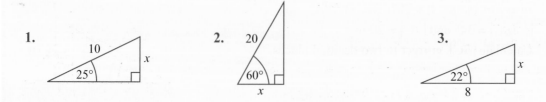

1.

2.

3.

4.

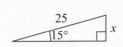

5.

6.

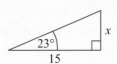

7.

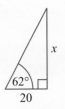

8.

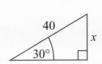

9.

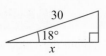

10.

11.

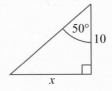

12.

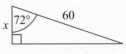

13.

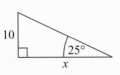

14.

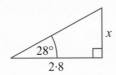

15.

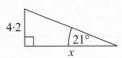

16.

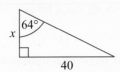

17.

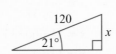

18.

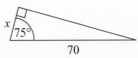

19. In $\triangle XYZ$, $|\angle XZY| = 90°$, $|\angle XYZ| = 27°$
and $|XY| = 5{\cdot}8$ cm.
Calculate $|YZ|$, correct to two decimal places.

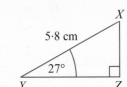

20. In $\triangle ABC$, $|\angle ABC| = 90°$, $|\angle BAC| = 34°$ and $|AB| = 20$.

 (i) Calculate $|BC|$.

 (ii) Hence or otherwise, calculate $|AC|$.

 Give both answers correct to two decimal places.

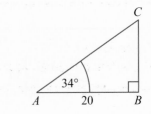

21. In the diagram, $XW \perp YZ$, $|XY| = 20$, $|\angle XYW| = 30°$
and $|\angle ZXW| = 40°$.

 (i) Calculate $|XW|$ (exactly).

 (ii) Calculate $|WZ|$, correct to two decimal places.

 (Hint: Draw $\triangle XYW$ and $\triangle XZW$ separately.)

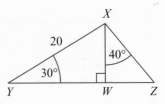

Finding the length of the hypotenuse

In some questions we are given the length of a side and an angle (other than the right angle) and asked to find the length of the hypotenuse. These questions are a little more difficult, as the length required, the hypotenuse, is on the bottom of the ratio and a few extra steps are needed to find its value.

EXAMPLE

Calculate the value of x, the hypotenuse of the right-angled triangle shown. Give your answer correct to two decimal places.

Solution:

We require the hypotenuse and know the adjacent.

Therefore, we use the cosine ratio, $\cos \theta = \dfrac{\text{Adjacent}}{\text{Hypotenuse}}$.

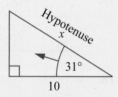

$\cos 31° = \dfrac{10}{x}$	(put in known values)
$x \cos 31° = 10$	(multiply both sides by x)
$x = \dfrac{10}{\cos 31°}$	(divide both sides by $\cos 31°$)
$x = 11{\cdot}66633397$	($\boxed{}$ 10 $\div$ $\cos$ 31 $=$)
$x = 11{\cdot}67$	(correct to two decimal places)

Exercise 34.4

Calculate the length of the hypotenuse, marked x, in each of the following triangles. (Where necessary, give answers correct to two decimal places. All dimensions are in centimetres.)

1.

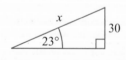

2.

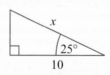

3.

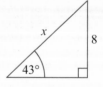

4.

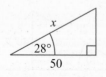

5.

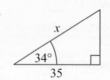

6.

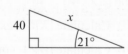

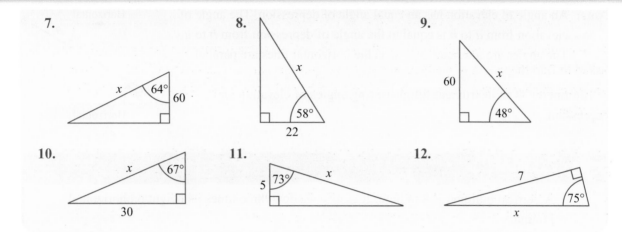

7.

x 64°   60

8.

x 58°   22

9.

60   x 48°

10.

x 67°   30

11.

5   73° x

12.

7   x 75°

Practical applications

Many practical problems in navigation, surveying, engineering and geography involve solving a triangle. In this section we will restrict the problems to those that involve right-angled triangles. When solving practical problems using trigonometry in this section, represent each situation with a right-angled triangle.

Mark on your triangle the angles and lengths you know and label what you need to calculate, using the correct ratio to link the angle or length required with the known angle or length.

Angles of elevation, depression and compass directions

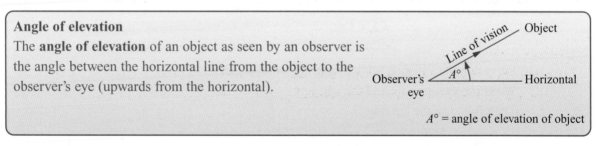

Angle of elevation
The **angle of elevation** of an object as seen by an observer is the angle between the horizontal line from the object to the observer's eye (upwards from the horizontal).

$A°$ = angle of elevation of object

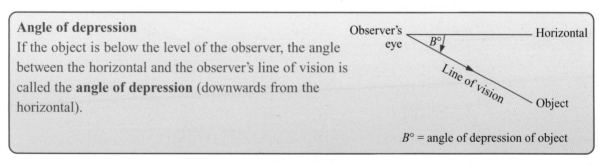

Angle of depression
If the object is below the level of the observer, the angle between the horizontal and the observer's line of vision is called the **angle of depression** (downwards from the horizontal).

$B°$ = angle of depression of object

Note: An angle of elevation has an equal angle of depression. The angle of elevation from a to b is equal to the angle of depression from b to a. The angles are alternate angles, as the horizontal lines are parallel.

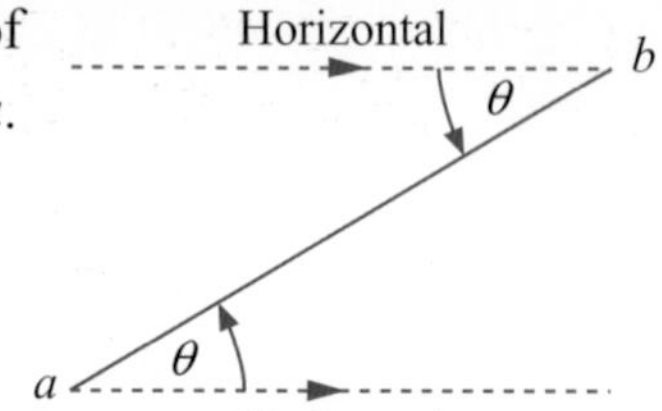

A **clinometer** is an instrument for measuring angles of elevation and depression.

EXAMPLE 1

A vertical building is 8 m high. It casts a shadow three times its height on horizontal ground.

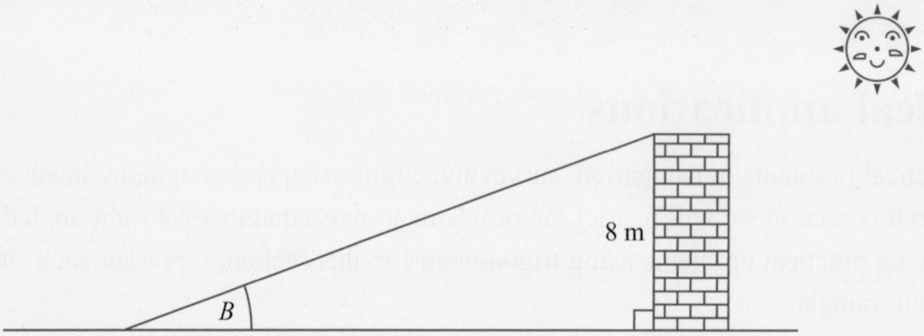

(i) Write down the length of the shadow.

(ii) Find B, the angle of elevation of the sun, correct to the nearest degree.

Solution:

(i) Length of the shadow = 3 times height of building

$= 3 \times 8$ m

$= 24$ m

(ii) Represent the situation with a right-angled triangle.
We know the opposite and the adjacent.
Therefore, use the tan ratio:

$$\tan B = \frac{\text{Opposite}}{\text{Adjacent}}$$

$$\tan B = \frac{8}{24}$$

$$\tan B = \frac{1}{3}$$

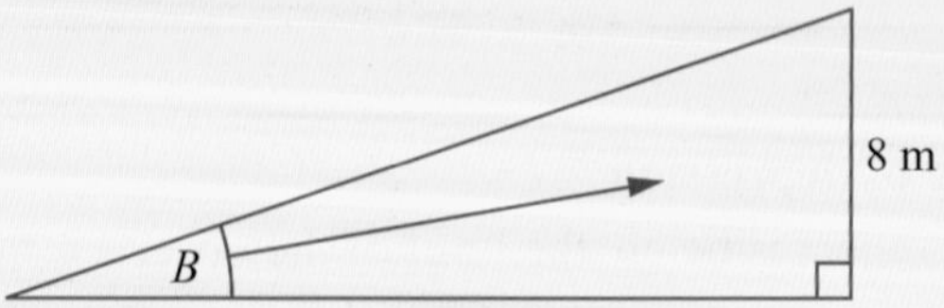

$$B = \tan^{-1}\left(\frac{1}{3}\right)$$

$B = 18{\cdot}43494882°$ (calculator: 2nd tan (1 ÷ 3) =)

$B = 18°$ (correct to the nearest degree)

EXAMPLE 2

Ciara wished to measure the width of a river.

She was at A on the riverbank, directly opposite B on the other bank.

Ciara walked from A to C, along the riverbank, at an average speed of 1·5 m/s.

It took Ciara 30 seconds to reach C.

She then measured $\angle ACB$ and found it to be 25°.

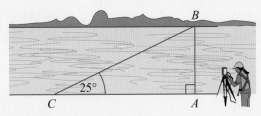

(i) Calculate $|AC|$, the distance walked by Ciara.

(ii) Hence, calculate $|AB|$, the width of the river.

Give your answer correct to the nearest metre.

Solution:

(i) $|AC|$

$\qquad$ Speed = 1·5 m/s $\qquad$ Time = 30 seconds

$\qquad$ Distance = speed × time

$\qquad\qquad\qquad = 1\cdot5 \times 30$

$\qquad\qquad\qquad = 45$

$\qquad \therefore \ |AC| = 45$ m

(ii) Calculate $|AB|$, the width of the river.

Represent the situation with a right-angled triangle.

Let w m = the width of the river.

We know the adjacent and need to find the opposite.

Therefore, use the tan ratio:

$$\tan A = \frac{\text{Opposite}}{\text{Adjacent}}$$

$\qquad \tan 25° = \dfrac{w}{45}$ $\quad$ (angle = 25°, adjacent = 45)

$\qquad 45 \tan 25° = w$ $\quad$ (multiply both sides by 45)

$\qquad 20\cdot98384462 = w$ $\quad$ (▣ 45 [tan] 25 [=])

$\qquad\qquad\quad 21 = w$ $\quad$ (nearest whole number)

Thus, the width of the river = 21 m (correct to the nearest metre).

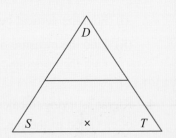

Exercise 34.5

1. From a point 12 m from the bottom of a wall, the angle of elevation to the top of the wall is 22°. Calculate the height of the wall, correct to two decimal places.

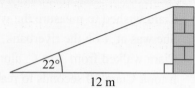

2. When the angle of elevation of the sun is 15°, an upright flagpole casts a shadow of length 18 m. Calculate the height of the pole, correct to one decimal place.

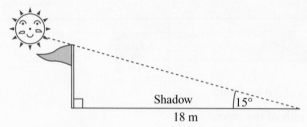

3. A ladder of length 3·7 m rests against a vertical wall so that the base of the ladder is 1·2 m from the wall.

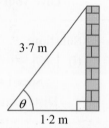

   (i) Find the vertical height that the ladder reaches on the wall.

   (ii) Find the measure of the angle, θ, which the ladder makes with the horizontal, correct to the nearest degree.

4. Kieran is trying to calculate θ, the angle of elevation of the sun. He measures Bernadette's height and then the length of her shadow. He calculates Bernadette's height to be 167 cm and the length of her shadow to be 120 cm. What is the angle of elevation of the sun, correct to one decimal place?

5. A girl is flying a kite. The length of string from her hand to the top of the kite is 60 m. The string, which is being held 1 m above the ground, makes an angle of elevation of 50° with the horizontal. Calculate the height of the kite above the ground, correct to the nearest metre.

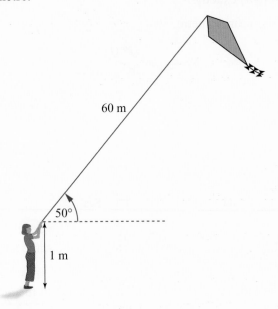

6. A person stands at the window of a building so that her eyes are 20 m above the level ground in the vicinity of the building.

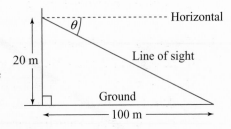

   An object is 100 m away from the building on a line directly beneath the person. Compute the angle of depression of the person's line of sight to the object on the ground correct to one decimal place.

7. [ZW] is a vertical television aerial mast.
   [XZ] and [YZ] are supporting cables.
   |XZ| = 15 m, |XW| = 12 m and |WY| = 40 m.

   (i) Calculate (a) |ZW| (b) |∠WYZ|, correct to two decimal places.

   (ii) What is the total length of wire used to support the aerial mast?

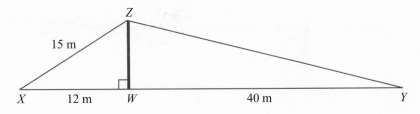

8. An aircraft takes off from a point P on a runway at a speed of 240 km/h. It remains at this speed while it climbs at an angle of 30° to the horizontal for 1·5 minutes until it reaches a point Q. Point Q is directly above a point R on the coastline.

   (i) Calculate (a) $|PQ|$ and (b) $|QR|$ exactly.

   (ii) Calculate $|PR|$ correct to the nearest metre.

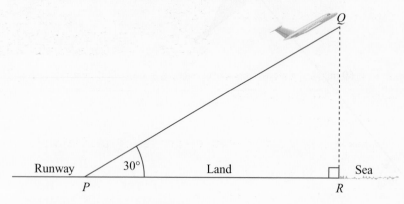

9. A ramp is made by placing a board on some steps. The steps are the same size, as shown, with all dimensions in centimetres.

   (i) Calculate the angle the board makes with the horizontal, correct to the nearest degree.

   (ii) Calculate the length of the board.

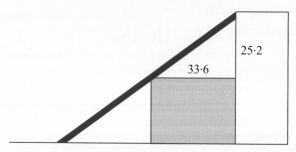

10. The diagram shows a farmyard gate. Its height is 1·6 m. The diagonal bar makes an angle of 30° with the horizontal ground. Calculate the length of the diagonal bar.

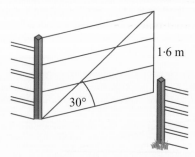

11. A girl is surfing the internet.

    (i) What height are her eyes above the centre of the screen?

    (ii) Find the horizontal distance from her eyes to the centre of the screen.

    Give each answer correct to one decimal place.

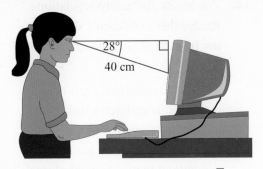

12. While trying to swim across a river, Gerry was swept downstream. The river is $150\sqrt{3}$ m wide, but Gerry had to swim 300 m to cross the river.

    (i) At what angle was he dragged downstream?

    (ii) Gerry took 2 minutes to cross the river. What was his average speed in m/s?

    (iii) How far downstream was Gerry dragged?

    (iv) Calculate the average speed of the river in m/s.

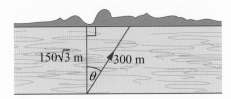

13. A ramp is to be built to allow manual wheelchairs to enter a building. The step is 45 cm and the ramp is to extend 4 m, as shown. A health and safety directive says, '*A ramp for wheelchairs must not be greater than 3°*'. Give two reasons for the directive. Does this ramp satisfy the directive?

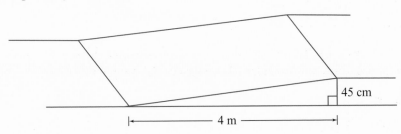

14. The health and safety regulations require that a children's slide must not be at an angle greater than 40°. The length of the slide is 20 metres.

(i) What is the maximum height that this children's slide can be set at to comply with the regulations? Give your answer correct to two decimal places.

(ii) Most children's slides are set at an angle between 30° and 40°. Give two reasons why most children's slides are set at an angle between 30° and 40°.

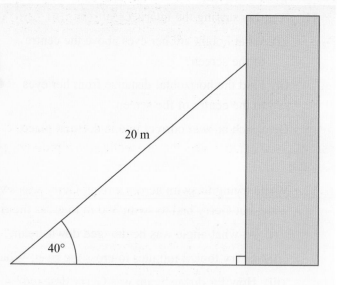

USING EQUATIONS TO SOLVE PROBLEMS

Forming expressions

Statements in words can be translated into algebraic expressions. It is common to let x represent the unknown number, usually the smallest, in a problem given in words. However, any other letter would do.

For example, if x represents an unknown number, then:

Words	Expression
5 more than the number	$(x + 5)$
2 less than the number	$(x - 2)$
3 times the number	$3x$
4 times the number, less 1	$(4x - 1)$
a third of the number	$\frac{1}{3}x \ or \ \frac{x}{3}$
the number subtracted from 6	$6 - x$
the difference between two numbers is 8	x and $(x + 8)$
two numbers add up to 10	x and $(10 - x)$

Steps in constructing an equation in solving a practical problem

A numerical problem given in words can often be translated into an equation. The solution of this equation will give the answer to the problem.

To solve a practical problem by constructing an equation, do the following.

1. Read the question carefully a few times.
2. Let x equal the unknown number that is required.
3. Write each statement in the problem in terms of x. Use a diagram if necessary.
4. Use the information in the problem to link the parts in step 3 to form an equation.
   Make sure both sides are measured in the same units.
5. Solve the equation (find the unknown number).
6. Test your solution in the problem itself – **not in your equation**, as your equation may be wrong.

Note: If the problem requires simultaneous equations to be solved, then step 2 becomes 'let x and y equal the unknown numbers that are required'.

When an equation is constructed from a problem given in words, it may lead to any one of three types of equation:

1. Simple linear equation   2. Simultaneous linear equations   3. Quadratic equation

1. Using simple equations to solve problems

 EXAMPLE 1

Alan has a number of marbles. His friend Brendan has 15 more than he has. Between them they have 39 marbles. How many marbles each have Alan and Brendan?

Solution:
Let x = the number of marbles Alan has.
Then $(x + 15)$ = the number of marbles Brendan has (15 more than Alan).
Link used to form the equation:
Given: (number of marbles Alan has) + (number of marbles Brendan has) = 39

$$x + (x + 15) = 39$$
$$x + x + 15 = 39$$
$$2x + 15 = 39$$
$$2x = 24$$
$$x = 12$$

Number of marbles Alan has = x = 12.
Number of marbles Brendan has = $(x + 15) = (12 + 15) = 27$.

 EXAMPLE 2

The perimeter of a rectangle is 46 cm. One side is 5 cm longer than the other. Calculate the area of the rectangle.

Solution:
Let x cm = the length of the shorter side.
Then $(x + 5)$ cm = the length of the longer side (5 cm longer).

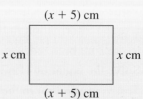

Link used to form the equation:

Given: Perimeter = 46 cm

$$(x + 5) + x + (x + 5) + x = 46$$
$$x + 5 + x + x + 5 + x = 46$$
$$4x + 10 = 46$$
$$4x = 36$$
$$x = 9$$

Width of the rectangle = x cm = 9 cm.

Length of the rectangle = $(x + 5)$ cm = $(9 + 5)$ cm = 14 cm.

Area = length × breadth = 14 × 9 = 126 cm^2.

EXAMPLE 3

This year, a woman is four times as old as her son. In five years' time she will be three times as old as him. What age is each of them now?

Solution:

Let x = the son's age now.

Then $4x$ = the mother's age now (four times as old).

In five years' time both mother and son will be five years older.

Therefore, in five years' time,

son's age = $(x + 5)$ years and mother's age = $(4x + 5)$ years (add 5 to both ages).

Link used to form the equation:

Given: in five years' time: mother's age = three times son's age

$$(4x + 5) = 3(x + 5)$$
$$4x + 5 = 3x + 15$$
$$4x - 3x = 15 - 5$$
$$x = 10$$

Son's age now = x years = 10 years.

Mother's age now = $4x$ years = 4 × 10 years = 40 years.

Exercise 35.1

In questions 1–12, do the following.

> 1. Let x = the unknown number.
>   (If there is a second unknown number, write this in terms of x.)
> 2. From the information in the question, look for a link to form an equation.
> 3. Solve the equation to find the unknown number, x.

1. A certain number is multiplied by 2 and then 5 is added on. The result is 11. Find the number.

2. A certain number is multiplied by 3 and then 2 is added on. The result is 14. Find the number.

3. A certain number is multiplied by 4 and then 3 is added on. The result is 27. Find the number.

4. A certain number is multiplied by 2 and then 5 is taken away. The result is 19. Find the number.

5. A certain number is multiplied by 3 and then 2 is taken away. The result is 13. Find the number.

6. When 6 is taken from four times a certain number, the answer is 22. Find the number.

7. A certain number is doubled and then 7 is added on. The result is the same if 10 is added to the number. What is the number?

8. A certain number is multiplied by 3 and then 5 is taken away. The result is the same as multiplying the number by 2 and then adding on 4. Find the number.

9. One number is 3 more than another number. If the two numbers are added, the result is 23. Find the numbers.

10. One number is 7 more than another number. If the two numbers are added, the result is 29. Find the numbers.

11. One number is 4 more than another number. If five times the smaller number is equal to three times the larger number, find the numbers.

12. 5 is added to a certain number and this new number is multiplied by 3. If the result is 21, find the original number.

13. The length of a rectangle is 4 cm greater than its breadth, as shown.
    (i) Find, in terms of x, the perimeter of the rectangle.
    If the perimeter of the rectangle is 32 cm:
    (ii) Use this information to form an equation.
    (iii) Solve the equation to find the value of x.

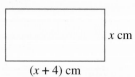

x cm

$(x + 4)$ cm

14. The length of a rectangle is 10 cm longer than the breadth. If the breadth is x cm:
    (i) Write down the length in terms of x.
    (ii) Draw a diagram of the rectangle.
    (iii) Write, in terms of x, the perimeter of the rectangle.
    If the perimeter of the rectangle is 56 cm:
    (iv) Use this information to form an equation.
    (v) Solve the equation to find the value of x.

15. The perimeter of a rectangle is 42 cm. The length of the rectangle is twice its width. If the width is x cm:
    (i) Write down the length in terms of x.
    (ii) Draw a diagram of the rectangle.
    (iii) Form an equation in x.
    (iv) Solve the equation to find the value of x.
    (v) Calculate the area of the rectangle.

16. This year, Catherine is x years old. Her brother Andrew is two years older. The sum of their ages is 38 years.
    (i) Write Andrew's age in terms of x.
    (ii) Form an equation in x.
    (iii) Solve the equation to find the value of x.
    (iv) How old is Andrew?

17. This year, Edward is x years of age. His sister Jane is six years older.
    (i) Write Jane's age in terms of x.
    (ii) Write down, in terms of x, both their ages two years from now.
    (iii) In two years, Jane will be twice as old as Edward. Use this information to form an equation.
    (iv) Solve the equation to find the value of x.

18. A woman's age this year is four times that of her son. In four years' time she will be three times as old as her son.
    (i) If the son's age is x years this year, find, in terms of x, his mother's age now.
    (ii) Write, in terms of x, their ages in four years' time.
    (iii) Form an equation in x.
    (iv) Solve the equation to find the value of x.

19. A pen costs 40 cent more than a pencil. The cost of a pencil is x cent.
    (i) Write down, in terms of x, the cost of:
        (a) A pen
        (b) 4 pencils
        (c) 3 pens

(ii) Four pencils and three pens cost €3·30. Using this information, write down an equation in terms of x.

(iii) Solve the equation to find x.

(iv) Calculate the cost of a pen.

20. The perimeter of the isosceles triangle shown is 64 cm.

    (i) Using this information, write down an equation in terms of x.

    (ii) Solve the equation to find x.

    (iii) What is the length of the base, $(5x - 1)$ cm?

21. Two cylindrical buckets hold 18 litres and 6 litres of liquid, respectively. To each bucket are now added another $2x$ litres of liquid, so that the first one now holds twice as much as the second one.

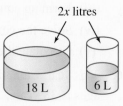

    (i) Express the volume of liquid in each bucket in terms of x.

    (ii) Form an equation in x.

    (iii) Solve the equation to find the value of x.

22. Three consecutive numbers (e.g. 3, 4, 5) are x, $x + 1$ and $x + 2$. When the three numbers are added together the result is 33.

    (i) Use this information to form an equation.

    (ii) Solve the equation to find the value of x.

    (iii) What are the three numbers?

23. Three consecutive odd numbers (e.g. 5, 7, 9) are x, $x + 2$ and $x + 4$. When the three numbers are added together the result is 45.

    (i) Use this information to form an equation.

    (ii) Solve the equation to find the value of x.

    (iii) What are the three numbers?

24. Find three consecutive numbers that add up to 21.

25. Find three consecutive numbers that add up to 45.

26. A girl bought a coat for $€\dfrac{x}{2}$ and a hat for $€\dfrac{x}{5}$.

The total amount of money she spent was €70.

    (i) Use this information to form an equation.

    (ii) Solve the equation to find the value of x.

    (iii) Find the cost of her hat.

27. Find the value of x and y in each of the following parallelograms.

(i)

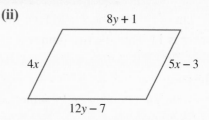

$2y + 3$

$3x - 1$

14

19

(ii)

$8y + 1$

$4x$

$5x - 3$

$12y - 7$

28. Molly ate x number of sweets. Laura ate two sweets less than Molly. Janice ate three sweets more than Molly and Laura combined. If they ate 27 sweets altogether, how many sweets did each of the girls eat?

29. Adam receives €x pocket money each week. Ryan gets one euro less than Adam. Mark receives two euro less than Adam and Ryan combined. If they receive €16 altogether, how much pocket money does each boy receive?

30. On a Friday evening, 200 people attended a concert, when the price was €10 per person.

  (i) How much money was taken at the door?

On a Saturday evening, $(200 - x)$ people attended the concert, when the price was €15 per person.

  (ii) Write, in terms of x, how much money was taken at the door on Saturday evening.

€400 more was taken in on Saturday evening than on Friday evening.

(iii) Form an equation to show the difference between the takings for both nights.

(iv) Solve the equation to find the value of x.

2. Using simultaneous equations to solve problems

Method

> 1. Let x = one unknown number and y = the other unknown number.
> 2. Look for **two** facts that **link** x and y and form two equations.
> 3. Solve these simultaneous equations.

EXAMPLE 1

The sum of two numbers is 8. Four times the first number less three times the second number is 11. Find the two numbers.

Solution:
Let x = the first number and y = the second number.

Two facts that link x and y:

1. The sum of the numbers is 8.

   Equation: $x + y = 8$ ①

2. Four times the first number less three times the second number is 11.

   Equation: $4x - 3y = 11$ ②

   Now solve the simultaneous equations ① and ②:

$$
\begin{array}{ll}
x + y = 8 & \text{①} \\
4x - 3y = 11 & \text{②} \\
\hline
3x + 3y = 24 & \text{① × 3} \\
4x - 3y = 11 & \text{②} \\
\hline
7x = 35 & \text{(add)} \\
x = 5 &
\end{array}
\qquad
\begin{array}{ll}
x + y = 8 & \text{①} \\
5 + y = 8 & \\
y = 3 &
\end{array}
$$

Put $x = 5$ into ① or ②.

Therefore, the first number is 5 and the second number is 3.

EXAMPLE 2

Five pens and two pencils cost €1·86. Three pens and four pencils cost €1·62. Find the cost of a pen and the cost of a pencil.

Solution:
Let x cent = the cost of a pen and y cent = the cost of a pencil.
€1·86 = 186c and €1·62 = 162c. Change the euro into cent to avoid decimals.

Two facts that link x and y:

1. Five pens and two pencils cost €1·86.

   Equation: $5x + 2y = 186$ ①   (both sides in cent)

2. Three pens and four pencils cost €1·62.

   Equation: $3x + 4y = 162$ ②   (both sides in cent)

Now solve the simultaneous equations ① and ②.

$$5x + 2y = 186 \quad ①$$
$$3x + 4y = 162 \quad ②$$
$$\overline{10x + 4y = 372} \quad ① \times 2$$
$$3x + 4y = 162 \quad ②$$
$$\overline{7x = 210} \quad \text{(subtract)}$$
$$x = 30$$

$$5x + 2y = 186 \quad ①$$
$$5(30) + 2y = 186$$
$$150 + 2y = 186$$
$$2y = 36$$
$$y = 18$$

Put $x = 30$ into ① or ②.

The cost of a pen is 30c and the cost of a pencil is 18c.

EXAMPLE 3

A concert was held in a hall that can hold 160 people. There are two prices of tickets, €5 and €3. On one evening when the hall was full, €600 was collected. Find how many of each ticket was sold on the night.

Solution:

Let x = the number of €5 tickets sold and y = the number of €3 tickets sold.

Two facts that link x and y:

1. There were 160 people in the hall.

   Equation: $x + y = 160$ ①

2. €600 was collected on the night.

   Equation: $5x + 3y = 600$ ②

   Now solve the simultaneous equations ① and ②.

$$x + y = 160 \quad ①$$
$$5x + 3y = 600 \quad ②$$
$$\overline{3x + 3y = 480} \quad ① \times 3$$
$$5x + 3y = 600 \quad ②$$
$$\overline{-2x = -120} \quad \text{(subtract)}$$
$$2x = 120$$
$$x = 60$$

$$x + y = 160 \quad ①$$
$$60 + y = 160$$
$$y = 100$$

Put $x = 60$ in ① or ②.

Therefore, the number of €5 tickets sold was 60 and the number of €3 sold was 100.

Exercise 35.2

In questions 1–8, let x = one number and y = the other number. Link x and y twice to form two equations and solve these equations to find the unknown numbers.

1. The sum of two numbers is 14. The difference is 4. Find the numbers.

2. The difference between two numbers is 8. The sum of the two numbers is 20. Find the numbers.

3. The sum of two numbers is 9. Three times the first number less twice the second number is 7. Find the numbers.

4. The sum of four times one number and three times another number is 41. If twice the first number less three times the second number is 7, find the numbers.

5. Find two numbers such that three times the first number added to twice the second number is 29, while four times the first number less twice the second number is 20.

6. Three times a number added to a second number is 13. The first number added to three times the second number is 7. Find the two numbers.

7. Twice one number added to a second number is 7, while three times the first number added to twice the second number is 13. Find the two numbers.

8. The difference between two numbers is 4. Four times the first number less three times the second number is 18. Find the two numbers.

9. Two apples and a banana cost 70c. One apple and a banana cost 50c.

    Let x cent be the price of an apple and y cent the price of a banana.

    (i) Write down an equation in x and y to show the price of

        (a) two apples and a banana   (b) one apple and a banana.

    (ii) Solve your two equations simultaneously.

    (iii) What is the price of (a) an apple   (b) a banana?

10. Five pens and two pencils cost €2·50. Three pens and two pencils cost €1·70.

    (i) Write (a) €2·50 and (b) €1·70 as cent.

    Let x cent be the price of a pen and y cent the price of a pencil.

    (ii) Write down an equation in x and y to show the price of the following.

        (a) Five pens and two pencils

        (b) Three pens and two pencils

    (iii) Solve your two equations simultaneously.

    (iv) What is the price of (a) a pen (b) a pencil?

11. Five packets of crisps and four bottles of lemonade cost €3·50.

    Two packets of crisps and two bottles of lemonade cost €1·60.

    (i) Write (a) €3·50 and (b) €1·60 as cent.

Let x cent be the price of a packet of crisps and y cent the price of a bottle of lemonade.

(ii) Write down an equation in x and y to show the price, in cent, of the following.

(a) Five packets of crisps and four bottles of lemonade

(b) Two packets of crisps and two bottles of lemonade

(iii) Solve your two equations simultaneously.

(iv) What is the price of (a) a packet of crisps and (b) a bottle of lemonade?

12. Seven books and three magazines cost €82.

Two books and one magazine cost €24.

Let €x be the price of a book and €y be the price of a magazine.

(i) Write down an equation in x and y to show the price of the following.

(a) Seven books and three magazines (b) Two books and one magazine

(ii) Solve your two equations simultaneously.

(iii) What is the price of (a) a book (b) a magazine?

(iv) Calculate the price of 10 books and six magazines.

13. Eight cans of cola and two packets of peanuts cost €5·30.

Six cans of cola and two packets of peanuts cost €4·10.

(i) Write (a) €5·30 and (b) €4·10 as cent.

Let x cent be the price of a can of cola and y cent the price of a packet of peanuts.

(ii) Write down two equations in x and y to represent the data.

(iii) Calculate the price of (a) a can of cola and (b) a packet of peanuts.

14. A school bought 20 tickets for a show. Some were teachers' tickets, costing €8 each, and some were pupils' tickets, costing €5 each. The total price of the tickets was €118. Let x be the number of teachers' tickets bought and y be the number of pupils' tickets bought.

(i) Write down an equation in x and y for the total **number** of tickets bought.

(ii) Write down an equation in x and y for the total **price** of the tickets.

(iii) Solve your two equations simultaneously.

(iv) How many of each type of ticket did the school buy?

15. A theatre with seating accommodation for 50 people took in €600 on a night when all the seats were sold. Seats were priced at €15 and €10.

Let x be the number of €15 seats sold and y the number of €10 seats sold.

(i) Write down an equation in x and y for the **number** of seats sold.

(ii) Write down an equation in x and y for the **price** of seats sold.

(iii) Solve your two equations simultaneously.

(iv) How many of each seat price were sold?

16. All 80 members of a club voted to elect the president of the club. There were only two candidates, Anne and Brian. Anne beat Brian by 20 votes.

Let x be the number of votes Anne received and y the number of votes Brian received.

 (i) Write an equation in x and y for the **number** of members in the club who voted.

 (ii) Write an equation in x and y for the **difference** between the number of votes Anne received and the number of votes Brian received.

(iii) Solve your two equations simultaneously.

(iv) How many members of the club voted for Anne?

17. The opposite sides in a parallelogram are equal in length. Use this information to calculate the values of x and y for the following parallelograms (all dimensions are in centimetres).

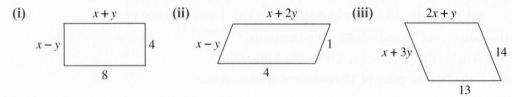

(i) $x + y$, $x - y$, 4, 8

(ii) $x + 2y$, $x - y$, 1, 4

(iii) $2x + y$, $x + 3y$, 14, 13

18. 1,500 tickets for a concert were sold. Tickets were priced at either €20 or €30. Ticket sales amounted to €38,000.

Let x be the quantity of €20 tickets sold and y the quantity of €30 tickets sold.

 (i) Write down an equation in x and y for the number of tickets sold.

 (ii) Write down an equation in x and y for the total cost of the tickets.

(iii) How many of each type of ticket were sold?

3. Using quadratic equations to solve problems

When we use an equation to solve a practical problem, the equation often turns out to be a quadratic equation. These equations usually have two solutions. If one of these makes no sense, for example producing a negative number of people, we reject it. Again, always look for the link in the question to set up the equation.

Note: The word 'product' means the result of multiplying.

EXAMPLE 1

When a number is added to its square, the total is 20.
Find the two possible numbers.

Solution:
Let x = the number; its square is x^2.

Link used to form the equation:
Given: (the number) + (the number)^2 = 20

$$x + x^2 = 20$$
$$x^2 + x - 20 = 0$$
$$(x + 5)(x - 4) = 0$$
$$x + 5 = 0 \quad \text{or} \quad x - 4 = 0$$
$$x = -5 \quad \text{or} \quad x = 4$$

Therefore, the numbers are −5 and 4.

EXAMPLE 2

The area of a rectangle is 44 cm^2. If the length is 7 cm longer than the breadth, find the length and breadth of the rectangle.

Solution:
Draw a diagram of the rectangle.
Let x cm be the breadth.
Then $(x + 7)$ cm is the length (7 cm longer).

Link used to form the equation:
Given: area of the rectangle = 44 cm^2

$$(\text{length})(\text{breadth}) = 44$$
$$(x + 7)(x) = 44$$
$$x^2 + 7x = 44$$
$$x^2 + 7x - 44 = 0$$
$$(x + 11)(x - 4) = 0$$
$$x + 11 = 0 \quad \text{or} \quad x - 4 = 0$$
$$x = -11 \quad \text{or} \quad x = 4$$

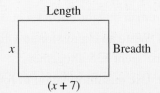

The negative value, $x = -11$, is not possible, so $x = -11$ is rejected.
Therefore, the breadth = x cm = 4 cm and length = $(x + 7)$ cm = $(4 + 7)$ cm = 11 cm.

Exercise 35.3

1. When a number x is added to its square, the total is 12. Find the value of x.

2. When a number x is subtracted from its square, the result is 30. Find the value of x.

3. A rectangle has a width of x m. Its length is 2 m longer than this.

    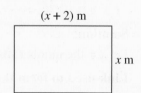

    (i) Write an expression in x for the area of the rectangle.

    If the area of the rectangle is 15 m²:

    (ii) Use this information to form an equation.

    (iii) Solve the equation to find the value of x.

4. A rectangle has a width of x cm. Its length is 5 cm longer than this.

    (i) Write an expression in x for the area of the rectangle.

    If the area of the rectangle is 36 cm²:

    (ii) Use this information to form an equation.

    (iii) Solve the equation to find the value of x.

5. A rectangle has a width of x cm. Its length is 4 cm longer than this.

    (i) Sketch the rectangle, marking the length and width in terms of x.

    (ii) Write an expression in x for the area of the rectangle.

    If the area of the rectangle is 21 cm²:

    (iii) Use this information to form an equation.

    (iv) Solve the equation to find the value of x.

6. A man bought x articles at a price of €$(x + 3)$ each.

    (i) Write an expression in x for the price of the articles.

    If he spent €28 altogether:

    (ii) Use this information to form an equation.

    (iii) Solve the equation to find the value of x.

7. A woman bought x articles at a price of €$(x - 2)$ each.

    (i) Write an expression in x for the price of the articles.

    If she spent €35 altogether:

    (ii) Use this information to form an equation.

    (iii) Solve the equation to find the value of x.

8. One positive number is 2 greater than another positive number.

    (i) If the smaller number is x, write the larger number in terms of x.

    (ii) Write, in terms of x, an expression for the product of the two numbers.

    Note: 'Product' means 'the result from multiplying'.

If the product is 8:

(iii) Use this information to form an equation.

(iv) Solve the equation to find x.

(v) What are the two numbers?

9. One positive number is 3 less than another number.

    (i) If the larger number is x, write the smaller number in terms of x.

  (ii) Write, in terms of x, an expression for the product of the two numbers.

If the product is 18:

(iii) Use this information to form an equation.

(iv) Solve the equation to find x.

(v) What are the two numbers?

10. A square has a length of x cm.

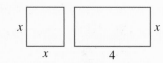

A rectangle has a length of 4 cm and a width of x cm.

Write, in terms of x, an expression for the area of:

  (i) The square.

 (ii) The rectangle.

If the area of the square added to the area of the rectangle is 12 cm^2:

(iii) Use this information to form an equation.

(iv) Solve the equation to find x.

11. A mug costs €$(x + 2)$ in a shop. A person bought x of these mugs at this price.

  (i) Write, in terms of x, how much the person spent.

If the person spent €24:

 (ii) Use this information to form an equation.

(iii) Solve the equation to find x.

(iv) What is the price of a mug?

12. A girl walked at a speed of x km/h for $(x - 3)$ hours.

  (i) Write, in terms of x, the distance walked by the girl.

    (Hint: distance = speed × time.)

If the girl walked a distance of 10 km:

 (ii) Use this information to form an equation.

(iii) Solve the equation to find x.

13. Find three consecutive natural number such that the product of the first two numbers is two greater than four times the third number.

14. Find three consecutive even numbers such that the product of the first two is two less than five times the third number.

Long division in algebra

Long division in algebra follows the same procedure as long division in arithmetic. The stages in dividing one algebraic expression by another are shown in the following examples.

EXAMPLE 1

Divide $3x^2 + 14x + 8$ by $x + 4$.

Solution:
$(3x^2 + 14x + 8) \div (x + 4)$

$$
\begin{array}{r}
3x + 2 \\
x + 4 \overline{)3x^2 + 14x + 8} \\
\underline{3x^2 + 12x} \\
2x + 8 \\
\underline{2x + 8} \\
0 + 0
\end{array}
$$

$(3x^2 \div x = 3x$, put $3x$ on top)

$(3x(x + 4) = 3x^2 + 12x)$

(subtract, bring down 8, $2x \div x = 2$, put 2 on top)

$(2(x + 4) = 2x + 8)$

(subtract)

$\therefore (3x^2 + 14x + 8) \div (x + 4) = 3x + 2$

EXAMPLE 2

Divide $2x^2 - 9x + 10$ by $2x - 5$.

Solution:
$(2x^2 - 9x + 10) \div (2x - 5)$

$$
\begin{array}{r}
x - 2 \\
2x - 5 \overline{)2x^2 - 9x + 10} \\
\underline{2x^2 - 5x} \\
-4x + 10 \\
\underline{-4x + 10} \\
0 + 0
\end{array}
$$

$(2x^2 \div 2x = x$, put x on top)

$(x(2x - 5) = 2x^2 - 5x)$

(subtract, bring down 10, $-4x \div 2x = -2$, put -2 on top)

$(-2(2x - 5) = -4x + 10)$

(subtract)

$\therefore (2x^2 - 9x + 10) \div (2x - 5) = x - 2$

Exercise 36.1

In questions 1–16, simplify the expression.

1. $\dfrac{5x}{x}$

2. $\dfrac{3x}{x}$

3. $\dfrac{2x}{x}$

4. $\dfrac{-2x}{x}$

5. $\dfrac{-6x}{x}$

6. $\dfrac{8x}{4x}$

7. $\dfrac{15x}{3x}$

8. $\dfrac{3x}{3x}$

9. $\dfrac{5x}{5x}$

10. $\dfrac{-8x}{8x}$

11. $\dfrac{2x^2}{x}$

12. $\dfrac{2x^2}{2x}$

13. $\dfrac{5x^2}{x}$

14. $\dfrac{-6x}{2x}$

15. $\dfrac{-16x}{8x}$

16. $\dfrac{-20x}{-4x}$

In questions 17–32, perform the division.

17. Divide $2x^2 + 11x + 12$ by $2x + 3$.

18. Divide $3x^2 + 5x + 2$ by $3x + 2$.

19. Divide $4x^2 + 11x + 6$ by $4x + 3$.

20. Divide $5x^2 + 13x + 6$ by $5x + 3$.

21. Divide $2x^2 + 5x + 3$ by $x + 1$.

22. Divide $3x^2 + 16x + 5$ by $x + 5$.

23. Divide $x^2 + 3x + 2$ by $x + 2$.

24. Divide $x^2 + 9x + 20$ by $x + 4$.

25. Divide $2x^2 + 9x - 5$ by $2x - 1$.

26. Divide $3x^2 - 7x - 6$ by $3x + 2$.

27. Divide $3x^2 + 7x - 6$ by $x + 3$.

28. Divide $2x^2 - 5x + 3$ by $x - 1$.

29. Divide $3x^2 + 10x - 8$ by $3x - 2$.

30. Divide $4x^2 - 21x + 5$ by $x - 5$.

31. Divide $8x^2 + 6x - 5$ by $2x - 1$.

32. Divide $6x^2 - x - 2$ by $3x - 2$.

33. Divide $2x^2 + 11x + 15$ by $x + 3$ and verify your answer by letting $x = 1$.

34. Divide $6x^2 + 17x + 5$ by $2x + 5$ and verify your answer by letting $x = 2$.

35. Write down an expression for the missing lengths, b, of each of the following rectangles.

(i)

b | Area $= 2x^2 + 11x + 5$

$2x + 1$

(ii)

b | Area $= x^2 + 7x + 12$

$x + 4$

(iii)

b | Area $= 6x^2 + 11x - 10$

$3x - 2$

Collecting data

Data are collected for many reasons. For example, a company may do some market research to find out if people like their new products or the Department of Education may collect information on the number of children in a certain area to see if they need to build more schools in that area. **Raw data** are the data as they were collected before any processing has been done. **Data logging** usually involves just counting. For example, if a shop owner wanted to record the number of customers that entered their shop, they can use a data logger, which would count customers as they enter. **Electronic data capture** is the process by which data are transferred from a paper copy, for example a questionnaire, to an electronic file, usually on a computer.

Primary data
Primary data (first-hand data) are data that you collect yourself or are collected by someone under your direct supervision.

Secondary data
Secondary data (second-hand data) are data that have already been collected and made available from an external source such as newspapers, government departments, organisations or the internet.

Primary and secondary data have their advantages and disadvantages.

Data	Advantages	Disadvantages
Primary	Know how it was obtained. Accuracy is also known.	Time consuming. Can be expensive.
Secondary	Easy and cheap to obtain.	Could be out of date. May have mistakes and be biased. Unknown source of collection.

Note: 'Data' is a plural word. So we really should say 'data are...', not 'data is...'. However, in everyday speech, most people use 'data' as a singular word. In this book we use data as a plural word.

Census

The **population** is the complete set of data under consideration. For example, a population may be all the females in Ireland between the ages of 12 and 18, all the sixth-year students in your school or the number of red cars in Ireland. A **census** is a collection of data relating to a population. A list of every item in a population is called a **sampling frame**.

Sample

A **sample** is a small part of the population selected for surveying. A **random sample** is a sample in which every member of the population has an equal chance of being selected. Data gathered from a sample are called **statistics**. Conclusions drawn from a sample can then be applied to the whole population (this is called statistical inference). However, it is very important that the sample chosen is representative of that population to avoid bias.

Bias

Bias (unfairness) is anything that distorts the data so that they will not give a representative sample. Bias can occur in sampling due to:

1. Failing to identify the correct population.
2. Choosing a sample that is not representative of the population.
3. A sample size that is too small (larger samples are usually more accurate).
4. Careless or dishonest answers to questions.
5. Using questions that are misleading or ambiguous.
6. Failure to respond to a survey.
7. Errors in recording the data, for example recording 23 as 32.
8. The data can go out of date, for example conclusions drawn from an opinion poll can change over a period of time.

Reasons for using samples

1. They are quick and cheap.
2. It is essential when the sampling units are destroyed (called destructive sampling). For example, we cannot test the lifetimes of every light bulb manufactured until they fail.
3. Quality of information gained is more manageable and better controlled, leading to better accuracy. (More time and money can be spent on the sample.)
4. It is often very difficult to gather data on a whole population.

Sample survey

A survey collects data (information). A sample survey is a survey that collects data from a sample of the population, usually using a questionnaire. Questionnaires are well-designed forms which are used to conduct sample surveys.

Note: It is good practice to do a **pilot survey**. A pilot survey is a small-scale survey carried out before the main survey. This helps to test your questions and the data collection method. It also helps to check if survey will produce the information required.

The main survey methods are:

Personal interview	People are asked questions directly. This is regularly used in market research.
Telephone survey	Often used for a personal interview.
Postal survey	A survey is sent to someone's address.
Online questionnaires	People fill out the questionnaire online.

Advantages and disadvantages are:

Method	Advantages	Disadvantages
Personal interview (face to face)	High response rate. Can ask many questions.	Can be expensive. Interviewer can influence response.
Telephone survey	High response rate. Can ask many questions. Can ask more personal questions.	Can be expensive. Interviewer can influence response. Easier to tell lies.
Postal survey	Relatively cheap. Can ask many questions. Can ask more personal questions.	Poor response rate. Partly completed. Limited in the type of data collected. No way of clarifying any questions.
Online questionnaires	Cheap and fast to collect large volume of data. More flexible design. Ease of editing. Can be sent directly to a database such as Microsoft Excel. No interviewer bias. Anonymity. No geographical problems.	Limited to those with access to an online computer. This leads to sample bias. Technical problems (crashes, freezes). Protecting privacy is an ethical issue.

Other methods for collecting data

Observational studies

Data obtained by making observations are called **observational studies**. The data is collected by counting, measuring or noting things that happen. For example, a traffic survey might be done in this way to reveal the number of vehicles passing over a bridge. Important factors are place, time of day and the amount of time spent collecting the data. Observational studies can be laborious and time consuming.

Designed experiments

The purpose of an experiment is to discover information. A **designed experiment** is a controlled study in which the researcher understands the cause-and-effect relationships. The study is controlled. This method of collecting data is very popular with drug companies testing a new drug to see if has any effect on those who take it. The experiment can usually measure the effects, if any, that result from changes in the situation. The experiment must be designed so that it will collect a sufficient amount of the right kind of information and does not mix up the information with something else. If the experiment is not well designed, any data you collect may be biased. An example of a good experiment is throwing a die many times to see if it is biased. The key things to remember are that the experiment must be repeated a number of times and that the experiment must be capable of being replicated by other people.

ANSWERS

Exercise 1.1

1. 16 **2.** 10 **3.** 23 **4.** 19 **5.** 7 **6.** 10 **7.** 11 **8.** 11 **9.** 5 **10.** 20

11. 11 **12.** 6 **13.** 18 **14.** 13 **15.** 1 **16.** 26 **17.** 2 **18.** 0 **19.** 2

20. 1 **21.** 1 **22.** (i) $6 + 2 - 5 = 3$ (ii) $4 \times 5 + 3 = 23$ (iii) $6 + 2 \times 4 = 14$

   (iv) $12 \times 2 \div 6 = 4$ (v) $4 \times 3 - 2 = 10$ (vi) $(20 - 8) \div 2 = 6$

23. Brian, because Aishling added before multiplying **24.** She subtracted before multiplying

25. $20 - 6 \times 3$ **26.** $4(3 + 2) = 20$

Exercise 1.2

1. 9 **2.** 16 **3.** 16 **4.** 25 **5.** 9 **6.** 20 **7.** 36 **8.** 150 **9.** 12 **10.** 16

11. 25 **12.** 8 **13.** 25 **14.** 10 **15.** 2 **16.** 3 **17.** 8 **18.** 4 **19.** 20

20. 31 **21.** 16 **22.** 26 **23.** 29 **24.** 80 **25.** 3 **26.** 9 **27.** 4 **28.** 6

29. 20 **30.** 35 **31.** 2 **32.** 5 **33.** 2 **34.** 4 **35.** 4 **36.** 2

37. Cerda. $\dfrac{8 + 4}{4 - 2} = (8 + 4) \div (4 - 2) = 12 \div 2 = 6$

38. He multiplied before squaring. $5(2)^2 = 5(4) = 20$ **39.** $5(3 + 1)^2 = 80$

Exercise 2.1

1. 1, 2, 3, 6 **2.** 1, 2, 4, 8 **3.** 1, 2, 5, 10 **4.** 1, 2, 3, 4, 6, 12 **5.** 1, 3, 5, 15

6. 1, 2, 3, 6, 9, 18 **7.** 1, 2, 4, 5, 10, 20 **8.** 1, 2, 3, 4, 6, 8, 12, 24 **9.** 1, 2, 4, 7, 14, 28

10. 1, 5, 7, 35 **11.** 1, 2, 4, 8, 16, 32 **12.** 1, 2, 4, 5, 8, 10, 20, 40

13. 1, 2, 3, 4, 6, 8, 12, 16, 24, 48 **14.** 1, 2, 5, 10, 25, 50 **15.** 1, 2, 4 **16.** 1, 3, 9

17. 1, 2, 4, 8, 16 **18.** 1, 5, 25 **19.** 1, 2, 4 **20.** 1, 5 **21.** 1, 2, 3, 4, 6, 12 **22.** 2

23. 3 **24.** 6 **25.** 10 **26.** 15 **27.** 9 **28.** 5 **29.** 4 **30.** (ii) 6 **31.** 2, 5

32. 3, 8 **35.** 8 and 16; 16 and 24; . . . **36.** 6 and 12; 12 and 18; 30 and 36; . . . **37.** Yes

Exercise 2.2

11. 3, 6, 9, 12, 15, 18 4, 8, 12, 16, 20, 24 5, 10, 15, 20, 25, 30

   6, 12, 18, 24, 30, 36 10, 20, 30, 40, 50, 60 12, 24, 36, 48, 60, 72

12. (i) 3, 6, 9, 12, 15, 18 (ii) 5, 10, 15, 20 (iii) 15 **13.** 12 **14.** 20 **15.** 24 **16.** 30

17. 36 **18.** 45 **19.** 18 **20.** 35 **21.** 12 **22.** 60 **23.** 30 **24.** 60

25. 120 seconds or 2 minutes; clock was started when both beams where on the ship

26. 30th June; Wednesday   27. 40 minutes   28. (i) 60 years   (ii) 15, 10 and 6   29. (i) 18

    (ii) 30   (iii) 13   (iv) 24 or 48 or 72 . . .   30. $48 \div 8 = 6$ 31. (i) 3   (ii) 5   (iii) 2

    32. 8 cm by 8 cm

Exercise 2.3

1. 2×3 2. 2×5 3. 3×5 4. 2×7 5. $2 \times 3 \times 3$ or 2×3^2 6. $2 \times 2 \times 5$ or $2^2 \times 5$

7. $2 \times 2 \times 2 \times 3$ or $2^3 \times 3$ 8. $2 \times 2 \times 7$ or $2^2 \times 7$ 9. $2 \times 2 \times 3 \times 3$ or $2^2 \times 3^2$

10. $2 \times 2 \times 2 \times 5$ or $2^3 \times 5$ 11. $3 \times 3 \times 5$ or $3^2 \times 5$ 12. $2 \times 2 \times 2 \times 7$ or $2^3 \times 7$

13. $2 \times 2 \times 3 \times 7$ or $2^2 \times 3 \times 7$ 14. $2 \times 2 \times 2 \times 3 \times 5$ or $2^3 \times 3 \times 5$

15. $2 \times 2 \times 3 \times 3 \times 3$ or $2^2 \times 3^3$ 16. $2 \times 3 \times 5 \times 5$ or $2 \times 3 \times 5^2$

17. $2 \times 2 \times 3 \times 3 \times 5$ or $2^2 \times 3^2 \times 5$ 18. $2 \times 2 \times 3 \times 5 \times 5$ or $2^2 \times 3 \times 5^2$ 19. 2

20. 3 and 7   21. 2 and 13   22. 2, 3 and 5   23. 3   24. 5

25. 2, 3, 5, 7, 11, 13, 17, 19, 23, 29, 31, 37, 41, 43, 47, 53, 59, 61, 67, 71, 73, 79, 83, 89, 97

26. $69 = 3 \times 23$; $205 = 5 \times 41$; $77 = 7 \times 11$ 27. (i) 10   (ii) 33   (iii) 35   (iv) 5

    (v) 25   (vi) 55   28. Present year $- 1980$

29. (i) 3,042,900   (ii) 55,110,055   (iii) 670,000,838   30. (i) $2 \times 2 \times 2 \times 3 \times 3$ or $2^3 \times 3^2$

    (ii) $2 \times 3 \times 5 \times 7$ (iii) $2 \times 2 \times 2 \times 3 \times 5 \times 5 \times 7$ or $2^3 \times 3 \times 5^2 \times 7$

31. (i) 2×5 (ii) $3 + 7$ or $2 + 3 + 5$ or $2 + 2 + 2 + 2 + 2$ or $2 + 2 + 3 + 3$

32. 7 and 17   33. 2,730   34. (i) False. 2 is prime and even   (ii) True, $1^2 = 1 \times 1$, $4 = 2 \times 2$, . . .

Exercise 3.1

1. (i) $a = 3, b = 6, c = -4, d = -6$ (ii) $a = -1, b = -2, c = 8, d = -6$ (iii) $a = 0, b = 4, c = -5$,

    $d = -7$ 2. $-€25$ 3. (i) $-€30$ (ii) $€70$

4. (i) $-1, 5$ (ii) $-3, 0, 2, 4$ (iii) $-5, -4, -2, 3$ 5. (i) $7°C$ (ii) $3°C$ (iii) $0°C$ (iv) $-3°C$

6. (i) -40 m   (ii) -65m   7. $5°C$ 8. $12°C$ 9. 250 m   10. (i) (a) Dorothy   (b) Andrew

    (ii) Dorothy, Hilda, Fiona, Brendan, Greg, Edward, Ciara and Andrew

11. (i) (a) Cairo   (b) Moscow   (ii) $-22°C, -3°C, -2°C, 1°C, 4°C$ (iii) Cairo

    (iv) (a) $3°C$ (b) $19°C$ 12. (i) 6   (ii) 1   (iii) -5 13. (i) $3 < 5$ (ii) $7 > 2$

    (iii) $3 > -2$ (iv) $1 > -2$ (v) $-3 < 4$ (vi) $0 > -2$ (vii) $-3 > -7$ (viii) $-4 < -3$

Exercise 3.2

1. (i) (a) 6   (b) 1   (c) 3   (d) -1 (e) -5 (f) -6 (g) -1 (h) 0

2. 2   3. 2   4. 3   5. 0   6. 7   7. 2   8. 5   9. 3   10. -6 11. -4 12. -2

13. -8 14. -2 15. 2   16. 3   17. -2 18. -2 19. -3 20. -7 21. 3

22. 2   23. 4   24. 2   25. 0   26. 3   27. 2

28. (i) 3   (ii) 4   (iii) 3   (iv) 10   (v) 2   (vi) −3   **29.** (i) 10   (ii) 5

30. $a = -7, b = 5$ **32.** −70 m   **33.** (i) 2 and 5   (ii) 3

36. (i) 1,300 m   (ii) 375 m   (iii) 150 m   (iv) 1,075 m

Exercise 3.3

1. −4   **2.** −15   **3.** 18   **4.** −20   **5.** −6   **6.** 16   **7.** −24   **8.** 15   **9.** −2   **10.** −5

11. −3   **12.** 5   **13.** −2   **14.** 4   **15.** −3   **16.** 2   **17.** 1   **18.** 9   **19.** 4   **20.** −8

21. −22   **22.** −3   **23.** −7   **24.** 5   **25.** −2   **26.** 3   **27.** 7   **28.** −4

30. (i) (a) −2   (b) −3   (c) −4

Exercise 3.4

1. 9   **2.** 25   **3.** 49   **4.** 1   **5.** 8   **6.** 27   **7.** 64   **8.** 4   **9.** 16   **10.** 25

11. 36   **12.** 1   **13.** −1   **14.** −125   **15.** 49   **16.** −27   **17.** 16

18. 100   **19.** 64   **20.** 144

Exercise 3.5

1. 17   **2.** 10   **3.** 14   **4.** 8   **5.** 5   **6.** 7   **7.** 5   **8.** 3   **9.** 14   **10.** 21   **11.** 1

12. 14   **13.** 2   **14.** 6   **15.** 2   **16.** 8   **17.** 7   **18.** 32   **19.** 3   **20.** 0   **21.** −8

22. 4   **23.** −2   **24.** −5   **25.** 5   **26.** −4   **27.** 2   **28.** 3   **29.** 0   **30.** 40

Exercise 3.6

1. 18   **2.** 20   **3.** 6   **4.** 4   **5.** 2   **6.** 3   **7.** 3   **8.** 2   **9.** 1   **10.** 4   **11.** 10   **12.** 4

13. 10   **14.** 24   **15.** 28   **16.** −12   **17.** 15   **18.** −4   **19.** 6   **20.** 8   **21.** 6   **22.** 2

23. 24   **24.** 0   **25.** 9   **26.** 18   **27.** 16   **28.** 12   **29.** 32   **30.** 48   **31.** 20   **32.** 61

33. 2   **34.** 9   **35.** 9   **36.** 16   **37.** 80   **38.** 12   **39.** 32   **40.** 3   **41.** 2   **42.** 1   **43.** 3

44. 2   **45.** 9   **46.** $-3^2 = -1 \times 3 \times 3 = -9; (-3)^2 = -3 \times -3 = 9$

Exercise 4.1

1. (i) $\dfrac{1}{2}$ (ii) $\dfrac{1}{4}$ (iii) $\dfrac{1}{4}$ (iv) $\dfrac{3}{4}$ (v) $\dfrac{1}{3}$ (vi) $\dfrac{1}{2}$ (vii) $\dfrac{2}{3}$ (viii) $\dfrac{7}{10}$ (ix) $\dfrac{2}{3}$ (x) $\dfrac{1}{3}$

2. (i) $\dfrac{5}{8}$ (ii) $\dfrac{1}{4}$ (iii) $\dfrac{5}{6}$ (iv) $\dfrac{1}{3}$ (v) $\dfrac{7}{8}$ (vi) $\dfrac{3}{4}$ (vii) $\dfrac{1}{2}$ (viii) $\dfrac{2}{3}$ (ix) $\dfrac{1}{4}$

3. (ii) $\dfrac{1}{4}$ **4.** (i) 2   (ii) 6   (iii) 20   (iv) 2   (v) 3   (vi) 2   (vii) 4   (viii) 15

   (ix) 4   (x) 6   (xi) 18, 8   (xii) 10; 2 and 4, 3 and 6, ...

5. Yes; $\dfrac{6}{8} = \dfrac{3}{4} = \dfrac{9}{12}$ **6.** $\dfrac{4}{18} = \dfrac{6}{27} = \dfrac{2}{9}$

7. No. $\dfrac{2}{3} = \dfrac{8}{12}$; John did not multiply top and bottom by same number

8. (i) $\dfrac{1}{4}$ (ii) (a) We can only multiply or divide the top and bottom by the same number (except 0)

(b) $\dfrac{12}{24} \neq \dfrac{1}{4}$ 9. $\dfrac{3}{5} = \dfrac{9}{15}; \dfrac{2}{3} = \dfrac{10}{15}; \quad \therefore \dfrac{2}{3} > \dfrac{3}{5}$

10. $\dfrac{10}{15} = \dfrac{2}{3}, \dfrac{15}{20} = \dfrac{3}{4}.$ Thus, Kate is wrong, as $\dfrac{2}{3} \neq \dfrac{3}{4}.$ 11. Between $\dfrac{3}{4}$ and 1

Exercise 4.2

1. $\dfrac{9}{4}$ 2. $\dfrac{13}{5}$ 3. $\dfrac{19}{4}$ 4. $\dfrac{15}{4}$ 5. $\dfrac{7}{5}$ 6. $\dfrac{33}{10}$ 7. $\dfrac{15}{8}$ 8. $\dfrac{27}{8}$ 9. $\dfrac{22}{5}$

10. $\dfrac{17}{3}$ 11. $\dfrac{30}{7}$ 12. $\dfrac{43}{5}$ 13. $1\dfrac{3}{4}$ 14. $2\dfrac{1}{6}$ 15. $6\dfrac{1}{4}$ 16. $3\dfrac{2}{3}$

17. $2\dfrac{3}{7}$ 18. $2\dfrac{3}{8}$ 19. $4\dfrac{2}{5}$ 20. $3\dfrac{1}{2}$ 21. $1\dfrac{1}{2}$ 22. $2\dfrac{2}{9}$ 23. $6\dfrac{3}{5}$ 24. $6\dfrac{5}{6}$

25. $\dfrac{4}{5}$ 26. $\dfrac{6}{7}$ 27. $\dfrac{1}{3}$ 28. $\dfrac{1}{8}$ 29. $\dfrac{2}{3}$ 30. $\dfrac{9}{10}$ 31. $\dfrac{3}{4}$ 32. $\dfrac{7}{6}$ or $1\dfrac{1}{6}$

33. $\dfrac{17}{12}$ or $1\dfrac{5}{12}$ 34. $\dfrac{3}{2}$ or $1\dfrac{1}{2}$ 35. $\dfrac{7}{20}$ 36. $\dfrac{1}{10}$ 37. $\dfrac{39}{8}$ or $4\dfrac{7}{8}$ 38. $\dfrac{109}{20}$ or $5\dfrac{9}{20}$

39. $\dfrac{45}{8}$ or $5\dfrac{5}{8}$ 40. $\dfrac{5}{2}$ or $2\dfrac{1}{2}$ 41. $\dfrac{11}{12}$ 42. $-\dfrac{11}{12}$ 43. $\dfrac{27}{8}$ or $3\dfrac{3}{8}$ 44. $\dfrac{37}{12}$ or $3\dfrac{1}{12}$

45. $-\dfrac{23}{20}$ or $-1\dfrac{3}{20}$ 46. $20\dfrac{1}{12}$ cm   47. $16\dfrac{7}{12}$ cm   48. $10\dfrac{1}{2}$ km

49. (i) $\dfrac{1}{4}$ (ii) Bren won; $\dfrac{2}{5} = \dfrac{8}{20}; \dfrac{1}{4} = \dfrac{5}{20}; \dfrac{2}{5} > \dfrac{7}{20}$ and $\dfrac{2}{5} > \dfrac{1}{4}$ 51. $x = \dfrac{5}{6}$

52. (i) $\dfrac{3}{5}, \dfrac{7}{10}$ (ii) $\dfrac{1}{4}, \dfrac{3}{8}, \dfrac{1}{2}$ (iii) $\dfrac{1}{8}, \dfrac{5}{16}, \dfrac{1}{2}, \dfrac{3}{4}$

53. $\dfrac{7}{10}; \dfrac{1}{2} = \dfrac{10}{20}, \dfrac{7}{10} = \dfrac{14}{20}$ and $\dfrac{3}{4} = \dfrac{15}{20}, \quad \therefore \dfrac{7}{10}$ is between $\dfrac{1}{2}$ and $\dfrac{3}{4}$

54. (i) The LCM of 2 and 3 is 6   (ii) $\dfrac{1}{6}$

55. (i) Rory subtracted the top of the second fraction from the top of the first fraction and subtracted the bottom of the second fraction from the bottom of the second fraction. This is an incorrect method. See the correct method in (ii).

(ii) $\dfrac{7}{8} - \dfrac{1}{5} = \dfrac{35}{40} - \dfrac{8}{40} = \dfrac{35-8}{40} = \dfrac{27}{40}$

57. (i) $\dfrac{5}{12}$ (ii) 4   58. (i) $\dfrac{1}{2}$ (ii) $\dfrac{3}{10}$ 59. (i) $\dfrac{1}{3}$ (ii) $\dfrac{3}{4}$ (iii) $\dfrac{5}{12}$ (iv) $\dfrac{1}{8}$

Exercise 4.3

1. $\dfrac{10}{21}$ 2. $\dfrac{3}{20}$ 3. $\dfrac{15}{28}$ 4. $\dfrac{1}{3}$ 5. $\dfrac{8}{21}$ 6. $\dfrac{3}{4}$ 7. $\dfrac{15}{16}$ 8. 3 9. $\dfrac{5}{6}$

10. $\dfrac{49}{12}$ or $4\dfrac{1}{12}$ 11. $\dfrac{3}{2}$ or $1\dfrac{1}{2}$ 12. $\dfrac{7}{2}$ or $3\dfrac{1}{2}$ 13. 10 14. $\dfrac{5}{16}$ 15. $\dfrac{54}{11}$ or $4\dfrac{10}{11}$ 16. $\dfrac{35}{36}$

18. $\dfrac{2}{5}$ of $8\dfrac{1}{2}$; $\dfrac{4}{5}$ of $4\dfrac{1}{8} = \dfrac{4}{5} \times \dfrac{33}{8} = \dfrac{33}{10}$; $\dfrac{2}{5}$ of $8\dfrac{1}{2} = \dfrac{2}{5} \times \dfrac{17}{2} = \dfrac{17}{5} = \dfrac{34}{10}$; $\dfrac{34}{10} > \dfrac{33}{10}$ 19. 10 km

20. (i) $\dfrac{8}{15}$ (ii) $\dfrac{2}{15}$ 21. (i) 72 m² (ii) $37\dfrac{2}{3}$ m 22. 9 tins 23. (i) $\dfrac{4}{15}$ (ii) 15

Exercise 4.4

1. $\dfrac{21}{20}$ or $1\dfrac{1}{20}$ 2. $\dfrac{6}{5}$ or $1\dfrac{1}{5}$ 3. $\dfrac{2}{5}$ 4. $\dfrac{4}{3}$ or $1\dfrac{1}{3}$ 5. $\dfrac{3}{2}$ or $1\dfrac{1}{2}$ 6. $\dfrac{1}{6}$ 7. 2 8. 4

9. $\dfrac{1}{3}$ 10. $\dfrac{5}{8}$ 11. $\dfrac{2}{5}$ 12. $\dfrac{6}{7}$ 13. $\dfrac{2}{3}$ 14. 3 15. $\dfrac{1}{2}$ 16. $\dfrac{7}{2}$ or $3\dfrac{1}{2}$

17. $\dfrac{21}{5}$ or $4\dfrac{1}{5}$ 18. $\dfrac{7}{3}$ or $2\dfrac{1}{3}$ 19. $\dfrac{15}{2}$ or $7\dfrac{1}{2}$ 20. $\dfrac{16}{5}$ or $3\dfrac{1}{5}$ 21. 20 22. $\dfrac{7}{20}$

23. 10 24. $\dfrac{10}{3}$ or $3\dfrac{1}{3}$ 25. 18 26. Yes; $12 \div \dfrac{2}{3} = 18$ or $17 \times \dfrac{2}{3} = 11\dfrac{1}{3}$

27. 22 28. 42 29. 12

Exercise 4.5

1. $\dfrac{1}{4}$ 2. $\dfrac{4}{9}$ 3. $\dfrac{9}{16}$ 4. $\dfrac{16}{25}$ 5. $\dfrac{1}{16}$ 6. $\dfrac{1}{9}$ 7. $\dfrac{1}{27}$ 8. $\dfrac{1}{125}$ 9. $\dfrac{27}{125}$

10. $\dfrac{25}{16}$ or $1\dfrac{9}{16}$ 11. $\dfrac{16}{9}$ or $1\dfrac{7}{9}$ 12. $\dfrac{49}{16}$ or $3\dfrac{1}{16}$ 13. $\dfrac{100}{9}$ or $11\dfrac{1}{9}$ 14. $\dfrac{144}{25}$ or $5\dfrac{19}{25}$

15. $\dfrac{27}{8}$ or $3\dfrac{3}{8}$ 16. $\dfrac{81}{25}$ or $3\dfrac{6}{25}$ 17. $\dfrac{8}{27}$ 18. $\dfrac{125}{8}$ or $15\dfrac{5}{8}$ 19. $\dfrac{1}{4}$ 20. $\dfrac{4}{9}$

Exercise 4.6

1. $\dfrac{17}{20}$ 2. $\dfrac{3}{5}$ 3. $\dfrac{7}{4}$ or $1\dfrac{3}{4}$ 4. $\dfrac{1}{4}$ 5. $\dfrac{5}{8}$ 6. $\dfrac{4}{3}$ or $1\dfrac{1}{3}$ 7. 2 8. $\dfrac{7}{8}$

9. $\dfrac{31}{16}$ or $1\dfrac{15}{16}$ 10. $\dfrac{5}{4}$ or $1\dfrac{1}{4}$ 11. $\dfrac{1}{4}$ 12. 1 13. 6 14. $\dfrac{1}{2}$ 15. $\dfrac{1}{5}$ 16. 1

17. $\dfrac{25}{36}$ 18. $\dfrac{1}{30}$ 19. Both equal $\dfrac{17}{20}$ 20. $\dfrac{1}{3}$ 21. (i) $\dfrac{3}{4}$ (ii) $\dfrac{3}{10}$ (iii) $\dfrac{11}{20}$

(iv) $\dfrac{9}{20}$ 22. (i) 250 g   (ii) $\dfrac{1}{4}$

23. (i) $\dfrac{3}{7}; \dfrac{2}{5}$ (iii) We always and up with the fraction we started with

Exercise 4.7

1. $\dfrac{3}{4}$ 2. $\dfrac{3}{5}$ 3. $\dfrac{2}{3}$ 4. $\dfrac{1}{5}$ 5. $\dfrac{5}{8}$ 6. $\dfrac{1}{3}$ 7. $\dfrac{1}{6}$ 8. $\dfrac{1}{4}$ 9. $\dfrac{1}{3}$ 10. $\dfrac{2}{7}$ 11. $\dfrac{1}{2}$

12. $\dfrac{3}{4}$ 13. $\dfrac{3}{10}$ 14. $\dfrac{1}{3}$ 15. $\dfrac{4}{5}$ 16. $\dfrac{5}{16}$ 17. $\dfrac{1}{5}$ 18. $\dfrac{2}{5}$ 19. $\dfrac{3}{7}$ 20. $\dfrac{1}{3}$

21. (i) $\dfrac{2}{5}$ (ii) $\dfrac{1}{3}$ (iii) $\dfrac{4}{15}$ 22. (i) $\dfrac{1}{3}$ (ii) $\dfrac{3}{10}$ (iii) $\dfrac{1}{5}$ (iv) $\dfrac{1}{6}$ 23. (i) 2   (ii) 4

(iii) 5   (iv) 9   24. 40   25. 24   26. 20   27. 24   28. 32   29. 54

30. €40   31. 450   32. (i) $P = \dfrac{5}{8}$ (ii) $Q = 60, R = 150$ 33. 75 cm

Exercise 5.1

41. (i) 2·7   (ii) 4·6   42. (i) (a) 23·47   (b) 2·347   (ii) (a) 163·8   (b) 1·638

(iii) (a) 51,296·0   (b) 5·1296   (iv) (a) 235·84   (b) 2,358·4   (c) 23·584

43. (i) 60·5   (ii) 5·06

Exercise 5.2

1. $\dfrac{2}{5}$ 2. $\dfrac{7}{10}$ 3. $\dfrac{3}{5}$ 4. $\dfrac{1}{5}$ 5. $\dfrac{9}{10}$ 6. $\dfrac{1}{4}$ 7. $\dfrac{3}{4}$ 8. $\dfrac{3}{20}$ 9. $\dfrac{7}{20}$

10. $\dfrac{11}{20}$ 11. $\dfrac{1}{8}$ 12. $\dfrac{3}{8}$ 13. $\dfrac{11}{10}$ or $1\dfrac{1}{10}$ 14. $\dfrac{23}{10}$ or $2\dfrac{3}{10}$ 15. $\dfrac{19}{5}$ or $3\dfrac{4}{5}$

16. $\dfrac{1}{20}$ 17. $\dfrac{49}{20}$ or $2\dfrac{9}{20}$ 18. $\dfrac{81}{25}$ or $3\dfrac{6}{25}$ 19. $\dfrac{14}{5}$ or $2\dfrac{4}{5}$ 20. $\dfrac{1}{16}$

21. $\dfrac{29}{25}$ or $1\dfrac{4}{25}$ 22. $\dfrac{29}{8}$ or $3\dfrac{5}{8}$ 23. $\dfrac{61}{25}$ or $2\dfrac{11}{25}$ 24. $\dfrac{27}{25}$ or $1\dfrac{2}{25}$ 25. $\dfrac{41}{20}$ or $2\dfrac{1}{20}$

26. (i) $\dfrac{4}{5}$ (ii) $\dfrac{1}{25}$ (iii) $\dfrac{2}{25}$ (iv) $\dfrac{1}{200}$

Exercise 5.3

1. 9·5   2. 6·2   3. 21·9   4. 11·1   5. 2·6   6. 4   7. 12·3   8. 24·2   9. 35·4

10. 19·7   11. 25·6   12. 5·94   13. 4·5   14. 0   15. 27   16. 12·348

17. −11·16   18. 5·8   19. 15·5   20. 4·07   21. 5·85   22. 1·92   23. 1·12

24. 40   **25.** 60   **26.** 32·5   **27.** 4   **28.** (i) 0·36 (ii) 0·64 (iii) 6·25 (iv) 2·5

30. (i) 18 (ii) 30 cm   **31.** 17·4 cm   **33.** 3 by 54c and 4 by 38c   **34.** (i) 0·75g (ii) 800

36. (i) $0·3 \times 0·8 = 0·24$ (ii) $1·5 \times 2·6 = 3·9$ (iii) $15·6 \div 0·3 = 52$

37. No. Mass of 10·2 tonnes   **38.** 648 mm   **39.** 30·16

Exercise 5.4

2. (i) 54,570 (ii) 54,600 (iii) 55,000 (iv) 50,000   **4.** (i) 75 (ii) 84

5. (i) 2,350 (ii) 2,449   **6.** Nearest 1,000   **7.** (i) 4,567 (ii) (a) 4,570 (b) 4,600

  (c) 5,000   **8.** (i) (a) 80 (b) 100 (ii) (a) 230 (b) 200 (iii) (a) 460 (b) 500

9. No; €19,000   **10.** 28·5 cm

Exercise 5.5

1. (i) 8·8 (ii) 3·5 (iii) 23·4 (iv) 1·8 (v) 3·9

2. (i) 6·14 (ii) 9·14 (iii) 31·27 (iv) 0·64 (v) 0·01

3. (i) 4·577 (ii) 0·123 (iii) 15·289 (iv) 0·038 (v) 2·480

4. (i) 11·54 (ii) 17·38 (iii) 39·44 (iv) 2·55

5. (i) 0·14 (ii) 1·67 (iii) 0·55 (iv) 0·28 (v) 0·06   **6.** (i) 4·4 (ii) 4·43

7. (i) 68·2 kg (ii) 68·25 kg (iii) 68 kg (iv) 70 kg   **8.** No; 0·556

Exercise 5.6

1. (i) 20 (ii) 600 (iii) 400 (iv) 20 (v) 0·09

2. (i) 470 (ii) 350 (iii) 4,800 (iv) 29 (v) 0·068

3. (i) 4,580 (ii) 7,590 (iii) 3,280 (iv) 24·9 (v) 0·0796

4. (i) 8,300 (ii) 9·3 (iii) 0·35 (iv) 0·29

5. (i) 0·67 (ii) 1·6 (iii) 0·64 (iv) 1·8 (v) 0·056

6. (i) 28·43 (ii) 28·4 (iii) 28 (iv) 30   **7.** No; 580

Exercise 5.7

1. 24; 24·51; 0·51   **2.** 6; 6·4; 0·4   **3.** 20; 18; 2   **4.** 3; 3·6; 0·6   **5.** 5; 5·15; 0·15

6. 3; 3·15; 0·15   **7.** 8; 7·6; 0·4   **8.** 5; 5·2; 0·2   **9.** 7; 6·94; 0·06   **10.** 4; 4·1; 0·1

11. 4; 4·05; 0·05   **12.** 6; 6·1; 0·1   **13.** $40 \times 4 = 160$

14. (i) 600; 20 (ii) 30; 32 (iii) 2

15. (i) 6,000 (ii) Both numbers were increased for the estimate

16. $4 \times 10 = 40$ **17.** (i) $\dfrac{21 - 5}{2} = \dfrac{16}{2} = 8$ (ii) 10 (iii) Should have used $(20·8 - 4·8) \div (1·6)$

Exercise 6.1

1. (i) 5   (ii) 6   (iii) 13   (iv) 9   2. (i) 8   (ii) 20   (iii) 17   (iv) 5
(v) 25   (vi) 22   (vii) 3   (viii) 3   3. (i) 7   (ii) 3   (iii) 12   (iv) 10
(v) 20   (vi) 0   (vii) 4   (viii) 16   4. (i) 2   (ii) 5   (iii) 7
5. 6   6. 17   7. 14   8. 19   9. 12   10. (i) 3   (ii) −4   (iii) 1   (iv) 0
(v) 9   (vi) 7   (vii) 1   (viii) −7   11. (i) 1   (ii) 3   (iii) 4   (iv) −2   (v) 8
(vi) 9   (vii) 3   (viii) 1   12. 9   13. (i) €21   (ii) €51   (iii) €81   (iv) €6
14. (i) €29   (ii) €35   (iii) €63   15. (i) 10°C   (ii) 25°C   16. (i) 900   (ii) 500
17. Alice, Easy Talk; Brian, Talk On; Ciara, Talk On; Dean, Easy Talk

Exercise 6.2

1. $5a$ 2. $9b$ 3. $7x$ 4. $8y$ 5. $3a$ 6. $4x$ 7. $3x$ 8. $6x$ 9. $7x$ 10. $6x$
11. $4a$ 12. $8q$ 13. $5a + 3$ 14. $7x + 6$ 15. $6a + 8b$ 16. $7p^2$ 17. $3x^2$ 18. a^2
19. $7p$ 20. $4x$ 21. $6q$ 22. $9ab$ 23. $6ab$ 24. $3ab$ 25. $-2x$ 26. $-3x$
27. $-2a$ 28. $-x$ 29. $-x$ 30. $-2a$ 31. $5x$ 32. 0   33. $3x$ 34. $x^2 + 6x + 8$
35. $x^2 + 2x - 15$ 36. $x^2 - 5x + 4$ 37. 0   38. 2   41. (i) $(3a + 2b)$ g   (ii) $(4p + 2q)$ g
(iii) $(3m + 4n)$ g   42. (i) $2a$ (ii) $4a$ (iii) a (iv) $2a + b$ (v) $6ab$ (vi) $2a^2$
43. (i) $6x$ cm   (ii) $3x$ cm   44. $(5x + 5y + 8)$ cm
45. (i) $(a + 4b + 4)$ kg   (ii) $(3x + 3y + 8)$ kg   (iii) $(5p + 6q + 8r)$ kg
46. (i) and (iii) as perimeter = $10a$ m; not (ii) as perimeter = $12a$ m > $10a$ m (too long)
47. sum = $3p$, sum = $3a$ 49. For example, $3a + 2a$; $6a − a$

Exercise 6.3

1. 12   2. −15   3. −8   4. 18   5. $10a$ 6. $12b$ 7. $10x$ 8. $16y$ 9. $8m$
10. $30x$ 11. $4x$ 12. $7x$ 13. a^2 14. $6a^2$ 15. $10a^3$ 16. $12a^3$ 17. $6ab$
18. $12pq$ 19. $2pq$ 20. $3k^2$ 21. $-8pq$ 22. $15ab$ 23. $12k^2$ 24. $-12ab$ 25. $-10x^2$
26. $6x^2$ 27. $-8x^2$ 28. $-2x^2$ 29. $-2x$ 30. $5x$ 31. $-4x$ 32. $3x^2$ 33. $-x^4$ 34. $-2x^3$
35. $4x^2$ 36. $5x^3$ 37. $3a \times 2 = 6a$; $3 \times a \times a = 3a^2$; $3a \times 2b = 6ab$; $3a \times 2ab = 6a^2b$

Exercise 6.4

1. $2x + 10$ 2. $3x + 6$ 3. $8x + 4$ 4. $12x + 8$ 5. $9 + 15a$ 6. $15 + 10p$ 7. $9a − 6$
8. $6 − 8b$ 9. $6x + 4y$ 10. $2x + 13$ 11. $3a + 10$ 12. $10a + 6$ 13. $8x + 3$
14. $4x − 10$ 15. $16x + 6$ 16. $6x + 8$ 17. $22a − 9$ 18. x 19. $-10 + 8x$
20. $-3 + 7x$ 21. $1 + 3x$ 22. $16x + 18$ 23. $11x + 13$ 24. 0   25. x 26. 12
27. −3   28. $4x$ 29. x 30. $2a$ 31. $5x$ 32. x^2 33. 0   34. 7
37. $4(x + 2) = 8 + 4x$; $4(2 − x) + 4x = 8$; $2(6x + 1) = 12x + 2$; $2(2x + 4) + 8x = 12x + 8$ 38. $5x$

Exercise 6.5

1. $2x^2 + 6x$ 2. $6x^2 + 15x$ 3. $4x^2 + 8x$ 4. $5a^2 + 20a$ 5. $2p^2 + 6p$ 6. $3q^2 - 3q$

7. $7x^2 - 14x$ 8. $24x - 6x^2$ 9. $10x^2 - 30x$ 10. $-2x^2 + 6x$ 11. $-6x^2 - 3x$

12. $-x^2 + 4x$ 13. $x^2 + 5x + 6$ 14. $x^2 + 6x + 9$ 15. $9x^2$ 16. $2x^2$ 17. $4x^2 + 9x$

18. $2x$ 19. 0 20. a 21. $8x^3$ 22. x^2

Exercise 6.6

1. $x^2 + 3x + 2$ 2. $x^2 + 5x + 6$ 3. $x^2 + 9x + 20$ 4. $x^2 + 7x + 6$ 5. $x^2 + 7x + 10$

6. $x^2 + 10x + 21$ 7. $2x^2 + 5x + 3$ 8. $2x^2 + 11x + 5$ 9. $3x^2 + 17x + 10$ 10. $x^2 + 3x - 10$

11. $x^2 + x - 6$ 12. $x^2 + 2x - 15$ 13. $x^2 - 6x + 8$ 14. $x^2 - 9x + 18$ 15. $x^2 - 3x + 2$

16. $2a^2 + a - 3$ 17. $2a^2 + 9a - 5$ 18. $2x^2 - x - 10$ 19. $3a^2 - 10a + 3$ 20. $2p^2 - 7p + 3$

21. $3x^2 + 11x - 20$ 22. $6x^2 + 11x + 3$ 23. $8a^2 - 10a - 3$ 24. $4x^2 - 9$ 25. $x^2 - 25$

26. $x^2 - 9$ 27. $x^2 - 1$ 28. $x^2 + 2x + 1$ 29. $x^2 - 6x + 9$ 30. $4x^2 + 4x + 1$ 31. x

32. 0 35. (i) $6x + 8$ (ii) $2x^2 + 9x - 5$ 36. (i) $3x^2$ (ii) $x^2 + 13x$ (iii) $5x + 5$

37. (i) $x^2 + 5x + 6$ (ii) $x^2, 3x, 2x, 6; x^2 + 3x + 2x + 6 = x^2 + 5x + 6$

Exercise 7.1

1. (i) 8   (ii) 6   (iii) 3   2. (i) 5   (ii) 2   (iii) 3

Exercise 7.3

1. 2   2. 4   3. 3   4. 5   5. 3   6. 5   7. 3   8. 2   9. 6   10. 11   11. -2

12. -3 13. -6 14. -5 15. 0   16. 0   17. 3   18. 5   19. 4   20. 6

21. -2 22. 3   23. 4   24. -4 25. 2   26. 2   27. -10 28. -6 29. 4

30. 2   31. 5   32. 7   33. 9   34. 14   35. 4   36. 11   37. 11   38. 5

39. 3   40. 9   41. 13   42. 5   43. 10   44. 11

45. (ii) $2t + 6$ (iii) $4t + 5 = 2t + 6$ (iv) 2 kg   46. (i) (a) $5a$ (b) $2a + 750$

(ii) $5a = 2a + 750$ (iii) 250 g

Exercise 7.4

1. 2   2. 4   3. 4   4. 1   5. 6   6. -5 7. 1   8. 4   9. 2   10. 4   11. 4

12. -1 13. 3   14. 3   15. -6 16. 2   17. 1   18. 3   19. 3   20. 1   21. 9

22. -4 23. 2   24. 5   25. 7   26. 2   27. 6   28. 1   29. 2   30. -3

Exercise 7.5

1. 3   2. 5   3. 1   4. 3   5. 1   6. 5   7. 2   8. 5   9. 10   10. -12

11. 2   12. -11 13. -6 14. 3   15. 4   16. 5   17. 4   18. 9   19. 4   20. 7

Exercise 8.1

1. 1 : 2   **2.** 3 : 4   **3.** 1 : 3   **4.** 2 : 5   **5.** 3 : 5   **6.** 2 : 3   **7.** 5 : 4   **8.** 5 : 3

9. 6 : 5   **10.** 3 : 2   **11.** 4 : 5   **12.** 1 : 5   **13.** 3 : 2   **14.** 4 : 3   **15.** 8 : 7

16. 5 : 8   **17.** 2 : 3 : 5   **18.** 3 : 4 : 5   **19.** 1 : 4 : 5   **20.** 3 : 4 : 7   **21.** 2 : 5

22. 3 : 4   **23.** 2 : 3   **24.** 1 : 3   **25.** 1 : 5   **26.** 3 : 8   **27.** 3 : 10   **28.** 9 : 10

29. 2 : 7   **30.** 3 : 1   **31.** 3 : 8   **32.** 1 : 5   **33.** 1 : 10   **34.** 8 : 15

35. (i) 1 : 3   (ii) 1 : 1   (iii) 2 : 3   (iv) 1 : 2   **36.** (i) 1 : 2   (ii) 1 : 3   **37.** (i) 1 : 3

    (ii) 2 : 5   (iii) 7 : 2   **38.** 6 : 5   **39.** 207 : 127 : 123   **40.** (i) 3 : 2   (ii) 3 : 10

    (iii) 5 : 1   **41.** 5 : 4

Exercise 8.2

1. $\frac{1}{4}$; 25%   **2.** (i) $\frac{1}{10}$ (ii) €120   **3.** (i) $\frac{5}{8}$ (ii) 144,000   **4.** €550   **5.** 27·2 km

Exercise 8.3

1. €6; €12   **2.** €12; €18   **3.** €6; €18   **4.** 15 kg; 25 kg   **5.** 12 mins; 16 mins

6. 30 cm; 20 cm   **7.** 6 months; 3 months   **8.** 20; 16   **9.** 56; 32   **10.** €75; €45

11. 200 pupils; 250 pupils   **12.** 120 g; 140 g   **13.** 90; 60   **14.** €16·24; €8·12

15. €6·12; €9·18   **16.** €24; €96; €60   **17.** 200 g; 160 g; 120 g   **18.** €1,000; €1,400; €1,600

19. 30 kg; 60 kg; 80 kg   **20.** 72 cm; 54 cm; 36 cm   **21.** €8; €16   **22.** €35; €15

23. €10; €20   **24.** €560   **25.** 180   **26.** €15   **27.** Boy €160; girl €240

28. 15 cm; 20 cm; 25 cm   **29.** Copper 42 kg; zinc 24 kg; tin 18 kg   **30.** €21,600; €34,560

31. A €3,000; B €2,000; C €1,500

Exercise 8.4

1. (i) €60; €60   (ii) €80; €40   (iii) €90; €30   **2.** A €60; B €80; C €40   **3.** P €60; Q €30; R €30

4. €12   **5.** (i) B   (ii) A €20; B €10; C €40   **6.** (i) X   (ii) X €30; Y €90; Z €180

Exercise 8.5

1. €60   **2.** (i) €42   (ii) €18   **3.** €200   **4.** (i) 819   (ii) 455   **5.** 64 km/h   **6.** 18 years

7. 25,000   **8.** (i) 56   (ii) 20   **9.** 75 cm   **10.** 63 cm   **11.** 162 cm

12. (i) €108   (ii) €24; €36   **13.** €400; €160   **14.** €91   **15.** €31·92

Exercise 8.6

1. (i) €80   (ii) €560   **2.** (i) €0·25   (ii) €0·75   (iii) €3   **3.** €2·40   **4.** (i) 40   (ii) 320

    (iii) 20   **5.** €300·80   **6.** €20·30   **7.** (i) 20   (ii) 1,400   (iii) 1,200   (iv) 1,100

8. (i) 0·2 kg or 200 g   **(ii)** 0·6 kg or 600 g   **(iii)** 8 kg   **9. (i)** €96   **(ii)** €24   **(iii)** €136
(iv) €152   **10.** 960 g   **11.** €588   **12.** $10\frac{1}{2}$ cm   **13.** 480

14. (i) (a) 20 km   **(b)** 80 km   **(c)** 5 km   **(d)** 15 km   **(e)** 3·5 km
   (ii) (a) 4 cm   **(b)** 6 cm   **(c)** 7·5 cm   **(d)** 15 cm   **(e)** 1·25 cm

15. (i) (a) 288 cm or 2·8 m   **(b)** 36 cm or 0·36 m   **(c)** 234 cm or 2·34 m   **(ii)** 3 cm

16. €270   **17. (i)** €6   **(ii)** €180   **18.** €30

Exercise 9.1

1. (i) $\frac{1}{5}$ **(ii)** 0·2   **2. (i)** $\frac{3}{10}$ **(ii)** 0·3   **3. (i)** $\frac{1}{2}$ **(ii)** 0·5   **4. (i)** $\frac{1}{4}$ **(ii)** 0·25

5. (i) $\frac{1}{10}$ **(ii)** 0·1   **6. (i)** $\frac{1}{20}$ **(ii)** 0·5   **7. (i)** $\frac{2}{5}$ **(ii)** 0·4   **8. (i)** $\frac{3}{4}$ **(ii)** 0·75

9. (i) $\frac{4}{5}$ **(ii)** 0·8   **10. (i)** $\frac{3}{5}$ **(ii)** 0·6   **11. (i)** $\frac{7}{20}$ **(ii)** 0·35   **12. (i)** $\frac{9}{20}$ **(ii)** 0·45

13. (i) $\frac{13}{20}$ **(ii)** 0·65   **14. (i)** $\frac{19}{20}$ **(ii)** 0·95   **15. (i)** $\frac{11}{20}$ **(ii)** 0·55   **16. (i)** $\frac{3}{25}$ **(ii)** 0·12

17. (i) $\frac{1}{25}$ **(ii)** 0·04   **18. (i)** $\frac{3}{20}$ **(ii)** 0·15   **19. (i)** $\frac{1}{50}$ **(ii)** 0·02   **20. (i)** $\frac{22}{25}$ **(ii)** 0·88

21. (i) $\frac{6}{5}$ **(ii)** 1·20   **22. (i)** $\frac{3}{2}$ **(ii)** 1·5   **23. (i)** $\frac{11}{10}$ **(ii)** 1·1   **24. (i)** $\frac{9}{5}$ **(ii)** 1·8

25. (i) $\frac{9}{4}$ **(ii)** 2·25   **26.** 12%   **27.** 30%   **28.** 23%   **29.** 18%   **30.** 3%

31. 68%   **32.** 2%   **33.** 4%   **34.** 160%   **35.** 240%   **36.** 50%   **37.** 25%

38. 75%   **39.** 20%   **40.** 40%   **41.** 30%   **42.** 90%   **43.** 44%   **44.** 85%

45. 66%   **46.** 9%   **47.** 2%   **48.** 120%   **49.** 150%   **50.** $12\frac{1}{2}$%

51. (i) $\frac{3}{5}$ **(ii)** 0·6   **(iii)** 60%   **52. (i)** $\frac{4}{5}$ **(ii)** 0·8   **(iii)** 80%   **53.** $\frac{1}{5}$; 22%; $\frac{2}{7}$; 0·3

54. 50% + $\frac{1}{2}$; 30% + $\frac{7}{10}$; 60% + $\frac{2}{5}$; $\frac{3}{4}$ + 0·25

55. $\frac{3}{4}$, 0·75, 75%; $\frac{1}{2}$, 0·5, 50%; $\frac{1}{4}$, 0·25, 25%; $\frac{1}{10}$, 0·1, 10%   **56. (i)** Maths, 81%

   (ii) History, 44%   **(iii)** History, Irish, Geography, French, Science, English and Maths

Exercise 9.2

1. 75%   **2.** 40%   **3.** 60%   **4.** 20%   **5.** 80%   **6.** 12%   **7.** 250%   **8.** 150%
9. 25%   **10.** 30%   **11.** 20%   **12.** 45%   **13.** 40%   **14.** 15%   **15.** 20%

16. 25% **17.** $33\frac{1}{3}$% **18.** 15% **19.** 120% **20.** 75% **21.** 35% **22.** 32% **23.** 35%

24. 16% **25. (i)** 60% **(ii)** 40% **26.** 71% **27.** 16%; 24%; 40%; 20%

28. 20 wins in 25 is 80%, 30 wins in 40 is 75% **29.** $2\frac{1}{2}$% **30. (i)** 25% **(ii)** 20% **31.** 70%

32. (i) 50% **(ii)** 40% **(iii)** 10% **(iv)** 70%

Exercise 9.3

1. 20% **2.** 50% **3.** 25% **4.** 10% **5.** 5% **6.** 12% **7.** 7% **8.** 9% **9.** 14%

10. 8% **11.** $12\frac{1}{2}$% **12.** 5% **13.** 7% **14.** 15% **15.** $12\frac{1}{2}$% **16.** $13\frac{1}{2}$%

17. $33\frac{1}{3}$% **18.** $66\frac{2}{3}$% **19.** 6% **20.** 2% **21.** 7% **22. (i)** 201·6 kg **(ii)** 12% **23.** 5%

Exercise 9.4

1. €38 **2.** €30 **3.** 84c **4.** €54·30 **5.** €6 **6.** 92 m **7.** 50 m **8.** €81·15

9. €182·07 **10.** 75·96 **11.** €38·50 **12.** 325 m **13.** €37·20 **14.** €120

15. €4 **16.** €23·80 **17.** 462 **18.** €2·01 **19.** 300 m **20.** €120

21. €496; €620; €992; €372 **22.** €9·52 **23. (i)** €12,600 **(ii)** €600

24. (i) €1,272; €960; €1,356 **(ii)** €312; €0; €396 **(iii)** 32·5%; 0%; 41·25%

25. (i) 62% **(ii)** 16 g; 124 g; 60 g

Exercise 9.5

1. (i) 330 **(ii)** 190 **(iii)** 96 km **(iv)** 598 m **(v)** €144 **(vi)** €86·40

2. 198 g **3. (i)** 9 g **(ii)** 69 g **4.** €540·80 **5.** €31·36 **6.** 615 kg **7.** 130·8 km/h

8. (i) €64 **(ii)** €135 **(iii)** €60 **(iv)** €9·60

9. Yes, Gail is wrong. 44% decrease, not 50% (hint: assume the price is €100).

10. $\frac{2}{5}$ off, as $\frac{2}{5}$ = 40% > $33\frac{1}{3}$% **11. (i)** 56 cm **(ii)** 15%

12. (i) €520; €416; €332·80 **(ii)** No; 60% reduction would reduce price to €260

13. (i) (a) 2,160 **(b)** 2,376 **(ii)** Decrease of 1% **14. (i)** €240 **(ii)** 3 years

Exercise 9.6

1. 300 **2.** €400 **3.** 1,200 **4.** 55 **5.** €600 **6.** 750 **7.** €1,500 **8.** 80 g

9. €550 **10.** 500 ml **11.** 350 **12.** 25 **13.** €540 **14.** 8 cm **15.** €32,000

16. 120 **17.** 400 g **18.** €2,000

Exercise 10.1

1. {2, 4, 6, 8}   2. {1, 3, 5, 7, 9}   3. {1, 2, 3, 4, 6, 12}   4. {S, U, C, E}

5. {2, 3, 5, 7, 11, 13}   6. {A, R, N, G, E, M, T}   7. {A, O, U, I, E}   8. {A, E, I}

9. {3, 6, 9, 12, 15, 18, 21}   10. {5, 10, 15, 20, 25, 30}

11. {Monday, Tuesday, Wednesday, Thursday, Friday, Saturday, Sunday}

12. {Saturday, Sunday}   13. {January, June, July}   14. {1, 2, 3, 4, 5, 6, 7, 8, 9}

15. {0, 1, 4, 9, 16, 25}   16. True   17. False   18. True   19. True   20. ∈   21. ∉

22. ∉   23. ∉   24. ∉   25. ∉   26. ∉   27. ∈   28. ∉   29. ∈   30. ∈   31. ∉

Exercise 10.2

1. (i) *P* and *S*; *Q* and *R*   (ii) (a) 7   (b) 16   3. (i) Yes   (ii) 8   4. Yes

5. (i) (a) $P = \{a, e, i\}$ (b) $Q = \{a, e\}$ (ii) No   (iii) 1   6. (i) 9   (ii) 34   (iii) 29   (iv) 25

7. (i) The null set, { } or ∅   (ii) 0   8. (i) (a) $A = \{r, e, a, n, g\}$ (b) $B = \{r, a, n, g, e\}$

   (ii) Yes   (iii) 0

Exercise 10.3

1. {6, 8, 10, 12, 14}   2. {3, 5, 7, 9, 11}   3. {T, E, N, S}   4. {T, O, M, R, W}

5. {1, 2, 4, 7, 14, 28}   6. {1, 2, 3, 4, 6, 9, 12, 18, 36}   7. {4, 8, 12, 16, 20, 24}

8. {2, 3, 5, 7, 11, 13, 17, 19}   9. {A, E, I, O, U}   10. {I, O, U}   11. {Tuesday, Thursday}

12. { } or ∅   13. { } or ∅   14. { } or ∅

Exercise 10.4

1. (i) True   (ii) False   (iii) True   (iv) True   (v) False   (vi) True   (vii) False   (viii) True

   (ix) False   (x) True

2. (i) {2, 4, 6, 8, 10}   (ii) {1, 3, 5, 7, 9}   (iii) {3, 6, 9}   (iv) {2, 3, 5, 7}   (v) {5, 10}

   (vi) {1, 2, 3, 4, 6, 8}   (vii) {1, 4, 9}   (viii) {1, 8} (ix) { } or ∅

3. (i)   (ii)   (iii)

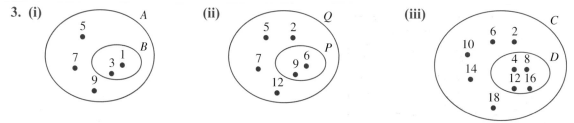

4. {231, 141, 600, 501}

5. (i) { }, {*p*}, {*q*}, {*r*}, {*p, q*}, {*p, r*}, {*q, r*}, {*p, q, r*} (ii) { }, {1}, {2}, {3}, {4}, {1, 2}, {1, 3},
   {1, 4}, {2, 3}, {2, 4}, {3, 4}, {1, 2, 3}, {1, 2, 4}, {1, 3, 4}, {2, 3, 4}, {1, 2, 3, 4}

6. {*a, b, c*}, {*a, b, d*}, {*a, c, d*}, {*b, c, d*}

Exercise 10.5

1. (i)

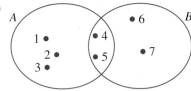

(ii) {4, 5}; {1, 2, 3, 4, 5, 6, 7}   **(iii)** 5   **(iv)** Yes

2. (i)

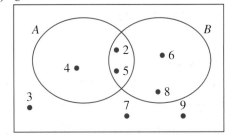

(ii) {b, d}; {a, b, c, d, e, f, g, h}   **(iii)** 4

3. (i)

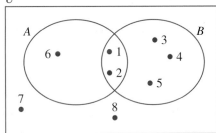

(ii) {e, f}; {c, d, e, f, g, h}   **(iii)** 4

4. (i) U

(ii) {2, 4, 5, 6, 8}; {2, 5}   **(iv)** 3

5. (i) True   **(ii)** True   **(iii)** False   **(iv)** True   **(v)** True   **(vi)** False   **(vii)** False   **(viii)** True
(ix) False   **(x)** False   **(xi)** {12, 13, 14}

6. (ii) U

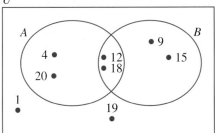

(iii) 2   **(iv)** {7, 8}

7. (i) ∈   **(ii)** =   **(iii)** ⊂   **(iv)** ⊂   **(v)** =   **(vi)** ∉   **(vii)** ∪ =   **(viii)** ∩ =   **(ix)** ⊂ ⊂

8. U

Exercise 10.6

1. (i)

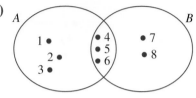

(ii) (a) {1, 2, 3} **(b)** {7, 8}

2. (i)

(ii) (a) {b, d} **(b)** {e, f, g} **(iii)** 1

3. (i) {r, s} **(ii)** {u, v, w} **(iii)** {r, s, u, v, w} **(iv)** { } or Ø

4. (i) True **(ii)** False **(iii)** False **(iv)** True **(v)** True

5. (i) {3, 4, 5} **(ii)** {1, 3, 4} **(iii)** {6, 7, 8} **(iv)** {1, 6, 8} **(v)** {1, 2, 3, 4, 5, 6, 7, 8}

(vi) {1, 3, 4, 6, 8} **(vii)** {2, 7} **(viii)** {1, 3, 4, 5} **(ix)** {1, 2, 5, 6, 7, 8, 9}

(x) {1, 5, 6, 8, 9} **(xi)** {7}

Exercise 10.7

1. {a, b}

2. {4, 6, 8}

3. (i) U

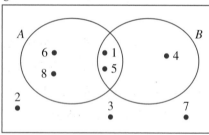

(ii) (a) {2, 3, 4, 7} **(b)** {2, 3, 6, 7, 8}

4. (i) U

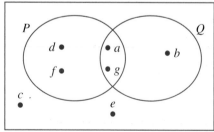

(ii) (a) {b, c, e} **(b)** {c, d, e, f} **(c)** {c, e} **(d)** {c, e} **(iii)** 5

5. (i) {a, b, g, h, t, k, m, n, r, s, v, p, q} **(ii)** {k, m, n, g, h, t} **(iii)** {g, h, t, r, s, v} **(iv)** {g, h, t}

(v) {k, m, n, g, h, t, r, s, v} **(vi)** {k, m, n} **(vii)** {r, s, v} **(viii)** {r, s, v, a, b, p, q}

(ix) {k, m, n, a, b, p, q} **(x)** {a, b, p, q} **(xi)** {a, b, p, q} **(xii)** {r, s, v} **(xiii)** {k, m, n}

(xiv) {a, b, k, m, n, g, h, t, p, q}

Exercise 10.8

1. (i) 15   (ii) 45   (iii) 27   (iv) 9   (v) 42
2. (i) 22   (ii) 34   (iii) 33   (iv) 5   (v) 23
3. (i) 4   (ii) 24   (iii) 28   4. (i) 11   (ii) 12   (iii) 2
5. (i) 28   (ii) 15   (iii) 7   6. 9   7. 35   8. 150
9. (i) 46   (ii) 10   (iii) 11   (iv) 18   (v) 39   (vi) 7   (vii) 25   (viii) 18   (ix) 36
10. 27   11. 10   12. 25   13. (i) 10   (ii) 8   14. 6   15. (i) 8   (ii) 15   (iii) 7
16. $28 - x = 22$; 6

Exercise 11.1

1. (i) 30   (ii) 45   (iii) 6   (iv) 24   (v) 5   (vi) 15   (vii) 40   (viii) 42   (ix) 32
2. (i) $\dfrac{1}{2}$ (ii) $\dfrac{1}{4}$ (iii) $\dfrac{1}{3}$ (iv) $1\dfrac{1}{2}$ (v) $\dfrac{2}{5}$ (vi) $\dfrac{7}{10}$ 3. (i) 3 hrs   (ii) 2 hrs

    (iii) 2 hrs 40 mins   (iv) 2 hrs 29 mins   (v) 3 hrs 46 mins   4. (i) 15:40   (ii) 13:03

    (iii) 12:18   (iv) 21:10   (v) 06:05   5. (i) 10:45   (ii) 20:50   (iii) 11:27   (iv) 10:03

    (v) 15:25   6. 3 hrs 40 mins   7. 18:02   8. 15:15   9. (i) 1 hr 35 mins

    (ii) 145 mins   10. 13:55   11. 03:05   12. 35 mins

13. 17:10, 17:45, 18:05, 18:35, 18:47, 19:12, 19:37, 20:02   14. 11:15   15. 03:00 or 15:00

16. 07:00, 19:00, 5:15 p.m., 7:45 a.m., 22:20, 10:49 p.m.   17. (i) 23:40, 00:25, 00:48, 02:10

    (ii) 2 hrs 40 mins   (iii) He was in bed   18. (i) 9 mins 45 secs   (ii) 38 mins 11 secs

    (iii) 53 mins 56 secs   19. (i) 5,040   (ii) 5,600   20. (i) 12:05   (ii) 05:25

Exercise 11.2

1. 53 mins, 46 mins, 35 mins, 1 hr 5 mins, 42 mins, 36 mins
2. 4 mins, 13 mins, 21 mins, 33 mins, 45 mins, 1 hr 3 mins
3. (i) Train 1 = 4 hrs 25 mins; Train 2 = 4 hrs 5 mins; Train 3 = 3 hrs 45 mins

    (ii) 40 mins   (iii) 08:53   4. (i) 16 hrs 45 mins   (ii) 68   (iii) 21

5. (i) 09:55   (ii) 55 mins   (iii) 17:25

6. (i) 8, $2\dfrac{1}{2}$, 6 hrs 40 mins, 8 hrs 20 mins, 8 hrs 45 mins, 8 hrs 55 mins, 8 hrs 20 mins

    (ii) $10\dfrac{1}{2}$, 41   7. (i) 20 hours   (ii) (a) Maths   (b) Irish   8. (i) 2 hrs 8 mins   (ii) 1 min

    (iii) 14:39   (iv) One   (v) 16:01, 21:39

Exercise 11.3

1. (i) 20 km/h (ii) 62·5 km/h (iii) 65 km/h (iv) 50 km/h (v) 24 km/h (vi) 36 km/h

2. (i) 101·4 km (ii) 75 km (iii) 294 km (iv) 15 km (v) 416 km (vi) 1·8 km

3. (i) 1 hour (ii) $\frac{1}{2}$ hour (iii) 40 hours (iv) $\frac{2}{3}$ hour (v) $\frac{1}{22}$ hour (vi) $13\frac{1}{3}$ hour

4. Table 1: 80 km/h, 4 hrs, 140 km, 4 hrs, 90 secs, 5 m/sec, 3,000 m

   Table 2: 96 km/h, 4 hrs 30 mins, 80 km/h, 208 km, 120 km, 40 km/h, 125 km

5. 5 hours   6. 15 km/h   7. 300 km   8. (i) 2·5 hrs (ii) 72 km/h   9. 150 km

10. 64 km/hr   11. 4 m/s   12. 18:30   13. (i) 4·25 hrs (ii) 60 km/h   14. 72 km/h

15. 91 km   16. (i) 1 hr 45 mins (ii) 84 km/h   17. (i) 2 hrs 45 mins (ii) 11:50

   (iii) 94 km/h   18. (i) Madrid and Oslo (ii) Oslo (iii) 2,475 km (iv) 470 km/h

   (v) 03:09   19. (i) 45,000 km/h (ii) 1·3 secs   20. 525,600,000 km

Exercise 12.1

1. Discrete numerical
2. Continuous numerical
3. Unordered categorical
4. Ordered categorical
5. Unordered categorical
6. Ordered categorical
7. Continuous numerical
8. Discrete numerical
9. Continuous numerical
10. Unordered categorical
11. Discrete numerical
12. Ordered categorical
13. Discrete numerical
14. Continuous numerical
15. Unordered categorical
16. Continuous numerical
17. Discrete numerical
18. Continuous numerical
19. (i) Colour of the car, Red (ii) Number of doors (iii) Diameter of the wheels.
20. (i) How many rooms in your house? (ii) What height are you?

   (iii) What is your favourite colour? (iv) What year are you in school?

Exercise 12.2

1. (i) 60 (ii) 8   3. (i) 36   5. (ii) 30 (iii) 80   6. (ii) 7

Exercise 12.3

Note: In many questions in this exercise there can be a few different answers. The answers below only give a selection of answers.

1. Primary data (first-hand data) are data that you collect yourself or are collected by someone under your direct supervision. Secondary data (second-hand data) are data that have already been collected and made available from an externel source such as news papers, government departments or the internet.

2. (i) Primary (ii) Secondary (iii) Secondary (iv) Primary

3. A census is a collection of data from the whole population. A sample is a collection of data from a small part of the population.

4. Sample. Otherwise they would have no batteries to sell.

5. (i) Leading question as it forces an opinion on the person being interviewed
    (ii) Overlapping boxes   (iii) Not enough response sections   (iv) Leading question as it forces an opinion on the person being interviewed that sweets are bad for you before they answer the question   (v) Biased question   (vi) Personal question

6. (i) Question is too vague. Does not give a time period, such as per week, per month or per year or what time of the year, school term or not school term   (ii) During school term, how many times per month do you attend the cinema? Please tick one box.

7. (i) (a) Does not give a time period, such as per week, per month or per year or what time of the year.   (b) Overlapping boxes   (ii) During school holidays, how many hours per week do you spend on the internet? Please tick one box.

8. (i) Overlapping boxes   (ii) No 4 in the boxes   (iii) No zero for people who work at home

9. Overlapping boxes

10. (i) Overlapping boxes. No greater than €1,000 box
    (ii) Question assumes that all people have a mortgage

11. Collecting the data during rush hour only would give biased results as the traffic would be going slower. Helen needs to collect the data at different times of the day and on different days of the week.

12. (i) Biased sample because: (a) many of the people who use the train may not be interested in a road by-pass of the town   (b) The first 50 people who leave the train in the town on a Friday in June would not be representative of the whole town   (ii) Ask the question in a few different places in the town such as shops, schools or work places and try to ask the question to people of different ages and different genders (male or female)

    (iii) Leading question which would lead to biased answers

13. (i) (a) These students are already using the school canteen and would be a biased sample. She also needs to ask the question to students who do not use the school canteen   (b) Leading question as it forces an opinion on the person being interviewed that the food prices are already overpriced   (ii) To find students opinion of the price of food in the school canteen and to see if the price affects the number of students who use the school canteen   (iii) Pick 10 students at random from the school register from each of the six year groups

14. (i) No boys are given the old brand and no girls are given the new brand. No adults in the experiment   (ii) The dentist needs to randomly give the new brand of toothpaste to both boys, girls, men and women and also randomly give the old brand to the same number of boys, girls, men and women.

15. Mark out an even number of different sections of the same field with the same area. Plant the new 'better grow' compost in half of these sections and plant its competitors compost in the other half of the these sections. It would be a good idea to use a few different **independent** growers. Then record which compost helps seeds germinate more quickly

16. For each question please tick one box.

   1. Gender: Male ☐   Female ☐

   2. What year group are you in?

     1. ☐   **2.** ☐   **3.** ☐   **4.** ☐   **5.** ☐   **6.** ☐

   3. What is your favourite type of music?

     Rock ☐   Pop ☐   Hip Hop ☐   RNB ☐

     Trad ☐   Dance ☐   Classical ☐   Other ☐

Exercise 13.1

1. (i) 3   (ii) 3   (iii) 2   (iv) 6   **2.** (i) 6   (ii) 2   (iii) 5   (iv) 10
3. (i) 5   (ii) 6   (iii) 4   (iv) 5   **4.** (i) 7   (ii) 5   (iii) 6   (iv) 5
5. (i) 6   (ii) 4   (iii) 7   (iv) 4   **6.** (i) 5   (ii) 9   (iii) 4   (iv) 8
7. (i) 5   (ii) 2   (iii) 4   (iv) 8   **8.** (i) 4   (ii) 8   (iii) 3   (iv) 8
9. (i) 4   (ii) 0   (iii) 3   (iv) 10   **10.** (i) 3   (ii) 4   **11.** (i) 4·5   (ii) 5
12. (i) 9   (ii) 9   **13.** (i) 1·4   (ii) 1·3   (iii) 0·8   (iv) 1·7
14. (i) 142 min   (ii) 44 min   **15.** (ii) (a) 10   (b) 10   (iii) (a) 9·8   (b) 5
16. (i) 12 min 26 sec   (ii) 12 min 42 sec   (iii) 3 min 35 sec

Exercise 13.2

1. 20   **2.** 40   **3.** 60   **4.** 5   **5.** 3   **6.** 7   **7.** 5   **8.** 16   **9.** (i) 15   (ii) 9
10. 7   **11.** 2   **12.** 8   **13.** 5   **14.** 77   **15.** (i) 40   (ii) 100

Exercise 13.3

1. (i) A: 62·75; 78   B: 63; 19   **2.** (i) Boys: 86; 86; 10   Girls: 87; 87; 27
4. (i) 50, 52, 22 and 48, 52, 14   **5.** (i) B: 3·5; C: 3·6   (ii) B: 7; C: 3

Exercise 13.4

1. (i) 3   (ii) 1   (iii) 2   (iv) 2   **2.** (i) 6   (ii) 7   (iii) 5   (iv) 5
3. (i) 8   (ii) 6   (iii) 4   (iv) 4   **4.** (i) 5   (ii) 2   (iii) 3   (iv) 2·6
5. (i) 4   (ii) 5   (iii) 6   (iv) 6·5   **6.** (i) 0–2   (ii) 3–5
7. (i) (a) 8   (b) 16   (ii) 2   (iii) 2·3   **8.** (i) 8   (ii) (a) 7   (b) 6·8
9. (i) 1   (ii) 2   **10.** (i) 25   (ii) 18   (iii) (a) 4   (b) 19
11. (i) (a) 2   (b) 3   (ii) (a) 4   (b) 3   **12.** (i) 2°C; 1°C   (ii) 6°C; 1°C

Exercise 14.1

1. (ii) English (iii) Science   2. (ii) 5c (iii) 20 (iv) €3·30
3. (ii) (a) Train (b) Walking (iii) 30   4. (ii) 7 (iii) 24 (iv) 25%
5. (ii) 7 cm (iii) 20%   6. (ii) 50 (iii) Coffee; 24%
7. (ii) 0 (iii) 9 (iv) 5 (v) 36 (vi) 5·5 (vii) $66\frac{2}{3}$%

Exercise 14.2

2. (ii) 4   3. (iii) (a) 5 (b) 0 (iv) 35%   4. (iii) €4 (iv) €4·40
5. (iii) 3 (iv) 20 (v) 3·2   6. (iii) 3 (iv) 24 (v) 2·75

Exercise 14.3

5. (i) 5   6. (iii) 2 (iv) 2·25   7. (ii) (a) 35 (b) 85 (iii) (a) 5 (b) 4·625   8. (i) 3·6°

Exercise 14.4

1. (i) 70° (ii) 720 (iii) 140   2. (i) 64° (iii) 1080
3. (i) 60° (ii) 120 (iii) 40   4. (i) 30° (ii) 8 (iii) 24 (iv) 20
5. (i) 20°   6. (i) 40°

Exercise 14.5

6. (i) 7 (iii) 10−15   7. (ii) 150−160   8. (iii) 60−80 (iv) 60−80
9. (ii) 4−8 (iii) 4−8   10. (ii) 25 (iii) 15 (iv) 1 (v) 07:40−07:50 (vi) 28% (vii) 15

Exercise 14.6

5. (ii) 31   6. (ii) (a) 34 (b) 27   7. (i) 18|2 = 182 cm (ii) 153 cm
  (iii) (a) 148 cm (b) 187 cm (iv) 39 cm (v) 164 cm (vi) no (vii) 165·5 cm
  (viii) 165 cm   8. (ii) (a) 1·9 sec (b) 5·9 sec (iii) 4 sec (iv) 3·3 sec (v) 3·65 sec
  (vii) 0·1 sec

Exercise 15.1

1. 18   2. 15   3. 12   4. 30   5. 18   6. 30   7. 12   8. (i) 10
9. (i) 12   10. (i) 18   11. (i) 6   12. 260

Exercise 15.2

1. (i) $\frac{2}{3}$ (ii) $\frac{1}{3}$ (iii) 0   2. (i) $\frac{1}{11}$ (ii) $\frac{4}{11}$ (iii) $\frac{4}{11}$ (iv) $\frac{2}{11}$ (v) 0

3. (i) (a) $\frac{4}{5}$ (b) $\frac{1}{5}$ 4. (i) $\frac{1}{2}$ (ii) $\frac{1}{4}$ (iii) $\frac{1}{52}$ (iv) $\frac{1}{13}$

5. (i) (a) $\dfrac{1}{2}$ (b) $\dfrac{1}{5}$ (c) $\dfrac{3}{10}$ (d) $\dfrac{7}{10}$ **6.** (i) (a) $\dfrac{7}{20}$ (b) $\dfrac{3}{5}$ **7.** $\dfrac{1}{7}$

8. (i) 6; (ii) (a) $\dfrac{1}{3}$ (b) $\dfrac{11}{24}$ (c) $\dfrac{19}{24}$ **9.** 0·85 or $\dfrac{17}{20}$ **10.** (i) (a) $\dfrac{4}{5}$ (b) $\dfrac{1}{5}$

14. (i) €20 **15.** (i) $\dfrac{2}{5}$ (ii) $\dfrac{3}{5}$ (iii) $\dfrac{1}{5}$ (iv) $\dfrac{7}{10}$ **16.** (i) $\dfrac{1}{2}$ (ii) $\dfrac{5}{12}$ (iii) $\dfrac{1}{12}$

17. (i) (a) $\dfrac{16}{25}$ (b) $\dfrac{9}{25}$ (c) $\dfrac{1}{5}$ (d) $\dfrac{6}{25}$ **18.** (i) (a) $\dfrac{3}{5}$ (b) $\dfrac{1}{5}$ (c) $\dfrac{9}{10}$ (d) 0

19. (ii) (a) $\dfrac{3}{5}$ (b) $\dfrac{3}{8}$ **20.** (ii) (a) $\dfrac{3}{8}$ (b) $\dfrac{5}{24}$ (c) $\dfrac{5}{12}$

21. (ii) (a) $\dfrac{13}{20}$ (b) $\dfrac{7}{20}$ (c) $\dfrac{1}{4}$ (d) $\dfrac{9}{40}$ (iii) $\dfrac{8}{13}$ (iv) $\dfrac{1}{3}$

Exercise 15.3

1. (ii) $\dfrac{1}{4}$ **2.** (ii) $\dfrac{1}{6}$ **3.** (ii) (a) $\dfrac{1}{5}$ (b) $\dfrac{3}{10}$

4. (ii) (a) $\dfrac{1}{6}$ (b) $\dfrac{1}{6}$ (c) $\dfrac{1}{12}$ (d) 0 (e) $\dfrac{1}{3}$ (f) $\dfrac{1}{2}$ **5.** (ii) (a) $\dfrac{1}{4}$ (b) $\dfrac{3}{8}$ (c) $\dfrac{3}{8}$

6. (ii) (a) $\dfrac{1}{6}$ (b) $\dfrac{1}{4}$ (c) $\dfrac{11}{24}$ (d) $\dfrac{5}{24}$ **7.** (ii) (a) $\dfrac{2}{15}$ (b) $\dfrac{2}{15}$

Exercise 15.4

1. $\dfrac{13}{20}$ or 0·65 **2.** 200 **3.** (i) $\dfrac{11}{50}$ (ii) 11

4. (i) $\dfrac{1}{10}; \dfrac{3}{25}; \dfrac{13}{100}; \dfrac{7}{40}; \dfrac{91}{500}; \dfrac{4}{25}; \dfrac{83}{500}$ (ii) 2000 **5.** (i) $\dfrac{3}{10}$ **6.** (ii) $\dfrac{1}{4}$

7. (i) $P(A) = \dfrac{7}{50}; P(B) = \dfrac{43}{100}; P(C) = \dfrac{2}{25}; P(D) = \dfrac{11}{50}; P(E) = \dfrac{13}{100}$ (ii) 20 times

8. (i) 400 (ii) (a) $\dfrac{8}{25}$ (b) $\dfrac{27}{100}$ (c) $\dfrac{41}{100}$ (iii) 1458

Exercise 16.1

1. €14; €154 **2.** €124·20; €664·20 **3.** €75; €675 **4.** €12·75; €162·75 **5.** 15%; €12

6. 18%; €27 **7.** 23%; €575 **8.** 8%; €156·60 **9.** €152·52 **10.** €4·83 **11.** €108

12. 12% **13.** 23% **14.** (i) 4,200 litres (ii) €3,402 (iii) 21% **15.** €82 **16.** €82

17. (i) €1,200 (ii) €1,452 **18.** €495·60 **19.** €72·80 **20.** €984

Exercise 16.2

1. (a) 2,559 (b) €204·72 (c) €213·50 (d) €29·89 (e) €243·39
2. (a) 6,285 (b) €565·65 (c) €577 (d) €80·78 (e) €657·78
3. (i) 2,735 (ii) €300·85 (iii) €308·40 (iv) €346·95
4. (i) €38·64 (ii) €49·92   5. Option B; Option A = €26·45; Option B = €24·55

Exercise 16.3

1. €2; 25%   2. €12; 10%   3. €27; 15%   4. €35; 10%   5. €400; 27%   6. €124; 24%
7. €6; 5%   8. €120; 24%   9. €248; 12.5%   10. €50; 18%   11. 25%   12. 21%
13. 12%   14. €9,500   15. €12,803   16. (i) €250 (ii) €220   17. €80   18. €3·75
19. (i) €288   (ii) (a) €244·80   (b) 2%   20. (i) €15,500   (ii) (a) €14,260   (b) 14%

Exercise 16.4

1. (i) €9; €141   (ii) €322; €1,978   (iii) €21; €399   (iv) €1,476; €10,824
   (v) €779; €7,421   (vi) €798; €3,002   2. (i) 20%; €320   (ii) 8%; €1,104   (iii) 10%; €117
   (iv) 16%; €3,150   (v) 25%; €11,700   (vi) 18%; €6,765   3. €11,040   4. €102   5. 5%
6. 12·5%   7. (ii) €1·74   (iii) €33·06

Exercise 16.5

1. (i) $150   (ii) €120   2. $90   3. $40   4. €320   5. €85   6. (i) $48   (ii) $966
   (iii) ¥59,616   (iv) €75   (v) €500   (vi) €720   7. (i) €1 = $1·40   (ii) €1 = $2·20
8. Ireland; €1·50   9. Canada; €5   10. South Africa; €62·50   11. (i) R1,920 (ii) R64

Exercise 16.6

1. €61·80   2. €410   3. €416   4. €521·64   5. €65·28   6. €73·08   7. €168
8. €499·20   9. €115·85   10. €649·28   11. €630·50   12. €1,910·16   13. €12·61
14. €2,497·28   15. €6,073·92   16. €4,775·40   17. (i) €13,206   (ii) €14,064·39
18. €9,447·84   19. (i) (a) €750   (b) €795   (c) €842·70   (ii) €14,887·70
20. (i) €400   (ii) €11,248·64   21. €21,854·54   22. (i) 5%   (ii) €630·50

Exercise 16.7

1. €736   2. €432·25   3. €11,448   4. €5,356   5. €1,755·52   6. €1,515·30
7. €19,776·96   8. €2,744·95

Exercise 16.8

1. €4,720   2. €2,712   3. €5,337   4. €5,549   5. €2,085·60

Exercise 16.9

1. €3,000; €1,000; €14,000
2. €4,600; €2,000; €21,000
3. €3,150; €900; €16,600
4. €4,655; €2,500; €22,000
5. €3,960; €2,070; €15,930
6. €3,298; €570; €18,830
7. €2,912; €1,060; €17,140
8. €4,516; €1,703; €20,877
9. €4,109·70; €2,027·70; €17,542·30
10. €4,653; €3,459; €17,691
11. (i) €4,400 (ii) €1,100 (iii) €20,900 (iv) 5%
12. (i) €3,420 (ii) €1,330 (iii) €17,670 (iv) 7%
13. (i) €4,318 (ii) €1,016 (iii) €24,384 (iv) €23,834
14. (i) €6,195 (ii) €3,095 (iii) €24,785
15. (i) €3,909·60 (ii) €2,069·60 (iii) €18,260·40
16. €81; €669
17. €82·20; €537·80
18. €24,600
19. €28,800

Exercise 17.1

1. 32 cm^2, 24 cm
2. 60 m^2, 32 m
3. 96 cm^2, 40 cm
4. 300 m^2, 70 m
5. 600 cm^2, 100 cm
6. 216 m^2, 60 m
7. (i) 25 cm^2 (ii) 20 cm
8. (i) 64 m^2 (ii) 32 m
9. (i) 100 cm^2 (ii) 40 cm
10. (i) 144 m^2 (ii) 48 m
11. (i) 6·24 cm^2 (ii) 10 cm
12. (i) 20·25 m^2 (ii) 18 m
13. (i) 40 cm (ii) 195 cm^2
14. (i) 86 cm (ii) 262 cm^2
15. (i) 56 cm (ii) 95 cm^2
16. 40 cm^2
17. 48 cm^2
18. 30 cm^2
19. 23 cm^2
20. 6 cm^2
21. 108 cm^2
22. (i) 24 m^2 (ii) 156 cm^2 (iii) 77 m^2
23. (i) 36 cm (ii) 72 cm^2
24. 22·5 m^2
25. 92 m^2
26. 299 m^2
27. 42·5 m^2
28. 136 m^2
29. 1,360 m^2
30. 240 m^2

Exercise 17.2

1. 5 m, 18 m
2. 7 m, 24 m
3. 4 m, 12 m^2
4. 6 m, 60 m^2
5. (i) 12 cm (ii) 40 cm
6. 45 cm^2
7. (i) 5 cm (ii) 25 cm^2
8. (i) 6 cm (ii) 24 cm
9. 10 cm
10. 12 cm
11. 18 cm
12. 6 cm
13. 12 cm
14. 6 cm

Exercise 17.3

1. (i) 6,000 m^2 (ii) 1,216 m^2 (iii) 304, €7,600
2. (i) 1,500 (ii) €2,250
3. 200
4. (i) 800 m^2 (ii) 124 m^2 (iii) 496
5. (i) 4,500 (ii) €12,600 (iii) €17,550
6. (i) 20 litres (ii) €508
7. €2,655
8. (ii) 12 shelves (iii) 3 sheets
9. (i) 252 m^2, 144 m^2 (ii) 0·4 m^2 (iii) 990 (iv) €8,415
10. A
11. (i) 13·25 m (ii) 15,900
12. 45 cm^2

Exercise 17.4

1. 31·4 cm, 78·5 cm^2
2. 62·8 m, 314 m^2
3. 125·6 mm, 1,256 mm^2
4. 75·36 cm, 452·16 cm^2
5. 37·68 m, 113·04 m^2
6. 25·12 mm, 50·24 mm^2
7. 81·64 cm, 530·66 cm^2
8. 188·4 cm, 2,826 cm^2
9. 53·38 m, 226·865 m^2

10. 15·7 cm, 19·625 cm²   **11.** 88 cm, 616 cm²   **12.** 44 cm, 154 cm²

13. 132 mm, 1,386 mm²   **14.** 176 cm, 2,464 cm²   **15.** 220 mm, 3,850 mm²

16. 13·2 m, 13·86 m²   **17.** 66 cm, 346·5 cm²   **18.** 8·8 m, 6·16 m²

19. 22 cm, 38·5 cm²   **20.** 30·8 cm, 75·46 cm²   **21.** 56·52 cm, 254·34 cm²

22. 12·56 m, 12·56 m²   **23.** 18·84 cm, 28·26 cm²   **24.** 3·14 m, 0·785 m²

25. 47·1 cm, 176·625 cm²   **26.** 6π cm, 9π cm²   **27.** 4π m, 4π m²

28. 22π mm, 121π mm²   **29.** 9π cm, 20·25π cm²   **30.** 3π m, 2·25π m²

31. (i) 113·04 cm²   (ii) 18·84 cm   (iii) 42·84 cm   **32.** (i) 25·12 cm²   (ii) 12·56 cm   (iii) 20·56 cm   **33.** (i) 235·5 cm²   (ii) 47·1 cm   (iii) 67·1 cm   **34.** (i) 18·84 cm²   (ii) 6·28 cm   (iii) 18·28 cm   **35.** (i) 25·12 cm²   (ii) 6·28 cm   (iii) 22·28 cm

36. (i) 84·78 cm²   (ii) 18·84 cm   (iii) 36·84 cm   **37.** 3,706·5 cm²   **38.** 299·97 cm²

39. 197·82 cm²   **40.** 21·5 cm²   **41.** 30·96 cm²   **42.** 616 cm²   **43.** 1,438·5 cm²

44. 644·9 cm²

Exercise 17.5

1. 16π cm², 4 cm   **2.** 81π cm², 9 cm   **3.** 62·8 cm, 10 cm   **4.** 94·2 m, 15 m

5. 1,386 mm², 21 mm   **6.** 88 cm, 14 cm   **7.** 8π cm, 4 cm   **8.** 490·625 m², 12·5 m

9. 176 cm, 28 cm   **10.** 18π cm, 9 cm   **11.** 3,850 m², 35 m   **12.** 188·4 mm, 30 mm

13. 22π m, 11 m   **14.** 251·2 cm, 40 cm   **15.** 22 m, 3·5 m   **16.** 346·5 cm², 10·5 cm

17. 44 cm   **18.** 25π m²   **19.** 12·56 cm   **20.** 4·5 m

Exercise 17.6

1. (i) 21 cm   (ii) 132 cm   (iii) 330 m   (iv) 200   **2.** 8,225 cm²

3. (i) 670·5 m²   (ii) €2,145·60   **4.** (i) 73·005 mm   (ii) 365·025 mm   (iii) 6

5. (i) 28 mm   (ii) 80·9 mm   (iii) (a) 2·25 mm   (b) 7·1 mm   **6.** (i) 0·77 km   (ii) 6,000

7. 3,080 cm²   **8.** (i) 49 m   (ii) 154 m   (iii) 600 m   (iv) 9   (v) 14·4 km/hr

9. (i) 154 cm²   (ii) 70 cm   (iii) 210 cm²   **10.** (i) 54·6 m   (ii) €43,411·20

11. (i) 0·785 m²   (ii) 1·6956 m²   (iii) 15·5662 m²   (iv) 86%   **12.** 116 cm

13. (i) 1,600   (ii) 576   (iii) 1,256   (iv) 912

Exercise 17.7

1. (i) 2·8 m   (ii) 0·6 m   (iii) 0·9 m   (iv) 1·2 m   **2.** (i) 8 cm   (ii) 2 cm   (iii) 11 cm   (iv) 1·2 cm   **3.** (i) 3·5 m   (ii) 8 m approx.   (iii) 1:35

4. (i) 22·5 m   (ii) 4 m   (iii) 7 cm   **5.** (ii) 520 m   **7.** (i) 31 m   (ii) 55 m²

8. (i) 105 m   (ii) 68 m   (iii) 346 m   (iv) 7,140 m²   (v) €119,920   (vi) 32·25 m

Exercise 17.8

1. 5 ml, 300 ml, 8 l, 150 ml, 1 l   **2.** 18 ml, 280 ml, 360 ml, 980 ml, 2,320 ml, 10·066 l

3. (i) (a) 480 cm^3 (b) 376 cm^2 (ii) (a) 225 cm^3 (b) 230 cm^2 (iii) (a) 64 cm^3 (b) 96 cm^2

4. 480 cm^3, 376 cm^2 **5.** 30 m^3, 62 m^2 **6.** 48 m^3, 92 m^2 **7.** 160,000 cm^3, 18,400 cm^2

8. 4,500 mm^3, 1,710 mm^2 **9.** (i) 126 cm^3, 162 cm^2 (ii) 27 cm^3, 54 cm^2 **10.** (iii)

13. (i) cube, 6, 8, 12   (ii) cuboid, 6, 8, 12   **14.** (i) 8 cm^3 (ii) 18   **15.** 13

16. (i) 46,400 cm^2 (ii) 4·64 m^3 **17.** (i) 26,400 cm^2 (ii) (a) 378,000 cm^3 (b) 0·378 m^3

   (c) 378 litres   **18.** 3,000   **19.** 36   **20.** 6,450 cm^3 **21.** 7,632 cm^3 **22.** 2,400 cm^3

23. (i) 350 cm^3 (ii) 3,632 g   **24.** (i) 36,000 cm^3 (ii) 12 mins   **25.** 54 mins   **26.** 50 hours

Exercise 17.9

1. (i) 8 cm   (ii) 1,160 cm^2 **2.** (i) 4 cm   (ii) 96 cm^2 **3.** (i) 2 cm   (ii) 8 cm^3

4. (i) 10 cm   (ii) 484 cm^2 **5.** (i) 7·5 m   (ii) 186·5 cm^2 **6.** (i) 7 cm   (ii) 0·14 litres

7. 150 cm^2 **8.** 40 cm   **9.** (i) 8 m   (ii) 3·6 m

Exercise 17.10

1. 1,540 cm^3, 440 cm^2, 748 cm^2 **2.** 1,570 mm^3, 314 mm^2, 471 mm^2

3. 49 cm^3, 280 cm^3, 3520 cm^2, 8448 cm^2 **4.** 22 cm^3, 608 cm^3, 3,768 cm^2, 4,672·32 cm^2

5. 192·5 m^3, 110 cm^2, 187 cm^2 **6.** (i) 13,860 cm^3 (ii) 1,320 cm^2 **7.** (i) 18 cm   (ii) 15 cm

   (iii) 12,723 cm^2 **8.** (i) 30,000π cm^3 (ii) 300π cm^3 (iii) 100   **9.** R   **10.** 58,875 cm^3

11. (i) 1,100 cm^3 (ii) (a) $h = 14$ cm, $l = 20$ cm, $b = 10$ cm   (b) 2,800 cm^3 (c) 600 cm^3

12. 23,550 m^3 **13.** (i) 1,800 m   (ii) 5·5 m   **14.** (i) 9 cm   (ii) 2 cm   **15.** (i) 550 cm^3

   (ii) 40   (iii) 10 cm   **16.** (i) 198 cm^3 (ii) 49,500 cm^3 (iii) 9,900 cm^3 (iv) 11 cm

17. (i) 18·48 litres   (ii) 84   **18.** 48 cm^2 **19.** (i) 10·99 cm   (ii) 60 cm

Exercise 18.1

1. 2^3 **2.** 3^4 **3.** 4^6 **4.** 6^7 **5.** 10^5 **6.** 8^6 **7.** 16   **8.** 81   **9.** 125

10. 100,000   **11.** 32,768   **12.** 1,024   **13.** 531,441   **14.** 823,543

Exercise 18.2

1. 3   **2.** 7   **3.** 9   **4.** 3·5   **5.** 2   **6.** 6   **7.** 4·5   **8.** 11   **9.** 10   **10.** 7

11. 72   **12.** 6   **13.** 77   **14.** 6   **15.** 4   **16.** 4   **17.** 144   **18.** 7   **19.** 5

20. 121   **21.** 64   **22.** 5·29   **23.** 6·40   **24.** 9·22   **25.** 7·35   **26.** 15·30   **27.** 35·69

Exercise 18.3

1. 2^7 2. 3^8 3. 4^5 4. 5^6 5. 6^9 6. 5^7 7. 3^6 8. 2^7 9. 4^{10} 10. 6^6

11. 4^1 12. 7^2 13. 3^3 14. 4^4 15. 2^3 16. 10^2 17. 9^2 18. 5^4 19. 6^4

20. 7^2 21. 2^6 22. 3^{12} 23. 5^8 24. 8^{10} 25. 7^{15} 26. 6^{20} 27. 4^{14} 28. 9^{18}

29. 6   30. 7   31. 5   32. 3   33. 2   34. 4   35. 10   36. 6   37. 4^2 38. 3^4

39. 2^3 40. 3^2

Exercise 18.4

1. 4×10^3 2. 5×10^4 3. 2×10^5 4. 3×10^6 5. 3×10^2 6. $7 \cdot 5 \times 10^3$

7. $3 \cdot 6 \times 10^4$ 8. $6 \cdot 5 \times 10^5$ 9. $2 \cdot 3 \times 10^6$ 10. $2 \cdot 08 \times 10^3$ 11. $6 \cdot 07 \times 10^3$

12. $3 \cdot 05 \times 10^4$ 13. $1 \cdot 58 \times 10^6$ 14. $2 \cdot 04 \times 10^4$ 15. $5 \cdot 03 \times 10^5$ 16. $8 \cdot 532 \times 10^6$

17. $1 \cdot 4 \times 10^3$ 18. $1 \cdot 44 \times 10^4$ 19. $4 \cdot 2 \times 10^3$ 20. $1 \cdot 45 \times 10^5$ 21. $1 \cdot 2 \times 10^5$

22. $3 \cdot 5 \times 10^4$ 23. $2 \cdot 5 \times 10^3$ 24. $4 \cdot 5 \times 10^3$ 25. $3 \cdot 2 \times 10^4$ 26. $5 \cdot 4 \times 10^4$

27. $2 \cdot 28 \times 10^5$ 28. $2 \cdot 6 \times 10^6$ 29. $1 \cdot 7 \times 10^5$ 30. $2 \cdot 7 \times 10^4$ 31. $4 \cdot 3 \times 10^4$

32. $3 \cdot 6 \times 10^4$ 33. $1 \cdot 5979 \times 10^6$

Exercise 18.5

1. $6 \cdot 2 \times 10^3$ 2. 6×10^4 3. $4 \cdot 6 \times 10^5$ 4. $3 \cdot 8 \times 10^6$ 5. 7×10^6 6. $6 \cdot 5 \times 10^5$

7. $7 \cdot 6 \times 10^4$ 8. 5×10^5 9. 6×10^3 10. 7×10^4 11. $2 \cdot 3 \times 10^5$ 12. $5 \cdot 2 \times 10^4$

13. $2 \cdot 8 \times 10^4$ 14. $2 \cdot 4 \times 10^4$ 15. $3 \cdot 2 \times 10^6$ 16. $2 \cdot 3 \times 10^6$ 17. $2 \cdot 6 \times 10^4$

18. 3×10^5 19. (i) $5 \cdot 6 \times 10^4$ (ii) $6 \cdot 2 \times 10^5$ 20. $2 \cdot 2 \times 10^3$ kg

21. (i) $1 \cdot 4 \times 10^3 \, \text{m}^3$ (ii) 140 mins

Exercise 18.6

1. 6×10^6 2. 8×10^8 3. $5 \cdot 2 \times 10^5$ 4. $8 \cdot 4 \times 10^6$ 5. $1 \cdot 8 \times 10^6$ 6. $4 \cdot 5 \times 10^7$

7. $7 \cdot 68 \times 10^8$ 8. $9 \cdot 45 \times 10^6$ 9. 4×10^2 10. 2×10^2 11. 4×10^4 12. $2 \cdot 5 \times 10^3$

13. $1 \cdot 4 \times 10^5$ 14. $2 \cdot 4 \times 10^3$ 15. $5 \cdot 8 \times 10^3$ 16. $1 \cdot 2 \times 10^2$ 17. 3×10^3

18. (i) $9 \cdot 5 \times 10^6$ (ii) $1 \cdot 6 \times 10^3$ 19. $5 \cdot 99 \times 10^{24}$ kg   20. $1 \cdot 25$ kg   21. $1 \cdot 08 \times 10^8$ km

22. $1 \cdot 2 \times 10^{-2}$ cm

Exercise 18.7

1. $\dfrac{1}{2}$ 2. $-\dfrac{1}{8}$ 3. $\dfrac{1}{7}$ 4. $-\dfrac{1}{6}$ 5. $\dfrac{3}{2}$ 6. $\dfrac{8}{5}$ 7. -9 8. $-\dfrac{7}{4}$ 9. 37   10. $-\dfrac{13}{7}$

11. $\dfrac{11}{12}$ 12. $-\dfrac{7}{10}$ 13. $\dfrac{3}{7}$ 14. $\dfrac{9}{13}$ 15. $\dfrac{7}{37}$ 16. $\dfrac{9}{32}$ 17. $0 \cdot 392$ 18. $-0 \cdot 312$

19. $1 \cdot 923$ 20. $0 \cdot 671$

Exercise 19.1

1. $4a$ **2.** $2p$ **3.** $2y$ **4.** 1 **5.** $3a$ **6.** $-2p$ **7.** x **8.** $-2p$ **9.** $3x$ **10.** $3r$

11. b **12.** 2 **13.** 1 **14.** $4a$ **15.** $2a$ **16.** $2(x + 2y)$ **17.** $5(a + 3)$ **18.** $x(x + 3)$

19. $a(c + d)$ **20.** $2p(q - 3r)$ **21.** $2x(2x - y)$ **22.** $a(a - 1)$ **23.** $5x(1 - 2y)$ **24.** $4(x + 2)$

25. $a(b + c)$ **26.** $3(a + b)$ **27.** $p(2 + q)$ **28.** $4(3a + 2b)$ **29.** $3(m + 2n)$ **30.** $x(x + 1)$

31. $x(x - 3)$ **32.** $2x(1 + 2x)$ **33.** $a(a + 5)$ **34.** $2p(2 + p)$ **35.** $5x(x + 2)$

36. $3x(a + 2b)$ **37.** $4a(b - 2)$ **38.** $2p(q - 3r)$ **39.** $6x(p - q)$ **40.** $5a(b + 2c)$

41. $7x(1 - 4y)$ **42.** $2a(1 - 2a)$ **43.** $3a(1 + 2b + 3c)$ **44.** $4a(a - 5b)$ **45.** $p(q + r - 1)$

46. $3x(2y - 3z)$ **47.** $q(r - 2s)$ **48.** $b(4a - 3b)$ **49.** $3x(x - 3y)$ **50.** $6pq(3p - 1)$

51. $4xy(x + 2y)$ **52.** $2ab(a + 3b)$ **53.** $5ab(2c - 3d)$ **54.** $a^2 + 3a;\ a(a + 3)$

55. (i) $4a(2b + 3)$ **(ii)** $2(2b + 3)$ **(iii)** $2a$

Exercise 19.2

1. $(a + b)(c + d)$ **2.** $(p + q)(r + s)$ **3.** $(x + a)(p + q)$ **4.** $(x - y)(m + n)$ **5.** $(y - 3)(2x + 5)$

6. $(c - 3d)(2a - b)$ **7.** $(x + y)(a + b)$ **8.** $(p + x)(q + r)$ **9.** $(m + n)(x + y)$

10. $(5 + x)(a + b)$ **11.** $(4 + z)(x + y)$ **12.** $(a + d)(b + c)$ **13.** $(3 + r)(p + q)$

14. $(a + p)(x + 4)$ **15.** $(5 + a)(x + y)$ **16.** $(a + b)(p + q)$ **17.** $(a + 2)(x - y)$

18. $(3 + r)(p - q)$ **19.** $(a + 4)(m - n)$ **20.** $(c + d)(a - b)$ **21.** $(3 - c)(a + b)$

22. $(p - 5)(q + r)$ **23.** $(x - y)(p + q)$ **24.** $(r - 2s)(p + q)$ **25.** $(a + 2)(a + b)$

26. $(x + z)(x - y)$ **27.** $(x + q)(x + 2p)$ **28.** $(x + y)(2 - x)$ **29.** $(m + 4)(m + n)$

30. $(p + q)(p - 3)$ **31.** $(a + 1)(b + c)$ **32.** $(p + 1)(q + r)$ **33.** $(x - 1)(a + b)$

34. $(x - 1)(y + z)$

Exercise 19.3

1. $-5(a + b)$ **2.** $-3a(b + c)$ **3.** $-2p(q + r)$ **4.** $-4x(a + b)$ **5.** $-3(a - b)$ **6.** $-q(r - 3s)$

7. $-5p(q - r)$ **8.** $-x(x - 2)$ **9.** $(a + b)(c + d)$ **10.** $(p + 3)(q + r)$ **11.** $(2 + x)(a + b)$

12. $(3 + z)(x + y)$ **13.** $(p - q)(x + y)$ **14.** $(2a - 5)(b + c)$ **15.** $(a + d)(b - c)$

16. $(2a - b)(p - q)$ **17.** $(x - 4)(a - p)$ **18.** $(3 - q)(a - b)$ **19.** $(p - s)(q - r)$

20. $(p - q)(a - b)$ **21.** $(x - 1)(a + b)$ **22.** $(p - q)(1 - 3a)$ **23.** $(p - 1)(a - b)$

24. $(1 + c)(a - b)$

Exercise 19.4

1. $(x + 2)(x + 1)$ **2.** $(x + 3)(x + 1)$ **3.** $(x + 1)(x + 5)$ **4.** $(x + 1)(x + 7)$ **5.** $(x + 1)(x + 11)$

6. $(x + 2)(x + 4)$ **7.** $(x + 4)(x + 1)$ **8.** $(x + 4)(x + 3)$ **9.** $(x + 2)(x + 5)$

10. $(x + 1)(x + 10)$ **11.** $(x + 6)(x + 2)$ **12.** $(x + 1)(x + 12)$ **13.** $(x - 2)(x - 7)$

14. $(x - 3)(x - 7)$ **15.** $(x - 2)(x - 6)$ **16.** $(x - 4)(x + 2)$ **17.** $(x + 10)(x - 2)$

18. $(x - 6)(x + 2)$ **19.** $(x + 5)(x - 3)$ **20.** $(x - 4)(x + 3)$ **21.** $(x + 6)(x - 5)$

22. $(x + 3)(x + 3)$ **23.** $(x + 2)(x + 2)$ **24.** $(x + 4)(x + 6)$ **25.** $(x + 2)(x - 1)$

26. $(x - 3)(x + 2)$ **27.** $(x - 8)(x + 3)$ **28.** $(x - 3)(x + 1)$ **29.** $(x + 6)(x - 1)$

30. $(x - 4)(x - 25)$ **31.** $(x + 3)(x + 16)$ **32.** $(x + 4)(x - 1)$ **33.** $(x + 5)(x - 4)$

34. $(x - 6)(x + 4)$ **35.** $(x - 5)(x + 2)$ **36.** $(x + 20)(x - 3)$ **37.** $(x - 7)(x + 5)$

38. $(x - 4)(x - 5)$ **39.** $(x - 7)(x + 6)$ **40.** $(x + 6)(x - 3)$ **41.** $(x + 9)(x + 5)$

42. $(x - 7)(x + 4)$ **43.** $(x - 7)(x + 2)$ **44.** $(x + 8)(x - 5)$ **45.** $(x - 9)(x + 3)$

46. $(x - 18)(x + 4)$ **47.** $(x + 30)(x - 2)$ **48.** $(x - 16)(x + 5)$

49. $x^2 + 9x + 20$; $(x + 4)(x + 5)$ **50.** $x^2 - 2x - 15$

Exercise 19.5

1. $(5)^2$ **2.** $(2)^2$ **3.** $(12)^2$ **4.** $(9)^2$ **5.** $(13)^2$ **6.** $(25)^2$ **7.** $(x + 4)(x - 4)$

8. $(x + 8)(x - 8)$ **9.** $(x + 11)(x - 11)$ **10.** $(x - 3)(x + 3)$ **11.** $(x - 6)(x + 6)$

12. $(a - 10)(a + 10)$ **13.** $(p - 9)(p + 9)$ **14.** $(7 - y)(7 + y)$ **15.** $(1 - x)(1 + x)$

16. 16 **17.** 48 **18.** 51 **19.** 21 **20.** 200 **21.** 1,200 **22.** 6 **23.** 10

24. 0·4 **25.** $x^2 - 9$; $(x + 3)(x - 3)$

Exercise 20.1

1. Not correct **2.** Correct **3.** Correct **4.** Not correct **5.** Not correct

6. Correct **7.** Not correct **8.** Not correct **9.** Correct

Exercise 20.2

1. $x = 4, y = 3$ **2.** $x = 6, y = 4$ **3.** $p = 6, q = 5$ **4.** $p = 17, q = 11$ **5.** $x = 5, y = 4$

6. $p = 2, q = 16$ **7.** $x = 5, y = 2$ **8.** $x = 4, y = 1$ **9.** $x = 5, y = 2$ **10.** $x = 2, y = 1$

11. $x = 3, y = -1$ **12.** $x = 3, y = 2$ **13.** $p = -2, q = 5$ **14.** $x = 1, y = -4$

15. $x = 0, y = -8$ **16.** $x = 7, y = 3$ **17.** $x = 6, y = 1$ **18.** $x = 4, y = 1$ **19.** $x = 5, y = 5$

20. $x = 6, y = -3$ **21.** $x = -1, y = 2$ **22.** $x = 1, y = 2$ **23.** $x = -2, y = 3$ **24.** $x = 0, y = -2$

25. (i) (a) 2 (b) 1 (ii) 4

Exercise 21.1

1. −3, 1 2. 3, 8 3. −5, −4 4. 0, 1 5. −4, 0 6. 0, 2 7. −4, 4 8. −2, 2
9. −12, 12 10. 1, 4 11. −4, −2 12. 3, 5 13. −4, 2 14. −2, 1 15. −3, 5
16. −7, −5 17. −4, 5 18. 2, 3 19. 0, 5 20. −2, 0 21. 0, 4 22. −3, 3
23. −8, 8 24. −10, 10 25. −1, 1 26. −9, 9 27. −7, 7 28. 0, 7 29. −1, 8
30. −11, 11 31. 4, 5 32. −1, 4 33. −8, 0 34. −1, 9 35. −6, 6 36. 3, 7
37. 2, 10 38. −2, 6 39. −5, 0 40. −5, 3 41. 2, 6 42. −2, 8 43. −3, 7
44. −4, 4 45. −4, 6

Exercise 22.1

1. (i) $\frac{10}{21}$ (ii) $\frac{43}{30}$ (iii) $\frac{25}{56}$ (iv) $\frac{9}{20}$ 2. (i) $\frac{11}{18}$ (ii) $\frac{-7}{18}$ (iii) $\frac{31}{18}$ (iv) $\frac{85}{18}$

3. (i) $\frac{47}{60}$ (ii) $\frac{9}{4}$ (iii) 2 (iv) $\frac{17}{20}$ 4. (i) $\frac{31}{12}$ (ii) $\frac{23}{12}$ (iii) $\frac{73}{12}$ (iv) $\frac{20}{27}$

Exercise 22.2

1. $\frac{5x}{6}$ 2. $\frac{7x}{12}$ 3. $\frac{9x}{20}$ 4. $\frac{7x}{18}$ 5. $\frac{x}{8}$ 6. $\frac{-5x}{12}$ 7. (i) $\frac{5}{9}$ (ii) $\frac{2x+21}{9}$

8. (i) $\frac{3}{10}$ (ii) $\frac{x-3}{10}$ 9. $\frac{2x+9}{2}$ 10. $\frac{7x+9}{12}$ 11. $\frac{8x+9}{4}$ 12. $\frac{9x-1}{6}$

13. $\frac{4x+11}{12}$ 14. $\frac{10x+47}{12}$ 15. $\frac{5x+6}{8}$ 16. $\frac{19x-13}{12}$ 17. $\frac{x+5}{6}$ 19. (i) $\frac{9x+33}{10}$

20. (i) $\frac{11x-6}{20}$

Exercise 22.3

1. $4a$ 2. $5x$ 3. $3p$ 4. $2b$ 5. $2a$ 6. $4p$ 7. $3x$ 8. 2 9. x 10. x 11. 1
12. 1 13. 1 14. $2a$ 15. $2x$ 16. $3a$ 17. $3b$ 18. $2q$ 19. $2a^2$ 20. $5x$

Exercise 22.4

1. 7 2. $\frac{1}{3-5x}$ 3. y 4. $\frac{5}{w+2}$ 5. x 6. 5 7. $\frac{1}{2}$ 8. $4y$ 9. 2 10. $-w$

11. $x-8$ 12. $\frac{1}{x+3}$ 13. $\frac{1}{x+3}$ 14. $\frac{x+5}{x}$ 15. $\frac{1}{x+5}$ 16. $\frac{x-4}{x+7}$ 17. $\frac{x-10}{x-9}$

18. $\frac{x+6}{x+5}$ 19. 6

Exercise 23.1

1. $<$ 2. $>$ 3. $<$ 4. $>$ 5. $>$ 6. $<$ 7. $>$ 8. $<$ 9. $<$ 10. 2, 3, 4, 5, 6

11. 3, 4, 5, 6, 7   12. 1, 0, -1, -2, -3 13. 0, 1, 2, 3, 4   14. 2, 3, 4, 5, 6

15. -3, -4, -5, -6, -7

Exercise 23.2

1. $x \geq 4$ 2. $x \leq 3$ 3. $x > 2$ 4. $x < 3$ 5. $x \geq -1$ 6. $x \leq -2$ 7. $x < 3$ 8. $x \geq 2$

9. $x \leq -2$ 10. $x = \{1, 2, 3, 4, 5\}$ 11. $x = \{1, 2, 3\}$ 12. 6   13. $x < \dfrac{1}{2}$ 14. $x \geq \dfrac{5}{3}$

15. $x > \dfrac{9}{4}$ 16. $x \leq \dfrac{6}{5}$ 17. 2   18. 5 cm   19. (6, 7)   20. (2, 6) or (3, 4)

21. (i) $3 + 0 \cdot 25x \leq 10$ (ii) 28   (iii) $3 + 0 \cdot 3x \leq 10$ (iv) 23   (v) 10c

Exercise 24.2

1. (i) 360°   (ii) full angle   2. (i) (a) 180°   (b) 90°   (c) 120°

   (d) 270°   (e) 72°   (f) 720°   (ii) $\dfrac{2}{3}$

3. (i) (a) 60°   (b) 300°   (ii) 45°   (iii) 03:15   6. (i) $A = 30$ (ii) $B = 40$ (iii) $C = 70$

   (iv) $D = 50$ (v) $x = 45$ (vi) $y = 15$ (vii) $a = 40$ (viii) $x = 20$

   (ix) $x = 120$, $y = 60$, $z = 60$ (x) $p = 70$, $q = 110$, $r = 110$ (xi) $a = 110$ (xii) $x = 30$

7. (i) 130°   (ii) 80°   (iii) 230°   8. (i) 90°   (ii) 110°   (iii) 290°

Exercise 24.3

1. $A = 70$, $B = 110$, $C = 110$ 2. $X = 135$, $Y = 135$, $Z = 45$

3. $P = 120$, $Q = 60$, $R = 60$, $S = 120$ 4. $A = 55$, $B = 55$, $C = 125$

5. $A = 80$ 6. $X = 105$ 7. $P = 125$, $Q = 55$ 8. $A = 130$, $B = 50$

9. $X = 25$, $Y = 155$ 10. $A = 55$, $B = 14$ 11. (i) $A = 25$ (ii) $B = 20$ (iii) $C = 30$

Exercise 24.4

1. $A = 75$ 2. $B = 50$ 3. $C = 45$ 4. $D = 30$ 5. $A = 50$, $B = 80$

6. $A = 45$ 7. $B = 65$ 8. $A = 55$, $B = 70$ 9. $A = 60$, $B = 68$

10. $X = 50$, $Y = 70$ 11. $P = 70$, $Q = 55$, $R = 55$ 12. $A = 112$, $B = 62$ 13. $A = 60$

14. $A = 105$ 15. $A = 65$, $B = 50$ 16. $A = 58$, $B = 64$, $C = 58$ 17. $A = 18$ 18. $x = 20$

19. $P = 135$, $Q = 90$, $R = 45$ 20. $X = 40$, $Y = 140$, $Z = 80$ 21. $X = 70$, $Y = 35$ 22. (ii) 132°

Exercise 24.5

3. 125°   **4.** $A = 80$ **5.** $A = 65, B = 115, C = 115$ **6.** $A = 105, B = 75, C = 75$

7. $A = 95, B = 85$ **8.** $A = 75$ **9.** $x = 80$ **10.** $A = 110°, B = 55$ **11.** $x = 36$

12. $x = 59$ **13.** $x = 50, y = 80, z = 50$ **14.** $x = 120, y = 120, z = 32$ **15.** $a = 115$

16. 30°   **17. (i)** 40° **(ii)** 70°   **18. (ii) (a)** 70° **(b)** 110° **(c)** 105° **(d)** 35°

Exercise 24.6

1. $A = 90, B = 30$ **2.** $P = 90, Q = 40$ **3.** $Q = 90, R = 20$ **4.** $A = 138$

5. $A = 35, B = 125$ **6.** $x = 45$ **7.** $A = 90, B = 90, C = 36, D = 65$

8. $A = 100, B = 80$ **9.** $x = 90, y = 18$ **10.** $a = 25$ **11.** $p = 55, q = 70$

12. $x = 50$ **13.** $p = 50, q = 80$ **14.** $x = 35$ **15.** $x = 48, y = 84$ **16.** $x = 60$

17. $x = 45$ **18.** $x = 60, y = 30$ **19.** $a = 37, b = 90, c = 53$

20. $p = 90, q = 26, r = 64$ **21.** $x = 52, y = 52$ **22.** $a = 90, b = 50, c = 50$

23. $a = 90, b = 70, c = 35, d = 55$ **24. (ii) (a)** 40° **(b)** 100° **(c)** 80° **(d)** 50°

25. (i) 100° **(ii)** 80°   **26. (i) (a)** 90° **(b)** 45°   **27. (i)** 60° **(ii)** 75°

Exercise 25.1

2. 5   **3.** 13   **4.** 8   **5.** 7   **6.** 20   **7.** 40   **8.** 34   **9.** 12   **10.** 11

11. 16   **12.** 5   **13.** 2   **14.** 4   **15.** 3   **16.** 2   **17.** 14   **18.** $\sqrt{13}$ **19.** $\sqrt{41}$

20. $\sqrt{24}$ **21.** $\sqrt{11}$ **22.** 2   **23.** 3   **24.** 5   **25.** 4   **28.** 12 cm   **29.** 5 cm

30. 4·8 m   **31.** $A = 225$ cm^2; $B = 31$ cm^2 **32.** 7·5 cm   **33. (i)** 5 **(ii)** 12   **34.** 78 mm

35. 18 cm   **37. (i)** 558 m **(ii)** 450 m **(iii)** 108 m **(iv)** Path; 21 seconds

38. (i) 5 cm **(ii)** 13 cm

Exercise 25.2

1. (i) 30 cm **(ii)** 40 cm^2 **2. (i)** 32 cm **(ii)** 30 cm^2 **3. (i)** 24 cm **(ii)** 28 cm^2

4. (i) 40 cm **(ii)** 84 cm^2 **5. (i)** 26 cm **(ii)** 35 cm^2 **6. (i)** 50 cm **(ii)** 120 cm^2

7. 8 cm   **8.** 5 cm   **9.** 6 cm   **10. (i)** 4 cm **(ii)** 40 cm^2 **11. (i)** 12 cm **(ii)** 180 cm^2

12. (i) 15 cm **(ii)** 300 cm^2 **13. (i)** 7 cm **(ii)** 20 cm **(iii) (a)** 52 cm^2 **(b)** 26 cm^2

14. (i) 9 cm **(ii)** 90 cm^2 **15. (i)** 20 cm^2 **(ii)** 5 cm

16. (i) (a) 52 cm **(b)** 6 cm **(c)** 8 cm **(ii) (a)** 128 cm^2 **(b)** 64 cm^2 **(c)** 40 cm^2

   (iii) 12·8 cm   **17.** 12

Exercise 26.1

7. (i) (a) $\triangle SRT$ (b) $[RT]$ (c) $\angle RST$ (ii) $\overrightarrow{QR}$ or $\overrightarrow{RT}$ (iii) P 8. (i) (a) $\triangle UTV$ (b) $[TV]$

   (c) $\angle TUV$ (ii) (a) $\triangle RUS$ (b) $[RS]$ (c) $\angle SUR$ (iii) (a) $\overrightarrow{TV}$ (b) $\overrightarrow{US}$ (c) $\overrightarrow{SR}$

9. (i) (a) $\triangle YZR$ (b) $[YR]$ (c) $\angle ZYR$ (ii) $XQZY$ or $XZRY$ (iii) $\angle QXP$ or $\angle YZR$ (iv) 40 cm^2

10. (i) (a) E (b) $[DC]$ (c) $\triangle DYF$ (d) $[CY]$ (e) $[YF]$ (f) $\triangle YDF$ (ii) $XCYD$ (iii) (a) 8 cm^2

   (b) 16 cm^2 (c) 32 cm^2 11. (i) (a) V (b) $[RS]$ (c) $\triangle SVU$ (d) $\angle USV$ (ii) $\overrightarrow{VS}$

   (iii) 10 cm^2 (iv) 120°

Exercise 26.2

6. (i) S (ii) Q (iii) $\triangle POQ$ (iv) $\angle PQO$ 7. (i) Q (ii) $[QO]$ (iii) $\triangle QOS$

8. (i) (a) F (b) E (c) B (d) A (e) D (f) C (g) Y (h) X (i) $[FE]$

   (j) $\triangle DAX$ (k) $\angle YFD$ (l) $\angle XCD$ (ii) (a) D (b) B (c) A (d) C (e) X

   (f) $\triangle ADX$ (g) $\angle DXC$ (h) $[XB]$ 9. (i) $\triangle BAK$ (ii) $ADCB$

   (iii) $\triangle ABD$; $\triangle ADC$; $\triangle DCB$; $\triangle CBA$ (iv) $[DC]$ 10. (i) (a) D (b) C (c) Q

   (d) $\triangle BZQ$ (e) $\angle ZPA$ (ii) (a) A (b) R (c) D (d) $\triangle QAP$ (e) $PZSD$ (iii) $[BR]$

   (iv) 32 cm^2

Exercise 26.4

5. (i) C (ii) D (iii) $[BA]$ (iv) $[CB]$ (v) $\triangle CDM$ (vi) $\angle DAM$

6. (i) R (ii) W (iii) S (iv) P (v) $[QY]$ (vi) $\triangle SZO$ (vii) $\triangle ZWS$ (viii) $YQXO$

7. (i) $[PQ]$; $[QR]$; $[SR]$; $[ST]$ (ii) (a) P (b) S (c) $[RS]$ (d) $\triangle RXQ$ (iii) (a) S (b) T

   (c) $[RT]$ (d) $\triangle RQY$ (e) $\angle TSQ$ (iv) $[ST]$ (v) T (vi) 40 cm^2 8. (i) $[AB]$; $[XD]$; $[BY]$

   (ii) $\triangle DAX$ (iii) $\triangle ACD$ (iv) $[BD]$ (v) 50° (vi) 64 cm^2

Exercise 28.2

14. (iii) (a) $\dfrac{1}{2}$ (b) $\dfrac{3}{2}$ (c) $\dfrac{9}{4}$ 15. $p = 8$ cm, $q = 10$ cm   16. $p = 7$ cm, $q = 6$ cm

17. $p = 12$ cm, $q = 6$ cm   18. $p = 25$ cm, $q = 16$ cm   19. $p = 8$ cm, $q = 15$ cm

20. $p = 6$ cm, $q = 10$ cm   21. $p = 20$ cm, $q = 9$ cm   22. $p = 8$ cm, $q = 6$ cm

23. $p = 12$ cm, $q = 6$ cm   24. $p = 6$ cm, $q = 15$ cm

25. (ii) 9 cm (iii) (a) 6 cm (b) 4 cm (c) 4 cm

26. (ii) 6 cm (iii) (a) 9 cm (b) 3 cm (c) 8 cm

27. (ii) 8 cm (iii) (a) 15 cm (b) 12 cm   28. (ii) 2 cm

Exercise 28.3

1. 7 m   2. 10 m   3. 16 m   4. 15 m   5. 96 cm   6. 9 m

Exercise 29.2

1. $(5, 3)$ 2. $(2, 4)$ 3. $(3, 2)$ 4. $(6, 3)$ 5. $(4, 6)$ 6. $(3, 5)$ 7. $(5, 3)$

8. $(2, 5)$ 9. $(1, 2)$ 10. $(3, -4)$ 11. $(-2, -3)$ 12. $(-4, -4)$ 13. $(4, 4)$

14. (i) $(6, 5)$ (ii) $(6, 5)$ 15. $A(5, 3), B(10, 6), C(15, 9)$

Exercise 29.3

1. 5 2. 10 3. 13 4. $\sqrt{89}$ 5. $\sqrt{5}$ 6. $\sqrt{20}$ 7. $\sqrt{17}$ 8. $\sqrt{26}$ 9. 6

10. $\sqrt{34}$ 11. 3 12. $\sqrt{32}$ 14. (i) $(5, 6)$ (ii) 5

17. (i) $(6, 1)$ (ii) (a) 4 (b) 3 (iii) 5 (iv) 5 (vii) (a) $|x_2 - x_1|$ (b) $|y_2 - y_1|$

Exercise 29.4

4. $\dfrac{3}{4}$ 5. $\dfrac{1}{2}$ 6. $\dfrac{2}{5}$ 7. $\dfrac{4}{5}$ 8. $\dfrac{1}{3}$ 9. $\dfrac{7}{5}$ 10. $\dfrac{2}{3}$ 11. $\dfrac{1}{2}$ 12. $\dfrac{5}{4}$ 13. $\dfrac{3}{2}$

14. $-\dfrac{2}{3}$ 15. 1 16. -1 17. 0 18. 2 21. $\dfrac{9}{40}$ 22. (i) 80 km/h (ii) 75 km/h

Exercise 29.5

9. 7 10. 4

Exercise 29.6

1. $y = 4x - 5$ 2. $y = 3x - 1$ 3. $y = 2x + 4$ 4. $y = x + 5$ 5. $y = -2x + 1$

6. $y = -3x + 1$ 7. $y = -5x - 17$ 8. $y = -4x$ 9. $y = \dfrac{1}{2}x + 1$ 10. $y = \dfrac{1}{3}x - 4$

11. $y = -\dfrac{2}{5}x + 3$ 12. $y = -\dfrac{5}{4}x - 13$ 13. $y = 3x - 7$ 14. $y = \dfrac{1}{2}x + 2$

Exercise 29.7

1. (i) 3 (ii) $y = 3x - 8$ 2. (i) 2 (ii) $y = 2x - 1$ 3. (i) $\dfrac{1}{2}$ (ii) $y = \dfrac{1}{2}x + 1$

4. (i) $-\dfrac{1}{3}$ (ii) $y = -\dfrac{1}{3}x + 4$ 5. $y = -x + 4$ 6. $y = -3x + 8$ 7. $y = -x + 7$

8. $y = 4x - 7$ 9. $y = -\dfrac{1}{2}x + 2$ 10. $y = \dfrac{3}{5}x + 3$ 11. (i) $(5, 3)$ (ii) $y = 2x - 7$

Exercise 29.8

1. $2; (0, 3)$ 2. $3; (0, 4)$ 3. $5; (0, -1)$ 4. $-4; (0, 1)$ 5. $-2; (0, 7)$ 6. $-7; (0, -3)$

7. $\dfrac{1}{2}; (0, -2)$ 8. $\dfrac{1}{3}; (0, -5)$ 9. $-\dfrac{3}{4}; (0, 2)$ 10. $-\dfrac{1}{2}; (0, -4)$ 11. $-\dfrac{5}{4}; (0, 7)$

12. $-\dfrac{7}{6}; (0, -8)$ 13. (i) 3 (ii) $y = 3x + 8$ 14. (i) $\dfrac{1}{2}$ (ii) $y = \dfrac{1}{2}x - 1$

Exercise 29.10

1. (1, 0); (0, 1)   2. (3, 0); (0, −3)   3. (2, 0); (0, −4)   4. (−1, 0); (0, 3)

5. (2, 0); (0, 8)   6. (−2, 0); (0, 10)   7. (4, 0); (0, 8)   8. (4, 0); (0, 12)

9. (1, 0); (0, 6)   10. (ii) M (3, 3)   (iv) 2   (v) $y = 2x − 3$ (vi) (0, −3)   (viii) −1

11. (i) $y = 2x + 8$ (ii) $S(0, 8)$ 12. (i) (a) (3, 6)   (b) $\sqrt{80}$ (c) −2   (d) $y = − 2x + 12$

    (iii) 2   (iv) $A(6, 0)$; $B(0, 12)$ (v) 36   13. (i) (a) (2, 6)   (b) $\sqrt{8}$ (c) −1

    (d) $y = − x + 8$ (iii) 2   (iv) $R(8, 0)$; $S(0, 8)$ (v) 32

14. (i) $\sqrt{116}$ (ii) $\dfrac{5}{2}$ and $\dfrac{−5}{2}$ (iii) $x − 2y + 2 = 0$

Exercise 30.1

1. $\{(1, 5), (2, 8), (3, 11), (4, 14), (5, 17)\}$

2. $\{(0, 1), (2, 9), (4, 17), (6, 25), (8, 33)\}$

3. $\{(−3, −5), (−2, −3), (−1, −1), (0, 1), (1, 3), (2, 5)\}$

4. $\{(−2, 1), (−1, 2), (0, 3), (1, 4), (2, 5), (3, 6)\}$

5. $\{(−5, −22), (−4, −17), (−3, −12), (−2, −7), (−1, −2), (0, 3), (1, 8), (2, 13)\}$

6. $\{(−2, −10), (−1, −7), (0, −4), (1, −1), (2, 2), (3, 5), (4, 8), (5, 11)\}$

7. $\{(−3, −11), (−2, −9), (−1, −7), (0, −5), (1, −3), (2, −1)\}$

8. $\{(−1, −4), (0, −3), (1, −2), (2, −1), (3, 0), (4, 1)\}$

9. $\{(0, 3), (1, 4), (2, 7), (3, 12), (4, 19), (5, 28), (6, 39)\}$

10. $\{(−2, −2), (−1, −2), (0, 0), (1, 4), (2, 10), (3, 18), (4, 28)\}$

11. (i) 22   (ii) 4

12. (i) 24   (ii) 15

13. (i) 34   (ii) 7

14. (i) 3(input) − 2

    (ii) Range = $\{−2, 1, 4, 7, 10, 13\}$

15. (i) (input)^2 + 2(input)

    (ii) Range = $\{3, 0, −1, 0, 3, 8, 15\}$

17. (i) It is your age three times

    (ii) Output = (input × 7) × 1443

    (iii) Output = (input × 10101)

18. (i) €0·60   (ii) $y = 1·3x$ (iii) B   (iv) B   (v) A

    (vi) Niamh should find out how many people will be coming to see the play.

Exercise 30.2

1. (i) 7   (ii) 9   (iii) 11   (iv) 13
2. (i) 4   (ii) 10   (iii) 16   (iv) 22
3. (i) 23   (ii) 7   (iii) 15   (iv) 11
4. (i) 1   (ii) −3   (iii) 3   (iv) 9
5. (i) −1   (ii) −4   (iii) 2   (iv) −7
6. (i) 3   (ii) 8   (iii) −7   (iv) −12
7. (i) 5   (ii) 7   (iii) 2   (iv) 12
8. (i) −6   (ii) −3   (iii) 9   (iv) 30
9. (i) 0   (ii) 2   (iii) 3   (iv) 12   (v) $-2 < 0$
10. (i) 3   (ii) 1   (iii) −1   (iv) 2   (v) $7 > 0$
11. (i) 7   (ii) 13   (iii) 7   (iv) 13   (v) $23 = 23$
12. (i) 2   (ii) 3   (iii) 4   (iv) 1   (v) 0   (vi) $6 > 5$
13. (i) 3   (ii) 8   (iii) −1   (iv) 3   (v) −4, 2
14. (i) −6   (ii) −6   (iii) −4   (iv) −1, 4

Exercise 30.3

1. (i) Range = {7, 9, 11, 13, 15}   (ii) f = {(1, 7), (2, 9), (3, 11), (4, 13), (5, 15)}
2. (i) Range = {8, 14, 20, 26}   (ii) f = {(2, 8), (4, 14), (6, 20), (8, 26)}
3. (i) Range = {−3, 1, 5, 9, 13}   (ii) f = {(0, −3), (1, 1), (2, 5), (3, 9), (4, 13)}
4. (i) Range = {−5, −3, −1, 1, 3, 5}   (ii) f = {(−2, −5), (−1, −3), (0, −1), (1, 1), (2, 3), (3, 5)}
5. (i) Range = {1, 2, 3, 4, 5, 6}   (ii) f = {(−3, 1), (−2, 2), (−1, 3), (0, 4), (1, 5), (2, 6)}
6. Range = {7, 10, 13}
7. Range = {−2, 3, 8}
8. Range = {1, 3, 5, 7, 9}
9. Range = {−8, −5, −2, 1}
10. Range = {5, 1, −3, −7}

Exercise 30.4

1. $a = 5, b = 9, c = 5$ 2. $p = 13, q = −5, r = 1$
3. $a = 7, b = −8, c = 3$ 4. $r = 9, s = −7, t = 2$
5. $x = 0, y = −2, z = −4$ 6. $a = 0, b = 2, c = 3$
7. (i) $p = 5$ (ii) $q = 1$ (iii) $r = 3$ (iv) $s = −3$

8. (i) $a = 9$ (ii) $b = -5$ (iii) $c = 3$ (iv) $d = 1$
9. (i) (2, 9) (ii) (0, 1) (iii) (1, 5) (iv) (−1, −3)
10. (i) (3, 1) (ii) (−3, −11) (iii) (4, 3) (iv) (−1, −7)

Exercise 31.3

1. (i) −3, 1 (ii) −4, 2 (iii) −1·75 (iv) −3·4, 1·4 (v) $x = -1$ (vi) 54
2. (i) −1, 4 (ii) −2·25 (iii) 0, 3 (iv) −1·4, 4·4
3. (i) 1, 2 (ii) 1 (iii) −0·8, 3·8 (iv) 0, 3
4. (i) 1, 5 (ii) −3·75 (iii) 54 (iv) 1·3, 4·7
5. (i) −1, 2 (ii) −2, 3 (iii) 0, 1
6. (i) −4, 2 (ii) −3, 1 (iii) $x = -1$ (iv) 128
7. (i) −3, 2 (ii) −2, 1 (iii) −3·7, 2·7
8. (i) −1, 5 (ii) 1, 3 (iii) $x = 2$
9. (i) −1, 3 (ii) −2, 4 (iii) 128 (iv) 8·25
10. (i) 1, 3 (ii) 4·25 (iii) 0·6, 3·4
11. (i) −2, 1 (ii) −1·25 (iv) −2·6, 1·6
12. (i) 1, 4 (ii) 2, 3 (iii) 1·75
13. (i) −4, 1 (ii) −4·4, 1·4 (iii) −5·8
15. (i) −1, 1·5 (ii) −1·5, 2
16. (i) 5 (ii) −2, 0·5 (iii) −1·5, 0
17. −2, 4
18. (0, 4) (3, −2)
19. (−2, −6) (2, 6)

Exercise 32.1

1. (i) \$4 (ii) €5 (iii) $y = 2x$
    (iv) The straight line through the origin/The equation of the line is in the form $y = mx$.
2. (i) €10 (ii) 4 hours (iii) $y = 4x$ (iv) 15 hours
3. (i) €36 (ii) 7 hours (iii) €9 (iv) $y = 9x$ (v) 28 hours
4. (ii) 3·5 hours (iii) $y = 60x$ (iv) 7·5 km
5. (ii) 216 km (iii) 27 litres (iv) €41·04
6. (ii) The straight line through the origin/The equation of the line is in the form $y = mx$.
    (iii) 6·74 v (iv) 3·5 A (v) $y = 1·5x$ (vi) 30 A

7. (ii) The straight line through the origin/The equation of the line is in the form $y = mx$.
    (iii) 10 N   (iv) 2·4 m/s^2 (v) $y = 2·5x$ (vi) 2·5 kg   (vii) 16 m/s^2
8. (i) 5·1 inches   (ii) 7·6 cm   (iii) $y = 2·54x$ (iv) 30·5 cm

Exercise 32.2

1. (i) 4 seconds   (ii) 1°C   (iii) 1°C
2. (i) €25   (iv) 35 weeks
3. (iii) 2·5 km   (iv) $a = 4, b = 3$
4. (iii) 12·5°C   (iv) 20°C
5. (ii) Green. After 5 weeks the green plant had a height of 22 cm and the height of the pink plant
        was 21 cm. The green plant was 1 cm taller.
    (iii) Yes. After 4 weeks both plants will have a height of 18 cm.

Exercise 32.3

1. (i) 18 km   (ii) 30 mins   (iii) 21 km/h
2. (i) 0 km   (ii) 14:30   (iii) 30 km   (iv) 20 km/h
3. (i) (a) 09:30   (b) 10:00   (c) 11:00
    (ii) (a) 50 km/h   (b) 75 km/h   (c) 50 km/h
    (iii) Tom will arrive 5 minutes early
4. (i) 1000 m/1 km   (ii) 5 m/s   (iii) 3 minutes   (iv) 2000 m/2 km   (v) 125 m/min
5. (i) 20 km   (ii) 20 minutes   (iii) Cathy's journey home.
6. (i) 40 km/h   (ii) 300 km   (iii) Lunch or meeting a client.
    (iv) Twice   (v) 50 km/h
7. (i) Twice   (ii) 2 minutes   (iii) 300 m   (iv) 1 minute
8. (i) 50 m   (ii) 4 lengths   (iii) 200 m   (iv) 5 minutes   (v) 0·67 m/s
9. (i) No. It started 15 m from the burrow.
    (ii) No. There is no flat section.
    (iii) Twice   (iv) (a) 7·5 m/s   (b) 10 m/s   (v) 7·5 m/s
10. (i) (a) 12:00   (b) 30 mins   (c) 10 km   (d) 20 km/h
    (ii) (b) 25 km/h   (c) 12·5 km/h
12. P = Fast average speed as its slope is very steep (high slope).
    Q = Not moving, stopped, as its slope is zero.
    R = Slow average speed as its slope is not steep (low slope).

13. (i) *P* = running as it has the next highest slope, (ii) *R* = cycling as it has the greatest slope, (iii) *Q* = swimming as it has the smallest slope.
    Note: It is assumed that Emma can cycle faster than she can run and that she can run faster than she can swim.

14. (i) 75 km (ii) 2 hours (iii) 40 km (iv) 11:24
    (v) (a) 25 km/h (b) 70 km/h (c) 80 km/h (vi) 15 km

15. (i) Larry set off from Wicklow at 09:00 and travelled for 75 km in one hour and then stopped for 20 minutes. He then travelled the remaining 75 km in 40 minutes. He then turned around and travelled the 150 km to Wicklow in one hour without stopping. (ii) Aoife set off at 09·20 travelled 50 km in 40 minutes and then stopped for 10 minutes. She then travelled the remaining 100 km in 40 minutes without stopping. (iii) 10:20, when both were 75 km from Wicklow.

16. At B, James turned off one tap, or reduced the flow of one tap, or reduced the flow of both taps, and the water rose 10 cm in 4 minutes. At C, James turned off both taps and there was no increase in the height of the water and maybe it took him 4 minutes to undress and get ready for the bath. At D, James got into the bath and the height of the water rose by 10 cm almost immediately. Between E and F, James had his bath and the height of the water remained the same for 12 minutes. At F, James got out of the bath and the height of the water fell by 10 cm almost immediately. At G, James pulled the plug and the height of the water fell by 30 cm in 4 minutes.

17. (i) 43°C (ii) 03:20 and 06:20 (iii) 07:20 (iv) 16°C (v) 2 hr 20 min

18. (i) 80 cans (ii) 40 cans (iii) 12:00 and 14:00 (iv) 13:15 – 14:00 (v) 140 cans

19. (i) 08:30 (ii) 8°C (iii) 5·5 hours

20. (i) 09:15 (ii) 300 m (iii) 30 mins (iv) 10 m/min (v) 2·5 hrs

21. (i) 07:00 (ii) 07:45 (iii) 1,400 m (iv) 09:00 (v) 1,000 m or 1 km

22. (i) 13 m (ii) Tree was topped (iii) 1975, 1990 (iv) 14·5 m

Exercise 32.4

1. (i) 9 m (ii) 3 seconds (iii) 6 seconds (iv) 2 seconds and 4 seconds
2. (iii) (a) 0·6 seconds and 5·4 seconds (b) 3 seconds
3. (i) 12 m (iv) 3·5 seconds
4. (i) 9 m/s (iv) 2·25 m/s
5. (i) 12°C (ii) 2·25°C (iii) 2 hours (iv) 4 hours (v) −4°C
6. (iii) (a) 13:15 and 15:45 (b) 68 km/h (c) 14:30 (lowest speed of 17·5 km/h)
7. (i) 16:15 (ii) October and January

Exercise 33.1

1. (ii) 1, 3, 5; Yes: odd numbers (iii) 2, 4, 6; Yes: even numbers (iv) Yellow
   (v) Green (vi) Green **2.** (i) 1, 4, 7 (ii) 2, 5, 8 (iii) 3, 6, 9 (iv) Blue (v) White (vi) Red

3. (i) 1, 4, 7 (ii) 2, 5, 8 (iii) 3, 6, 9 (iv) Yellow (v) Blue (vi) 15 (vii) 22

4. (ii) 2, 4, 6, . . . ; Even numbers (iii) 4, 8, 12, . . . ; Yes (iv) No (v) (a) ☉ (b) ♥
   (c) ♥ (d) ♥

5. (i) Yellow: 1, 5, 9; Purple: 2, 6, 10; Green: 3, 7, 11; Blue: 4, 8, 12 (ii) Blue (iii) Purple
   (iv) Green (v) 31 (vi) 37

Exercise 33.2

1. 10, 12, 14, 16; Start with 2, add 2 each time

2. 13, 16, 19, 22; Start with 1, add 3 each time

3. 17, 21, 25, 29; Start with 1, add 4 each time

4. 20, 15, 10, 5; Start with 40, subtract 5 each time

5. 6, 5, 4, 3; Start with 10, subtract 1 each time

6. 15, 18, 21, 24; Start with 3, add 3 each time

7. −3, −1, 1, 3; Start with −11, add 2 each time

8. 1, −2, −5, −8; Start with 13, subtract 3 each time

9. 4·1, 4·5, 4·9, 5·4; Start with 2·5, add 0·4 each time

10. 0·4, −0·2, −0·8, −1·4; Start with 2·8, subtract 0·6 each time

11. 2, 5, 8, 11   12. 1, 5, 9, 13   13. 10, 15, 20, 25   14. 5, 7, 9, 11   15. 12, 9, 6, 3

16. 18, 16, 14, 12   17. 41, 48, 55, 62   18. 36, 44, 52, 60   19. 87, 78, 69, 60

20. 54, 43, 32, 21   21. (i) 4, 7, 10, 13 (ii) Yes. A constant (3) is added each time (iii) 19

22. (i) 4, 8, 12, 16 (ii) Yes. A constant (4) is added each time (iii) Add 4
    (iv) Number of tiles = 4 times pattern number (v) 24 (vi) 10th

23. (i) 3, 6, 9 (ii) Yes. A constant (3) is added each time (iii) Add 3 (iv) 4, 7, 10; Yes; Add 3
    (v) 19 (vi) 17th

24. (i)

Pattern	1	2	3	4
Number of discs	3	6	9	12

(ii) Yes. A constant (3) is added each time (iii) Add 3
(iv) Number of green discs = 3 times pattern number (v) 30 (vi) 50th

Exercise 33.3

1. 5, 7, 9, 11   2. 4, 7, 10, 13   3. 3, 7, 11, 15   4. 2, 7, 12, 17

5. −1, −3, −5, −7   6. −1, −5, −9, −13   7. 6, 9, 14, 21   8. 3, 8, 15, 24

9. $2, \dfrac{3}{2}, \dfrac{4}{3}, \dfrac{5}{4}$ 10. $1, \dfrac{4}{3}, \dfrac{3}{2}, \dfrac{8}{5}$ 11. 2, 4, 8, 16   12. 3, 9, 27, 81

13. (i) 2, 5, 8, 11   14. (i) 9, 14, 19, 24

Exercise 33.4

1.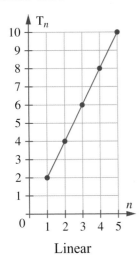
Linear

2.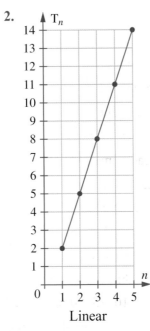
Linear

3.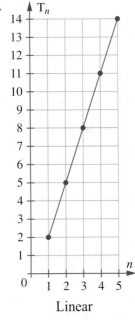
Linear

4.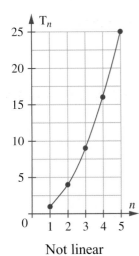
Not linear

5.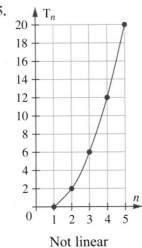
Not linear

6.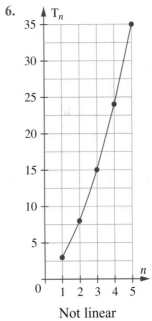
Not linear

7.

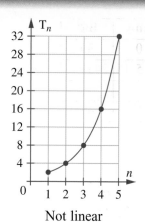

Not linear

8.

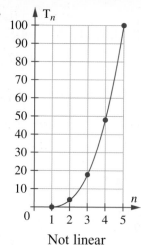

Not linear

9. (i) 5, 7, 9, 11

(ii)

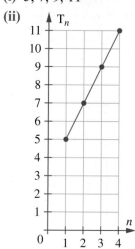

10. (i) 1, 4, 7, 10

(ii)

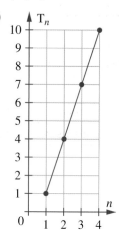

11. (i)

Day	1	2	3	4	5
€	4	6	8	10	12

(ii)

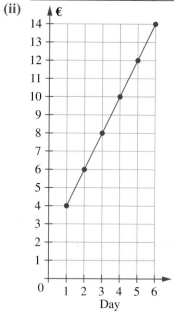

(iii) (a) €22 (b) €52

(v) €202 (vi) €18 (vii) 19 days

12. (i)

Day	1	2	3	. . .	10
€	1	4	7	. . .	28

(ii)

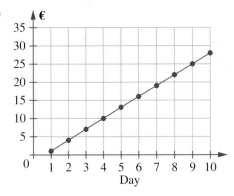

(iii) The values grow more quickly

13. (i)

Day	Amy	Bill
Start (1)	0	30
Day 2	5	33
⋮		
Day 6	25	45

(ii) Bill

(iii)

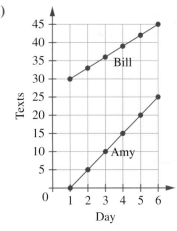

(iv) Linear (v) Day 18 (vi) No

14. (i)

Day	Lenny	Jane
Start (1)	20	0
Day 2	22	3
⋮		
Day 10	38	27

(ii)

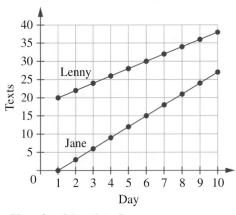

(iii) Yes; day 21 (iv) Jane

15. (i) 6, 10, 14 (ii)

Pattern	1	2	3
Rods used	6	10	14

(iii)

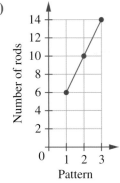

16. (i) 1 m, 1·25 m, 1·5 m, 1·75m, 2 m

   (ii) Yes; Constant difference of 0·25 m

   (iii) 4·25 m

17. (i)

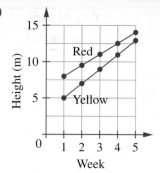

   (ii) Yellow flower

   (iii) Yes

Exercise 33.5

1. Multiply the position by 2 and add 3

2. Multiply the position by 2 and add 2

3. Multiply the position by 3 and add 1

4. Multiply the position by 3 and add 2

5. Multiply the position by 5 and subtract 1

6. Multiply the position by 6 and subtract 5

7. (i) Multiply the position by 8 and subtract 3   (ii) 157

8. (i) Multiply the position by 12 and subtract 2   (ii) 118   (iii) $T_n = 12n - 2$

9. (i)

Journey (km)	1	2	3	4	5	6
Cost (€)		5	8	11	14	17	20

   (ii) (a) €2   (b) €3

10. (i) 9, 11, 13   (ii) Linear   (iii) $T_n = 2n = 1$ (iv) 101

11. (i) 35 mins **(ii)**

Weight (kg)	1	2	3	4	5	6
Time (mins)	35	50	65	80	95	110

(iii)

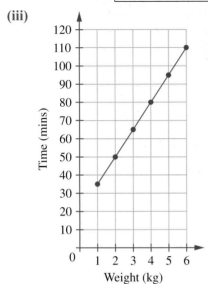

(iv) 140 mins

12. (i) 17, 21, 25 **(ii)** $T_n = 4n = 1$ **(iii)** 12th

Exercise 33.6

1. 2, 5, 10, 17 **2.** −1, 2, 7, 14 **3.** 2, 6, 12, 20 **4.** 5, 8, 13, 20 **5.** 2, 8, 16, 26

6. 0, 0, 6, 18 **7.** 7, 13, 21 **8.** 4, 11, 21 **9.** 4, 9, 12, 13

10. (i) 9 m, 16 m, 21 m, 24 m, 25 m, 24 m **(ii)** No. The differences are different.

(iii)

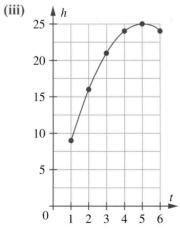

(v) Yes; 25 m

Exercise 33.7

1. 3, 9, 27, 81   2. 4, 10, 28, 82   3. 5, 7, 11, 19   4. 6, 18, 54, 162   5. 6, 12, 24, 48

6. 6, 10, 18, 34   7. (i) Red: 16, 32, 64, 128; Grey: 6, 18, 54, 162

(ii)

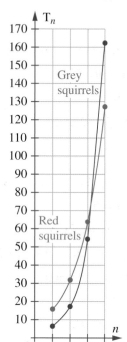

(iii) The grey squirrels outnumbered the red ones

Exercise 34.1

5. (i) 6   (ii) (a) $\dfrac{6}{10}$ or $\dfrac{3}{5}$ (b) $\dfrac{8}{10}$ or $\dfrac{4}{5}$ (c) $\dfrac{6}{8}$ or $\dfrac{3}{4}$ 6. (i) 3   (ii) (a) $\dfrac{3}{5}$ (b) $\dfrac{4}{5}$ (c) $\dfrac{3}{4}$

Exercise 34.2

1. $A = 31°$ 2. $B = 33°$ 3. $C = 35°$ 4. $D = 66°$ 5. $E = 52°$ 6. $F = 44°$

7. $G = 36°; H = 54°$ 8. $P = 43°; Q = 47$ 9. $R = 21°; S = 69°$

10. $X = 30°; Y = 60°$ 11. $W = 38°; Z = 52°$ 12. $T = 34°; K = 56°$

13. (i) 34° (ii) 56°   14. (i) $\dfrac{1}{2}$ (ii) (a) 30° (b) 60°   16. yes

Exercise 34.3

1. 4·23 cm   2. 10 cm   3. 3·23 cm   4. 6·47 cm   5. 24·51 cm   6. 6·37 cm

7. 37·61 cm   8. 20 cm   9. 28·53 cm   10. 11·35 cm   11. 11·92 cm

12. 18·54 cm   13. 21·45 cm   14. 1·49 cm   15. 10·94 cm   16. 19·51 cm

17. 43·00 cm   18. 18·12 cm   19. 5·17 cm   20. (i) 13·49 (ii) 24·12

21. (i) 10 (ii) 8·39

Exercise 34.4

1. 76·78 cm   2. 11·03 cm   3. 11·73 cm   4. 56·63 cm   5. 42·22 cm   6. 111·62 cm
7. 136·87 cm   8. 41·52 cm   9. 80·74 cm   10. 32·59 cm   11. 17·10 cm   12. 7·25 cm

Exercise 34.5

1. 4·85 m   2. 4·82 m   3. (i) 3·5 m (ii) 71°   4. 54·3°   5. 47 m   6. 11·3°
7. (i) (a) 9 m (b) 12·68° (ii) 56 m   8. (i) (a) 600 m (b) 300 m (ii) 520 m
9. (i) 37° (ii) 84 cm   10. 3·2 m   11. (i) 18·5 cm (ii) 57·1 cm
12. (i) 30° (ii) 2·5 m/s (iii) 150 m (iv) 1·25 m/s   13. no   14. (i) 12·86 m

Exercise 35.1

1. 3   2. 4   3. 6   4. 12   5. 5   6. 7   7. 3   8. 9   9. 10, 13   10. 11, 18
11. 6, 10   12. 2   13. (i) $(4x + 8)$ cm   (ii) $4x + 8 = 32$ (iii) $x = 6$
14. (i) $(x + 10)$ cm   (iii) $(4x + 20)$ cm   (iv) $4x + 20 = 56$ (v) $x = 9$ 15. (i) $2x$ cm
   (iii) $2(x) + 2(2x) = 42$ (iv) 7   (v) 98 cm^2 16. (i) $(x + 2)$ years   (ii) $(x) + (x + 2) = 38$
   (iii) 18   (iv) 20 years   17. (i) $(x + 6)$ years   (ii) $(x + 2)$ years, $(x + 8)$ years
   (iii) $2(x + 2) = x + 8$ (iv) 4
18. (i) $4x$ years   (ii) $(x + 4)$ years; $(4x + 4)$ years   (iii) $4x + 4 = 3(x + 4)$ (iv) 8
19. (i) (a) $(x + 40)$c   (b) $(3x)$c   (c) $3(x + 40)$c   (ii) $4x + 3(x + 40) = 330$ (iii) 30   (iv) 70c
20. (i) $(4x) + (4x) + (5x - 1) = 64$ (ii) 5   (iii) 24 cm   21. (i) $(18 + 2x)$ litres; $(6 + 2x)$ litres
   (ii) $18 + 2x = 2(6 + 2x)$ (iii) 3
22. (i) $(x) + (x + 1) + (x + 2) = 33$ (ii) $x = 10$ (iii) 10, 11, 12
23. (i) $(x) + (x + 2) + (x + 4) = 45$ (ii) 13   (iii) 13, 15, 17
24. 6, 7, 8   25. 14, 15, 16   26. (i) $\frac{x}{2} + \frac{x}{5} = 70$ (ii) $x = 100$ (iii) €20
27. (i) $x = 5, y = 8$ (ii) $x = 3, y = 2$ 28. 7, 5, 15   29. 5, 4, 7
30. (i) 2,000   (ii) $3,000 - 15x$ (iii) $(3,000 - 15x) - 2,000 = 400$ (iv) 40

Exercise 35.2

1. 5, 9   2. 6, 14   3. 5, 4   4. 8, 3   5. 7, 4   6. 4, 1   7. 1, 5   8. 6, 2
9. (i) (a) $2x + y = 70$ (b) $x + y = 50$ (ii) $x = 20; y = 30$ (iii) (a) 20c   (b) 30c
10. (i) (a) 250c   (b) 170c   (ii) (a) $5x + 2y = 250$ (b) $3x + 2y = 170$ (iii) $x = 40, y = 25$
   (iv) (a) 40c   (b) 25c   11. (i) (a) 350c   (b) 160c   (ii) (a) $5x + 4y = 350$
   (b) $2x + 2y = 160$ (iii) $x = 30, y = 50$ (iv) (a) 30c   (b) 50c
12. (i) (a) $7x + 3y = 82$ (b) $2x + y = 24$ (ii) $x = 10; y = 4$ (iii) (a) €10   (b) €4   (iv) €124

13. (i) (a) 530c (b) 410c (ii) $8x + 2y = 530, 6x + 2y = 410$ (iii) (a) 60c (b) 25c

14. (i) $x + y = 20$ (ii) $8x + 5y = 118$ (iii) $x = 6; y = 14$ (iv) 6 teacher tickets, 14 student tickets

15. (i) $x + y = 50$ (ii) $15x + 10y = 600$ (iii) $x = 20; y = 30$ (iv) 20 €15 tickets, 30 €10 tickets

16. (i) $x + y = 80$ (ii) $x - y = 20$ (iii) $x = 50; y = 30$ (iv) 50

17. (i) $x = 6; y = 2$ (ii) $x = 2; y = 1$ (iii) $x = 5; y = 3$

18. (i) $x + y = 1,500$ (ii) $20x + 30y = 38,000$ (iii) 700 €20 tickets; 800 €30 tickets

Exercise 35.3

1. $3; -4$ **2.** $6; -5$ **3.** (i) $x^2 + 2x$ (ii) $x^2 + 2x = 15$ (iii) $x = 3$ m

4. (i) $x^2 + 5x$ (ii) $x^2 + 5x = 36$ (iii) $x = 4$ m **5.** (ii) $x^2 + 4x$ (iii) $x^2 + 4x = 21$

  (iv) $x = 3$ cm **6.** (i) €$(x^2 + 3x)$ (ii) $x^2 + 3x = 28$ (iii) $x = 4$ **7.** (i) €$(x^2 - 2x)$

  (ii) $x^2 - 2x = 35$ (iii) 7 **8.** (i) $x + 2$ (ii) $x^2 + 2x$ (iii) $x^2 + 2x = 8$

  (iv) 2 (v) 2, 4 **9.** (i) $x - 3$ (ii) $x^2 - 3x$ (iii) $x^2 - 3x = 18$ (iv) 6 (v) 3, 6

10. (i) x^2 (ii) $4x$ (iii) $x^2 + 4x = 12$ (iv) $x = 2$ **11.** (i) €$(x^2 + 2x)$ (ii) $x^2 + 2x = 24$

  (iii) 4 (iv) €6 **12.** (i) $(x^2 - 3x)$ km (ii) $x^2 - 3x = 10$ (iii) $x = 5$

13. 5, 6, 7 **14.** 6, 8, 10

Exercise 36.1

1. 5 **2.** 3 **3.** 2 **4.** -2 **5.** -6 **6.** 2 **7.** 5 **8.** 1 **9.** 1 **10.** -1

11. $2x$ **12.** x **13.** $5x$ **14.** -3 **15.** -2 **16.** 5 **17.** $x + 4$ **18.** $x + 1$

19. $x + 2$ **20.** $x + 2$ **21.** $2x + 3$ **22.** $3x + 1$ **23.** $x + 1$ **24.** $x + 5$ **25.** $x + 5$

26. $x - 3$ **27.** $3x - 2$ **28.** $2x - 3$ **29.** $x + 4$ **30.** $4x - 1$ **31.** $4x + 5$ **32.** $2x + 1$

33. $2x + 5; (28) \div (4) = 7$ **34.** $3x + 1; (63) \div (9) = 7$ **35.** (i) $x + 5$ (ii) $x + 3$ (iii) $2x + 5$